Letts

GCSE CLASSBOOK

Maths

INTERMEDIATE

Peter Sherran • Mary Rouncefield

First published 1996
Reprinted 1997
Second edition 2001

Letts Educational
Aldine House
Aldine Place
London W12 8AW
Tel: 020 8740 2266
Fax: 020 8743 8451
www.letts-education.com

Design, page layout and illustrations: Ken Vail Graphic Design

Cover design by Santamaria

British Library Cataloguing-in-Publication Data

A CIP record for this book is available from the British Library

ISBN 1 84085 561 4

Printed and bound in the United Kingdom

Letts Educational Limited, a division of Granada Learning Limited. Part of the Granada Media Group.

CONTENTS

INTRODUCTION

This Letts GCSE Mathematics classbook has been specially written for the 2001 GCSE specifications. It is closely linked to the National Curriculum and will help you to master the key concepts in Key Stage 4 Mathematics, and refresh your memory of the important topics from Key Stage 3.

This classbook has been written in 40 units to coordinate the development of:

1 Number and algebra

2 Shape, space and measures

3 Data handling

Each of the units is clearly written and illustrated, and there are many worked examples to help you grasp the ideas involved. The numerous questions in each unit have been carefully designed to develop your understanding and will provide you with plenty of practice.

To allow you to check that you fully understand a topic, key questions have been marked with the symbol ✓. This means that the answer to this question is in the back of the book. Once you have thoroughly attempted such a question, check the answer. If you do not have the right answer, re-check your working. If you still cannot see how to get the correct answer, you should then ask your teacher to explain where you are going wrong.

To help remind you of work you may have done some time before, this book contains five review chapters. There is also a large bank of GCSE-style exam questions to help you practice and prepare as you get nearer your final exams.

This updated version of the classbook includes several new features. There is a glossary which you can use to find the meaning of key mathematical terms during your course and for revision. **ICT Extra!** boxes appear throughout the book and suggest opportunities for using ICT in a Maths context. At the back of the book you will find examples of evidence in the classbook which you could use to build a Key Skills level 2 portfolio.

We hope that this classbook will help you to progress in GCSE Mathematics, as it has been written by experienced examiners and teachers, very much with exam success in mind. But as well as helping you to achieve your desired grade, we hope that these books will give you an insight into and enjoyment of Mathematics.

NUMBER SYSTEMS

1.1 Ancient and Modern

To appreciate fully the power of the number system that we use today, we need to look at a different number system and try using it for everyday calculations.

The ancient Greeks and Romans used letters of the alphabet in their number systems. The Romans used the following letters:

The total value of a number written in this way is found by adding the values of the letters shown; except when a letter is written to the *left* of one of higher value, in which case its value is subtracted.
For example:
XX = 20 XXX = 30 XXII = 22 but XL = 40 and IV = 4

1 Write these ancient Roman numbers in the modern way:
a) II b) VII c) XI d) XD ✓
e) XXV ✓ f) DXXI g) MCM

2 How many Kings of England were called Henry before Henry VIII?

3 Write these numbers using Roman numerals:
a) 3 b) 400 ✓ c) 6
d) 9 e) 38 f) 215
g) 560 h) 12 i) 849 ✓

4 The year in which a film, or TV programme, is made is often shown in Roman numerals during the final credits. When were these Charlie Chaplin films made?
a) The Gold Rush MCMXXV ✓ b) The Vagabond MCMXVI
c) City Lights MCMXXXI d) The Great Dictator MCMXL

5 Check which of the following statements are true and which are false:
a) XXI + XII = XXXIII
b) LXV + XI = LXXVI
c) LXI + V = LXIV
d) XIV + I = XV
e) XIV + XVI = XX
f) XIV + XIV = XXII
g) XC + X = C
h) XC + X = CXX

6 Work out, leaving your answers in Roman numerals:
a) XXV + XI b) XXXIII + XXVII ✓ c) CCXL + XV d) XXVI − XI
e) MLX − XXX f) DCL − LX g) DXCI − XI ✓

7 Find the value of the following, giving your answers in Roman numerals. You may find it easier to do the calculation in modern notation.
a) XXV multiplied by VII b) XLVIII divided by XXIV

1.2 Place value

In a number such as Roman III, each I has the same value regardless of its position. Compare this with the modern number 111 in which the place values of the 1s are all different. The ancient system may *appear* simpler but calculations involving multiplication and division, for example, are much more difficult. The system that we use today is based on the number ten and is known as the **decimal system** from the Latin word *decem* meaning ten.

1 In the number 471, the 7 stands for 7 tens. What does the 7 stand for in each of these numbers?
a) 71 b) 701 c) 7001 ✓ d) 17
e) 107 f) 1007 g) 170 h) 1070
i) 10 070 j) 1700 k) 10 700 l) 7010

2 The ancient Roman system didn't have a symbol for zero. Why is zero so important in the decimal system?

3 a) Which number is ten times as large as 63?
b) Describe a method for multiplying any whole number by ten.
c) Explain why your method works.
d) Describe a method for multiplying any whole number by 100.
e) Describe a method for multiplying any whole number by 30.

4 Write down the value of the following:
a) 108 × 10 b) 47 × 100 c) 21 × 30 d) 83 × 200
e) 506 × 40 f) 3007 × 60 g) 204 × 500 h) 3100 × 600

5 The smallest number that can be made with 7, 9 and 1 is 179. Find the smallest number that can be made with:
a) 3, 7, 9 and 1 b) 2, 5, 9 and 3 c) 8, 2, 7, 6 and 1 d) 1, 2, 1, 6 and 4

6 a) Explain what is *wrong* with each of these calculations:
(i) 234 + 41 = 644 (ii)
```
  24
× 36
 144
  72
 216
```
(iii) 3000 − 1726 = 2726

b) Find the *correct* answers – without using a calculator.

7 Find the value of these and show your method clearly:

a) 8431 − 1726 b) 6500 − 1432 c) 9000 − 6514 ✓ d) 3215 − 216
e) 2403 − 1074 f) 137 × 40 g) 632 × 70 h) 712 × 60
i) 63 × 47 ✓ j) 91 × 24 k) 743 × 35 l) 375 × 83

1.3 Extending the system

The pattern of place values for whole numbers may be extended as far to the *left* as we like.

… Th H T U

This allows us to represent very large numbers without having to introduce any new symbols.

Extending the pattern to the *right* allows us to represent **fractions** in the same system.

A decimal point is used to separate the whole number part from the fraction part of a number.

… Th H T U $\frac{1}{10}$ $\frac{1}{100}$ …

Example

Each of the following numbers has the place value of one of its figures shown above it, but the decimal point is missing. Re-write the numbers using a decimal point and put them in order of size, smallest first.

T	$\frac{1}{10}$	$\frac{1}{100}$	U
4 6 1	2 8 9	8 1 2	1 5 4 2

Answer

T U $\frac{1}{10}$	U $\frac{1}{10}$ $\frac{1}{100}$	$\frac{1}{10}$ $\frac{1}{100}$ $\frac{1}{1000}$	T U $\frac{1}{10}$ $\frac{1}{100}$
4 6 1 = 46.1	2 8 9 = 2.89	8 1 2 = 0.812	1 5 4 2 = 15.42

In order of size, smallest first, these are: 0.812, 2.89, 15.42, and 46.1.

---

1 Re-write the following numbers using a decimal point and put them in order of size, smallest first:

U	$\frac{1}{10}$	T	$\frac{1}{1000}$
2 9 7	3 4 1	8 7 3 2	6 5 4 2

2 The value of the 9 in the number 431.9 is 9 tenths. State the value of the 9 in each of these numbers:

a) 43.19 b) 927.8 c) 96.5 d) 0.09 e) 8.92 f) 80.92

3 Write these numbers using a decimal point:

a) $\frac{7}{10}$ b) $\frac{3}{100}$ c) $5\frac{1}{10}$ d) $12\frac{3}{100}$ e) $\frac{27}{100}$ f) $\frac{39}{1000}$

4 List these numbers in order of size, smallest first:

0.743, 0.734, 2, 1.46, 1.999, 0.09999

5 Which figure in 23.745 has the same place value as the 8 in 6.18? Explain how you were able to decide.

6 a) If a decimal number is multiplied by 10, what happens to the place value of each figure?
b) Find the value of: (i) 6.73 × 10 (ii) 0.8 × 10 (iii) 147 × 10

7 a) A calculator shows that 26.7 ÷ 10 = 2.67. Explain what has happened to the place value of each figure.
b) Find the value of: (i) 3.56 ÷ 10 (ii) 2.45 ÷ 10 (iii) 8.7 ÷ 10 16 ÷ 10

8 Work out without using a calculator:
a) 0.7 × 10 b) 0.7 × 100 c) 0.7 × 1000 d) 0.07 × 1000
e) 8.6 ÷ 10 f) 8.6 ÷ 100 g) 8.6 ÷ 1000 h) 860 ÷ 1000

9 Re-write the following numbers, missing off any zeros that aren't needed:
a) 0060.030 ✓ b) 0707.070

10 Find the values needed to complete these statements:
a) … × 0.81 = 81 ✓ b) … ÷ 10 = 4.67 c) … × 100 = 0.6
d) 32 ÷ … = 0.032 e) … × 10 = 86 f) … × 0.23 = 230
g) 68.4 ÷ … = 0.0684

1.4 Reading scales

The top scale is marked in tenths so each division is 0.1.

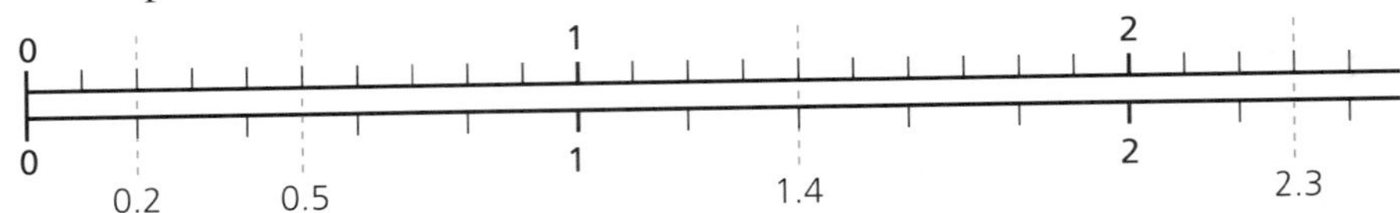

The bottom scale is marked in fifths so each division is 0.2.
(*Note*: $\frac{1}{5} = \frac{2}{10} = 0.2$)

1 What numbers do these arrows point to?

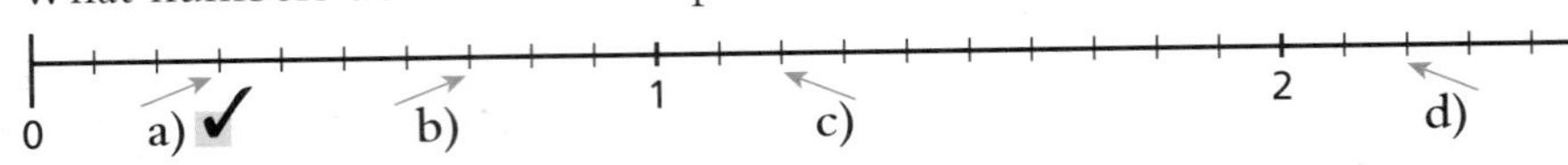

2 What values are shown here?

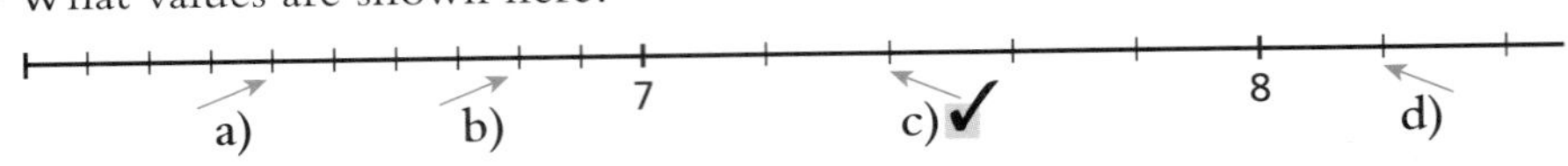

3 a) What is the value of each division on this scale?

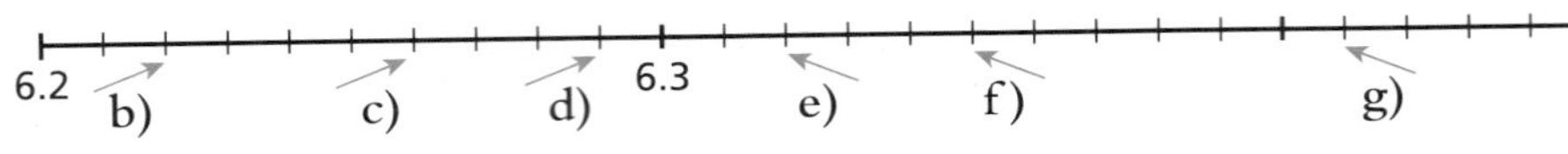

b) to g) Find the labelled values.

4 Work out which number is half-way between:
a) 2 and 3 b) 87 and 88 c) 2.1 and 2.2
d) 1.9 and 2 e) 3.72 and 3.73

5 Write down the whole number nearest to each of the following:
a) 6.37 b) 2.58 c) 4.47 d) 7.28
e) 12.49 f) 2.6143 g) 8.0976 h) 15.5102

6 For each of the following pairs of numbers, state which one is nearer to the number given in brackets:
a) 8.6, 8.7 (8.63) ✓
b) 2.3, 2.4 (2.347)
c) 4.2, 4.3 (4.271)
d) 6.5, 6.6 (6.5638)
e) 3.46, 3.47 (3.468)
f) 0.369, 0.370 (0.369 27)
g) 0.183, 0.184 (0.183 51)
h) 0.012, 0.013 (0.012 49)

You may find it helpful to write down the mid-value of each pair first, e.g. the mid-value of 8.6 and 8.7 is 8.65.

7 For each of the following pairs of numbers, decide which one is nearer to 3.714 6. Use a number line to show your reasoning.
a) 3 or 4 b) 3.7 or 3.8 ✓ c) 3.71 or 3.72 d) 3.714 or 3.715

8 Decide which of the following is nearer to 3.141 592:
a) 3 or 4 b) 3.1 or 3.2 c) 3.14 or 3.15 d) 3.141 or 3.142
e) 3.141 5 or 3.141 6 f) 3.141 59 or 3.141 60

1.5 Decimal places

A carpenter needs to saw a piece of wood, 182.5 cm long, into 6 equal lengths. Using a calculator, 182.5 ÷ 6 is displayed as 30.41666667.

Discussion point

Is it sensible to say that each piece will be 30.416 666 67 cm long? What is a sensible level of accuracy to use?

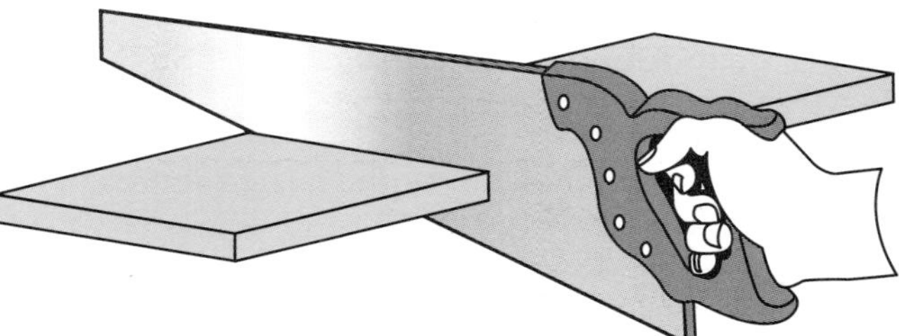

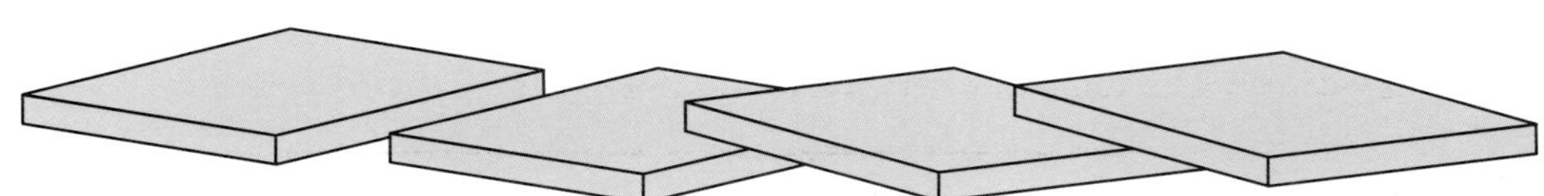

The number 2.137

has 3 figures to the right of the decimal point.
We say that this number has **3 decimal places** (D.P.).

The final stage of a calculation often involves rounding off the answer to reduce the number of decimal places to a sensible level.

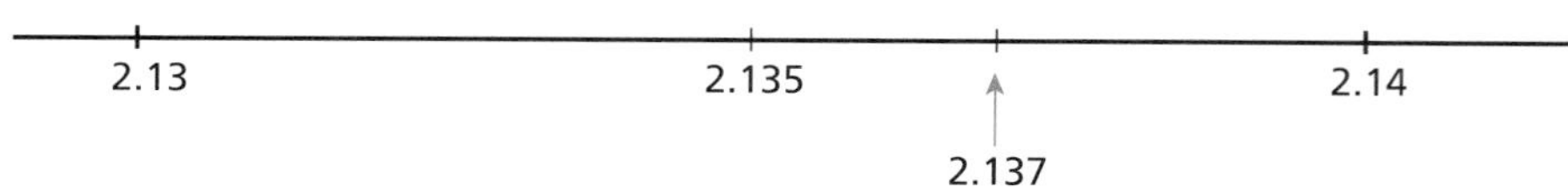

Since the third decimal place is *more than 5*, it follows that 2.137 is nearer to 2.14 than 2.13. We say that 2.137 **rounds off** to 2.14 correct to 2 decimal places (2 D.P.).

1 Suppose that 2.137 is to be rounded to one decimal place.
a) Between which two values does it lie? ✓
b) Which value is it closer to?
c) Explain how you can round 2.137 to one decimal place by considering the second decimal place.

2 Round these off to one decimal place:

a) 5.68	b) 0.09	c) 1.399
d) 1.3399	e) 5.99 ✓	f) 7.042

3 Round off to two decimal places:

a) 0.239	b) 4.542	c) 8.703	d) 2.967
e) 3.296	f) 0.0374	g) 0.1234	h) 0.0709

4 Which of the following numbers would round off to 2.67 to two decimal places?

a) 2.674	b) 2.669	c) 2.659	d) 2.701
e) 2.664	f) 2.667	g) 2.6708	h) 2.6748

The number 7.25 is exactly halfway between 7.2 and 7.3 and so it isn't clear how to round it to one decimal place. The usual way of dealing with this problem is to **round up** to the larger value. So 7.25 is given as 7.3 to one decimal place.

5 Round these off to the nearest tenth:

a) 0.65	b) 2.35	c) 18.45	d) 11.55
e) 16.95	f) 4.05		

6 Round 7.349 **a)** to two decimal places **b)** to one decimal place.
Explain what goes wrong if you try to use your answer to part **a)** to find the answer to part **b)**.

7 A group of seven friends wins a £10 000 National Lottery prize. They have an agreement that any winnings are to be shared equally.
You are asked to work out how much each prize-winner should receive.
a) Use a calculator to work out 10 000 ÷ 7.
b) To be as accurate as possible, how much should each person receive?
c) How much money is left over?
d) What happens if you are told to share out the money to the nearest £10 each and to keep the rest for yourself?

8 Round off to the nearest penny:

a) £5.678 54 ✓ b) £14.995 643 c) £0.873 216 d) £11.464 9723
e) £365 ÷ 9 f) £761 ÷ 6 g) £5000 ÷ 11 h) £2500 ÷ 17

9 The cost of electricity in the home depends on the number of *units* used. A typical household may use around 2000 units, per quarter, and the cost per unit is usually given in pence to two decimal places. The figure calculated is rounded to the nearest penny.
(*Note*: the total cost usually includes a standing charge together with VAT but this question deals only with the cost of the units.)
a) Work out the cost of 1788 units at 7.07p per unit.
b) If the charges are increased to 7.09p per unit, find the new cost of 1788 units.
c) If the cost per unit is increased by one penny, what difference would this make to the cost of 2000 units?
d) Why do you think the cost of units is given to $\frac{1}{100}$th of a penny?

1.6 Without a calculator

When adding or subtracting decimals, you should first position the numbers so that the decimal points are in line.

Discuss the rule. Why does it work?

1 Work out:

a) 21.34 + 6.5 b) 7.3 + 1.67 c) 0.0583 + 0.765 d) 12.43 + 7
e) 235 + 6.79 f) £32.48 + £9 g) £431 + £17.50 h) £3.27 + 146p

2 Find the value of:

a) 64.78 − 7.3 b) 12.9 − 2.47 c) 8.6 − 0.042 e) 6.781 − 3
e) 45 − 8.67 f) £16 − £4.37 g) 746p − £2.30 h) £34 − 123p

One approach to multiplying decimals is to start with some results that are known and extend the pattern.

$6 \times 4 = 24$		
$6 \times 40 = 240$	$60 \times 4 = 240$	
$6 \times 400 = 2400$	$60 \times 40 = 2400$	$600 \times 4 = 2400$

3 What result is suggested, by extending the pattern in the first column *upwards*, for the value of 6×0.4? ✓

4 By extending the other columns upwards, find two other pairs of numbers that make 24 when multiplied.

5 What is 6×0.04?

6 Find two other products that give the same result as question 5. ✓

7 What is 0.6×4?

8 What are the missing entries in this pattern?
(You will find it *easier* if you follow the order given by the letters.)

(g)	(h)	$900 \times 0.007 = 6.3$
$9 \times 7 = 63$	(e)	(f)
$9 \times 70 = 630$	(c) ✓	(d)
(a)	$90 \times 70 = 6300$	(b) ✓

9 Complete the steps in this process to find the value of 0.16×0.352:

$16 \times 352 = 5632$
$1.6 \times 352 =$
$0.16 \times 352 =$
$0.16 \times 35.2 =$
$0.16 \times \ldots = \ldots$
$\ldots \times \ldots = \ldots$

10 The process used in question 9 can be made quicker by missing out some of the steps.

Try the approach below to find the value of 0.71×1.43, given that $71 \times 143 = 10153$.

$71 \times 143 = 10153$
$0.71 \times 143 =$
$0.71 \times 1.43 =$

Describe how to work out the answer using a single step.

11 Use the fact that $7 \times 16 = 112$ to work out:
a) 70×16 b) 7×1.6 c) 0.7×0.16 ✓ d) 1.6×0.7

12 Given that $147 \times 23 = 3381$, find the value of:
a) 14.7×23 b) 1.47×2.3 c) 0.147×23

13 Work out 36×142 and hence find the value of:
a) 36×14.2 b) 0.36×142 c) 3.6×1.42

14 Find:
a) 0.3×0.2 b) 6.8×24 c) 2.7×3.61

15 Given that $17 \times 243 \times 18 = 74\,358$, find the value of:
a) $1.7 \times 2.43 \times 18$ b) $18 \times 24.3 \times 0.017$

16 Given that $32 \times 14 = 448$, copy and complete:
a) $32 \times \ldots = 4.48$ b) $\ldots \times 1.4 = 0.0448$

1.7 More or less?

The symbol < used to stand for 'is less than' and the symbol > is used to stand for 'is more than'.

(To remember this, you might think of < for <ess than.)

---

1 Which of the following statements are true?
a) $3.12 < 3.21$ b) $0.8 > 0.09$ c) $2.409 > 2.48$ d) $\frac{7}{10} < 0.699$

2 Compare these pairs of values and insert the appropriate symbol, < or >:
a) $8 \times 0.9 \ldots 8$ b) $24 \ldots 24 \times 1.2$ c) $0.3 \times 0.3 \ldots 0.3 \times 0.3 \times 0.3$

A statement such as $7 < x < 10$ (or $10 > x > 7$) tells us that x is a number which lies between 7 and 10.

3 Find any number x to make these statements true:
a) $6 < x < 7$ b) $8.1 < x < 8.2$ c) $9.36 > x > 9.35$ d) $4 < x < 4.1$

2 ANGLES AND SYMMETRY

2.1 Angles

An angle is an amount of turn or rotation.

One complete turn or revolution is 360°

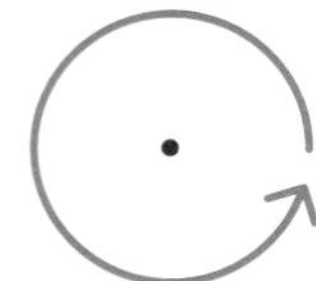

A half turn is 180°.

A quarter turn is 90°. This is also called a **right angle.**

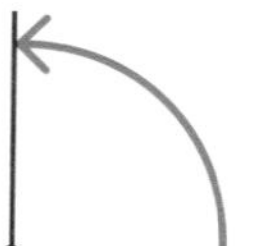

45° is half of a right angle.

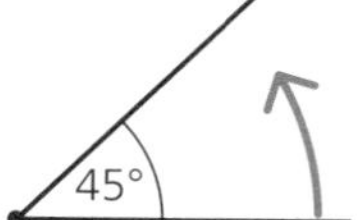

1 Without using your protractor or angle measurer, try to identify each of the angles drawn here. In order to help you there are three possible answers for you to choose from.

Guess the size.

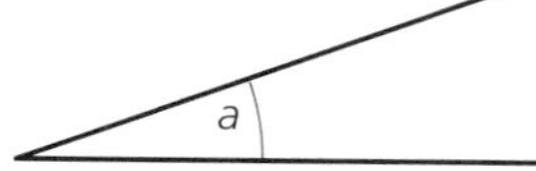

a) Is this 20°, 40° or 60°?

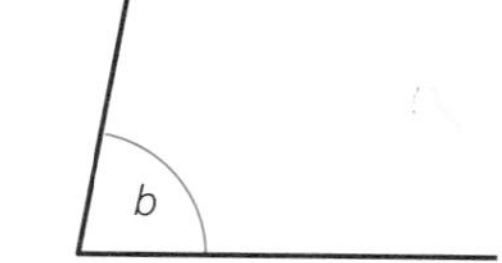

b) Is this 60°, 80° or 100°?

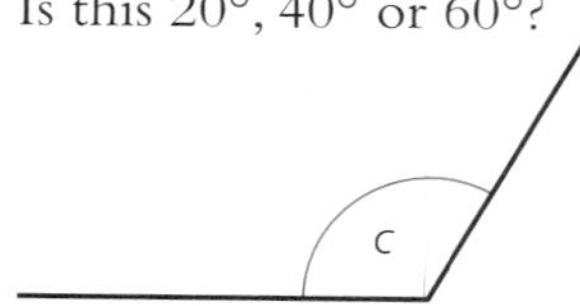

c) Is this 100°, 120° or 140°?

d) Is this 40°, 60° or 30°?

When you have decided, measure each angle to check your answers.

2.2 Naming angles

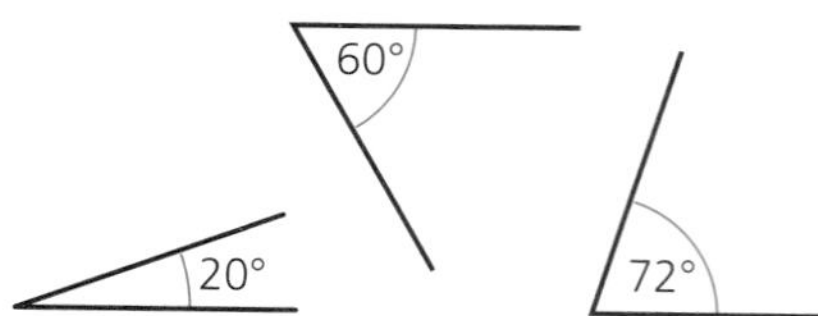

An angle which is less than 90° is called an **acute angle**.

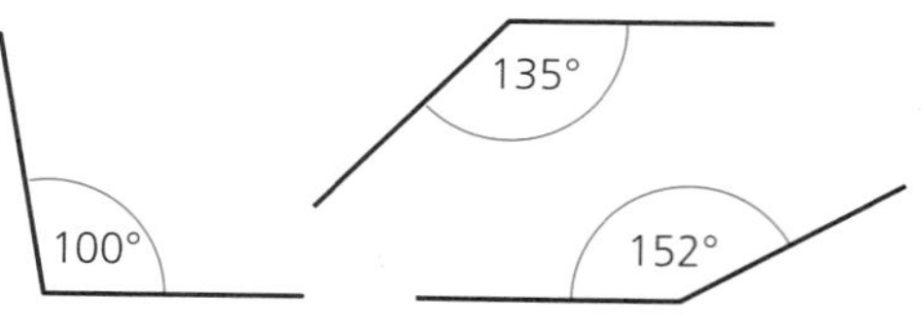

An angle bigger than 90° but less than 180° is called an **obtuse angle**.

An angle which is bigger than 180° is called a **reflex angle**.

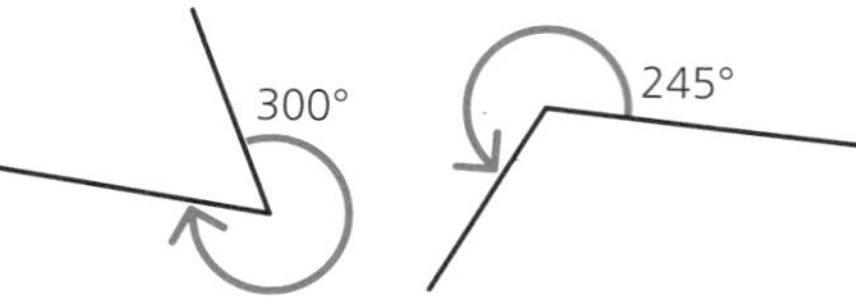

1 Draw a table like this:
Write these angles in the correct column

(i) 18°	(ii) 173°	(iii) 250°	(iv) 185°
(v) 56°	(vi) 283°	(vii) 155°	(viii) 128°
(ix) 222°	(x) 111°	(xi) 11°	(xii) 143°
(xiii) 163°	(xiv) 209°	(xv) 325°	(xvi) 69°

Acute angle	Obtuse angle	Reflex angle

2 Joe has drawn some angles in his maths book, but has measured them wrongly. Can you decide what he has done wrong?

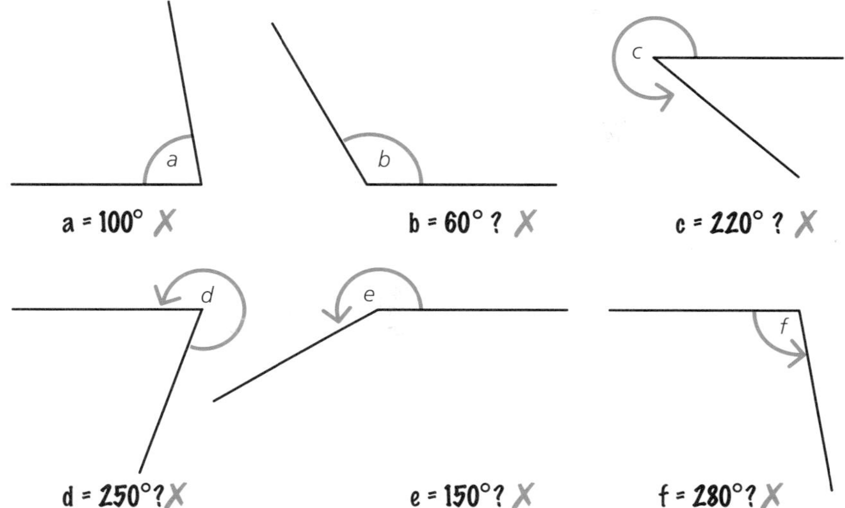

Write down the correct size for each angle.

2.3 Scale drawings

Scale drawings are very useful for finding disatnces and angles that cannot be measured directly.

Here is a *sketch* showing a tree and some measurements. The height of the tree in the sketch, for example, doesn't help us to work out the actual height of the tree.

If, instead, the diagram is *drawn to scale* then each measurement on the diagram can give us information.

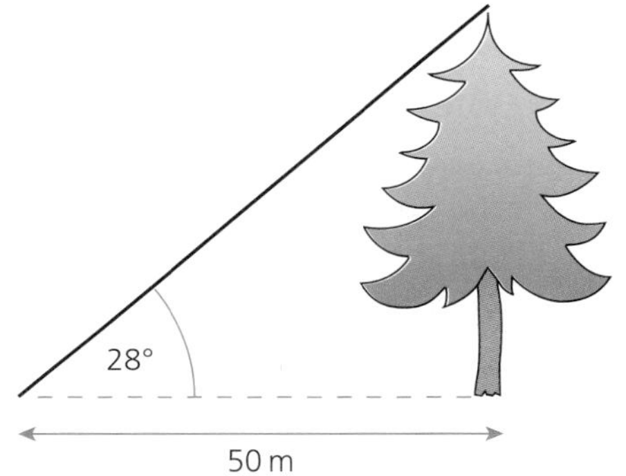

(continued)

To draw the diagram to scale you need to:

- decide on a scale to use e.g. 1 cm : 10 m
- use the scale to represent 50 m distance (draw a line 5 cm long)
- draw the angles accurately (28° and 90°)

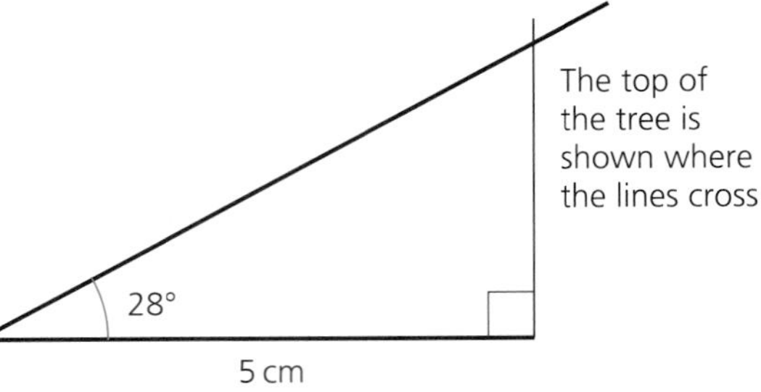

You can measure the height of the tree on the scale drawing. Check that this is 2.7 cm to 1 D.P.

The actual height of the tree is given by 2.7 × 10 m = 27 m

1 In the seaside town where Joe lives, local residents are complaining about a new block of flats which has been built on the sea front. They can't see the sea any more and they say the flats are too tall. The builders say they have planning permission to build the block 65 feet tall, and that this is what they have done. The county architect is called in. Here are the measurements he has made. Who is right?

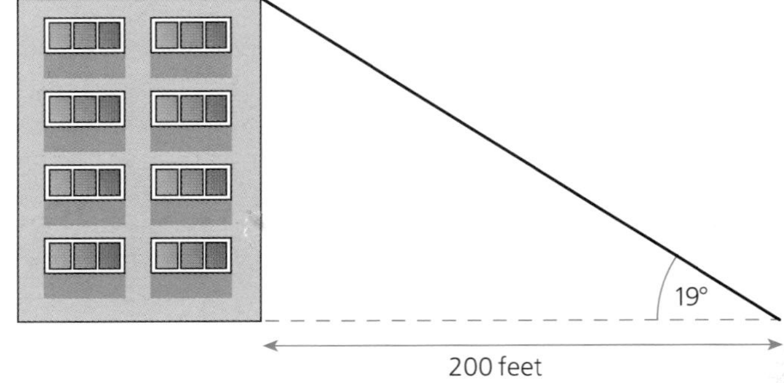

2 Laura's history class go on a trip to a ruined castle. Their teacher asks them to make sketches of the castle and to draw plans. Laura decides to find the height of the castle walls. Unfortunately there is a deep ditch (which was the moat).
She starts at A on the diagram and finds the angle of elevation. It is 25°. She walks 50 metres towards the castle to B and measures the angle of elevation again. It is 42°. Make a scale drawing using a scale of 1 cm for 10 m. Find the height of the castle walls.

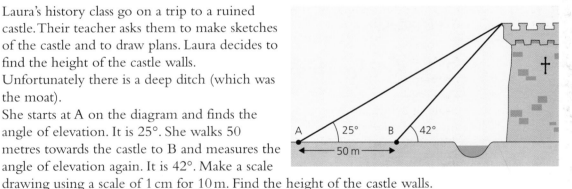

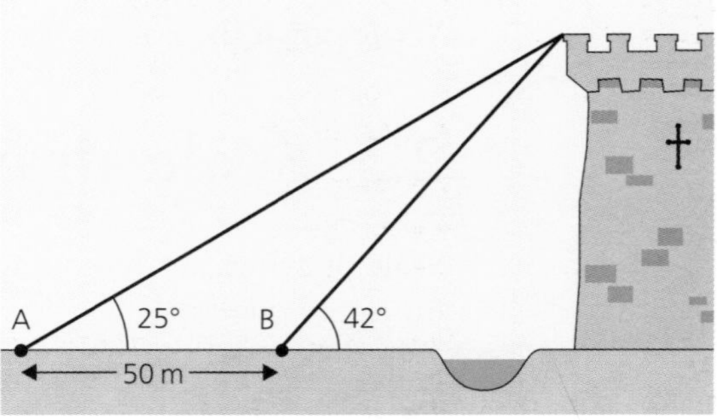

3 Make a scale drawing to find the height of the tower, using the measurements in this sketch.

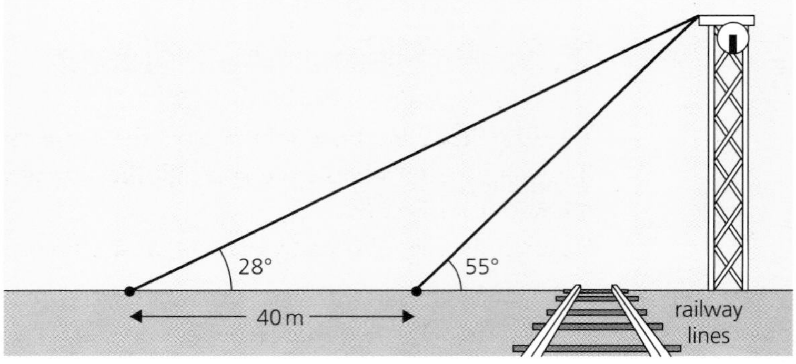

2.4 Tessellations

A tessellation is a pattern that you can make by repeating the same shape without leaving any gaps.

1 Here is a **tessellation** made using the same triangle over and over again.

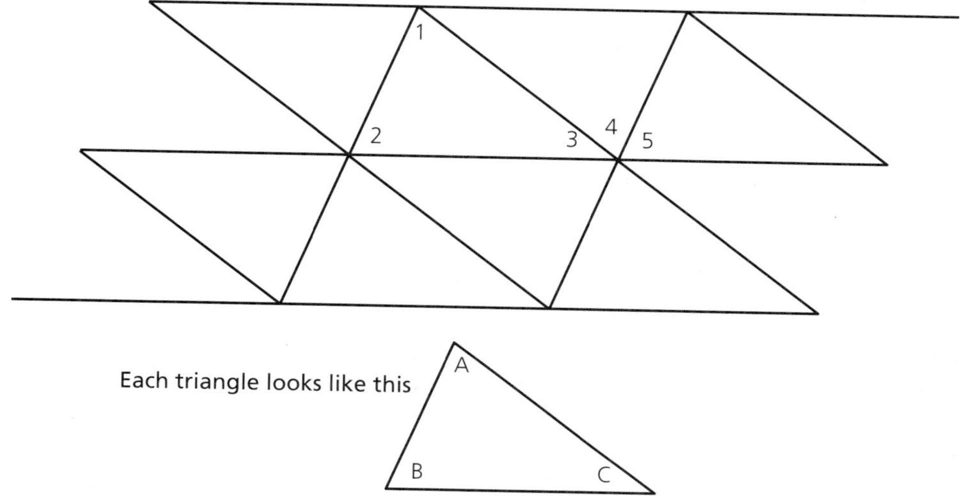

Which of these angles, A, B or C, corresponds to each numbered angle on the tessellation?

1 = Angle …
2 = Angle …
3 = Angle …
4 = Angle …
5 = Angle …

How does this demonstrate that the angles in the triangle total 180°?

2 Draw a tessellation of your own based on triangles. Can you explain why you can use *any* triangle to draw a tessellating pattern?

2.5 Angles and lines

Parallel lines are lines which have the same direction.
They are the same distance apart all the way along.
They will never cross.
Parallel lines are shown by arrows on the lines:

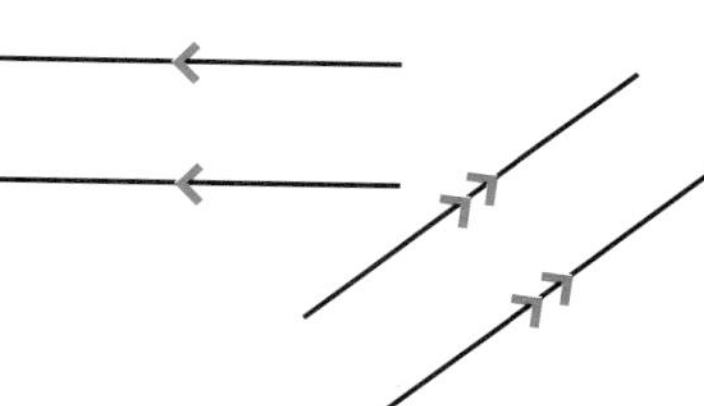

1 Use your protractor to measure the angles marked in each diagram.

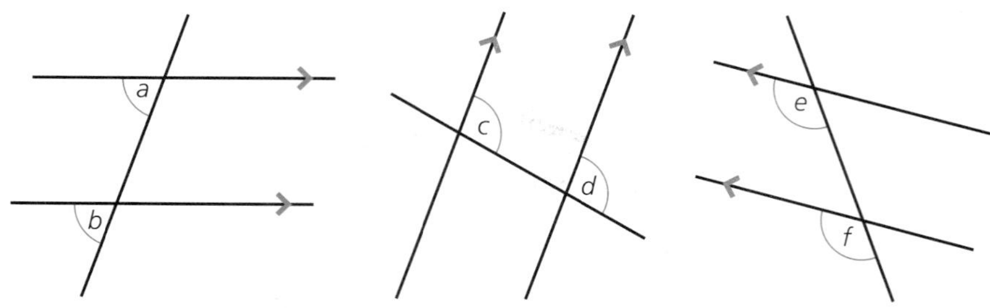

In these diagrams *a* and *b*, *c* and *d*, and *e* and *f*, are all pairs of **corresponding angles**. Corresponding angles are in corresponding positions.
One angle such as angle *a* can be slid down or translated onto the corresponding angle.

Write a statement about corresponding angles. ✔

2 Use your protractor to measure the angles marked here.

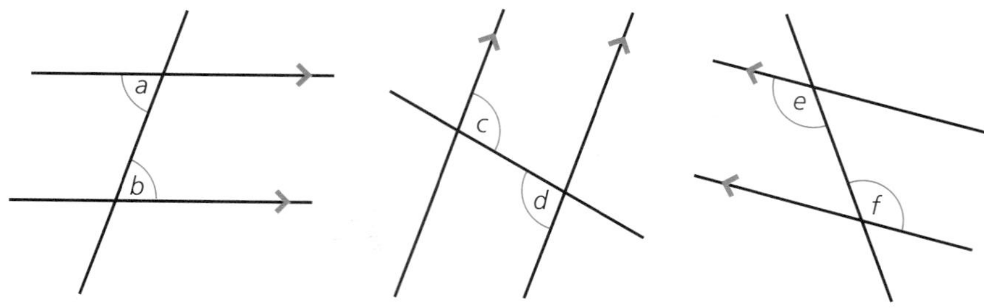

In these diagrams *a* and *b*, *c* and *d*, and *e* and *f*, are all pairs of **alternate angles**. Alternate angles are both inside the parallel lines, but they are on opposite sides of the **transversal** (the third line which crosses the parallel line). One angle can be rotated round to fit onto the other.
Write a statement about alternate angles. ✔

3 Intersecting lines are lines which cross each other.
Measure angles a, b, c and d in this diagram.

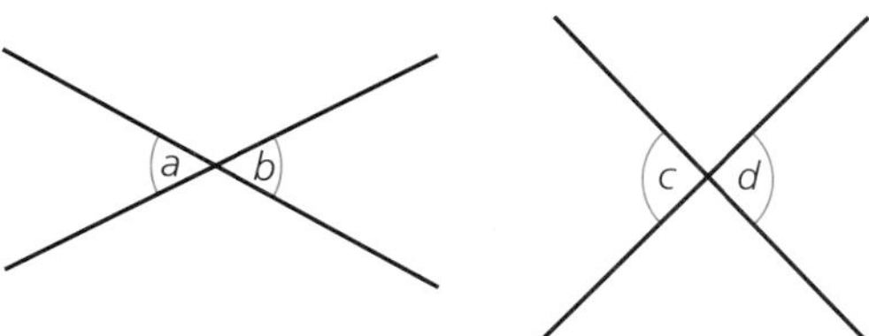

Angles a and b and angles c and d, are pairs of **vertically opposite** angles.
Write a statement about vertically opposite angles. ✓

4 In each diagram work out the angles marked with a letter.

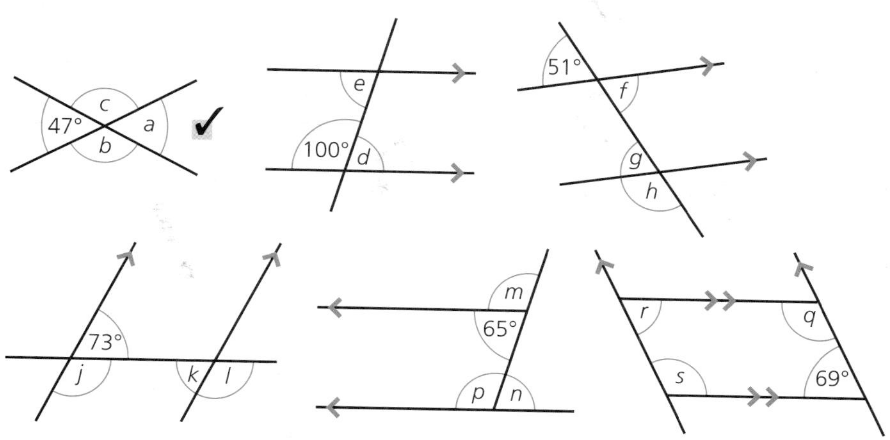

You can use the results of this section to *prove* that the angles of a triangle add up to 180°.

5 **a)** Copy the diagram and label an alternate angle to angle b.

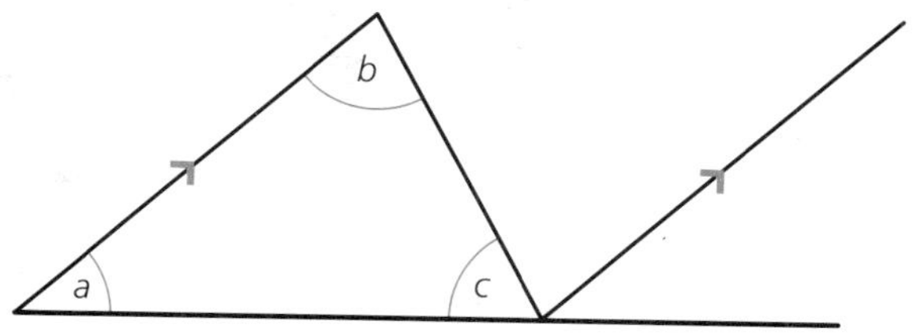

b) Label an angle corresponding to angle a.
c) Explain why $a + b + c$ must be 180°.

2.6 Reflections and line symmetry

In nature there are many examples of line symmetry.

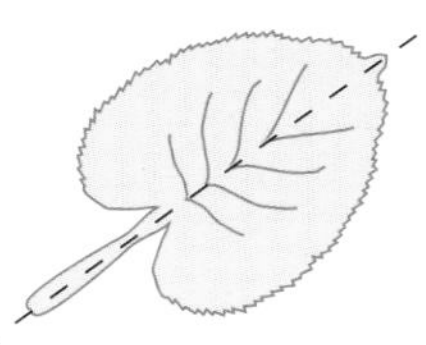

Most types of leaves are symmetrical. Do you think you are symmetrical? You may think you are – but it is quite unlikely. Many people have one foot larger than the other, or even different sized eyes.

Here is a photograph of a face. Try using a mirror to reflect each side of the person's face in turn.

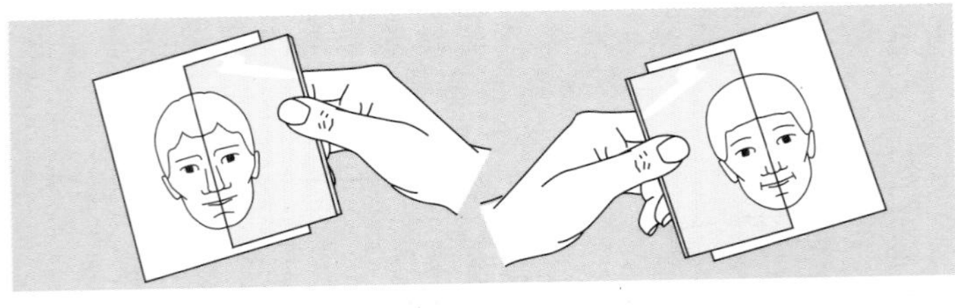

How do the two reflected faces compare?
Try this at home with other photographs of faces.

Each dotted line on this diagram is a line of symmetry.

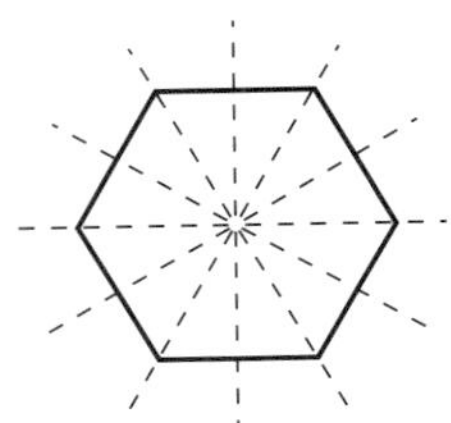

1 How many lines of symmetry do these shapes have?

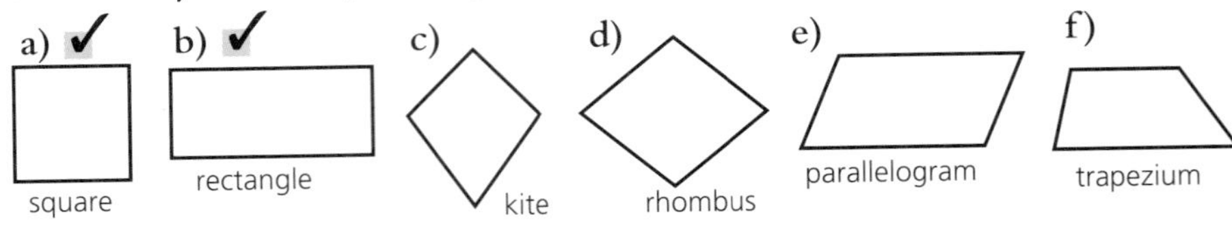

2 Which of these letters have a line of symmetry? JELLY

3 Reflect the word POTATO in the x-axis (so that the x-axis is the mirror line or line of symmetry). Use a mirror to check.

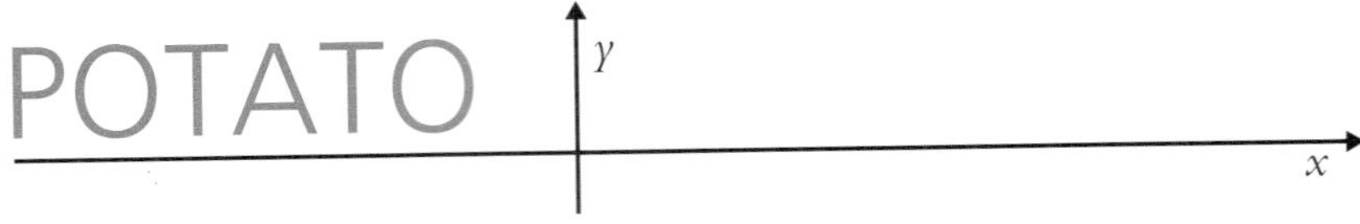

4 Reflect the word BREAD in the y-axis. Use a mirror to check.

BREAD

5 Reflect this triangle in the x-axis. Reflect it in the y-axis.

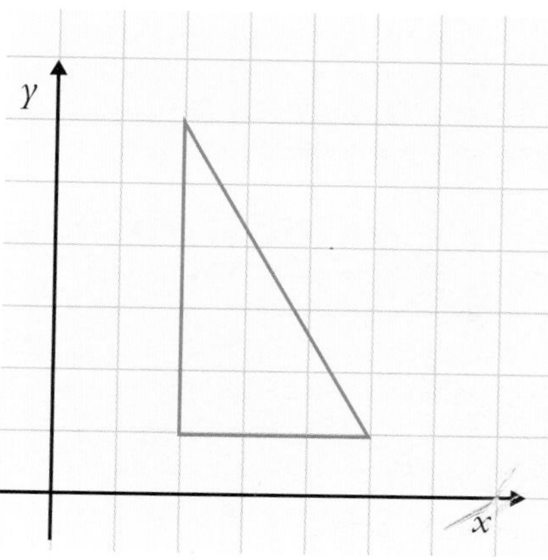

6 a) Plot the points below and join them up in order:

a (1, 1) b (4, 1) c (4, 2) d (2, 2) e (2, 3) f (4, 3) g (4, 4)
h (2, 4) i (2, 5) j (4, 5) k (4, 6) l (1, 6) m (1, 1)

b) Reflect this shape in the x-axis.

c) Reflect it in the y-axis.

d) Complete your drawing so it has two lines of symmetry.

7 Copy this shape onto graph paper.

Reflect it in the line labelled 'L' in the diagram.

When the point (4, 1) is reflected in the line 'L' where does it go?

Where does the point (4, 2) go?

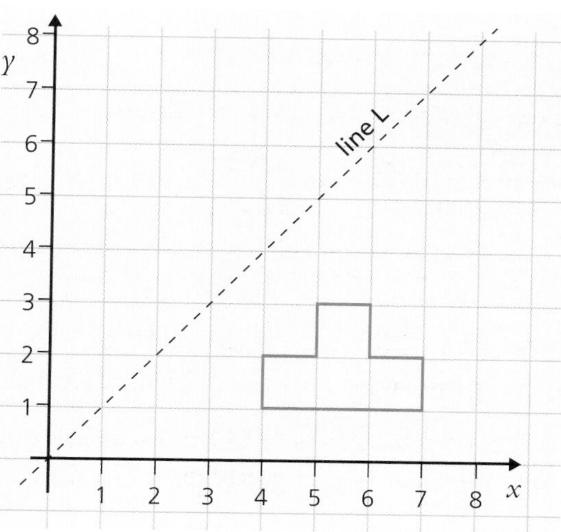

2.7 Rotational symmetry

If this shape were cut out and a pin put through the centre, it could be rotated. As it turned it would appear to be in the same position three times in one complete turn.

It has **rotational symmetry order 3**.

This next shape has **rotational symmetry order 4**.

1 For each shape give its order of rotational symmetry:

a) 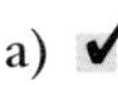

b) 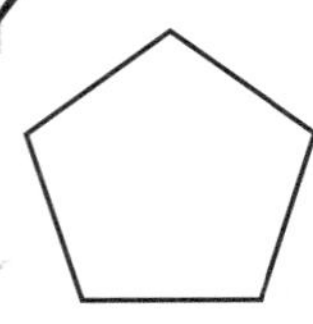

c) 

d) 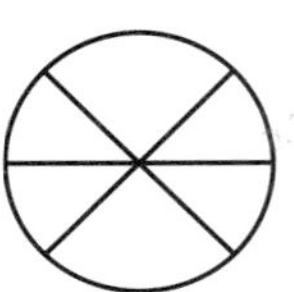

e) 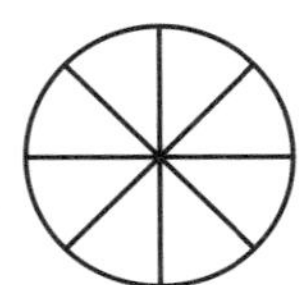

f) 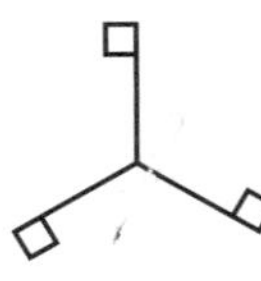

g) 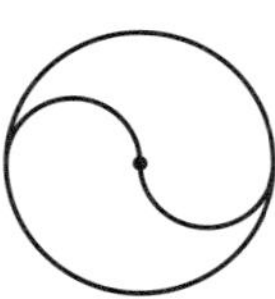

h) 

i) 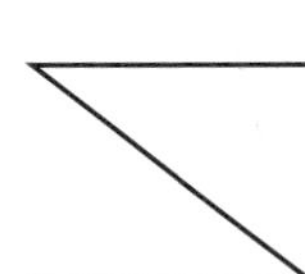

2 Complete each diagram so that it has rotational symmetry about the given point:
Use a protractor to help you measure angles correctly.

a) 

b) 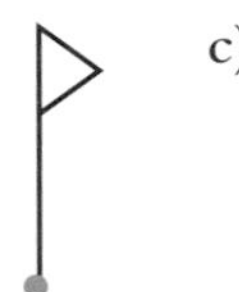

c) 

3 Copy this diagram:
Rotate the shape through 90° anticlockwise.

Repeat this twice more so that you have a shape with rotational symmetry order 4.

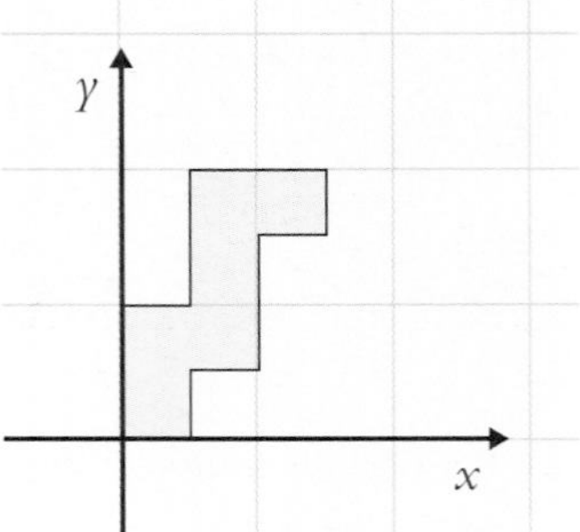

4 This ingenious tessellation was drawn by the Dutch artist M. C. Escher.

There are two centres of rotational symmetry through the design marked by ▲ and ■ which are easy to see.

a) What is the order of rotational symmetry at the centres marked ▲?
b) ... at the centres marked ■?
c) Can you find the hidden centres of rotational symmetry order 2?

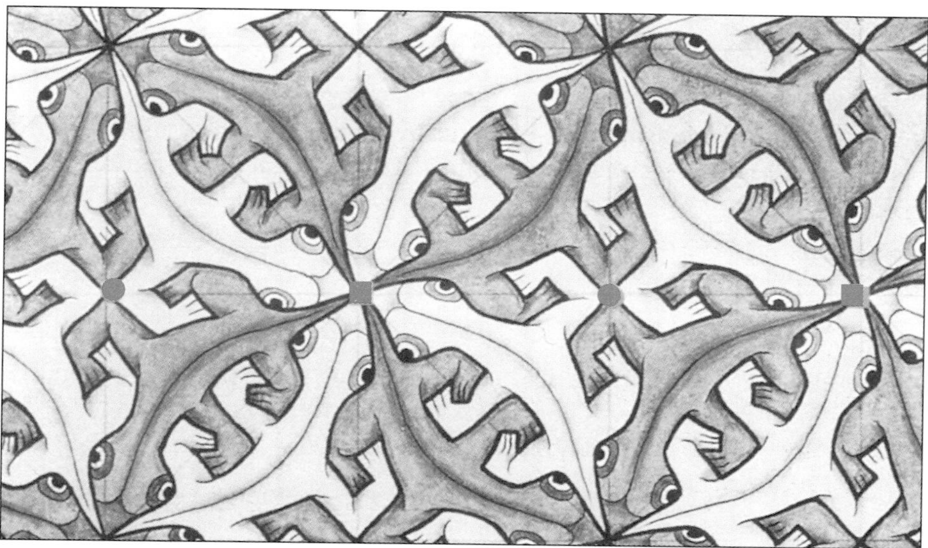

5 a) Each point marked by a ■ is a centre of rotation. What is the order of that rotation?
b) Each point marked by a ● is also a centre of rotation; of what order?

3 DIVISION

3.1 Division of whole numbers

Even though calculators are widely available, it is still important to know how to obtain the answers without one.

Example

What is 875 ÷ 5?

Answer

$$5\overline{)8^{3}75} \quad \text{quotient } 1$$

1 ← 5 fits into 8 once, with a remainder of 3 which is carried onto the next figure

$$5\overline{)8^{3}7^{2}5} \quad \text{quotient } 1\ 7$$

7 ← 5 fits into 37 7 times, with a remainder of 2

$$5\overline{)8^{3}7^{2}5} \quad \text{quotient } 1\ 7\ 5$$

5 ← 5 fits into 25 5 times

And so 875 ÷ 5 = 175.
Since there is no remainder, we can say that:

- 875 is **divisible** by 5
- 5 and 175 are **factors** of 875

---

1 Find the value of these without a calculator:
a) 924 ÷ 7 b) 6525 ÷ 5 c) 1968 ÷ 6 d) 4344 ÷ 8

2 Which of the following numbers is divisible by 7? Show your working.
a) 2884 b) 3777 c) 6993 d) 2442

3 Which of these are factors of 360?
a) 8 b) 7 c) 12 d) 15 e) 16 f) 35

The digit sum of a number is found by adding its digits and then, if necessary, repeating the process until the result is a single figure.

Example

Find the digit sum of 873 496.

Answer

8 + 7 + 3 + 4 + 9 + 6 = 37	This is not a single figure so the process is continued.
3 + 7 = 10	The result is still not a single figure.
1 + 0 = 1	The digit sum of 873 496 is 1.

---

4 Find the digit sum of each of the following numbers:
a) 46 532 b) 75 522 c) 87 945 d) 43 677 e) 86 593

5 Check which of the numbers in question 4 is divisible by:
a) 3 b) 9
and try to find a connection with the digit sums. Describe your findings clearly.

6 Use your answer to question 5 to decide which of the following numbers is:
a) divisible by 3 b) divisible by 9.
(i) 46 732 (ii) 72 314 (iii) 65 472 (iv) 811 233 (v) 412 365

7 How can we recognise a number that is divisible by:
a) 2 b) 5?

A prime number is a whole number, greater than 1, whose only factors are itself and 1.

It follows that the only *even* prime number is 2, which is also the *smallest* prime number.

8 List all of the prime numbers between 1 and 100.

9 Only one of the following numbers is prime. Which is it?
Explain your reasoning.
a) 534 794 b) 632 615 c) 131 071 d) 854 103

10 a) Write down any 3-figure number, then repeat it to make a 6-figure number.
b) Choose a prime number between 6 and 16.
c) Divide your 6-figure number by the prime number selected in **b)**.
Your maths teacher will pay you the value of your remainder in £s.

3.2 Division of decimals

The technique for dividing whole numbers extends easily to the division of decimals since the decimal fractions are an extension of the whole number system. However, we do need to keep track of the decimal point.

Example

Find 6.35 ÷ 5.

Answer

```
  1 . 2  7
5)6 ¹. 3 ³5
```

... and so we put a decimal point in the answer

the division has moved across the decimal point ...

Check – does the method give a sensible answer?

$635 \div 5 = 127$

÷100 ÷100

$6.35 \div 5 = 1.27$

Note: 5 ÷ 5 = 1 and so we should expect 6.35 ÷ 5 to be slightly more than 1

Example

What is 3.7 ÷ 4?

Answer

$$4\overline{)3.7^{1}0^{2}0} = 0.925$$

The extra zeros are needed to complete the working

1 Copy and complete

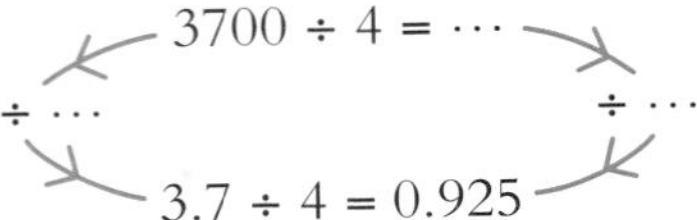

2 Find the value of these, making your method clear:

a) 17.6 ÷ 4 b) 20.52 ÷ 6 c) 2.268 ÷ 7 d) 0.114 ÷ 3

e) 41.6 ÷ 4 f) 38.6 ÷ 5 g) 0.0145 ÷ 8 h) 289.5 ÷ 6

Try these questions without using a calculator.

3 An athlete completes 4 laps of a running track in 3 minutes 59.2 seconds.

a) Convert the time taken to seconds.

b) What is the average time taken per lap?

4 Sarah works 7 hours overtime and earns an extra £47.81. What is her hourly rate of pay for the overtime?

5 Keith wants to buy a single videotape from the local store. The tapes are normally sold in packs of 5 for £8.75. If the shopkeeper agrees to split the pack, without making any extra charge, how much will Keith have to pay?

6 The total purchase price of a CD Midi System is £319.99. Helen pays £64.99 as a deposit and spreads the balance over 6 equal monthly payments. How much does Helen pay each month if there are no interest charges?

7 A car travels 376 miles on 9 gallons of fuel. Calculate the average fuel consumption in miles per gallon, to one decimal place.

(*Hint*: do the calculation to 2 decimal places and round off the answer.)

8 Find the cost of each of these carpets per m^2 and comment on whether the advert is fair.

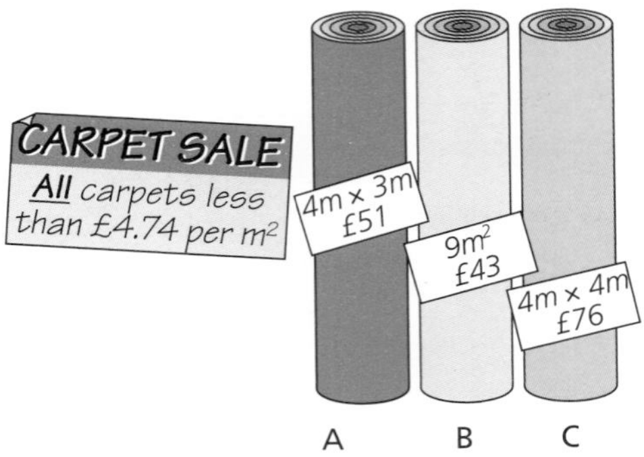

3.3 Equivalent fractions

1 a) Copy the figure and shade $\frac{3}{7}$ of it.

b) Use your diagram to help you complete the statement $\frac{3}{7} = \frac{}{14}$.

c) In the same way, copy and complete $\frac{4}{7} = \frac{}{14}$ and $\frac{6}{7} = \frac{12}{}$

Fractions such as $\frac{3}{7}$ and $\frac{6}{14}$ which are the same size, even though they are expressed in different terms, are said to be equivalent.

2 Describe the amount of shading in the diagram in two different ways, to find another pair of equivalent fractions.

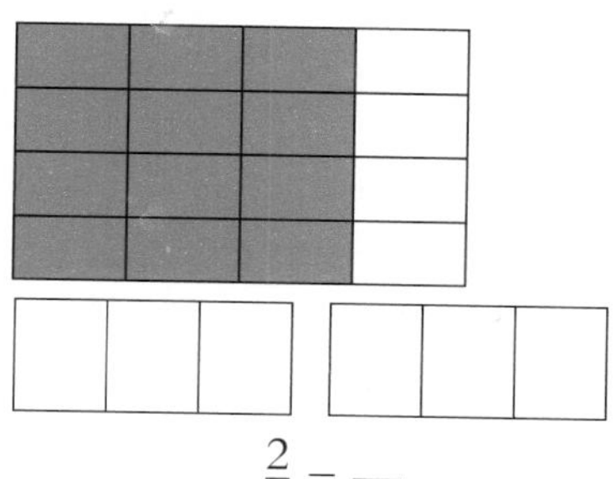

3 Copy these diagrams and add shading and extra lines, as necessary, to match the statement below. Copy and complete the statement.

$\frac{2}{3} = \frac{}{15}$

4 Given any fraction, if the top number (the **numerator**) is multiplied by some value, what must be done to the bottom number (the **denominator**) to make an equivalent fraction? ✓

5 Copy and complete these pairs of equivalent fractions.

a) $\frac{5}{6} = \frac{20}{}$ ✓ b) $\frac{8}{9} = \frac{}{27}$ c) $\frac{3}{8} = \frac{15}{}$ d) $\frac{24}{30} = \frac{}{5}$

Fractions with different denominators are difficult to compare directly. Choosing to work with equivalent fractions that have the same denominators makes the task much easier.

Example

Which of these two fractions is the larger, $\frac{5}{9}$ or $\frac{7}{12}$?

Answer

Both fractions can be written with a denominator of 36.

$\frac{5}{9} = \frac{20}{36}$, whereas $\frac{7}{12} = \frac{21}{36}$ and so $\frac{7}{12}$ is the larger fraction, i.e. $\frac{7}{12} > \frac{5}{9}$.

6 Write these fractions in order of size, smallest first.

a) $\frac{5}{8}, \frac{3}{4}, \frac{7}{12}, \frac{5}{6}$ b) $\frac{2}{3}, \frac{5}{6}, \frac{7}{10}, \frac{3}{5}$ c) $\frac{4}{9}, \frac{2}{3}, \frac{1}{2}, \frac{11}{18}$

Some fractions can be converted to decimals by finding an equivalent fraction with a denominator of 10, 100, 1000, etc.

Example

Turn these fractions into decimals: $\frac{3}{5}$, $\frac{2}{25}$.

Answer

$\frac{3}{5} = \frac{6}{10} = 0.6$

$\frac{2}{25} = \frac{8}{100} = 0.08$

7 Write each of these fractions with a denominator of 10, 100 or 1000 and convert the result to a decimal:

a) $\frac{2}{5}$ b) $\frac{11}{20}$ c) $\frac{49}{50}$ d) $\frac{4}{5}$ e) $\frac{9}{20}$ f) $\frac{9}{30}$ g) $\frac{7}{25}$ h) $\frac{24}{2000}$

3.4 Decimal patterns

An alternative method for converting fractions to decimals is to use division. For example, $\frac{3}{5}$ may be regarded as $3 \div 5$ which is the same as $3.0 \div 5$.

$5\overline{)3.{}^{3}0}$ = 0.6 giving $\frac{3}{5} = 0.6$ as in the example above.

The method can be used to convert any fraction to a decimal. It is also very easy to apply with a calculator.

1 Convert these fractions to decimals by division:

a) $\frac{2}{5}$ b) $\frac{3}{4}$ ✓ c) $\frac{37}{125}$ d) $\frac{261}{375}$

Fractions which do not have an equivalent with a denominator as a power of 10, convert to decimals with a **recurring** pattern.

For example, $\frac{1}{3} = 0.333\,333\,3\ldots$ which we write as $0.\dot{3}$.

$\frac{1}{6} = 0.166\,666\,6\ldots$ which is written as $0.1\dot{6}$

$\frac{123}{999} = 0.123\,123\,123\ldots$ is written as $0.\dot{1}2\dot{3}$ to show that the 123 repeats.

2 Write the following fractions as recurring decimals:

a) $\frac{1}{9}$ b) $\frac{4}{9}$ c) $\frac{7}{9}$ d) $\frac{3}{9}$

3 a) Check that your answer to 2 d) is the same as the result for $\frac{1}{3}$.

b) What do the results of question 2 suggest for the value of $\frac{9}{9}$?

4 Convert these fractions to recurring decimals and comment on the patterns found:

a) $\frac{1}{7}$ b) $\frac{2}{7}$ c) $\frac{3}{7}$ d) $\frac{4}{7}$

5 Work out 142 857 × 7. What does this suggest for the value of $\frac{7}{7}$? ✓

6 Find $\frac{1}{11}$ as a recurring decimal. What does this suggest for the value of $\frac{11}{11}$?

7 Use the results of questions 3, 5 and 6 to write 0.999 999 999 999 999... in its *simplest* form.

8 Write these as recurring decimals and describe the special nature of the patterns produced:

a) $\frac{31}{99}$ b) $\frac{7}{99}$ c) $\frac{456}{999}$ d) $\frac{12}{999}$

9 Write these recurring decimals as fractions:

a) 0.678 678... b) $0.\dot{4}\dot{1}$ c) $0.\dot{0}2\dot{9}$ d) $0.\dot{0}020\dot{8}$

3.5 Division by decimals

Example

Find 1.2 ÷ 0.06.

Answer

This may be written as $\frac{1.2}{0.06}$ and, using the idea of equivalent fractions, we can find an equivalent form in which the denominator is a whole number.

Therefore $\frac{1.2}{0.06} = \frac{120}{6} = 20$.

---

1 Find an expression equivalent to each of the following, such that the denominator is a whole number:

a) $\frac{4.71}{0.3}$ ✓ b) $\frac{2.75}{0.5}$ c) $\frac{0.196}{0.07}$ d) $\frac{0.384}{1.2}$

2 Complete the calculation of the expressions given in question 1 by carrying out the division by whole numbers.

3 Work out, without using a calculator:

a) 1.6 ÷ 0.05 b) 19.6 ÷ 0.4 c) 8.6792 ÷ 0.01

In some cases, the calculations may be simplified by cancelling common factors before completing the division.

Example
What is 0.56 ÷ 2.4?

Answer

$\frac{0.56}{2.4} = \frac{56}{240}$ It's probably much simpler to make both the numerator and the denominator into whole numbers first.

$= \frac{7}{30}$ A common factor of 8 may now be cancelled to simplify the fraction. Alternatively, the fraction can be simplified in stages.

$= \frac{0.7}{3}$ e.g. $\frac{56}{240} = \frac{28}{120} = \frac{14}{60} = \frac{7}{30}$

$= 0.2\dot{3}$

---

4 Use the method shown in the example to work out:
a) 0.49 ÷ 1.4 b) 7.2 ÷ 0.48 c) 99 ÷ 13.2
d) 8.5 ÷ 1.25 e) 0.279 ÷ 1.8 f) 17.64 ÷ 8.4

5 There are approximately 2.5 cm in one inch. How many inches are there in 30 cm?

6 A bag of potatoes weighs 5.5 lb. Given that there are 2.2 lb in 1 kg, how many kg do the potatoes weigh?

3.6 Percentages

Percentages are a convenient way of describing parts of a whole, in terms of hundredths, and are very commonly used in a wide range of situations. It is important to understand the connection with fractions and decimals.

1% means 1 part in 100 which may be written as $\frac{1}{100}$

and in the same way, 25% = $\frac{25}{100}$ which may be simplified to $\frac{1}{4}$.

Algebra may be used to give the rule for writing a percentage as a fraction.

In general, n% becomes $\frac{n}{100}$ when written as a fraction.

---

1 Write the following percentages as fractions in their simplest terms:
a) 50% b) [illegible] c) 12.5% d) 75% e) 20% f) 60%
g) 80% h) [illegible] i) [illegible] j) 30% k) 5% l) 2.5%

Having established how to convert percentages to fractions, we will now consider how to reverse the process.

Example

Convert $\frac{6}{25}$ to a percentage.

Answer

A fraction such as $\frac{6}{25}$ may be converted to a percentage by finding an equivalent fraction with a denominator of 100.

$\frac{6}{25} = \frac{24}{100}$ and so it follows that $\frac{6}{25} = 24\%$.

2 Write these fractions as percentages:

a) $\frac{7}{20}$ b) $\frac{11}{25}$ c) $\frac{9}{10}$ d) $\frac{31}{50}$ e) $\frac{4}{5}$ f) $\frac{42}{200}$ g) $\frac{42}{300}$ h) $\frac{42}{700}$

3 Convert these to percentages:

a) $\frac{9.1}{50}$ b) $\frac{8.3}{25}$ c) $\frac{16.8}{200}$ d) $\frac{15.6}{300}$ e) 11.4 out of 50

f) 9.72 out of 25 g) 18.8 out of 200

The process for converting a percentage to a fraction is easily extended to convert a percentage to a decimal.

$n\% = \frac{n}{100}$ which means the same as $n \div 100$.

Example

What are **a)** 25% **b)** 17.5% as decimals?

Answer

a) 25% = 25 ÷ 100 = 0.25

b) 17.5% = 17.5 ÷ 100 = 0.175

4 Write these percentages as decimals:

a) 37%	b) 83%	c) 7%	d) 6.8%	e) 27.5%	f) 4.67%
g) 0.7%	h) 0.219%	i) 1.43%	j) 97%	k) 28%	l) 0.03%

The process of converting a percentage to a decimal and vice versa is shown in this diagram.

÷ 100

percentage → decimal

decimal → percentage

× 100

Example

Convert to percentages: 0.73, 0.091.

Answer

0.73 = (0.73 × 100)% = 73%

0.091 = (0.091 × 100)% = 9.1%

5 Write the following decimals as percentages:

a) 0.72 b) 0.8 c) 0.09 d) 0.375

e) 0.431 f) 0.067 g) 0.523 h) 0.0076

In general, an expression can be converted to a percentage by first putting it into decimal form and then multiplying by 100.

Example

Using a calculator, follow the instructions shown in the table to check the conversion of the given expressions to percentages correct to 1 decimal place.

Answer

Expression	Work out	Result displayed	Solution
a) $\frac{23}{57}$	23 ÷ 57 × 100	40.350 877 19	40.4%
b) $\frac{0.1179}{3.48}$	0.1179 ÷ 3.48 × 100	3.387 931 034	3.4%
c) 743 out of 984	743 ÷ 984 × 100	75.508 130 08	75.5%

6 Use a calculator to convert the following to percentages, correct to one decimal place:

a) $\frac{23}{48}$ b) 39 out of 72 c) $\frac{41.97}{800}$

d) 112 out of 123 e) $\frac{7.439}{63.82}$ f) 5789 out of 11 000

g) 17.8 out of 23 h) 31.7 out of 32 i) 0.651 out of 2.67

PROBABILITY (1)

4.1 Probability and games

Probability or 'chance' is measured on a scale from 0 to 1.

An event which is certain to happen has a probability of 1.

Something which is impossible has a probability of 0.

In some situations it is possible to calculate the probability of an event happening providing:

- all the possible outcomes in that situation can be listed and counted and
- all those outcomes are equally likely.

$$\text{The probability of an event} = \frac{\text{number of ways that an event can happen}}{\text{total number of different outcomes}}$$

It is easy to learn about probability by thinking about familiar games using dice and cards.

Suppose we throw a dice. We can work out the probability of scoring a '2', say, by considering all the possible outcomes.

As there are six faces on a dice and each is equally likely, the probability of each score is 1 out of 6 or $\frac{1}{6}$. (This will only be true, of course, if the dice is symmetrical (or 'fair').)

The probability of scoring an odd number is 3 out of 6 or $\frac{3}{6}$, because there are 3 odd number scores.

The probability of scoring either a 5 or a 6 is $\frac{2}{6}$.

---

1 Imagine you are going to throw a dice. Here are some of the outcomes which you might consider:

(i) You will score a 1
(ii) You will score an even number
(iii) You will score a 7
(iv) You will score a 5 or a 6
(v) You will score a number between 1 and 6

a) Which of these is impossible (probability = 0)?
b) Which of these has an 'evens' chance (probability = $\frac{1}{2}$)?
c) Which of these is certain to happen (probability = 1)?
d) Which has a less than 'evens' chance?

For questions 2 to 16, write down the answer as a fraction.

2 When a dice is thrown, what is the probability of getting a number bigger than 4?

3 At the end of a game of Snakes and Ladders I either need a 1 or a 2 or else I can't move. What is the probability that I can't move? ✓

4 In a game of Monopoly I will go to jail if I throw a 3. What is the probability that I DO NOT go to jail?

5 In a game of Ludo the next player will take one of my counters if he scores a 5. What is the probability that I am safe?

6 In a raffle 150 tickets have been sold. There are three prizes.
I have bought one ticket.
What is the probability that I will win:
a) the first prize
b) any prize?

7 In a game there are 4 spinners to choose from.

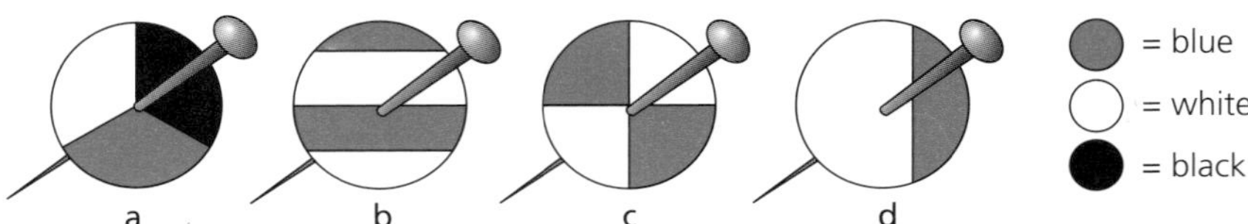

a) Which spinners give white and blue an equal chance?
b) If I am allowed to choose either 'blue' or 'white', which colour should I choose?

8 A pack of playing cards has four suits: clubs, diamonds, hearts and spades.

♣ clubs ♢ diamonds ♡ hearts ♠ spades

In each suit there are the numbers 1 (called an 'Ace') up to 10, plus three picture cards Jack, Queen and King. So there are 13 cards in each of 4 suits making 52 cards in all.

Pick a card from a pack at random (that is, without looking!). What is the probability that it is:
a) a black card ✓
b) a two
c) the Queen of Hearts
d) a heart
e) not a heart
f) a black Jack?

9 I take the thirteen spades out of the pack, shuffle them and turn the top one over. What is the probability it is:
a) the seven
b) an odd number
c) a 'picture' card?

10 I take the 12 picture cards (Jacks, Queens and Kings) out c
shuffle them. If I pick a card, what is the probability it is:
a) a club **b)** a King **c)** either a King or a clu

11 In a game of 'Black Lady' I have seven cards which include two c
hearts and a diamond. What is the probability that the next player p
diamond card when they have to take one of my cards?

12 I have been dealt three cards and they are all clubs. What is the probabi
that the next card I am dealt is a club also? ✓

13 I am dealing cards to my partner. So far I have dealt her two cards and they are both Aces. What is the probability that the next card is also an Ace?

14 Sally has 7 pairs of tights in a drawer. She knows 3 pairs have ladders in them. When she picks a pair out of the drawer, what is the probability she has picked a pair with no ladder?

15 Five letters arrive in the post addressed to 'J Jones'. If three are meant for Jenny and two are meant for John, what is the probability that the first letter Jenny opens is really for her?

16 On my bingo card there are 15 numbers. If the caller can shout out any number between 1 and 99, what is the probability that she calls one of my numbers?

4.2 Relative frequency

We know now that the *probability* in theory of scoring five when you throw a dice is $\frac{1}{6}$. If you throw the dice 60 times, roughly how many fives would you expect? Here is an experiment to find out.

Dice experiment

Copy the table below:

Number of throws	Number of 5s scored	Total frequency of 5s so far	Relative frequency of 5s so far
20			$\frac{\quad}{20} = 0. \ldots$
40			$\frac{\quad}{40} = 0. \ldots$
60			$\frac{\quad}{60} = 0. \ldots$
80			
100			
120			
140			
160			
180			
200			

Working with a partner, record the number of fives scored for every 20 throws of the dice. Keep a running total of the total number of fives in column 3. The last column is used to calculate the proportion of fives you have scored so far. This proportion is called the **relative frequency**.

Theoretically the probability of obtaining a five is $\frac{1}{6} = 0.166666\ldots$ or 0.17 to 1 D.P.

How do your relative frequencies compare to this probability?

Plot a graph like this, using the values in the first and last columns in your results table:

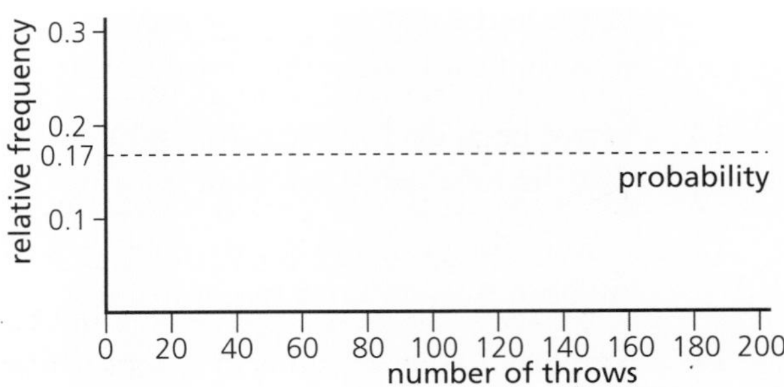

1 Discuss how the relative frequency changes as the number of throws increases. 

What would happen to the relative frequency in 600 throws? ... 6000 throws? There are some quicker ways of finding an answer. Section 4.4 shows you how to do a simulation using a graphics calculator. Section 4.5 gives instructions for a spreadsheet simulation.

In the dice experiment we used an experiment to confirm the probability we had worked out earlier. In the next experiment it's not so easy to make a guess at the probability.

Shove-penny experiment

You will need:

- a ruler
- a penny
- the shove penny grid (see end of book)
- an extra book to lean on

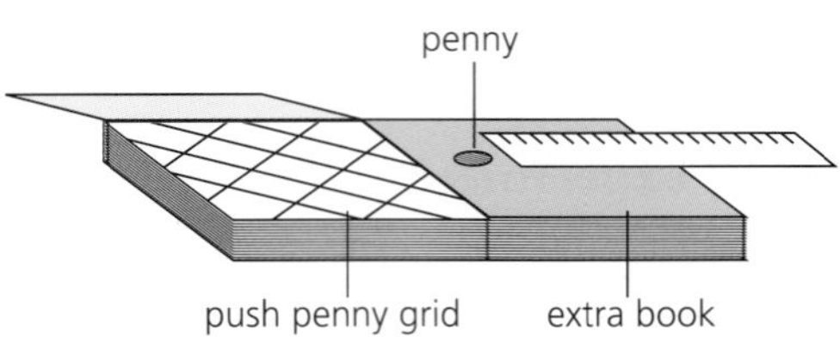

Use your ruler to push the penny onto the shove-penny grid.

If your penny lands completely inside a square (AND DOES NOT CROSS ANY LINES) you have scored a point.

1 How many points would you expect to score in 20 tries? Make a guess.

Repeat the experiment 20 times. Keep a count of your points. Collect up the results for the whole class.

Write everyone's results on a table similar to the table on page 31 (for the dice experiment). Change the column headings on the table to fit this experiment.

Use your results to draw a graph of the 'relative frequency of points scored'. (This is the last column on your table.)

2 Can you guess what your chances of scoring a point are by looking at the graph?

3 Does the relative frequency change with more trials?

Later on in the chapter we will come back to this experiment to see if we can work out what the theoretical probability of scoring a point should be.

Discussion point

How could you use the ideas in this section to find out:

- What proportion of people wear glasses ✓

or

- What proportion of people are left-handed?

4.3 Measuring chance

Probability theory is the branch of mathematics which we use to measure chance.

In some situations, where there is symmetry, we can work out probabilities theoretically. So if we throw a dice we know that we have six equally likely outcomes (providing the dice really is 'fair' or symmetrical) and we can use this to calculate probabilities.

In many real-life situations outcomes are not equally likely and probabilities have to be found using a different approach. You may have noticed that when you repeated the dice experiment a large number of times, the relative frequency settled down or levelled off on your graph. It should settle down to a value close to the probability we calculated using theoretical ideas of symmetry.

This suggests that if it is impossible for us to calculate a probability in any other way, we can use the relative frequency to estimate the probability.

There are many events in everyday life in which the outcome is uncertain, and probability can be useful in some of those situations.

In the weather forecast, for instance, the weather forecaster gives you an idea of what the chances are of rain that day.

If the probability is given as 50% it means that the chance of rain and the chance of fine weather are equal, on that particular day. This can be written as 0.5 or $\frac{1}{2}$.

A 70% chance means that it is more likely to rain than not. Your probability of rain is 0.7 or $\frac{7}{10}$. This is worked out by looking back at days when the wind direction, temperature, cloud cover and air pressure patterns were all similar, and finding the proportion of those days on which it did rain in the past. There is no way of estimating the probability by any other method, because the possible outcomes are not equally likely. There is no choice here but to use the relative frequency to estimate probability.

---

1 How do you think an insurance company can work out the probability of your house being burgled?

2 Why do insurance companies charge lower premiums for houses which have burglar alarms?

3 What other factors might lower your house insurance premiums?

Remind yourself of the 'Shove-penny' rules (page 32).

You score a point if you are able to push the penny so that it lands completely inside a square. You do not score a point if the penny crosses a line.

Can you guess the probability that you do score a point? Here is a way of working this out.

---

4 Measure the side of a square on the grid.

5 Measure the diameter of a penny.

6 What is the radius of the penny?

7 Think about the centre of the penny. How close to the sides of the square can the centre of the penny land without it crossing a line? ✔

8 a) How big is this square inside which the centre of the penny can land?
b) What is the area of each (big) square on the shove penny grid?
c) What is the area of the small square inside which the centre of the penny can land?

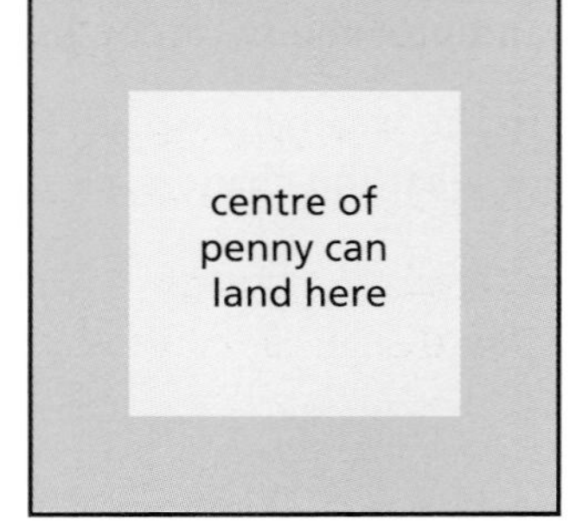

9 What is the probability that the penny lands completely inside a square? How does this compare with the results of your experiment?

10 ✓ Will the probability of scoring a point change if you use a smaller coin (e.g. 5p)? Choose the right answer below and explain your decision:
a) the probability will stay the same
b) the probability will increase
c) the probability will decrease.

11 Will the probability of scoring a point change if you use a larger coin (e.g. 2p or 10p)? Choose the right answer below and explain your decision:
a) the probability will stay the same
b) the probability will increase
c) the probability will decrease.

4.4 Random numbers

Random numbers can be used to simulate an experiment such as tossing a dice. Each number has an equal probability of appearing.

Many calculators have a random number generator. Look on your calculator for a key marked:

[Ran] or [Rand] or [Ran#]

Graphics calculators may have the random number command listed on a menu.

Press the random number key. You may need to press [SHIFT] (or [INV] or [2nd Fn]) then [Ran#]. (You may need to consult your manual.)

Do this several times.

Write down the number you obtain each time.

---

1 What is the largest number you obtain?
What is the smallest?

2 What happens if you turn your calculator off and then start again?
Do you get the same numbers as before?

3 What happens if you generate a random number and multiply it by 10?
Repeat this six times. Write down your answer each time.

4 Now generate a random number and multiply it by 6.
Repeat this six times. Write down your answer each time.

5 What happens when you generate a random number and *add* 6?
Do this six times, writing down your answer each time.

6 Describe the procedure which should give you the required range for the following random numbers:
a) numbers between 0 and 1
b) numbers between 0 and 5 ✓
c) numbers between 1 and 2 ✓
d) numbers between 0 and 100.
Try out your idea each time by keying in your procedure several times.

Now that you have had practice at generating random numbers we can use a calculator to run a simulation of the dice experiment:

- Key in

[Your calculator may have a key labelled RANDOM in place of Ran#.]
- Write down the number which comes before the decimal point. (Your answer should be from 1 to 6 inclusive.)
- Repeat this 20 times. Count how many times you scored five.
- Do this for 2 or 3 groups of 20 numbers.

You can collect up results from everyone in the class so that you have simulated 600 or 900 throws of a dice.

- Copy the table for the dice experiment shown earlier in this chapter. You will need to make your table longer to accommodate the total number of throws for the class. Calculate the relative frequency of fives scored every 20 throws. Draw a graph to show these cumulative relative frequencies. How does this compare with your earlier result using the dice?

4.5 Spreadsheet simulation

This section shows you how to simulate the dice experiment using the Excel spreadsheet.

RAND( ) generates a random number in the range 0 to 1.

INT(RAND( )*6+1) randomly generates a whole number from 1 to 6 inclusive.

The INT part of this command takes the whole number part and ignores the figures appearing after the decimal point.

Step 1 On Excel enter the command:
=INT(RAND( )*6+1)
into the cell B1.

This command can be copied into all the cells in rows 1 to 20 and in as many columns as you like.

Spreadsheet

	A	B	C	D	E	F	G
1		6	3	5	4	4	5
2		3	3	3	3	3	1
3		2	6	6	5	6	5
4		3	5	1	6	3	5
5		5	1	3	6	2	6
6		1	2	3	2	5	2
7		1	1	5	2	5	6
8							
17							
18		5	4	3	1	6	3
19		4	3	4	5	5	5
20		2	1	3	4	3	1
21							
22	FIVES	3	4	2	4	5	3
23	TOTAL	3					
24	TRIALS						
25	REL,FR.						

The computer will generate a simulated set of results for throwing a dice.

Step 2 Enter the command
= COUNTIF (B1:B20,5)
into the cell B22. Copy this across row 22.

Step 3 Enter the same number into B23 as is in B22.
Enter the command
=B23+C22
into the cell C23. Copy this across row 23.

Step 4 Enter the number 20 into cell B24.
Enter the command
=B24+20
into the cell C24. Copy this across row 24.

Step 5 Enter the command
=B23/B24
into cell B25. Copy this across row 25.

See if you can produce a graph showing the cumulative relative frequencies.

How do your results compare with the earlier dice 'experiments'? Which do you think is the best method?

ICT Extra!

Follow the instructions for the spreadsheet simulation of the experiment described on page 31. Then see if you can modify the instructions to produce a simulation of a coin spinning experiment. You will need to randomly generate the results '1' and '2'; where 1 stands for heads and 2 stands for tails. Your simulation should count the number of heads in 20 spins and repeat this 50 times.

5 WORKING WITH FRACTIONS

5.1 Fractional parts

Example

During a yacht race, four members of the crew take turns to cover an 11 hour watch during one of the stages. How long is each share of the duty?

Answer

The number of hours is given by 11 ÷ 4 which can be written as $\frac{11}{4}$.

This kind of fraction, in which the numerator is greater than the denominator, is known as a **top-heavy**, or **improper**, fraction.

$\frac{11}{4} = 2\frac{3}{4}$ ← 4 fits into 11 twice ...with 3 left over

Each share of the duty lasts $2\frac{3}{4}$ hours.

$2\frac{3}{4}$ is called a mixed number because it is made up of a mixture of a whole number and a fraction.

---

1 Convert these improper fractions to mixed numbers:

a) $\frac{25}{4}$ ✓ b) $\frac{17}{2}$ c) $\frac{18}{5}$ d) $\frac{14}{3}$

e) $\frac{9}{2}$ f) $\frac{15}{4}$ g) $\frac{27}{8}$ h) $\frac{39}{10}$

2 Work out as mixed numbers:

a) 9 ÷ 5 b) 21 ÷ 2 c) 23 ÷ 4 d) 49 ÷ 5

e) 76 ÷ 10 f) 46 ÷ 3 g) 49 ÷ 12 h) 111 ÷ 2

3 In these questions, cancel the improper fraction before converting to a mixed number:

a) 147 ÷ 28 b) 48 ÷ 15 c) 200 ÷ 60 d) 310 ÷ 20

e) 550 ÷ 330 f) 1700 ÷ 400 g) 240 ÷ 25 h) 729 ÷ 36

4 A car maintains a steady speed of 70 m.p.h. on a motorway.
How long does it take to reach the services?

$$\text{time} = \frac{\text{distance}}{\text{speed}}$$

SERVICES 21 MILES

Using fractions to solve problems often involves calculating a **fraction of an amount**.

Example

How long is $\frac{4}{5}$ hour, in minutes?

Answer

$\frac{4}{5}$ of 60 $= \frac{4}{5} \times 60 = \frac{4 \times 12}{1} = \frac{48}{1} = 48.$ $\quad \therefore \frac{4}{5}$ hour = 48 minutes.

'of' means 'times'.

the calculation is simplified by cancelling as far as possible before multiplying

Example

An author aims to complete a book of 18 chapters in one year. How much should have been completed after 7 months?

Answer

$\frac{7}{12}$ of 18 $= \frac{7}{12} \times 18 = \frac{7 \times 3}{2} = \frac{21}{2} = 10\frac{1}{2}.$

After 7 months, the author should have written approximately $10\frac{1}{2}$ chapters.

---

5 Find the number of minutes in these fractions of an hour:

a) $\frac{7}{12}$ ✓ b) $\frac{2}{3}$ c) $\frac{3}{5}$ d) $\frac{9}{20}$

6 Calculate the number of hours in these fractions of a day:

a) $\frac{5}{6}$ b) $\frac{7}{12}$ c) $\frac{2}{3}$ d) $\frac{3}{4}$

7 Work out:

a) $\frac{7}{16} \times 20$ ✓ b) $\frac{4}{5} \times 30$ c) $\frac{5}{12} \times 16$ d) $\frac{3}{8} \times 24$ e) $\frac{4}{15} \times 25$

f) $\frac{5}{36} \times 18$ g) $20 \times \frac{4}{5}$ h) $12 \times \frac{5}{8}$ i) $72 \times \frac{11}{54}$

8 In a particular school, three-fifths of the candidates entered for the GCSE examination are entered for the Intermediate tier. If there are 160 candidates altogether, how many are at Intermediate level?

9 I plan to travel from Stafford to Chester and consider two possible routes. I can either travel largely on the motorway, which is a distance of 65 miles, or take a more direct route of 50 miles across country. If my average speed on the motorway route is 60 m.p.h. and on the other route is 40 m.p.h. calculate:

a) the time taken in each case

b) the latest time I can leave Stafford to arrive in Chester by 3 p.m.

In solving some problems, fraction notation may provide a useful way of setting out a calculation even when decimals are involved. However, in such situations the methods may need to be adapted to allow for the use of a calculator. This is illustrated in the following example.

Example

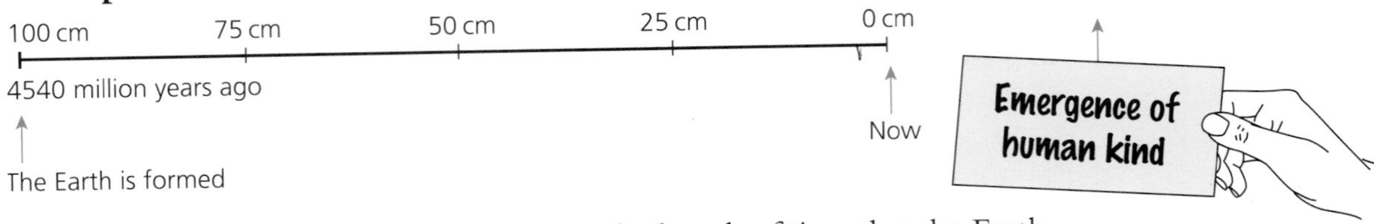

The diagram shows a time-line to represent the length of time that the Earth has been in existence. Taking the length of the line as 1 metre, make a guess at where the 'emergence of humankind' label should be placed.

The options given below refer to distances from the 'Now' end. Select the nearest one to your guess.

a) 50 cm b) 5 cm c) 75 cm d) 5 mm e) 20 cm f) 0.5 mm

Answer

The age of the Earth is currently put at about 4540 million years and yet it is thought that the earliest humans appeared only 2.4 million years ago.

The required time-line position can be calculated as a fraction of the length of the line given by $\frac{2.4}{4540} \times 100$ cm.

This can be worked out on a calculator as $2.4 \div 4540 \times 100 = 0.0528634361...$

So the correct answer is 0.5 mm.

---

10 Dinosaurs ruled the Earth between 225 million and 65 million years ago. How much of the time-line would be needed to represent this period?

An alternative way to illustrate the scale of events in time is to compare the time of the Earth's existence to a calendar year. In order to do this we need to develop some further calculator techniques.

Example

Work out 0.271 43 of a day in hours and minutes.

Answer

Using a calculator, $0.27143 \times 24 = 6.51432$
(Note that this is not the same as 6 hours 51 minutes)

To convert the decimal part of an hour into minutes, subtract 6 so that the display changes to 0.514 32 and then calculate this part of 60 minutes.

Check that this works out as 6 hours 31 minutes (to the nearest minute).

11 Calculate the following parts of a day in hours and minutes:

a) 0.876 49 ✓ b) 0.752 16 c) 0.583 74 d) 0.786 32

e) $\frac{7}{11}$ f) $\frac{8.73}{31}$ g) $\frac{47.8}{685.3}$ h) $\frac{7.689}{156.8}$

12 a) Changing the time-line scale of the example to 365 days, what calculation is needed to work out the number of days to represent mankind's presence on Earth?

b) From the result of part a) what would be the corresponding date if the Earth was formed on 1 January?

c) Work out the time on that date to the nearest minute at which mankind first appeared.

13 Work out the dates and times of the beginning and end of the dinosaur period using the one year scale.

5.2 Significant figures

The most significant figure in any number is the non-zero figure with the highest place value.

For example, in each of these numbers, the most significant figure is underlined.

<u>4</u>270 <u>2</u>.964 0.<u>8</u>71 0.00<u>1</u>48

1 Copy these numbers and underline the most significant figure in each case:

a) 8765 b) 0.389 c) 3050 d) 87.01

e) 0.0427 f) 0.0035 g) 0.000 19 h) 100.009

In some situations, such as when dealing with money, it may be sensible to round a value to two decimal places, i.e. to the nearest penny. However, in other situations such as calculating the distance to a star in miles, it would be much more sensible to round to a number of significant figures.

Example

Round 4270 to 1 S.F. (i.e. 1 significant figure).

Answer

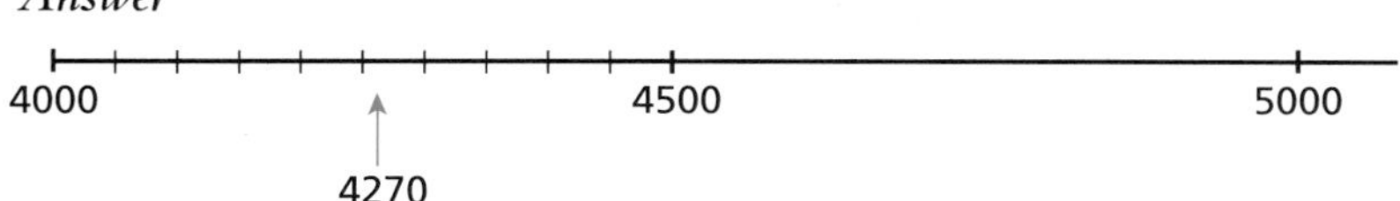

4270 is nearer to 4000 than 5000 and so 4270 = 4000 to 1 S.F.

The next most significant figure is less than 5 so 4270 rounds *down* to 4000.

The zeros are needed to maintain the place value

2 Use a diagram to show that 2.964 = 3.0 to 2 S.F. Note that the zero is needed as one of the significant figures.

3 Round each of these to 1 S.F.:

a) 6419 ✓ b) 3827 c) 0.934 d) 0.006 53

4 Round each of these to 2 S.F.:

a) 8.764 b) 9.276 c) 0.985 1 d) 0.099 72 ✓
e) 986 436 f) 6974 g) 0.003 614 h) 5.952

5 Round the numbers given in the following data to 2 S.F.

a) The equatorial diameter of the Earth is 7 926.380 3 miles.
b) The greatest circumference of the Earth, at the equator is 24 901.458 miles.
c) The distance of the Earth from the Sun is 92 955 900 miles.
d) The outermost planet in the solar system is Pluto, whose distance from the Sun is 3 674 488 000 miles.
e) The average speed of the Earth, in orbit around the Sun, is 18.505 5 miles per second.

5.3 Estimation

The technique of reducing the number of significant figures by rounding allows us to simplify a calculation to the point where we can work out a reasonable estimate of the answer. This means we can check whether answers obtained, possibly with a calculator, are of the right order of size.

Example

Estimate the value of 9.8763 × 0.006 154 78.

Answer

Rounding to 1 S.F.:

9.876 3× 0.006 154
10 × 0.006 = 0.06

This is in line with a calculator answer of 0.060 786 453 7.

(*Note*: even the calculator answer isn't exact because the true answer contains more figures than the calculator can display. In practice, the answers displayed on a calculator often contain far more figures than are needed and require rounding to a sensible level of accuracy.)

---

1 Estimate the values of these calculations by rounding the numbers to 1 S.F.:

a) 4.896 31 × 0.194 376 ✓
b) 18.276 54 ÷ 2.887 634
c) 7.239 84 × 14.786 35
d) 3.976 213 4 ÷ 1.989 671 2
e) 58 743 + 12 896
f) 375 864 + 896 142
g) 123 789 – 62 163
h) 87 352 + 42 863 – 68 123
i) 2.1587 × 5.7653 × 0.39721
j) 36.87 × 8.2447 ÷ 15.689

2 Use a calculator to find the values of the expressions given in question 1 and round the answers to 3 S.F. Compare these answers with your original estimates.

When estimating the value of a calculation, it may be useful to know whether the result is an **under-estimate** or an **over-estimate** of the true answer.

Example

Estimate: a) 8.3215 × 6.4217 b) 4.7863 × 3.6218.

Answer

a) 8.3215 × 6.4217 ≈ 8 × 6 = 48

This result must be an under-estimate of the true answer because both of the original figures were rounded down.

A calculator gives the answer as 53.438 176 55 = 53.4 to 3 S.F.

b) 4.7863 × 3.6218 ≈ 5 × 4 = 20

This result must be an over-estimate of the true answer because both of the original figures were rounded up.

A calculator gives the answer as 17.335 021 34 = 17.3 to 3 S.F.

3 State whether rounding the numbers in the following expressions to 1 S.F. will produce an under-estimate or an over-estimate of the true answer. Check your predictions using a calculator.

a) 9.876 54 × 0.058 653 b) 0.276 34 × 0.382 16 c) 42.76 × 837.92
d) 0.746 83 + 0.836 27 e) 38 456 + 19 112 f) 82.513 + 23.784 321

In some situations, it isn't clear whether a result is an under-estimate or an over-estimate.

Example

Estimate 8.9244 × 3.1762.

Answer

8.9234 × 3.1672 ≈ 9 × 3 = 27

over under

4 Copy and complete the table below to show how approximations combine:

Approximation	Operation	Approximation	Estimate
over	×	over	
over	×	under	not clear
under	×	over	
under	×	under	

5 What if the operation is changed to addition? Do any changes need to be made to the table?

We will now look at division and subtraction in the same way.

Example

Estimate 11.4784 ÷ 4.567 15.

Answer

11.4784 × 4.567 15 ≈ 10 ÷ 5 = 2

under over

This result must be an under-estimate.
A calculator gives the answer as 2.513 252 247 = 2.51 to 3 S.F.

6 Try some more examples of combining approximations under division. Use your results to complete a table of results for division as in question 4.

7 Make a table of results for combining approximations under subtraction.

5.4 Percentages of an amount

Some percentages can be worked with most simply by converting them to fractions. You should know the following results:

$50\% = \frac{1}{2}$ $25\% = \frac{1}{4}$ $12\frac{1}{2}\% = \frac{1}{8}$ $33\frac{1}{3}\% = \frac{1}{3}$ $10\% = \frac{1}{10}$

Other percentages can be obtained from these, such as $30\% = \frac{3}{10}$ i.e. $3 \times \frac{1}{10}$.

Example

What is 25% of 32 ... $66\frac{2}{3}\%$ of 21?

Answer

25% of $32 = \frac{1}{4}$ of $32 = 8$

$66\frac{2}{3}\%$ of $21 = \frac{2}{3}$ of $21 = 2 \times 7 = 14$

---

1 Work out:

a) 50% of 24 b) 25% of 24 c) $12\frac{1}{2}\%$ of 24 d) $33\frac{1}{3}\%$ of 15
e) $66\frac{2}{3}\%$ of 15 f) $66\frac{2}{3}\%$ of 45 g) 25% of 36 h) $12\frac{1}{2}\%$ of 36
i) 75% of 36 j) 10% of 90 k) 20% of 90 l) 5% of 90
m) 10% of 68 n) 30% of 68 o) 5% of 68

2 (Note: 10% of 21 = 2.1 but 10% of £21 must be written as £2.10.)
Find the value of:

a) 10% of £63 b) 10% of £97 c) 10% of £118 d) 10% of £800
e) 10% of £409 f) 10% of £68.30 g) 10% of £78.50 h) 10% of £97.60
i) 20% of £43 j) 30% of £46 k) 70% of £24 l) 5% of £38
m) 60% of £46 n) 5% of £409 o) 15% of £409

In a SALE, prices will often be reduced by a percentage.

Example

A coat, normally priced at £79, is reduced by 10% in a sale. What is the sale price?

Answer

	£
Normal price	79.00
Reduction	7.90
Sale price	71.10

The sale price is £71.10.

3 If all items in a sale are reduced by 10%, calculate the sale price on items originally priced at:

a) £58 ✓ b) £32 c) £119 d) £312
e) £49.90 f) £87.90 g) £699.90 h) £19.90

4 Some shops label each item in the sale to show the 'was' price and the 'now' price.
Find the 'now' prices for these labels if the items are reduced by 30%.

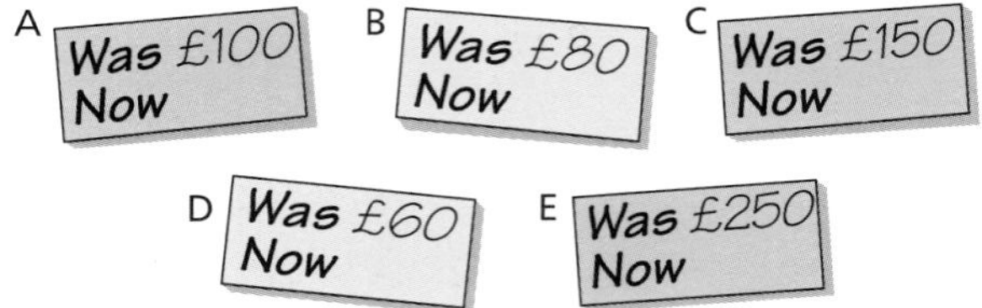

5 In one shop, the prices of a number of items end in £...9.99. For these items, the manager decides to work out the sale price as shown.

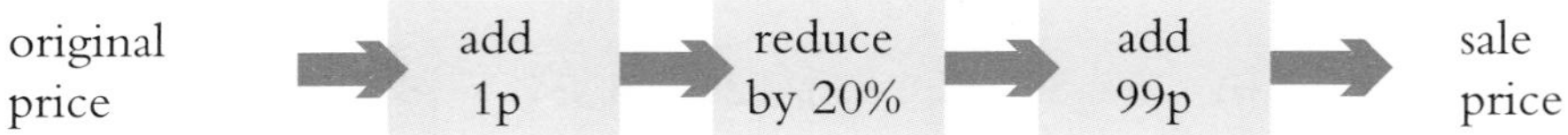

For example:

£39.99 → £40 → £32 → £32.99

The sale price is £32.99.

Use the manager's method to find the sale price for each of these:

a) £59.99 b) £99.99 c) £149.99
d) £89.99 e) £139.99 f) £249.99
g) £9.99 h) £499.99 i) £799.99

Would it be fair to claim that these prices were reduced by 20%? Explain.

6 Estimate the value of these by rounding the amounts to the nearest £ first:

a) 30% of £11.95 b) 40% of £15.87 c) 25% of £31.92
d) 20% of £49.79 e) 60% of £13.68 f) 75% of £119.85

7 Are your answers to question 6 under-estimates or over-estimates? Explain.

8 Find estimates of the following by rounding each percentage to the nearest 10% first. State, in each case, whether your estimate is an under-estimate or an over-estimate.

a) 19% of 40 ✓ b) 31% of 82 c) 9.8% of 179
d) 11.37% of 347 e) 19.83% of 436 f) 27.96% of 8.3

Percentage results can be combined to give new information.

Example

Find $42\frac{1}{2}$% of £24 ... 17.5% of £90.

Answer

	30% of £24 = £7.20			10% of £90	= £9
and	$12\frac{1}{2}$% of £24 = £3			5% of £90	= £4.50
so	$42\frac{1}{2}$% £24 = £10.20			2.5% of £90	= £2.25
			so	17.5% of £90	= £15.75

9 Given that $12\frac{1}{2}$% of £37.60 = £4.70 and that 30% of £37.60 = £11.28, find:
a) $42\frac{1}{2}$% of £37.60 **b)** 25% of £37.60 **c)** 37.5% of £37.60
d) 60% of £37.60 **e)** 72.5% of £37.60 **f)** 85% of £37.60

10 **a)** Work out: (i) 10% of £140 (ii) 5% of £140 (iii) 2.5% of £140
b) Hence find the value of 17.5% of £140.

11

What is the true price of these items if VAT is charged at 17.5% ?

12 How much VAT (at 17.5%) would be charged on the price of a luxury car advertised at £64 000 + VAT ?

Not all percentages convert to fractions that are simple to work with. An alternative approach is to use decimals, making use of a calculator as appropriate.

Example

What is: **a)** 8% of 42 **b)** 17.5% of £380 **c)** 6.9% of 731kg?

Answer

a) 8% of 42 = 0.08 × 42 = 3.36
b) 17.5% of £380 = 0.175 × £380 = £66.50
c) 6.9% of 731kg = 0.069 × 731 kg = 50.439 kg.

13 Calculate, giving your answers in the appropriate units:

a) 27% of 64 m b) 31.2% of 86 kg c) 7.9% of 2600 km
d) 49% of £97 e) 38% of $674 f) 0.6% of 18.7 m^2

14 Calculate to the nearest penny:

a) 17.5% of £47.99 b) 12.5% of £17.95 c) 37.5% of £176.50
d) 2.9% of £754.33 e) 8.7% of £5463.87 f) 19.6% of £63.81

15 Find to 3 significant figures:

a) 11.9% of 572 b) 16.3% of 0.178 c) 0.9% of 4.324
d) 29.3% of 0.0398 e) 0.176% of 0.36 f) 7.03% of 0.8713

Some scientific calculators have a REPLAY or PLAYBACK key. This allows, for example, the same percentage of different amounts to be found very efficiently.

Example

Find 17.5% of a) £86 b) £37.50

a) Key in 0.175 × 86 =
This gives 15.05 so the answer is £15.05.

b) Key in [◄] and edit the display to show 0.175 × 37.5
Press = to give 6.5625
So the answer is £6.56 to the nearest penny.

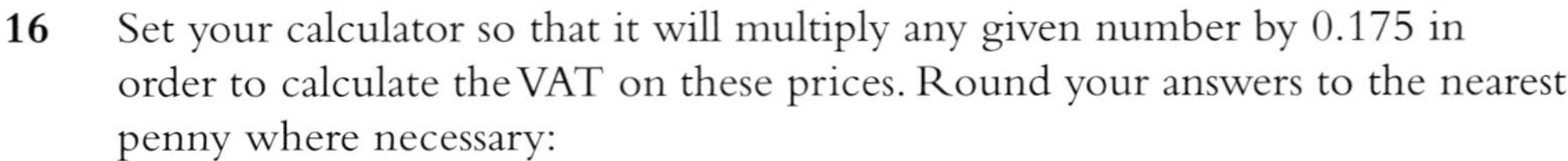

---

16 Set your calculator so that it will multiply any given number by 0.175 in order to calculate the VAT on these prices. Round your answers to the nearest penny where necessary:

a) £145 b) £1800 c) £23.49 d) £931.50
e) £2509 f) £1.78 g) £19.99 h) £27 000

17 A catalogue offers $12\frac{1}{2}$% commission on the value of each order. Find, as efficiently as possible, the value of the commission on these amounts to the nearest penny:

a) £128.57 b) £60.42 c) £212.99 d) £132.76
e) £41.95 f) £83.49 g) £476.35 h) £867.64

ORGANISING DATA

6.1 Which kind of average?

Look at these questions.

- My friend feels ill, is her temperature too high?
- How long does it take you to get here in the mornings?
- What should my pulse rate be?
- How much does a newborn baby weigh?

If you were asked a question like one of these, you would probably try to answer by giving a **typical** or **average** value.

The following are often used as typical values:

1 the mean
2 the result which occurs most often, called the mode
or **3** a 'middling result' called the median.

These are three different kinds of average and will be used in different situations.

The range of a set of values is the difference between the highest value and the lowest.

Another useful tool for comparing sets of data is the **range**. Suppose you are choosing a player for your cricket team. Both have the same batting average but one has a much larger range than the other. Which would you choose?

Example

Alison asked each of her friends how many computer games they own.
Here are their answers:
14, 0, 5, 22, 9
What is the median of these values? What is the range?

Answer

The median is the middle value in a set of results.

To find the median, the results must be listed in order:
0, 5, 9, 14, 22
So 9 is the median value.

The range is the difference between the highest and lowest values.
So range = 22 – 0 = 22

What will the median be if Alison includes her own answer which is 19?
The results now are:
0, 5, 9, 14, 19, 22

Now there is no single number in the middle. The median is halfway between the *two* middle results:

$$\text{median} = \frac{9 + 14}{2} = \frac{23}{2} = 11\tfrac{1}{2}$$

The mean is found by adding the results and dividing that total by the number of results used.

The mean is the value that most people think of as the 'average'. In fact the mode, the median and the mean are all different kinds of average. They are all used to give people an idea of what would be a 'typical' result.

Example

Here (again) are the numbers of computer games owned by Alison's friends: 0, 5, 9, 14 and 22

What is the mean of these values?

Answer

The mean is the total of these numbers divided by 5.

$$\text{mean} = \frac{0 + 5 + 9 + 14 + 22}{5} = \frac{50}{5} = 10$$

The mode is the result which occurs with the greatest frequency (i.e., most often).

Example

The numbers of computer games owned by Joe and his friends are 10, 0, 15, 18, 12, 10, 11.

What is the mode of these values?

Answer

The mode among this group of friends is 10 games. Alison's friends all had differing answers so there was no mode.

---

1 Issy has done a survey of how many fizzy drinks school pupils drink in a day. Here are the answers given by two groups of pupils:

Year 7 pupils													
4	0	3	2	6	5	7	6	6	8	5	2	1	
Year 10 pupils													
3	0	0	1	3	3	2	1	1	0	5	2	2	3

a) Find the median, mean, and mode for each group. ✓
b) Find the ranges for both groups of pupils.
c) Which group seems to drink more fizzy drinks?
d) Which group gave the most varied answers?

2 Here are the lengths of the annual holidays taken by the various employees of the 'Moving Pictures' TV company:

Job	Numbers of people	Holiday
Chairman of board	1	9 months
Managing director	1	3 months
Accountant	1	2.5 months
Cleaner	2	2 months
Secretary	2	1.5 months
Camera man/woman	5	0.75 months
Sound man/woman	4	0.5 month
Lighting man/woman	2	0.5 month
Scene shifters	2	0.5 month

a) Find the mean, median and mode for holiday entitlements among employees. If there are, say, 5 people with the same results, be sure to include them all.

b) The trade union representative is campaigning for extra holiday entitlements for employees. She says that the average holiday entitlement is too low. The managing director claims that the average holiday entitlement is more than generous.
Which of the three types of 'average' will be chosen by:
(i) the trade union representative?
(ii) the managing director?

c) Explain why similar tactics might be used when wage levels are being discussed.

3 For each of the following statements say whether the average used is likely to be a mean, median or mode.
(i) Miss Average weighs 135 lb.
(ii) Miss Average has an office job.
(iii) Mr Average is 5 feet 7 inches tall.
(iv) The average new house has 2.67 bedrooms.
(v) Mr Average attends the cinema 1.5 times per year.
(vi) Shoe stockists always make sure that they stock more shoes in size 6 than any other size.
(vii) An alien visiting planet Earth would say that the average Earth inhabitant speaks Chinese.
(viii) Fifty per cent of mothers are less than 27.5 years old at the time their baby is born.
(ix) The average wedding takes place on a Saturday.
(x) Miss Average is likely to live until she is 76 years old.

6.2 Qualitative or quantitative data

For each person in your class, find out:

- how many magazines did he/she read in the last week
- which kind of magazine was each one.

Decide on which categories you need for the answers to the second question.
Record their answers on two tables like this:

How many magazines did you read?

number of magazines	tally	frequency
0		
1		
2	I	
3		
4		
5		
6 or more		

What kind of magazines?

type of magazine	tally	frequency
fashion		
music		
computer	I	
car		
science fiction		
comic	I	
sport		

The tally marks show Joe's answers. He read two magazines. One was a computer magazine, the other was a comic.
Were there some magazines which did not fit easily into any of your categories?

1 Can you give the mode and the range for the answers to the first question? What are they?

2 Why is it impossible to give the range for the second question?

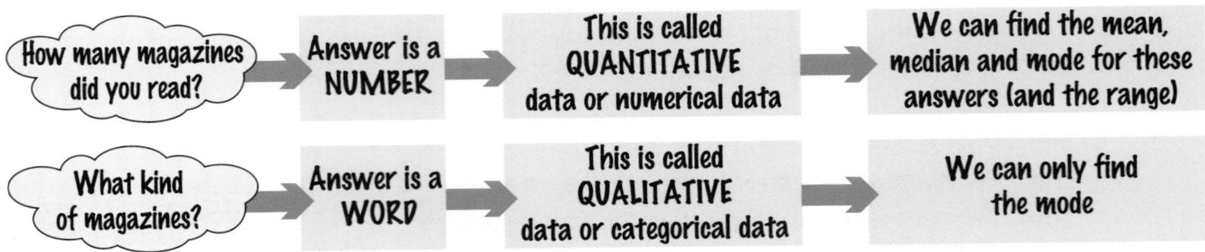
How many magazines did you read?
Answer is a NUMBER
This is called QUANTITATIVE data or numerical data
We can find the mean, median and mode for these answers (and the range)
What kind of magazines?
Answer is a WORD
This is called QUALITATIVE data or categorical data
We can only find the mode

6.3 Graphs, pictograms and pie charts

We use different ways of representing quantitative and qualitative data.
For *qualitative data* we often draw a bar graph. A bar graph helps you to see the important features in a set of results. The mode (or modal class) is then easy to identify.

Below are the results of a national survey into which newspapers are read by young adults aged 15 to 24 (national readership survey in *Social trends*, HMSO). They are shown as a bar graph.

The same survey also asked people of other age groups which newspapers they read. Below are the replies of people aged over 65 shown as a pictogram.

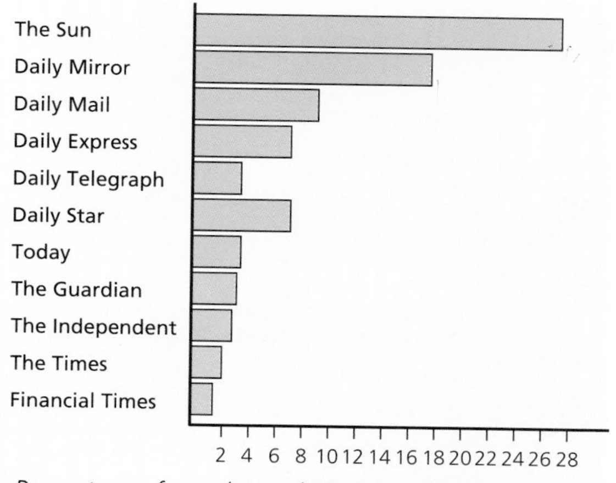

Percentage of people aged 15–24 reading each newspaper (1992)

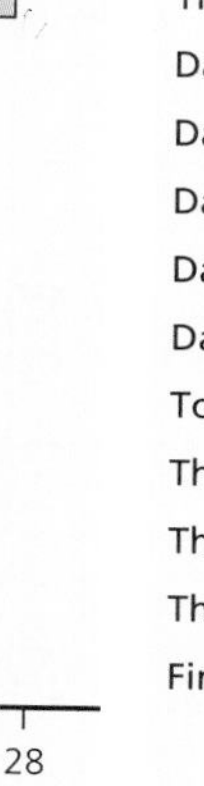

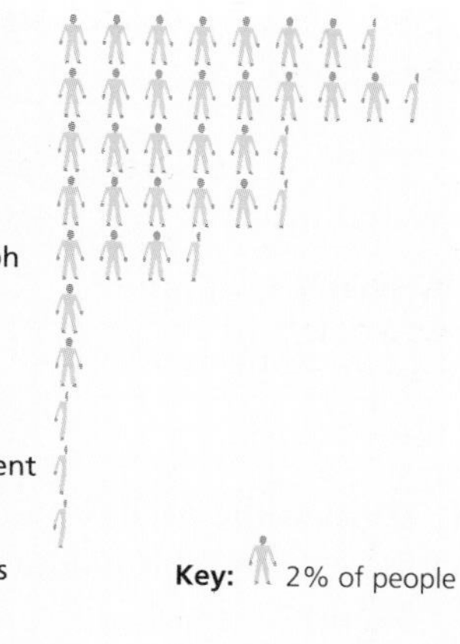

Percentage of people aged over 65 reading each newpaper (1992)

1 a) Which newspaper is most popular among older people (over 65)?
b) Which newspapers are least popular among older people?
c) Which newspaper is most popular among younger readers aged 15–24?
d) Which newspaper is least popular among younger readers?
e) What percentage of younger readers read the Daily Mail?
f) What percentage of older readers read the Daily Mail?
g) Are there any other papers besides the Mail which have a larger percentage of the older readers?
h) Which papers have a larger percentage of the younger readers?

2 Name one advantage and one disadvantage of pictograms.

3 This pie chart shows how Joe spent his time yesterday.
a) How many different activities did Joe decide to include in his pie chart?
b) Can you think of any activities he has missed out? Why do you think he missed them out?
c) Which item used up the most time?
d) Which item used up the least time?
e) Can you tell from the pie chart how long Joe spends watching TV?
f) Which activity takes nearly as much time as sleeping?
g) Which activity takes twice as long as eating?
h) Which two activities take the same length of time?

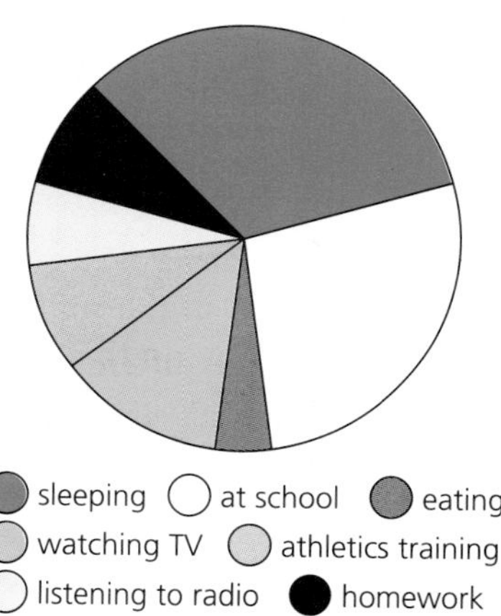

4 A pie chart helps you compare items. You can also see what fraction (or proportion) each item is compared to the total.
Here is the list of Joe's activities and the time for each one.

Activity	Time in hours
Sleeping	8
At school	$6\frac{1}{2}$
Eating	1
Watching TV	3
Athletics training	2
Listening to radio	$1\frac{1}{2}$
Homework	2

a) What is the total for all Joe's activities?
b) Joe spends 8 hours out of 24 sleeping. What fraction is that?
c) What is one third of 360°?
d) Check the angle for 'sleeping' on the pie chart.

How to calculate angles for a pie chart:
1 Find the total for the categories or items listed
2 Find the fraction of the total for each item
3 Multiply this fraction by 360° to find each angle

Here is Joe's working out:

Activity	Time (hours)	Fraction	Angle
Sleeping	8	$\frac{8}{24}$	120°
At school	$6\frac{1}{2}$	$\frac{6\frac{1}{2}}{24}$	98°
Eating	1	$\frac{1}{24}$	15°
Watching TV	3		
Athletics	2		
Listening to radio	$1\frac{1}{2}$		
Homework	2		
TOTAL	24		

Check this using your calculator.
Key in:
6.5 [÷] 24 [×] 360 [=]

e) Fill in the missing calculations on Joe's chart.
f) Why do the angles add up to 361°? Does this matter?

ICT Extra!

Draw a pie chart using a spreadsheet. Enter the data for one of the questions in this section into a spreadsheet such as Excel. Use the Chart Wizard to draw a pie chart.

5 Nicky ate a meal at lunch time which contained 600 calories. Here's how his meal shaped up!

a) Copy this table and fill in the missing calculations.

b) Use these results to draw a pie chart.

Food item	Calories	Fraction	Angle
2 sausages	190	$\frac{190}{600}$	$\frac{190}{600} \times 360° = 114°$
Mashed potato	140		
Baked beans	120		
Sponge pudding	130		
Custard	20		
TOTAL	600		

6 A survey of all BBC radio programs showed what percentage of all their time was allocated to various types of program.

a) Draw a pie chart to illustrate the results of this survey.

b) Can you think of programs which would fit into two of these categories? Can you think of any programs which would fit into none of them? Are these percentages likely to be exactly right? Explain your answer.

Type of program	Percentage of total air time
Music	57
Documentaries and current affairs	22
News	5
Sport	5
Drama	3
Light entertainment	2
Religion	1
Education	5

7 Alison asked all the members of form 10X where and what they ate for lunch yesterday. Draw a pie chart to illustrate this survey.

Type of lunch eaten	Number of pupils
Brought sandwiches	7
School snack bar	9
Hot lunch in cafeteria	8
Salad lunch in cafeteria	4
Went home	3

8 a) Look back to your magazine survey. What kind of graph could you draw to show how many magazines students read in your survey? ✔

b) Draw a suitable graph to show how many magazines students read in your survey.

c) What kind of graph could you draw to show what kinds of magazines students read? ✔

d) Draw a pie chart to show what kinds of magazines students read in your survey.

e) Which type of magazine forms the largest fraction of the total?

g) If you carried out the same survey with year 7 pupils, would you expect their pie chart for 'What kind of magazines' to be similar to yours? Explain your answer.

7 PROCESS AND PRIORITY

7.1 Checking calculations

One way to check an answer to a calculation is to re-do it in the same way and hope to spot any error that was made. Unfortunately, this approach often fails because the original mistake is simply repeated.

Example

Divide 4525 by 5.

Answer

$$5\overline{)4525}\ \to\ 95$$ ✗

The error made here is not likely to be found by repeating the calculation

WRONG

An alternative approach is to use the inverse process as shown in the diagram on the right.

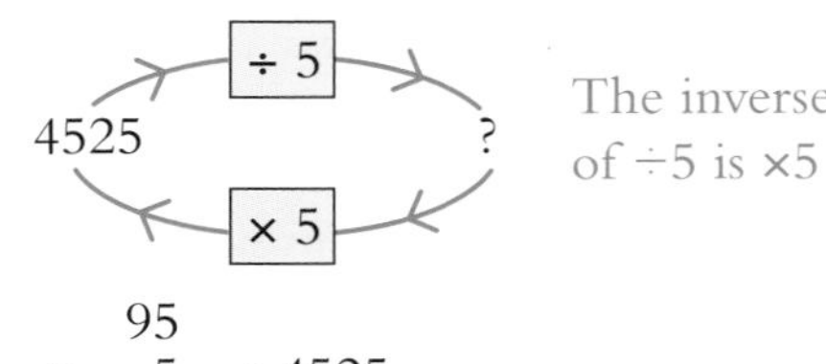

The inverse of ÷5 is ×5

That is, work out 95 × 5 and compare the result with 4525.

$$95 \times 5 = 475 \neq 4525$$

... and so there must be an error at some point in the working.
(*Note*: this also shows that the true answer must be much larger than 95.)

---

1 Divide 4525 by 5 and check your answer by multiplication. Show all the necessary steps in your working.

2 The inverse process undoes the original. Find the inverse of:
a) Divide by 0.73 b) Subtract 6.47 c) Multiply by 9 d) Add 543

3 Work these out, without using a calculator, and check your answers by using the inverse. Show all the necessary working.
a) 5712 – 3825 b) 10 000 – 3671 c) 71 421 ÷ 3 d) 164 ÷ 0.2
e) 471 × 200 f) 37.1 ÷ 4 g) 5 – 2.36 h) 21.3 × 0.5

4 Copy and complete these diagrams:

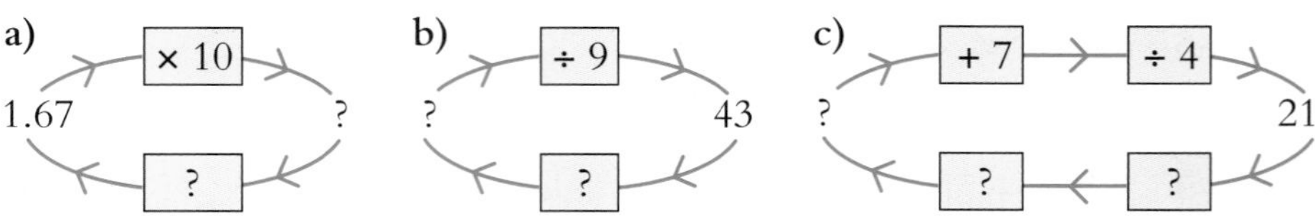

5 Which of the following are true statements? You may find it easier to check by using the inverse process.
a) 706 ÷ 46 = 11 b) 512 – 176 = 336 c) 8150 ÷ 163 = 50
d) 8123 – 679 = 7424 e) 31 898 ÷ 778 = 41 f) $\frac{1}{3}$ of 87.93 = 27.32

An alternative method of detecting 'obvious errors' is to use estimation. The calculation shown at the start of this unit may be simplified as follows.

$4525 \div 5$ is approximately the same as $5000 \div 5 = 1000$.

This result is an over-estimate of the true answer but is enough to show that $4525 \div 5 \neq 95$.

---

6 Use estimation to find the incorrect statements:
a) $8.65 \times 19.1 = 165.215$ **b)** $179.6 \div 39.2 = 44.582$ **c)** $47.2 \times 0.95 = 44.84$
d) $34.2 \div 0.95 = 360$ **e)** $56088 \div 456 = 123$ **f)** $0.367 + 0.196 + 5 = 0.568$

In some cases, a combination of methods may be needed.

Example

Check these statements: **a)** $\frac{1}{3}$ of $59.94 = 21.98$ **b)** $\frac{1}{3}$ of $59.94 = 19.89$

Answer

By estimation, $\frac{1}{3}$ of $59.54 \approx \frac{1}{3}$ of $60 = 20$.

However, this is an over-estimate which means that the answer cannot be 21.98. On this basis, the answer 19.89 is of the right order but some calculation is needed to be certain whether it is true or false.

The diagram shows the various options for checking the calculation.

59.94 → $\times\frac{1}{3}$ / $\div 3$ → 19.89? ; 19.89? → $\times 3$ → 59.94

Using the reverse process gives:

$$\begin{array}{r} 19.89 \\ \times \quad 3 \\ \hline 59.67 \end{array}$$

These results show that neither of the given statements is true.

---

7 **a)** Use estimation to decide which of the following statements must be false.
b) Check the remaining statements by calculation to find which are true.
(i) $47.89 \div 8.01 = 7.89$ (ii) $29.6 \times 8.5 = 251.6$ (iii) $8.37 + 6.79 + 7 = 19.16$
(iv) $6.75 \div 0.15 = 4.5$ (v) $6.75 \div 0.25 = 27$ (vi) $14 - 4.3712 = 9.6288$
(vii) $\frac{1}{3}$ of $91.41 = 30.57$ (viii) $\frac{1}{3}$ of $91.41 = 29.37$ (ix) $\frac{1}{3}$ of $91.41 = 30.47$

8 Tickets to see a live band are on sale for £25 each and the cost of hiring a coach for the journey is £188.50. A local tour organiser calculates the minimum charge per person for a party of 29 people in order to cover the costs. The first figure calculated is £29.50 but a second attempt produces £31.50.
a) Use estimation to decide which answer cannot be correct. Explain your reasoning.
b) Is the other answer correct?

7.2 Making statements – it's easier with algebra!

When using mathematics to solve problems it is important to be able to make clear statements.

Statement (1)	Statement (2)
If an object moves with constant acceleration then its velocity after a given time may be found by adding its initial velocity to the product of its acceleration and the time for which it has been accelerating.	$v = u + at$

Don't worry. You are not expected to *understand* statement (1). It is there only to show how difficult it can be to describe a process accurately without using algebra.

Statement (2) contains the same information as statement (1), once the use of the symbols is understood, but has a number of advantages:

- it is shorter and more easily remembered
- it is easier to use
- it can be written into computer, or graphics calculator, programs
- it can be rearranged to provide new information, e.g. $u = v - at$.

---

1 Re-write the following statements using symbols:

a) The value of y is 4 more than the value of x. ✓
b) Seven less than the value of y is the same as x.
c) The value of x, when added to y, produces 9 as the result.
d) When three is subtracted from the value of p, the value of q is found.
e) If the value of m is multiplied by 4, and 5 is added to the result, then this is the same as dividing n by 3.
f) If the product of x and y is subtracted from 8, then this gives the same result as adding x and y together.

When written in symbolic form, all the statements given in question 1 contain an '=' sign. Statements such as these are called equations.

2 Re-write the following statements as equations, using x to represent the unknown value in each case.

a) When this number is multiplied by 4, the result is the same as adding this number to 50. ✓
b) If you multiply this number by itself and then subtract the result from 10, you will get the same answer as multiplying the number by 3 and adding on 2.
c) Dividing this number by 7 gives the same result as subtracting 7 from it.
d) Dividing 12 by this number gives 4.5 as the answer.

Information about relationships can often be obtained from a diagram.

Example

From the diagram, form an equation giving:
a) p in terms of r and t;
b) q in terms of s and u.

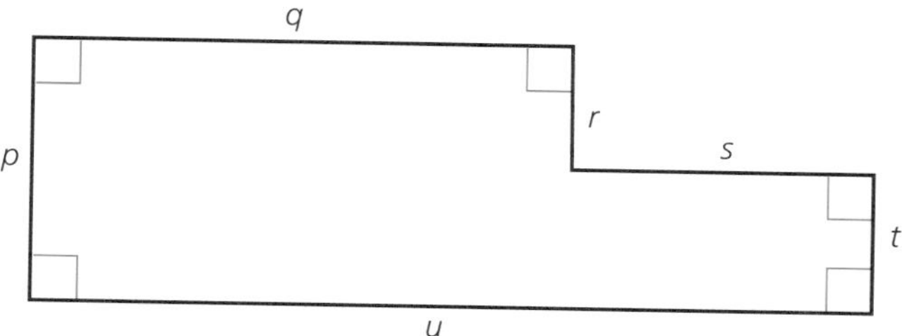

Answer

(*Note*: to give p in terms of r and t, we must write an equation in which p is on one side and some expression involving r and t is on the other. In this situation, p is referred to as the subject of the equation.)

a) $p = r + t$ (p represents the total vertical distance)
b) $q = u - s$ (q is the difference between u and s).

3 Use the diagram above to form an equation giving:
a) u in terms of q and s b) t in terms of p and r c) s as the subject.

4 Use this diagram to make each of the following the subject of an equation:
a) i b) l c) k d) j e) m f) n.

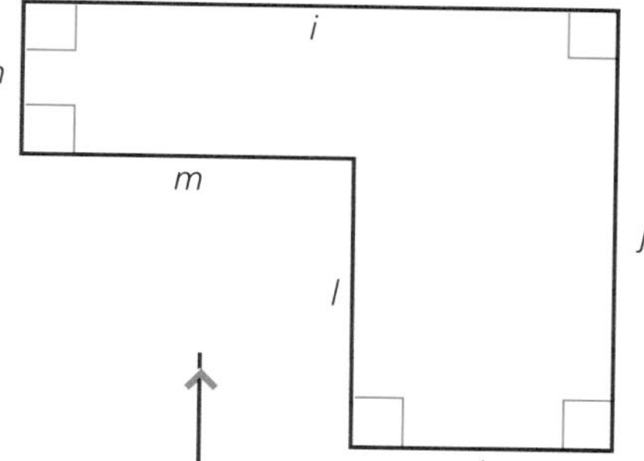

5 For each of these diagrams, form an equation in which x is the subject.

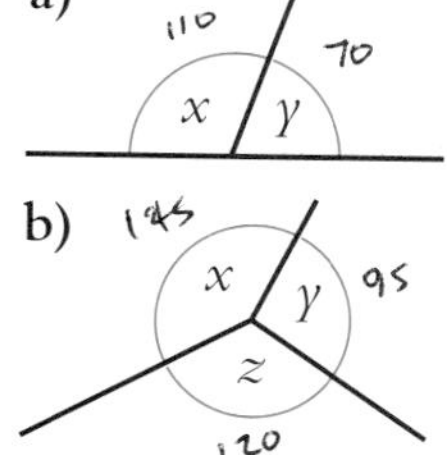

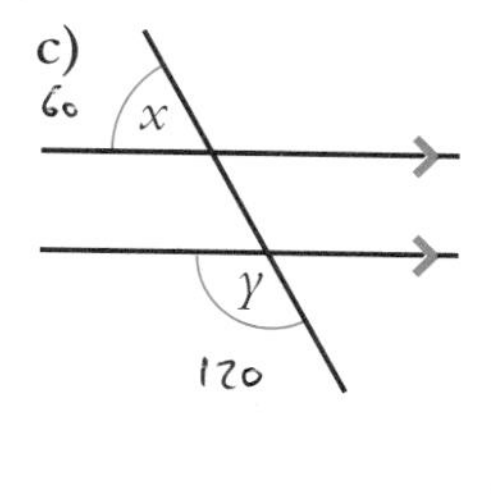

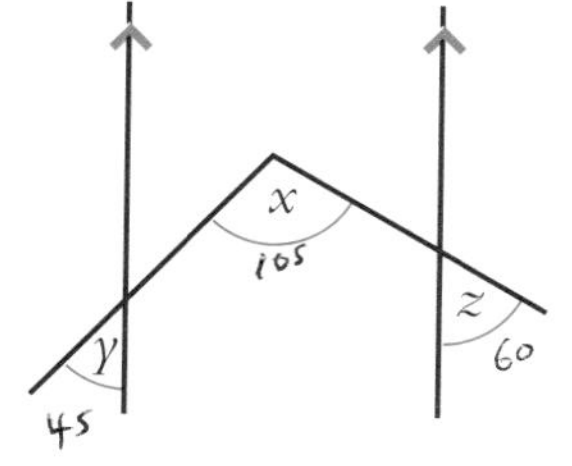

7.3 Simplifying expressions

Expressions in algebra can often be simplified and this makes it easier to solve problems.

When adding or subtracting we can only simplify expressions which contain **like terms**, i.e. terms in which the letters and powers are identical.

Adding and subtracting	*Multiplying*
$x + x = 2x$ $x + 2x = 3x$ $2y + 5y - 3y = 4y$ but $2x + 3y$ cannot be simplified. $5x + 3y - 2x + y = 5x - 2x + 3y + y$ $= 3x + 4y$	$x \times x = x^2$ $x \times x^2 = x^3$ $2y \times 3y = 6y^2$ $2x \times 3y = 6xy$ $5xy \times 3x = 15x^2y$

1 Simplify these expressions:

a) $a + a + a + a$ b) $5n + 3n - n$ c) $x \times x \times x \times x$
d) $4p \times 3p$ e) $4p + q - p + q$ ✓ f) $3p \times 4pq$ ✓
g) $6r + 3s - r - s$ h) $2xy + 3xy$ i) $4a^2b + 2a^2b - a^2b$ ✓
j) $4ab \times 3ab$ k) $2a \times b \times c$ l) $2a \times 3ab \times a$
m) $d^2 + d^2$ n) $2d^3 + 5d^3 + 3d^3$ o) $4cd \times 3de$

2 For each of these diagrams, form an equation in which x is the subject.

In a diagram, lengths (or angles) are only labelled with the same letter if they are equal.

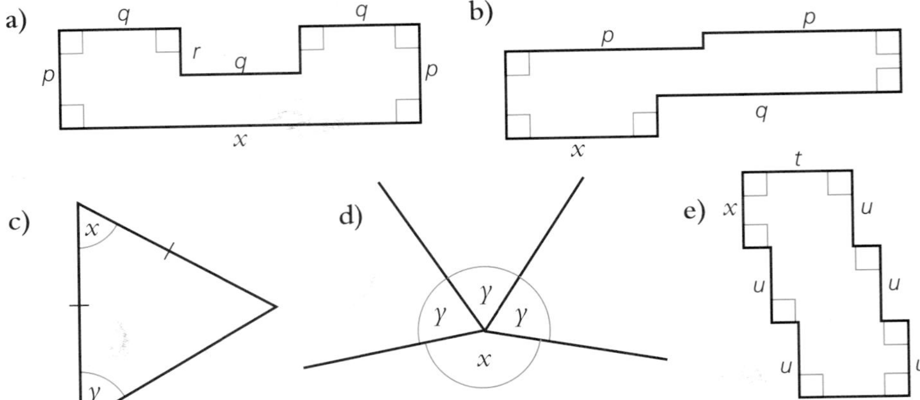

7.4 Order of operations

The order in which the operations of addition, subtraction, multiplication, division and raising to a power are carried out, can make a big difference to the outcome. Algebra is only useful as a means of communication, if everyone follows the same rules.

The equation $y = 3x^2$ contains information about how to convert a value, called x, into a new value called y. The process can be shown in a flow diagram as follows.

$x \rightarrow$ square $\rightarrow$ $\times 3$ $\rightarrow y$

A common error is to use the process shown below.

$x \rightarrow$ $\times 3$ $\rightarrow$ square $\rightarrow y$

However, this process represents the equation $y = (3x)^2 = 3x \times 3x = 9x^2$

For example, when $x = 4$, $3x^2 = 3 \times 16 = 48$ whereas $(3x)^2 = 12^2 = 144$.

In general, the operations should be carried out in the following order:

- **Brackets** calculations inside brackets should be done first
- **Powers and roots** as in the example above
- **Multiplication and division** can be done in either order
- **Addition and subtraction** again, can be done in either order

1 Draw flow diagrams for each of these equations:

a) $y = x^2 + 3$ b) $y = (x + 3)^2$ c) $y = 3\sqrt{x}$

d) $y = \frac{x}{3} + 2$ e) $y = 5(2x - 3)$ f) $y = 3(x + 1)^2$

2 Given that $v = 9$, find the value of these without using a calculator:

a) v^2 b) $1 + v^2$ c) $(1 + v)^2$ d) $\sqrt{v}$

e) $4\sqrt{v}$ f) $8 - \frac{v}{3}$ g) $4 + 2v$ h)

$2v^2$

i) $20 - v - 3$ j) $20 - (v - 3)$ k) $20 - v + 3$ l) $20 - (v + 3)$

Note: $\sqrt{9} + 16 = 3 + 16 = 19$ whereas $\sqrt{9 + 16} = \sqrt{25} = 5$

i.e. extending the line at the top of the square root symbol is equivalent to writing $\sqrt{}.(9 + 16)$ which means that the addition is carried out first.

In a similar way, $\frac{x + a}{b}$ means $(x + a) \div b$

and $\frac{b}{x + a}$ means $b \div (x + a)$.

---

3 Given that $p = 3$ and $q = 4$ find the value of the following without using a calculator:

a) $\sqrt{q} + 32$ b) $\sqrt{q + 32}$ c) $\sqrt{2p + q - 1}$ d) $\sqrt{p^2}$

e) $\sqrt{q^2}$ f) $\sqrt{p^2} + \sqrt{q^2}$ g) $\sqrt{p^2 + q^2}$ h) $\sqrt{p^2q^2}$

4 Decide whether each of these statements is *always* true, *sometimes* true or *never* true. In each case, give a reason for your decision:

a) $\sqrt{a + b} = \sqrt{a} + \sqrt{b}$ ✓

b) $\sqrt{ab} = \sqrt{a} \times \sqrt{b}$

(*Hint*: use a calculator and experiment with different values for a and b.)

5 Substitute $x = 5$ and $y = 6$ to find the value of these, without using a calculator:

a) $x + \frac{y}{2}$ b) $\frac{x + y + 1}{4}$ c) $\frac{12}{y - 2}$ d) $\frac{12}{y} - (x - 3)$

When multiplying numbers, calculations can be carried out in any order.

$\frac{1}{2} \times 7 \times 6$ can be worked out as: $\left(\frac{1}{2} \times 7\right) \times 6 = 3\frac{1}{2} \times 6 = 21$

or $\frac{1}{2} \times (7 \times 6) = \frac{1}{2} \times 42 = 21$

or $\left(\frac{1}{2} \times 6\right) \times 7 = 3 \times 7 = 21$

---

6 Find the value of $\frac{1}{2}ab$, *without* a calculator, in each of the following cases:

a) $a = 4, b = 7$ b) $a = 9, b = 16$ c) $a = 19.8, b = 20$

d) $a = 9, b = 3$ e) $a = 36, b = 27$ f) $a = 0.046, b = 1000$

7.5 Using a calculator

A **scientific** calculator follows the same rules that are used in algebra, whenever more than one operation is involved. For example the value of $2 + 3 \times 4$ is given as 14 (*not* 20). However, a calculator cannot recognise some expressions in the way that they would normally be written. You need to allow for this when you enter a key sequence.

Example

Expression	*Key in as*	*Result*
$\frac{8.71 - 3.01}{1.9}$	$(8.71 - 3.01) \div 1.9$	3
$\sqrt{17.3 + 7.7}$	$\sqrt{\ }(17.3 + 7.7)$	5
$\sqrt{\frac{208.8}{5.8}}$	$\sqrt{\ }(208.8 \div 5.8)$	6

Check these results using your own calculator.

1 Find the value of these. As a check, in each case the result should be a whole number.

a) $5 + \frac{130.9}{18.7}$ b) $\frac{36.7 + 59.2}{11.9875}$ c) $\frac{164.08}{8.45 + 3.27}$

d) $\sqrt{13.2496} + 4.36$ e) $\sqrt{213.2 + 147.8}$ f) $96.522 - 5 \times 3.62^2$

2 Calculate the value of each of the following expressions to 3 significant figures and check your answers by estimation:

a) $18.9 - \frac{11.37}{2.18}$ b) $\frac{67.89 + 91.4}{38.7 - 18.36}$ c) $\frac{41.3 + 62.8}{19.78} + 11.2$

d) $\sqrt{37.45} + 14.321$ e) $\frac{1}{2.137} + \frac{1}{3.985}$ f) $\sqrt{\frac{23.762}{5.971}}$

g) $27.36 - (11.93 - 1.27)$ h) 4.89×2.03^2 i) $(4.89 \times 2.03)^2$

7.6 Using a number line

A number line provides us with a way of representing numbers that is particularly useful for dealing with **negative** values.

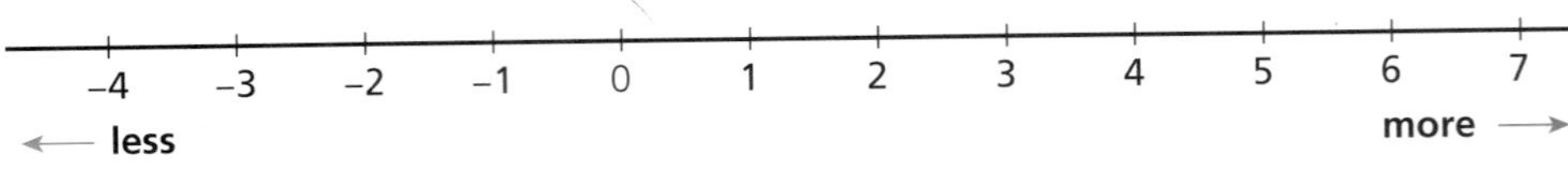

By using a number line, negative numbers are seen to be an extension of the familiar system rather than something completely new.

For example, the idea that the set of numbers given by $x < 5$, lies to the *left* of 5 on the number line, extends to the negative numbers.

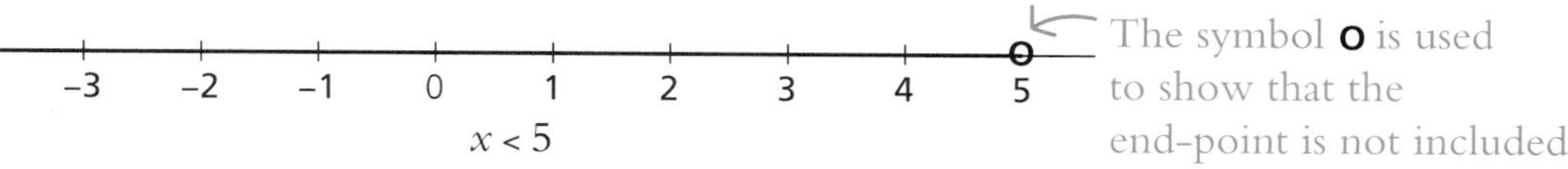

In the same way, numbers larger than a given value are shown to its *right*.

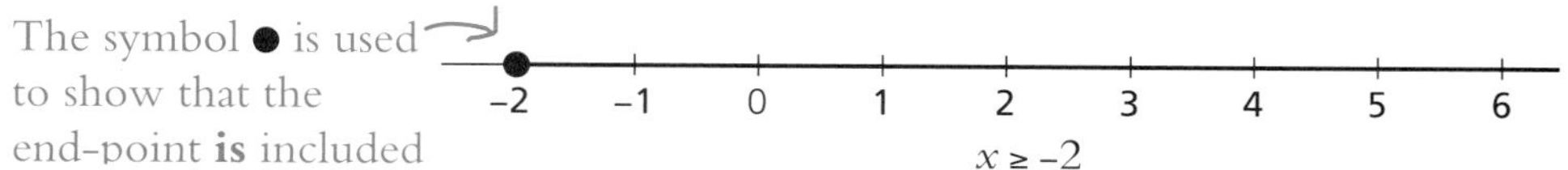

1 Show how each of the following inequalities may be represented on a number line:

a) $x < 3$ b) $x \le -1$ c) $x > -4$ d) $-2 \le x$

e) $-3 < x < 2$ f) $-5 \le x < -2$ g) $-3 < x \le 0$ h) $3 > x \ge -4$

2 List these numbers in order of size, smallest first:

a) 4, 9, −2, −5, 0, −7, 3, −10 b) 0.75, −0.5, 0.2, −0.2, −1, −0.75, 1

3 For each inequality, state a possible value of x:

a) $x < -10$ b) $-5 \le x < -1$ c) $-7 < x < -6$ d) $-2 > x > -3$

The operations of addition and subtraction can be shown as movements along the number line.

Example

Find the value of −4 − 3. (Note the two different uses of the minus sign.)

Answer

−4 − 3

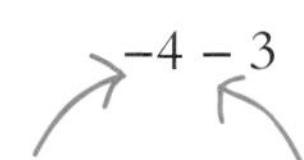

This represents the **sign of the number**. *Start* at −4.

This represents the **operation of subtraction**. Move 3 places to the left.

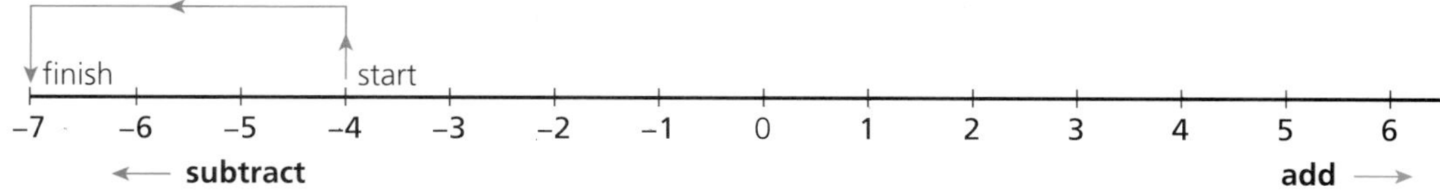

From the diagram, −4 − 3 = −7

4 Use a number line to find the value of:

a) −3 + 2 b) 3 − 5 c) −1 − 1 d) −1 + 1

e) −2 + 5 f) 3 − 5 − 4 g) −2 − 5 + 3 h) −8 + 5 + 3

i) −5 − 3.6 j) −5 + 3.6

When the number to be added (or subtracted) is negative, the normal direction of movement is reversed.

For example, $-3 - -2$ is the same as $-3 + 2 = -1$.

This negative sign switches the direction

Start at -3 and move 2 places to the *right*

5 Use the method shown above to work out:
a) $-5 - -7$ ✓ b) $4 + -6$ c) $-4 + -6$ d) $-8 - -8$
e) $4 + (3 - 9)$ ✓ f) $-2 - (-1 - 3)$ g) $-9 + (-11 + 10)$ h) $-2 - (-1 + -1)$

6 Work out question 5 using a calculator. Take care to distinguish between the different uses of the minus sign when entering the calculations.

7 Copy and complete:
a) $-3 + ? = -5$ b) $-5 - ? = 4$ c) $? + (-3 -6) = 0$ d) $-2 - (-8 + ?) = 3$

7.7 Negatives in real situations

The Book of Heroic Failures, by Stephen Pile, contains the following account of an early space exploration attempt under the heading 'The Greatest Mathematical Error!'.

> 'The Mariner I space probe was launched from Cape Canaveral on 28 July 1962 towards Venus. After 13 minutes flight a booster engine would give acceleration up to 25 820 m.p.h.
>
> After 44 minutes 9800 solar cells would unfold; after 80 days a computer would calculate the final course corrections and after 100 days the craft would circle the unknown planet scanning the mysterious cloud in which it is bathed.
>
> However, with an efficiency that is truly heartening, Mariner I plunged into the Atlantic Ocean only four minutes after take off.
>
> Enquiries later revealed that a minus sign had been omitted from the instructions fed into the computer. 'It was human error' a launch spokesman said. This minus sign cost £4 280 000.'

A change of sign is often associated with a change of direction.

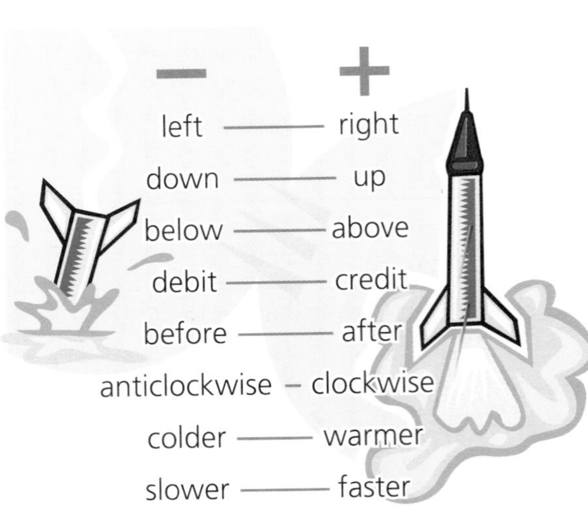

1 a) What is the special significance of a negative temperature on the Celsius (Centigrade) scale?

b) The cooling effect of the wind on a cold day is known as wind chill, and gives the sensation that the temperature becomes lower as the wind speed increases. Find the effect of a windchill of −10 °C on each of these temperatures.

(i) 3 °C (ii) −1 °C (iii) −8 °C (iv) −15 °C

2 In 1848 the physicist William Thomson, later Lord Kelvin, devised the Absolute Temperature Scale in which absolute zero corresponded to −273 °C, the temperature at which atoms and molecules stop moving. More recently, this has become known as the Kelvin scale, in which 0 K = −273 °C, 10 K = −263 °C and so on.

Describe each of the following temperatures using the Kelvin scale.

a) The freezing point of water 0 °C ✓
b) Room temperature 18 °C
c) Summer in the desert 51 °C
d) A cool day in Antarctica −30 °C
e) A sunny day on Mercury 450 °C
f) Mercury at night −170 °C

3 a) What do the letters BC stand for?

b) What would be an alternative way to describe the year 753 BC? ✓

c) According to legend, Rome was founded by Romulus and Remus in 753 BC and 244 years later the Romans set up a Republic. In what year was this?

d) The calculation for part c) could be carried out using negative numbers. Copy and complete the following statement.

… + 244 = …

4 In the game of golf, the score for each hole is compared to an established standard as follows:

Par	The number of strokes that an expert would be expected to take
Bogey	A score of one over par
Birdie	A score of one under par
Eagle	A score of two under par
Albatross	A score of three under par

The table below shows the results of some golfers over the first five holes.

a) The results combine to give A. Swinger a score of 3 under par. Work out the scores for the other players.

b) Copy the table but write each of the results and scores as numbers.

Names	Results	Score
A. Swinger	PAR BIRDIE PAR EAGLE PAR	3 UNDER PAR
G. Club	BIRDIE PAR BOGEY BOGEY ALBATROSS	
D. Bunker	PAR PAR BIRDIE BIRDIE BOGEY	
S. Wood	BOGEY BIRDIE PAR EAGLE EAGLE	
J. Irons	PAR ALBATROSS BIRDIE EAGLE BIRDIE	

5 In tournaments, it is common practice to display the scores of the top players on a **Leader Board.**

The Leader Board for the top four players in a tournament, played over 72 holes, is as follows:

Names	Holes played	Score
A. Slice	70	-10
L. Fairway	68	-9
H. Green	63	-7
R. Driver	65	-6

All the remaining holes are played to par, with the following exceptions:

L. Fairway plays a Birdie and a Bogey; H. Green plays a Birdie; R. Driver plays an Eagle and an Albatross.

State the final score for each player and put them in order of merit.

8.1 Measuring length

It's useful to be able to estimate lengths in both metric and imperial units.

1 Try to match up each line with its correct length.
(Do not use a ruler to measure.)

A

B

C

D

E

Choose your answers from these measurements:

a) 10.5 cm
b) 5 inches
c) 50 mm
d) 2.8 cm
e) 2.75 inches

Reminder: metric measures of length
10 millimetres (mm) = 1 centimetre (cm)
100 centimetres = 1 metre (m)
1000 millimetres = 1 metre
1000 metres = 1 kilometre (km)

2 Measure the length and height of this rectangle in millimetres. ✓

What is the perimeter of the rectangle (the distance round all four sides)?

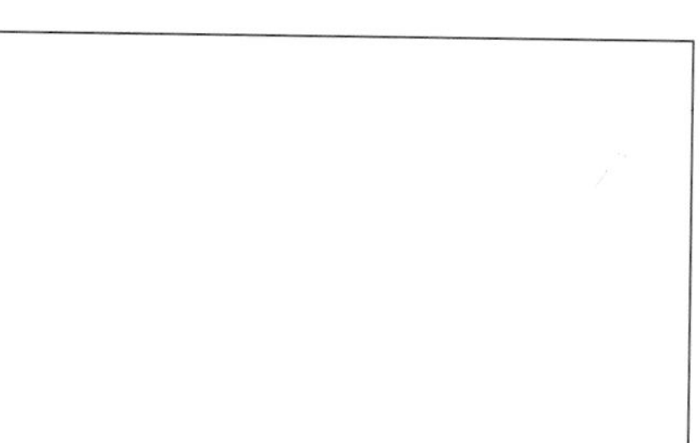

3 Draw a rectangle 12 cm long and 5 cm high.
What is the length of a diagonal?

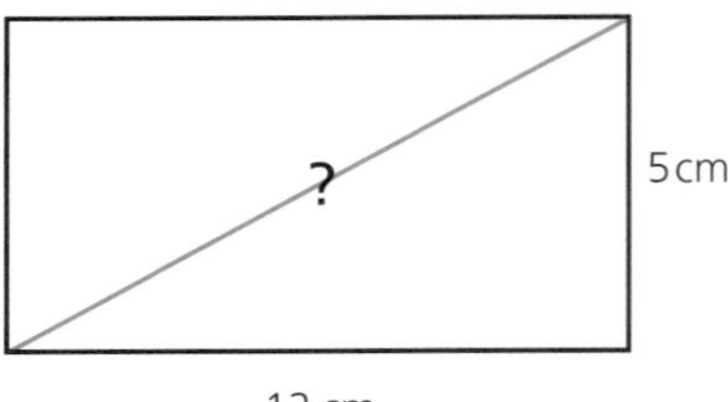

4 Measure the size of the page of this book. Give your answers in
a) millimetres, b) centimetres.

5 This diagram shows the end of a rack designed to hold compact discs. Make an accurate drawing and measure the length of the sloping edge.

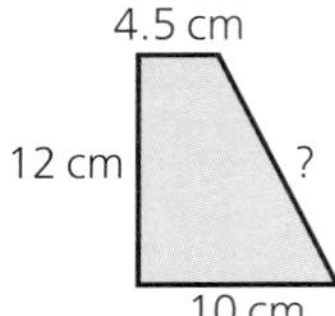

6 How many millimetres are there in:

a) 3 cm b) 5.8 cm ✓ c) 11.4 cm d) 14 m ✓ e) 8.3 m
f) 14.6 cm g) 14.6 m h) 530 cm i) 2 km j) 2.9 km?

7 How many centimetres are there in:

a) 48 mm ✓ b) 100 mm c) 63 mm d) 925 mm e) 1852 mm
f) 4 m g) 8.3 m h) 195 m i) 4 km j) 6.9 km?

8 How many metres are there in:

a) 153 cm ✓ b) 9000 mm c) 650 cm?

Most older people will tell you their height in feet and inches. Inches, feet, yards and miles are all *imperial measurements*. There are:

12 inches in 1 foot
3 feet in 1 yard
1760 yards in 1 mile

It can be quite difficult to convert from imperial measurements to metric ones. Here are some approximate conversions:

1 inch is slightly more than $2\frac{1}{2}$ cm
1 foot is approximately 30 cm
1 yard is about 90 cm
$\frac{1}{2}$ mile is approximately 1 km
(or 5 miles = 8 km approximately)

9 a) How many feet are there in 5 yards? ✓

b) How many yards are there in $\frac{1}{2}$ mile?

c) Is 800 m more or less than $\frac{1}{2}$ mile?

d) How many inches are there in 3 feet 6 inches?

e) Is $\frac{1}{4}$ mile more or less than 500 yards?

10 How may inches are approximately equal to: a) 10 cm b) 5 cm c) 20 cm d) 1 m?

11 How many centimetres are approximately equal to a) 3 feet b) 10 inches c) 6 inches?

12 a) How many km are approximately equal to (i) 10 miles (ii) 15 miles?
b) Are 20 miles more or less than 50 km?

13 Mrs Williams is 5 feet 6 inches tall. How tall is this in inches? How tall is this in centimetres (approximately)?

8.2 Measuring weight

Small light objects are weighed in grams while heavier objects are weighed in kilograms.

Sugar is usually sold in 1 kilogram bags while a jar of jam may be 500 grams (= half a kilogram).

Reminder: metric measurements of weight
1000 milligrams (mg) = 1 gram (g)
1000 grams = 1 kilogram (kg)
1000 kilograms = 1 tonne

Example

A recipe for buns requires the following ingredients:

500 g plain flour
200 ml of warm water (weighs 200 g)
50 g mixed peel
50 g melted butter
75 g currants
50 g sugar

If this mixture makes 12 buns, how much will each bun weigh (to the nearest gram)?

Answer
First we need to find the total weight of the ingredients.

Total weight = 500 g + 200 g + 50 g + 50 g + 75 g + 50 g = 925 g
Weight of one bun = 925 g ÷ 12
= 77.08
= 77 g to the nearest gram

1 A group of pupils are going on their Duke of Edinburgh Bronze Award expedition. They need to know how much weight they will have to carry.

Here is a list of the basic kit each pupil needs:

Sleeping bag	1.5 kg
Spare sweater	850 g
Spare socks and pants	125 g
Cup and plate, cutlery	530 g
Towel and soap	475 g

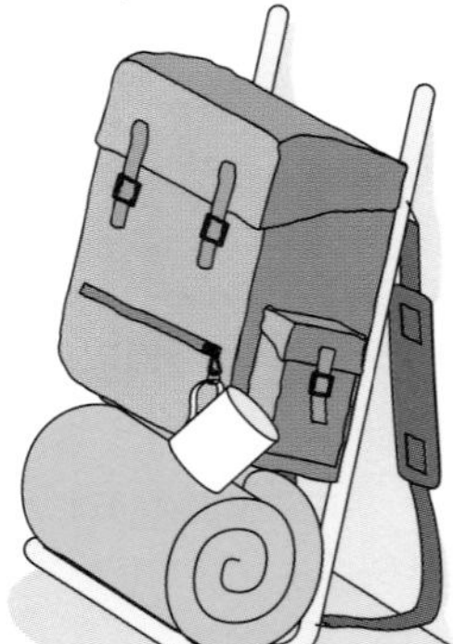

Find the total weight of these items in grams.

2 Breakfast for three pupils consists of:

6 eggs weighing	450 g
6 rashers of bacon	475 g
1 tin baked beans	450 g
Small loaf of bread	480 g
Margarine	75 g

a) Find the total weight of breakfast for three pupils if they must also include 1 litre of water (for tea or coffee), and 1 litre of water weighs 1 kg. ✓

b) What will be the total weight for 24 pupils (water and food)?

3 a) A large cheese weighs 5.6 kg. How many 125 g portions can be cut from this cheese?

b) Each pupil and each of the two expedition leaders is given a portion of cheese, making 26 portions altogether. How much cheese is left?

4 A can of soup weighs 475 g.

a) How much will a pack of four tins weigh?

b) How heavy will a box of 24 tins be, weighed in kilograms?

5 If a packet of 80 tea bags weighs 240 g, how much does one tea bag weigh?

6 Find the weight of 26 Mars Bars if one bar weighs 62 g.

Vegetables and fruit are still sold loose in pounds weight in many shops and market stalls. Pounds, ounces, stones, hundredweights are all *imperial measurements.*

There are:

16 ounces (oz) = 1 pound (lb)
14 pounds = 1 stone (st)
8 stones = 1 hundredweight (cwt)
20 hundredweights = 1 ton

Here are some approximate conversions:

1 kilogram is about 2.2 pounds
125 grams is about 4 ounces

---

7 How many ounces are there in:

a) $\frac{1}{4}$ lb ✓ b) $2\frac{1}{2}$ lb c) 5 lb

8 Which of the following is closest to one ounce:
a) 3 g b) 30 g c) 300 g d) 3 kg

9 a) Simone weighs 7 stones. What is this in pounds?
b) Which of the following is closest to Simone's weight:
(i) 4.5 kg (ii) 45 kg (iii) 450 kg

10 The ingredients for a cake are:
$\frac{1}{4}$ lb flour
$\frac{1}{4}$ lb sugar
$\frac{1}{4}$ lb margarine
1 egg (= 2 ounces)

a) What is the total weight of one cake in ounces?
b) What is the total weight of 5 cakes in pounds and ounces?

11 Is a metric tonne heavier or lighter than an imperial ton? Explain your answer.

12 What roughly is the weight of this kind of lorry?

13 In 1992 Cathy Millen set the world power lifting record for women at 250 kg, using the 'dead lift'. How many people (roughly) would have a combined weight of 250 kg?

8.3 Measuring capacity

Capacity is a measure of the amount of space, or cubic content, occupied by a liquid, a gas, etc.

As with measures of length and weight, we still use both metric and imperial measurements.

Here is a summary of different measures of capacity.

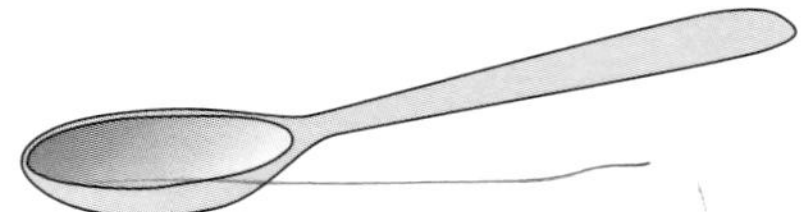

A medicine spoon holds 5 ml.
1 litre of water weighs 1 kilogram.

Reminder: metric measures of capacity
1000 millilitres (ml) = 1 litre (l)
1000 cm^3 = 1 litre
Sometimes the centilitre is also used:
100 cl = 1 litre

We still use imperial measures of capacity. There are:

20 fluid ounces in 1 pint
2 pints in 1 quart
8 pints in 1 gallon

Here are some approximate conversions:

'A litre of water's a pint and three quarters'
1 gallon is approximately $4\frac{1}{2}$ litres
30 ml is approximately 1 fluid ounce

Milk may be sold in pints or litres.

---

1 A can of cola contains 330 ml. I buy six cans. My friend buys a 2-litre bottle of cola and says she has more cola than I do. Is she right?

2 I need 3 cans of oil to change the oil in my car. Each can contains 440 ml of oil. I can buy oil also in a large 5-litre container.
a) How much oil do I need for one oil change?
b) How many oil changes will I get from 5 litres?

3 A litre is about $1\frac{3}{4}$ pints. How many litres of milk do I buy in a week, if I buy one pint each day for seven days?

4 A bottle of medicine holds 75 ml. How many doses (each a 5 ml spoonful) can I pour from this bottle?

5 A bottle of cola contains 1.5 litres. How many glasses containing 250 ml can be filled from this bottle?

6 Are 120 ml approximately equal to:
a) 1 b) 2 c) 3 d) 4 fluid ounces?

7 Are 3 gallons of petrol more or less than 15 litres?

8 How many pints are there in $5\frac{1}{2}$ gallons?

9 Change 0.75 litres to centilitres.

10 How many fluid ounces are there in $\frac{3}{4}$ pint?

11 How many ml are there in 1.3 litres?

12 Are 2 gallons approximately equal to:
a) 3 **b)** 9 **c)** 12 **d)** 15 litres?

8.4 Conversion graphs

This conversion graph has been drawn to make it easy to convert from miles to kilometres (and vice versa).

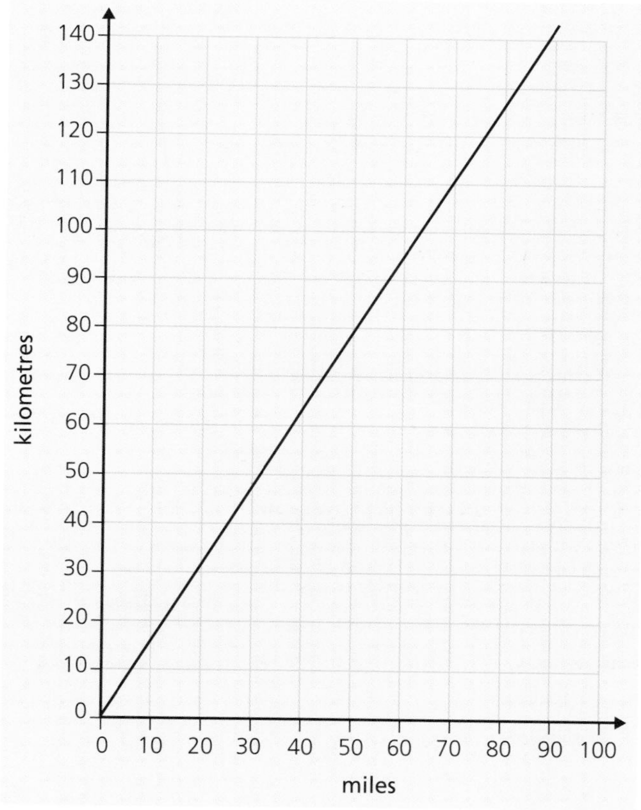

1 **a)** What is 30 miles in kilometres?
b) What is 30 kilometres in miles?
c) What is 80 miles in kilometres?
d) What is 80 kilometres in miles?

This is a conversion graph to convert temperature from Centigrade (Celsius) to Fahrenheit scales.

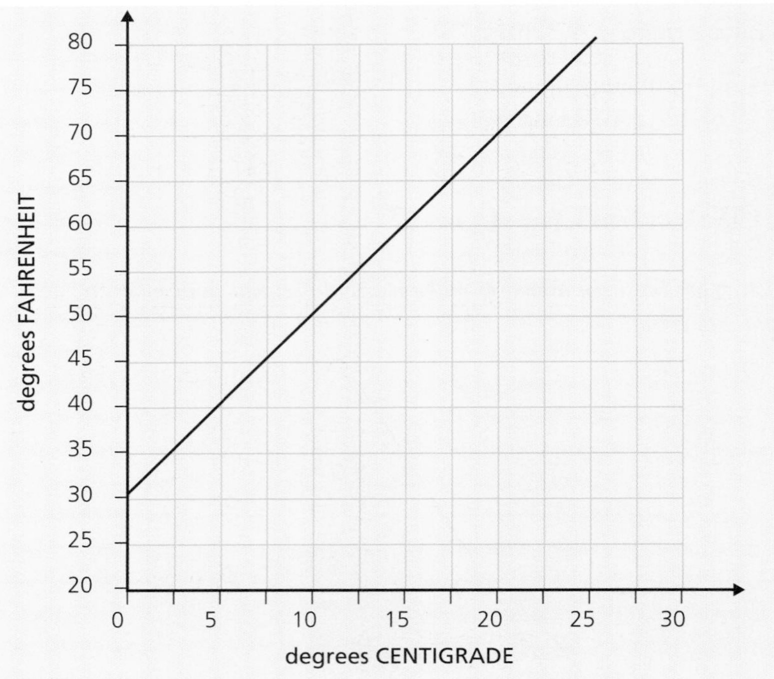

2 a) Freezing point is 0 °C. What is this in degrees Fahrenheit?
b) What is 20 °C in degrees Fahrenheit?
c) What is 50 °F in degrees Centigrade?
d) What is 60 °F in degrees Centigrade?

3 To convert inches to centimetres you multiply by 2.54.
a) Fill in this table:
b) Use these results to draw a conversion graph with inches on the horizontal axis (up to 40 inches) and centimetres on the vertical axis.
c) What is 50 centimetres in inches?
d) What is 15 inches in centimetres?

Inches	Centimetres
0	0
1	2.54
10	
20	

REVIEW 1

Unit 1 Number systems

1 Try these without using a calculator:

a) 1476 + 3867 + 981
b) 27 638 + 8176 + 6534
c) 7612 − 4816
d) 9130 − 7826
e) 5000 − 1276
f) 38 000 − 9437
g) 432 × 6
h) 5632 × 4
i) 36 × 24
j) 23 × 57
k) 49 × 200
l) 326 × 72
m) 7625 ÷ 5
n) 2454 ÷ 6

2 What values are shown here?

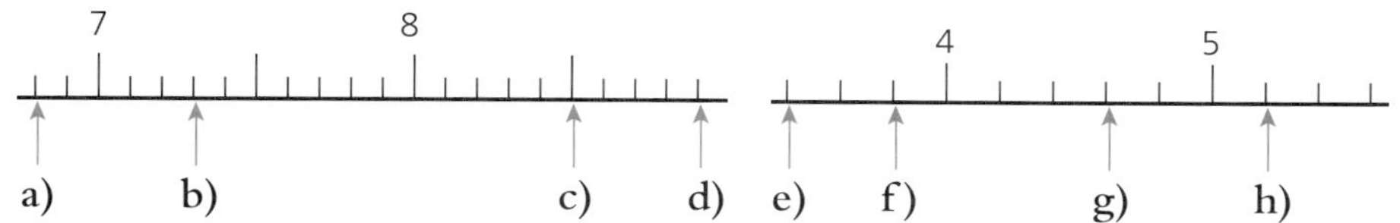

3 Write as decimals:

a) $\frac{7}{10}$
b) $\frac{2}{5}$
c) $3\frac{1}{2}$
d) $12\frac{1}{4}$

4 State the place value of the 9 in each of the following:

a) 59 653
b) 2.395
c) 19.82
d) 0.0091

5 Round each of the following to one decimal place.

a) 0.7652
b) 11.438
c) 16.449
d) 18.35
e) 6.972
f) 0.99

6 Round to the nearest penny:

a) £34.6748
b) £271.3864
c) £249.3451
d) £8 463.464 99
e) £45 672.3956
f) £273 148.435 09

7 Round to the nearest £10:

a) £654.87
b) £3786.92
c) £27 145.63
d) £82 464.92
e) £239.476 231
f) £8.734 126

8 Find the value of these without using a calculator:

a) 346 × 10
b) 279 ÷ 10
c) 528 ÷ 100
d) 0.76 × 10
e) 3.4 ÷ 1000
f) 2.9 × 1000
g) 12.62 + 3.7
h) 16 − 5.23
i) 5.81 + 12.5 − 0.732
j) 0.3 × 0.2
k) 12.4 × 0.5
l) 3.42 × 2.3

9 Find the value of the missing figures:

a) 0.261 × … = 2.61
b) 0.047 × … = 47
c) … × 100 = 3.8
d) … × 10 = 0.0423
e) 62.7 ÷ … = 6.27
f) 36 ÷ … = 0.36
g) … ÷ 10 = 0.72
h) … ÷ 100 = 2.9

Unit 2 Angles and symmetry

10 A hiker walks 100 m up a slope of 14° and then 50 m up a slope of 12°. How much higher is she than when she started? Make an accurate scale drawing to find your answer.

11 a) What is the least number of lines which must be added to the figure on the right to give it one and only one axis of symmetry?

b) In how many ways can this be done?

12 a) Find the values of x, y and z.

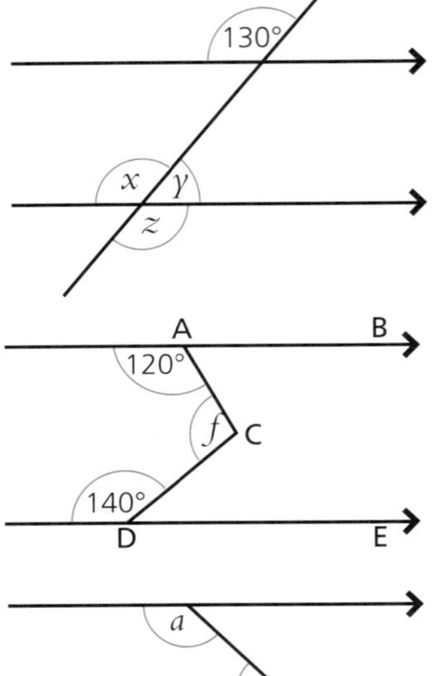

b) Copy this diagram.

c) Draw an extra line through point C which is also parallel to AB and DE.

d) Use this to help you find angle f.

e) Write down an equation giving b in terms of a and c.
$b = \ldots$

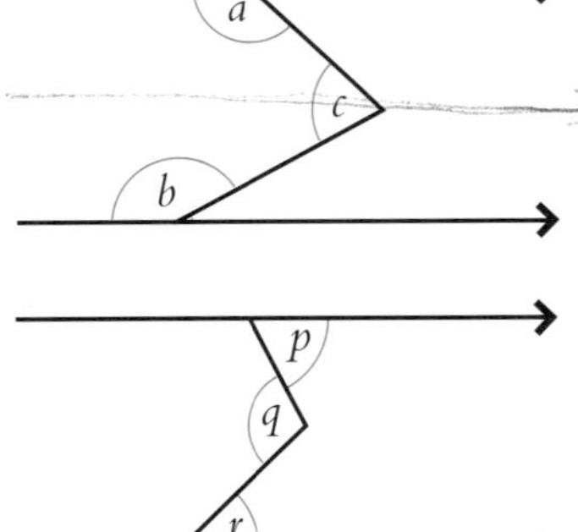

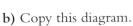

f) Write down an equation giving q in terms of p and r.

13 a) Find a, b and x.

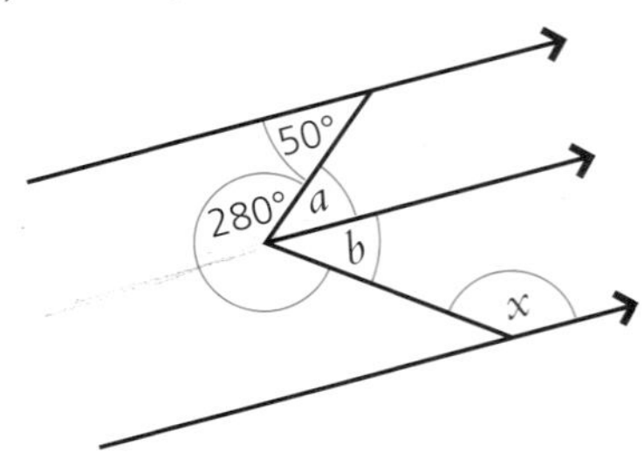

b) Find the value of c. (To do this copy the diagram and draw in a third parallel line.)

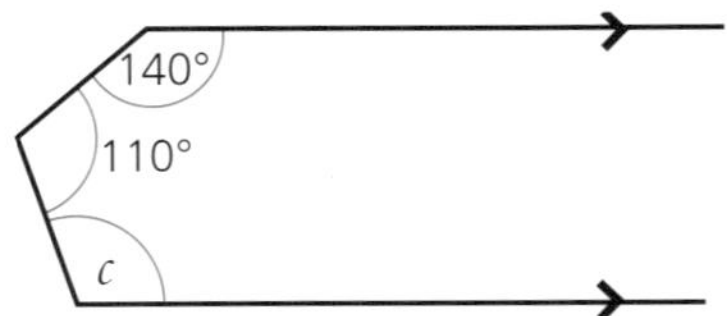

Unit 3 Division

14 Which of the following numbers are divisible by 5?
1463, 23 410, 8672, 23 145, 7115, 89 354, 49 000, 67 003

15 Find the digit sum of each of these numbers:
a) 3 481 b) 26 342 c) 762 325 d) 721 302

16 Which of the numbers given in question 15 is divisible by 3?

17 Which of the following numbers is divisible by 9?
2345, 3015, 26 423, 126 423, 261 423, 61 328, 641 328, 671 328

18 Rearrange the digits in these numbers to make the largest number you can that is divisible by 5:
a) 345 126 b) 36 251 c) 80 876
d) 9 213 527 e) 630 514 f) 905 056

19 Rearrange the digits in these numbers to make the largest number you can that is divisible by 6:
a) 4 371 b) 12 435 c) 90 768
d) 23 454 e) 753 825 f) 9 347 652

20 List the prime numbers between 100 and 150.

21 Only one of the following numbers is prime. Which is it? Explain your reasoning.
81 776, 81 775, 81 677, 81 777, 81 477

22 The program given below is written for a Casio graphics calculator and may be used to test whole numbers greater than 1 to find whether they are prime or not. The program may be adapted to work on a computer or on other makes of calculator.

```
? → X
2 → C
Lbl 1
C > √ X ⇒ Goto 3
X ÷ C → Y
Y = Int Y ⇒ Goto 2
Isz C
Goto 1
Lbl 2
"NOT PRIME"
Goto 4
Lbl 3
"PRIME"
Lbl 4
```

(continued)

ICT Extra!

Pick a number.
Is it a prime number?
Use this program for a Casio graphics calculator to test whether it is a prime number or not.

In response to the question mark prompt, key in the number that you wish to test and press EXE. The calculator will then display either "PRIME" or "NOT PRIME". Press EXE again twice to re-run the program.

(*Note*: the program is designed only to check whole numbers greater than 1 and will give false results for other numbers.)

a) Test the program for numbers that you know are prime or not prime.
b) What is the smallest prime number greater than 10 000?
c) $2^3 - 1 = 7$ which is prime. (Key in 2 x^y 3 – 1 EXE in response to the ?). Try $2^4 - 1$. Experiment further.

Unit 4 Probability (1)

23 Nicky writes down (at random) a whole number larger than 1 and smaller than 11. Find the probability that it is:
a) odd b) even c) prime d) a perfect square
e) a square root of a number less than 50.

24 What is the probability that a letter of the alphabet selected at random is a vowel?

25 Using only the figures between 1 and 5 inclusive, Ramesh writes down a proper fraction (not necessarily cancelled down into its lowest terms). List all the fractions he can make. Find the probability that his fraction:
a) is less than $\frac{1}{2}$
b) is greater than $\frac{1}{2}$
c) is in its lowest terms
d) is a perfect square
e) is equal to a recurring decimal

26 This diagram shows the face of a digital watch. Sarah has put her digital watch away in a drawer. When she takes it out, she finds that her watch has stopped and that she will need to buy a new battery.
Find the probability that:
a) the number in column B is a '4'
b) the number in column A is less than 5
c) the number in column B is a '2'
d) the number in column B is an '8'
e) the number in column C is a '6'
f) the number in column C is a '1'
g) the number in column D is less than 4
h) the number in column D is a '3'

Unit 5 Working with fractions

27 Find the value of these without using a calculator:

a) $7.8 \div 2$ b) $28.5 \div 5$ c) $11.28 \div 4$ d) $4.9 \div 2$
e) $17.1 \div 5$ f) $37.8 \div 4$ g) $2.8 \div 7$ h) $0.75 \div 3$
i) $0.55 \div 11$ j) $0.24 \div 6$ k) $32 \div 5$ l) $17 \div 2$
m) $21 \div 4$ n) $21 \div 40$ o) $2.1 \div 400$ p) $15 \div 6$
q) $15 \div 0.6$ r) $15 \div 0.006$

28 Find the missing values:

a) $\frac{3}{5} = \frac{12}{\ldots}$ b) $\frac{4}{7} = \frac{\ldots}{21}$ c) $\frac{24}{36} = \frac{2}{\ldots} = \frac{\ldots}{27}$

d) $\frac{2.9}{0.2} = \frac{\ldots}{2}$ e) $\frac{2.35}{0.47} = \frac{\ldots}{47}$ f) $\frac{0.764}{0.04} = \frac{\ldots}{4}$

29 Work out without using a calculator:

a) $2.36 \div 0.4$ b) $3.25 \div 0.5$ c) $0.462 \div 0.07$
d) $1.38 \div 0.006$ e) $0.47 \div 0.02$ f) $35 \div 0.8$

30 Write as recurring decimals:

a) $\frac{4}{9}$ b) $\frac{7}{11}$ c) $\frac{7}{3}$

31 Write as fractions in their simplest terms:

a) 50% b) 25% c) 75% d) $12\frac{1}{2}\%$ e) $33\frac{1}{3}\%$
f) $37\frac{1}{2}\%$ g) 20% h) 60% i) 70%

32 Write as decimals:

a) 17.5% b) 23.8% c) 9.6% d) 4.35% e) 81% f) 0.81%

33 Express each of these as a percentage:

a) 0.73 b) 0.04 c) 0.65 d) 0.761 e) 0.056 f) 0.009

34 Write these as mixed numbers:

a) $\frac{17}{4}$ b) $\frac{25}{3}$ c) $\frac{31}{2}$ d) $\frac{19}{5}$ e) $\frac{45}{7}$ f) $\frac{75}{12}$

35 Round to 3 significant figures:

a) 5648 b) 27 382 c) 9374 d) 12 953
e) 19 976 f) 9999 g) 8.764 h) 0.074 23
i) 0.047 56 j) 118.763 k) 34.2398 l) 4.9978
m) 0.399 67 n) 0.029 99 o) 0.002 099

Unit 6 Organising data

36 A line graph is used to show how a measurement has changed over a period of time. Here is a line graph reproduced from *Social trends* (HMSO 1994). It shows trade deliveries to shops of LPs, cassettes, compact discs and singles.

a) Which kinds of music recordings have been rising in popularity over the time period shown?
b) Which ones have been falling in popularity?
c) In what year (roughly) did sales of cassettes reach their peak?
d) In what year (roughly) were CDs first sold?
e) In what year did the sales of singles reach a peak?

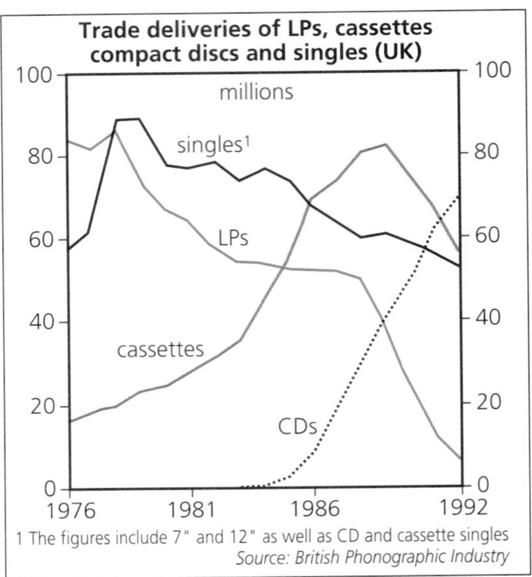

1 The figures include 7" and 12" as well as CD and cassette singles
Source: British Phonographic Industry

37 This line graph was reproduced from *Social trends* 1994.

a) Which fats have been falling in consumption?
b) Which fats are becoming more popular?

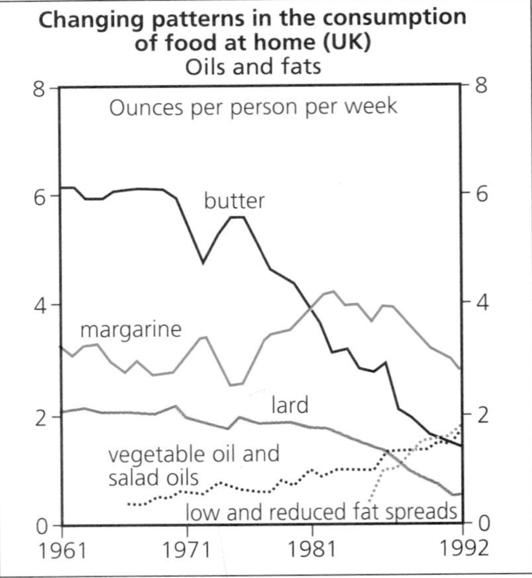

	Average total consumption	
	1961	1991
Butter	?	1.5oz
Margarine	3oz	?
Lard	?	?
Vegetable oil	0	?
Low fat spread	0	?
Total	**11oz**	**9.5oz**

c) Use the graph to help you fill in the missing values on this table (estimated to the nearest $\frac{1}{2}$ ounce).

d) Use these figures to draw two pie charts showing average weekly fat consumption in 1961 and 1991.

Unit 7 Process and priority

38 a) Round 88.76 and 1.97 to 1 significant figure.
b) Use your answers to part a) to estimate the value of 88.76 × 1.97.
c) Is the true answer more or less than your estimate?

39 Estimate the value of each of the following by rounding the numbers to 1 S.F. first. In each case state whether your answer is an over estimate or an under estimate.
a) 68.962 × 1.863 b) 57 349 + 38 654 c) 63 458 + 21 972
d) 89 865 – 34 787 e) 59.768 ÷ 12.263 f) 423.87 ÷ 0.4998

40 Describe the process that would undo each of the following.
a) Add 2.67 b) Divide by 0.873 c) Subtract 129
d) Subtract 0.046 e) Multiply by 7.65 f) Divide by 18.32

41 Find the missing values:
a) ? → [– 4.19] → 12.63 b) ? → [÷ 2.81] → 10

42 Find the value of these without a calculator:
a) 25% of 84 b) 10% of 700 c) 20% of 700
d) 10% of £45 e) 5% of £45 f) 15% of £45
g) $12\frac{1}{2}$% of £24 h) $33\frac{1}{3}$% of £99 i) $66\frac{2}{3}$% of £120

43 Use a calculator to find the value of the following:
a) 23% of £86 b) 11.8% of £340 c) 7.6% of £2 300
d) 57% of £325 e) 87.6% of £715 f) 2.73% of £8 600

44 a) A triangle has sides of length a cm, $(a + 3)$ cm and $(a + 5)$ cm. Find an expression for the perimeter of the triangle in terms of a.
b) A quadrilateral has sides of length x cm, $(x + y)$ cm, $2x$ cm and $3y$ cm. If the perimeter is P cm, find an equation giving P in terms of x and y.
c) Adjacent sides of a rectangle have lengths $2x$ cm and $3y$ cm. Find expressions for the area and perimeter of the rectangle.

45 Use a calculator to find the value of the following to 3 S.F.:
a) $9.87 + \frac{12.5}{3.9}$ b) $\frac{4.23 + 17.45}{3.42}$ c) $\frac{87.64}{19.8 - 6.573}$
d) $\sqrt{8.76} + \sqrt{5.9}$ e) $\sqrt{8.76 + 5.9}$ f) $\sqrt{2.79 \times 3.26}$
g) 7.84×2.37^2 h) $(34.2 - 1.98)^2$ i) $2.78^2 + 5.36^2$

46 Find the missing values:
a) −6 + … = 2 b) −3 − … = −10 c) −5 − … = 2
d) … + 7 = 3 e) … + 9 = −2 f) … −4 = −7

47 List the following in order of size, smallest first:
a) 8, −2, 0, 5.6, −10, 0.8 b) −6.6, 0.01, −4.72, −11, 0, −0.34

Unit 8 Length, weight and capacity

48 For each part of this question, pick the correct answer A, B, C or D.

a) 58 100 m expressed in kilometres is:

A 5.81 B 58.1 C 581 D 5810

b) 750 mm expressed in metres is:

A 0.075 B 0.75 C 7.5 D 75

c) A metre rule is broken into 4 equal pieces. The length of each piece is:

A 10 cm B 20 cm C 25 cm D 50 cm

d) The difference between 2 kg and 1300 grams, in grams, is:

A 70 B 7 C 1.3 D 700

e) If 1 km = 0.6 miles, then 60 miles is equivalent to:

A 36 km B 100 km C 360 km D 1000 km

f) What is the cost of 300 g of cheese if 3 kg costs £12.20?

A 40p B £4.05 C £1.22 D £12.20

g) How many tins of talcum powder, each containing 240 g, can be filled from a drum containing 120 kg?

A 5 B 50 C 500 D 5000

49 4 ounces is almost exactly equivalent to 114 g.

a) How many grams are equivalent to 8 ounces?

b) How many grams equal 12 ounces?

c) Use your answers to parts **a)** and **b)** to draw a conversion graph. Show amounts up to 20 ounces on the horizontal axis with the equivalent in grams shown on the vertical axis.

d) Use your graph to convert 9 ounces to grams.

e) How many ounces are equivalent to 500 g?

f) A piece of cheese weighs 3 oz. What is this in grams?

SIGNS, EQUATIONS, SEQUENCES

9.1 Changing signs

Positive and negative numbers, taken together, are sometimes referred to as **directed** numbers because a change of sign may be represented by a change of direction.

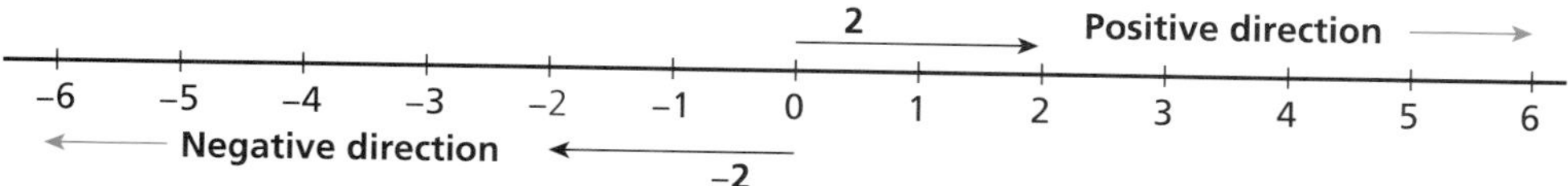

Multiplication by a positive number may be represented by a s t r e t c h i n g effect without a change of direction.

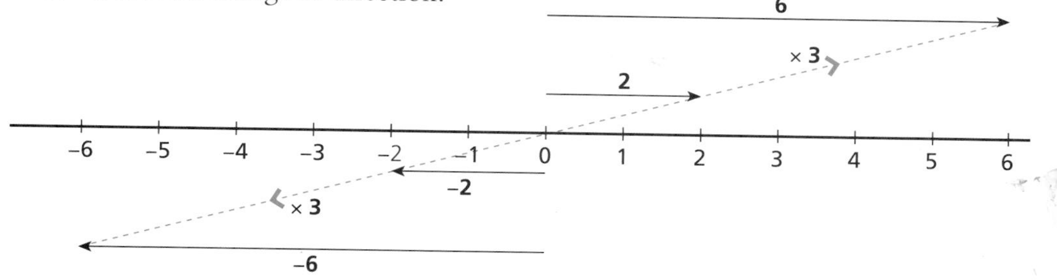

The results shown by the diagram are:

$2 \times 3 = 6$ (as we should expect)

and $-2 \times 3 = -6$

---

1 Use a diagram to show:

a) 2×4 b) -2×4 c) -4×2 d) -5×3 e) -2.5×3

If a and b are any two numbers then $ab = ba$, i.e. the order in which the numbers are multiplied doesn't make any difference to the answer.

Since $-2 \times 3 = -6$

it must follow that $3 \times -2 = -6$

The change of order suggests a new diagram:

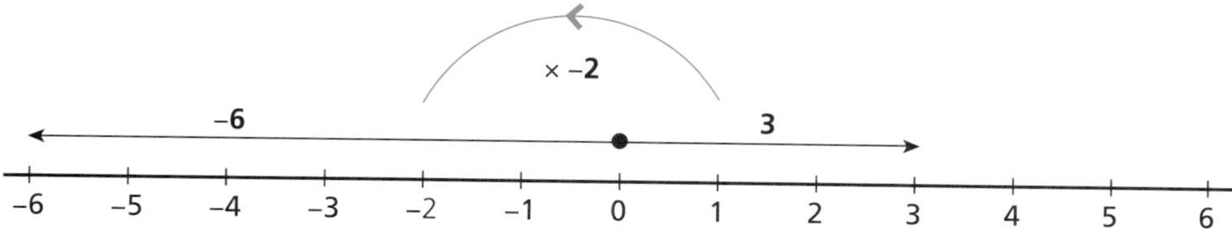

Note that multiplication by −2 is shown on the number line by a stretching effect together with a *change of direction*.

---

2 Draw diagrams to show:

a) -5×2 and 2×-5 b) -1.5×2 and 2×-1.5

3 Use a diagram to find the value of:
a) -2×-3 b) -3×-15
Show that reversing the order gives the same result.

4 Copy and complete the table:

positive	×	positive	=	positive
positive	×	negative		
	×	positive		
	×			

5 Work out:
a) -4×3 b) -2×5 c) 4×-1 d) -8×-10 e) 3×-11
f) -10×10 g) 6×-2 h) -3×-5 i) -7.5×10

6 Copy and complete:
a) $-5 \times \ldots = -10$ b) $4 \times \ldots = -16$ c) $-6 \times \ldots = 24$
d) $\ldots \times 7 = -14$ e) $\ldots \times -3 = 21$ f) $\ldots \times -2.5 = -10$
g) $\ldots \times -3 = -15$ h) $10 \times \ldots = -30$ i) $-10 \times \ldots = 27$

Reversing the process provides information about how directed numbers combine under division.
Using the fact that $-2 \times 3 = -6$ gives $-6 \div 3 = -2$.

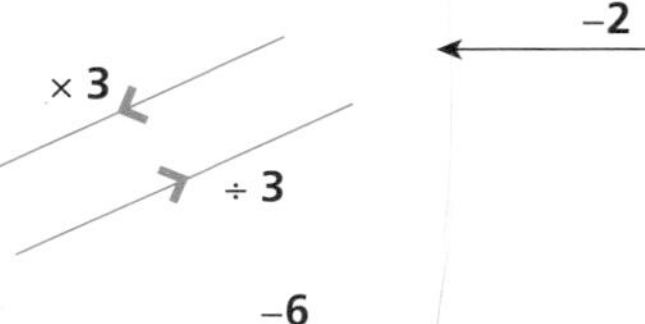

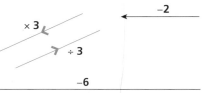

7 Show the following calculations, together with the reverse process, on a diagram like the one above. State the corresponding result as a division.
a) $-5 \times 4 = -20$ b) $3 \times -6 = -18$ c) $-2 \times -11 = 22$

8 Copy and complete the table:

positive	÷	positive	=	positive
positive	÷	negative		
	÷	positive		
	÷	negative		

9 Find the value of:
a) $-8 \div 2$ b) $-30 \div -10$ c) $27 \div -3$ d) $12 \div -10$
e) $-7.5 \div -2.5$ f) $18 \div -1.8$ g) $-7.8 \div 3$ h) $-12 \div -8$

10 Copy and complete:
a) $-20 \div \ldots = -5$ b) $12 \div \ldots = -6$ c) $-15 \div \ldots = -3$
d) $-36 \div \ldots = 12$ e) $\ldots \div 3 = -7$ f) $\ldots \div -5 = -2$

11 Work out:
a) $(-3 \times -2) \times -5$ b) $-3 \times (-2 \times -5)$ c) $-4 \times (3 - 5)$
d) $(-2 + 5) \times (-2 - 5)$ e) $(-12 - 9) \div (-4 - 3)$ f) $(-8 + 20) \div (-15 + 9)$

9.2 Substituting directed numbers

Taking $a = -3$, $b = -5$, then:

$a^2 = (-3)^2 = -3 \times -3 = 9$ and $a^3 = (-3)^3 = -3 \times -3 \times -3 = 9 \times -3 = -27$

In the same way:

$b^2 = 25$ and $b^3 = -125$

$ab = -3 \times -5 = 15$ $\quad a^2b = (-3)^2 \times -5 = 9 \times -5 = -45$

$a - b = -3 - -5 = -3 + 5 = 2$ $\quad a + 2b = -3 + 2 \times -5 = -3 + -10 = -13$

$\frac{a+b}{2} = \frac{-3 + -5}{2} = \frac{-8}{2} = -4$ $\quad \frac{3a - b}{b - a} = \frac{-9 - -5}{-5 - -3} = \frac{-9 + 5}{-5 + 3} = \frac{-4}{-2} = 2$

---

1 Given that $x = -4$, find the value of:

a) x^2 b) x^3 c) $2x$ d) $-3x$

e) $x - 5$ f) $5 - x$ g) $2 - 3x$ h) $20 - x^2$

i) $\frac{x}{2}$ j) $\frac{x}{2} - 3$ k) $\frac{12}{x}$ l) $\frac{x-5}{x+1}$

2 Find the value of these expressions, given that $p = -3$ and $q = -2$:

a) $p + q$ b) $p - q$ c) $p^2 + q$ d) $p^2 - q$

e) $p + q^3$ f) $p - q^3$ g) $(p + q)^2$ h) $(p - q)^2$

i) $2p + q$ j) $2(p + q)$ k) $p + 2q$ l) $2p - 3q$

3 Explain the difference between $(-3)^2$ and $-(3)^2$.

4 What is the smallest possible value that x^2 can take? Explain your answer.

5 Each of the following expressions has the value 5, −6.2 or −10.81. Use estimation to decide which is the most likely value and check with a calculator. Take $x = -4.3$, $y = 6.7$ and $z = -2.9$:

a) $xy + 18$ b) $24.43 + yz$ c) $y^2 - x^2 + 2(x - 12)$

d) $x + z + 1$ e) $x - y - \frac{z+1}{10}$ f) $\frac{3(z+1) - y}{2}$

6 Use the same values for x, y and z as in question 5 and try to find some more expressions that have the value 5, −6.2 or −10.81.
Exchange ideas with a partner.

9.3 Solving equations

The diagram shows where the process of solving equations fits into the larger process of using mathematics to solve problems. The solution of equations makes the vital link between the problem and its solution.

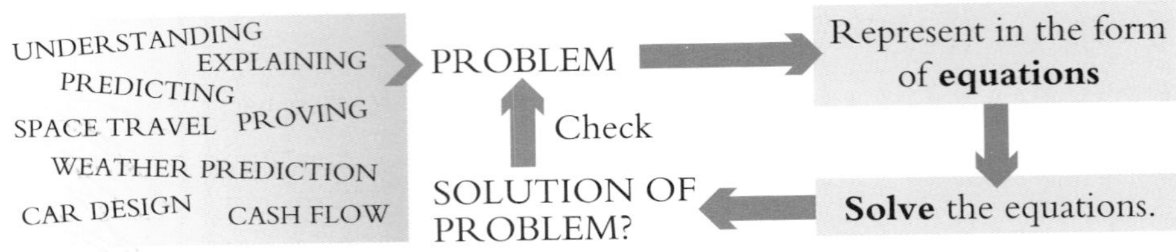

We now look at techniques for solving equations of a particular type, in which the unknown value only appears once.

Consider $3x - 7 = 4$. We want to find the value of x that makes the equation work.

One method is to draw a flow diagram. It shows the process to get from x to 4.

$x \rightarrow \boxed{\times 3} \rightarrow \boxed{-7} \rightarrow 4$

You can solve the equation by reversing the process:

$x \leftarrow \boxed{\div 3} \leftarrow \boxed{+7} \leftarrow 4$

---

1 Complete the solution of the equation given above. Give the solution:
a) as an improper fraction ✓
b) as a mixed number ✓
c) as a recurring decimal ✓
d) to 3 decimal places ✓
e) to 3 significant figures. ✓

2 Reverse the process shown in this flow diagram to find the value of x:

$x \rightarrow \boxed{\div 4} \rightarrow \boxed{-3} \rightarrow 8$

3 Find the values of x given in these flow diagrams:
a) $x \rightarrow \boxed{\div 5} \rightarrow \boxed{+2} \rightarrow 7$
b) $x \rightarrow \boxed{\times 10} \rightarrow \boxed{-3} \rightarrow 12$
c) $x \rightarrow \boxed{-17} \rightarrow \boxed{\times 3} \rightarrow 2.4$
d) $x \rightarrow \boxed{+11.8} \rightarrow \boxed{\div 2.5} \rightarrow 8$

4 For each of these equations, draw a flow diagram and find the solution by reversing the process. State the solution in any convenient form.
a) $5x + 1 = 10$ b) $\frac{x}{3} - 2 = 2.6$ c) $\frac{x}{5} + 6 = 9.8$
d) $\frac{x+5}{3} = 2.5$ e) $4(x - 6) = 7$ f) $10(x + 0.47) = 9$

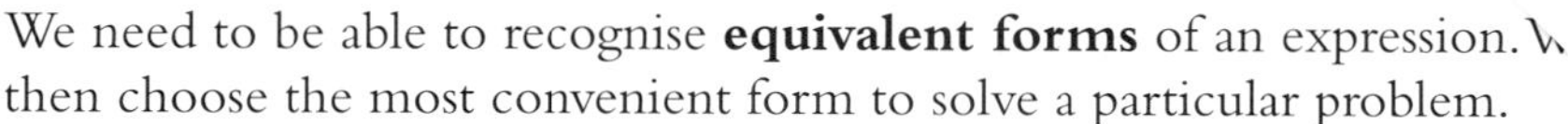

We need to be able to recognise **equivalent forms** of an expression. W… then choose the most convenient form to solve a particular problem.

We have already made use of equivalent forms in dealing with fractions, decimals and percentages. The following equivalent forms are useful when dealing with equations that involve fractions.

$$\frac{1}{3} \times \boxed{\text{ANYTHING}} = \boxed{\text{SAME THING}} \div 3$$

That is, $\frac{1}{3}x \equiv \frac{x}{3} \equiv x \div 3$

Also $\frac{2}{3}x \equiv \frac{2x}{3} \equiv x \times 2 \div 3 \equiv x \div 3 \times 2$

in general $\frac{a}{b}x \equiv \frac{ax}{b} \equiv x \times a \div b \equiv x \div b \times a$

The symbol ≡ is used to show that the expressions are equivalent, that is, they are the same for all values of x.

---

5 Use flow diagrams to solve these equations. Choose the most convenient form to work with. There is no need to use a calculator.

a) $\frac{3}{5}x = 9$ b) $\frac{11x}{3} = 77$ c) $\frac{2}{3}\left(x + 4\right) = 3\frac{1}{3}$

d) $\frac{7x}{4} - 9 = 12$ e) $\frac{8}{5}\left(x - 1\right) = 24$ f) $\frac{49.7x}{5.5} = 99.4$

The flow diagram method can also be used to solve equations involving powers and roots, provided that the unknown value only appears once.

Example

Solve $\sqrt{\frac{x-5}{2}} = 3$.

Answer

$x \longrightarrow \boxed{-5} \longrightarrow \boxed{\div 2} \longrightarrow \boxed{\sqrt{}} \longrightarrow 3$

$x \longleftarrow \boxed{+5} \longleftarrow \boxed{\times 2} \longleftarrow \boxed{\text{SQUARE}} \longleftarrow 3$

And so the solution is $x = 23$.

(*Note*: care must be taken where negative numbers may be involved. For example, $3^2 = 9$ and $(-3)^2 = 9$ so if the only information that we have is that $x^2 = 9$ there are two possible values of x, i.e. $x = 3$ or $x = -3$. This is normally written as $x = \pm 3$.)

Example

Solve $\frac{x^2 - 4}{3} = 7$.

Answer

$x \longrightarrow \boxed{\text{SQUARE}} \longrightarrow \boxed{-4} \longrightarrow \boxed{\div 3} \longrightarrow 7$

$x \longleftarrow \boxed{\pm\sqrt{}} \longleftarrow \boxed{+4} \longleftarrow \boxed{\times 3} \longleftarrow 7$

The solution is $x = \pm 5$.

6 Solve these equations without using a calculator:

a) $\sqrt{2x+1} = 7$ ✓ b) $\sqrt{\frac{x+8}{3}} = 4$ c) $\frac{3+\sqrt{x}}{4} = 2.5$

d) $\sqrt{\frac{x}{3}} - 5 = -3$ e) $\frac{5}{4}\sqrt{x} - 10 = -5$ f) $\frac{\sqrt{x}-20}{3} - 4 = -9$

7 Solve $\frac{\sqrt[3]{x}-6}{2} = -35$.

8 Solve these equations without using a calculator:

a) $x^2 - 11.8 = 4.2$ ✓ b) $2x^2 - 9 = -1$ c) $\frac{x^2}{3} - 48 = 0$

d) $(x+5)^2 = 36$ ✓ e) $(x-3)^2 = 25$ f) $(x+5)^3 = 64$

9 Use a calculator to solve these equations. Give your answers correct to 3 significant figures.

a) $5.18x = 11.92$ b) $0.23x = 17.5$ c) $\frac{x}{12.6} = 18.4$

d) $\frac{x}{7.3} = -5.48$ e) $6.7(x - 0.85) = 17.5$ f) $9.8x - 2.67 = -3.14$ ✓

g) $\frac{x}{4.62} + 13.8 = -0.47$ h) $\frac{0.27x - 0.48}{0.039} = -6$ i) $\sqrt{x} + 11.3 = 14.7$

j) $\sqrt{x} - 5 = \sqrt{2}$ k) $\frac{\sqrt{x}}{7.1} = 2.25$ l) $\frac{3\sqrt{x}}{2} = 17$

10 Form, and solve, an equation involving x for each of the following diagrams.

a)

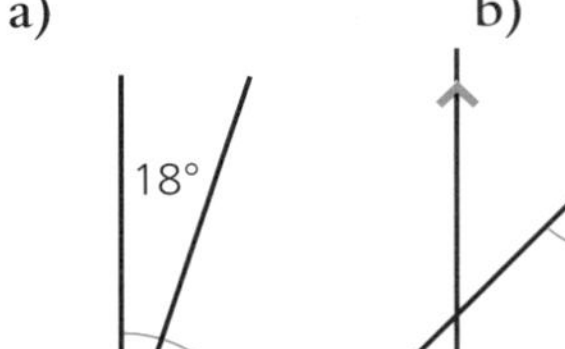

b)

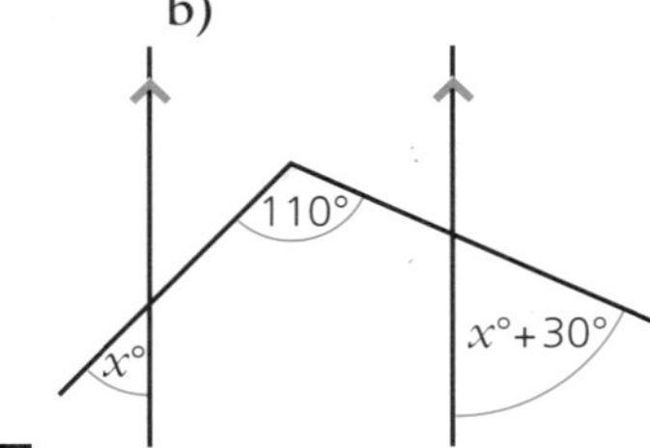

c)

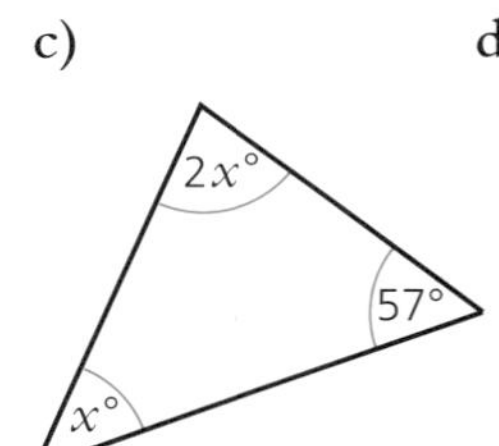

d)

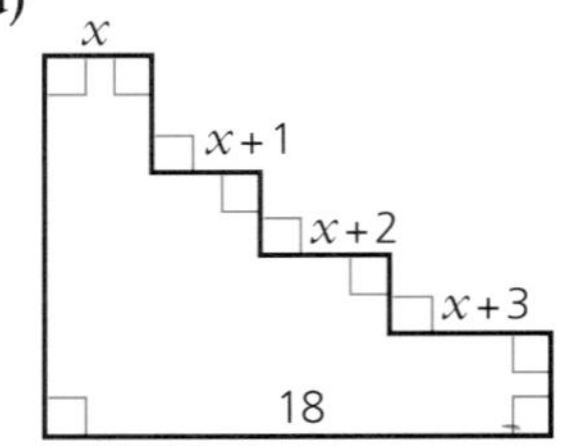

11 Re-write the following statements as equations, using x to represent an unknown value. Solve the problems by solving the equations.

a) Sam is three years older than Ben, who is two years older than Lucy. How old will they each be when the sum of their ages is 52?

b) My combined score in French, history and maths is 186 marks. I scored twice as many marks in history as in French and one more mark in maths than in history. What were my results?

12 Let $x = 0.373\,737\,373\,737\ldots$

a) Find the value of $100x$.

b) Work out $100x - x$. ✓

c) Use your answer to part b) to write $0.\dot{3}\dot{7}$ as a fraction. Check by division.

d) Adapt the method to write $0.\dot{1}4\dot{2}$ as a fraction.

9.4 Sequences

A list of numbers in a particular order, that follows some rule for producing further values, is called a sequence.

Each value in the list is referred to as a term.

Pattern plays an important part in mathematics and a knowledge of sequences can help in the recognition, description and application of pattern to the solution of problems.

1 List the first five terms of the sequences given by the following instructions.
  a) Start with zero. Add 3 to find the next term, then add 3 to find the term after that and so on.
  b) Start with 100. Subtract 5 to find the next term, then subtract 5 again to find the term after that and so on.
  c) Start with 1. Multiply by 2 to find the next term, then multiply by 2 again to find the term after that and so on.
  d) Start with 128. Each new term is found by dividing the last term by 2.
  e) Start with 1000. Each new term is found by dividing the last term by 10.

2 You can use your calculator to produce a sequence.
Key in [0] [=] [+] [3] then keep pressing the [=] key. Check that this gives the sequence you found in question **1a**.

3 Write down the next two terms in each of the following sequences:
  a) 5, 8, 11, 14, ... b) 50, 44, 38, 32, ... c) 2, 4, 6, 8, ...
  d) 2, 4, 8, 16, ... e) 1, −1, −3, −5, ... f) 1, −2, 4, −8, ...

4 Describe in words how each of the sequences given in question 3 is formed.

A sequence may be defined by giving a rule that relates the value of each term to its position.

Example

Consider the sequence 2, 4, 6, 8, 10, ... What is its rule?

Answer

Position number	1	2	3	4	5
Sequence	2	4	6	8	10

The value of each term is 2 × its position in the sequence.

ICT Extra!

Use your calculator to produce a number sequence.
THEN try using a spreadsheet to do the same thing.

5 List the first five terms of the sequences in which each term is given by:
a) one more than its position number
b) three times its position number
c) one-tenth of its position number
d) the square of its position number
e) the cube of its position number
f) one less than the square of its position number
g) one more than the cube of its position number
h) the product of its position number with the next position number
i) half of the product of its position number with the next position number.

We often need to know the value of a particular term (the third, say, or the tenth). This is much easier if the value of the term can be worked out directly from its position.

Example

Find the 100th term of the sequence 2, 4, 6, 8, 10, ...

Answer
Since the value of each term is 2 × its position number, the 100th term is given by 2 × 100 = 200.

Using the letter n to stand for the position number, the value of the term in that position is $2n$. The sequence may now be described by saying that the **nth term** is given by $2n$.

---

6 Re-write the rule for each sequence described in question 5 by finding an expression for the nth term.
List any advantages that you can think of for describing a sequence in this way.

7 List the first five terms of the sequence in which the nth term is given by:

a) $3n$	b) $2n + 1$	c) $2n - 1$
d) $n^2 + 1$	e) $(n + 1)^2$	f) $(n - 1)(n + 1)$

8 Work out the value of the 20th term of each of the sequences defined in question 7.

Example

Find the 8th term of the sequence given by $u_n = \frac{n}{2} + 1$.

You can write u_n to stand for the *n*th term of a sequence.

Answer
The 8th term is $u_8 = \frac{8}{2} + 1 = 5$

---

9 Find the 4th, 20th and 100th terms of the sequence given by $u_n = 2n - 1$.

10 A sequence is given by $u_n = n^2 + 5$. Find the values of:

a) u_1 b) u_5 c) u_{10} d) u_{20}

Some sequences have names that describe the patterns that can be made using dots to represent the value of each term. One particularly important example is the sequence of **triangle numbers** which often occurs in investigations.

1st	2nd	3rd	4th
$u_1 = 1$	$u_2 = 3$	$u_3 = 6$	$u_4 = 10$

The sequence of diagrams may be continued by adding an extra row each time. Note that although a single dot doesn't make a triangle, the number 1 is taken to be a triangle number because it fits the pattern - reverse the sequence shown above by removing a row at a time.

To continue the number sequence without drawing the diagrams we need to consider the **differences** between the terms.

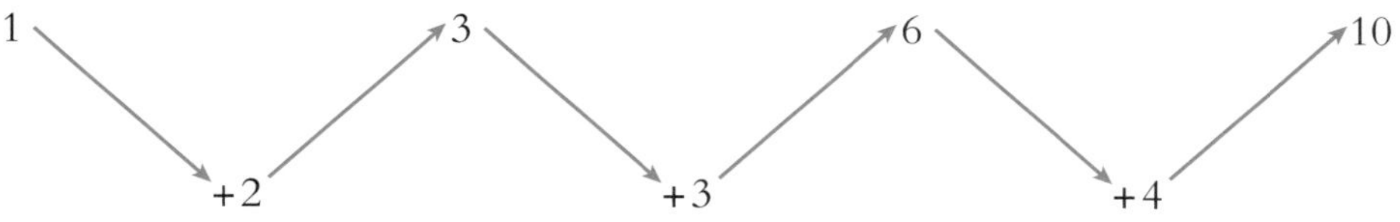

---

11 List the first ten triangle numbers.

12 Find the first five terms of the sequences given by:

a) $u_n = 2n - 1$ b) $u_n = \frac{n}{2}(n-1)$ c) $u_n = \frac{n^2 - n}{2}$ d) $u_n = \frac{n}{2}(n+1)$

13 Which of the sequences given in question 12 can be used to produce the triangle numbers? Check the result for the tenth triangle number.

14 a) Describe two methods for finding the value of the 100th triangle number.

b) What is the value of the 100th triangle number? Use the method that you think is the best.

10 PROBABILITY (2)

10.1 Equally likely outcomes

This first section revises ideas which you have already met in Unit 4. In games and situations in which all the outcomes are *equally likely*, probabilities can be worked out logically as:

$$\text{probability of an event} = \frac{\text{number of ways that event can happen}}{\text{total number of different outcomes}}$$

Example

There are 12 chocolates left in a box – but Daniel has lost the piece of paper which describes what the centres are.

Daniel knows that 7 of the chocolates have soft creamy centres while 5 have hard centres. If he picks a chocolate at random, what is the probability that he picks a chocolate with:

a) a hard centre
b) a soft centre
c) a jelly centre?

Answer

a) probability (hard centre) $= \frac{5}{12}$

b) probability (soft centre) $= \frac{7}{12}$

c) probability (jelly centre) = 0

---

1 On a library shelf there are 30 books. Fifteen are written in French, six are in Italian and the rest are in Spanish. I ask my younger brother to bring me a book in French, but he has no idea which language is which.
What is the probability he picks:
a) a French book ✔
b) a book written in Spanish
c) a book which is not in French
d) a Russian book?

2 A two-digit number is to be made by choosing 2 *different* digits from 1, 5, 7 and 9.
a) Write down all the two-digit numbers which can be made (there are 12). ✔
Find the probability that if one of these is picked at random it is:
b) a number divisible by 5
c) a number not divisible by 5
d) an odd number
e) a number divisible by 3.

3 A bag contains red counters and blue counters only. The probability of picking a blue counter is $\frac{5}{8}$.

a) What is the probability of picking a red counter?
b) If there are 6 red counters, how many counters are there altogether? ✓
c) How many blue counters are there?

4 Ramesh has designed a dart game for the school Summer Fair. The main board measures 40 cm by 20 cm. Each number (1 to 6) is written on a card 8 cm by 8 cm. My friend is not very good at playing darts but is fairly sure he can at least hit the board.

a) What is the area of the board?
b) What is the area of one card?
c) What is the probability that my friend's dart hits *any* of the six numbers?
d) What is the probability that he hits an odd numbered card and wins a prize?

5 ✓ a) If a person is picked at random from a studio audience the probability of picking a man is $\frac{5}{8}$. There are 400 people in the audience. How many men are there?
b) How many women are there? Check your answers give the correct total.
c) What is the probability that a woman is picked?

6 During a game of Scrabble I have these eight letters on my rack:
A B E T E E Q M
As I should only have seven letters one of the other players removes one letter without looking at it. What is the probability that she takes:

a) an E
b) a vowel
c) not an A
d) the Q
e) not an E
f) M T or B?

7 There are 7 red counters and 13 blue counters in a black bag. In a white bag there are 11 red counters and 25 blue counters.

a) What is the probability of choosing a red counter from the black bag?
b) What is the probability of choosing a red counter from the white bag?
c) If you need to pick a red counter to win the game, should you choose from the black bag or the white bag to give you the better chance?

10.2 Equally likely?

A friend of mine was about to go on a 'blind date' with a girl he had never met before (he had answered an advert). He was very optimistic about the outcome saying 'Well, there's a 50–50 chance that we will get on well. Either we will like each other or we won't.'

Was this correct?

He has assumed that it is equally as likely that they will like each other as dislike each other. Do you think this is true?

In real life, outcomes often are not equally likely.

1 Look at these situations. Are the outcomes equally likely or not?

Outcome 1	Outcome 2	Equally likely?
It will rain tomorrow	It will be sunny tomorrow	No
a) I will be run over when I cross the road.	I will cross the road safely.	
b) I will score an even number when I throw a dice	I will score an odd number.	
c) I have a 50p coin in my pocket and a 10p. I pick out 10p	I pick out 50p.	
d) I shuffle a pack of cards and pick a card without looking I pick a spade.	I pick a diamond.	
e) The next person I meet will be wearing glasses.	The next person I meet will not be wearing glasses.	
f) The next person I meet will be female.	The next person I meet will be male.	
g) I have an apple a banana and an orange in a bag. I pick a banana.	I pick an orange.	
h) I throw a dice and I score 6.	I throw a dice and I score 2.	
i) I toss a coin and it lands heads.	I toss a coin and it lands tails.	

2 Explain why, in (g), the probability I select a banana is not $\frac{1}{3}$.

10.3 Probability games

In this section we use probabilities to explain why some games are not as fair as they seem.

Section 10.5 gives instructions for carrying out a spreadsheet simulation of the difference game (game 1).

Making spinners for probability games
If you do not have dice available for the first two games you can use spinners instead.
To make a 6-sided spinner for games 1 and 2:

- Draw a circle.
- Use your compasses to mark off six equal arcs around the circumference.
- Join each mark to the centre and to the next mark on the circumference.
- Cut out your spinner and number the sections.
- What shape is the spinner?
- What kind of triangle does it contain?

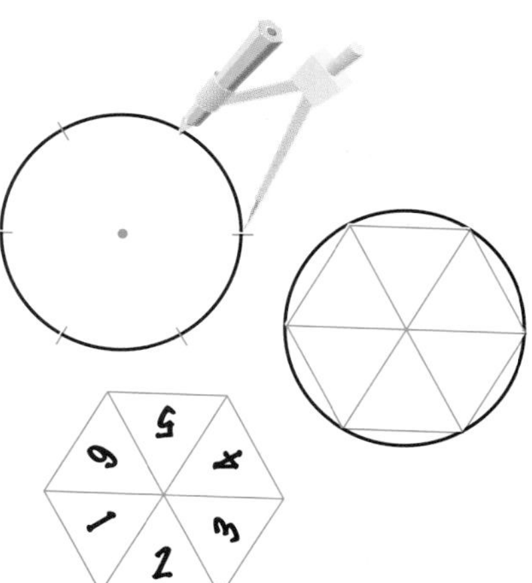

Game 1 Differences

You need either:

a) 2 ordinary dice, one white, one coloured
or b) 2 spinners (different colours)
or c) If you have 2 pencils with hexagonal cross-sections you can use them like this: write the numbers 1 to 6 round the end. Roll the pencil and take the number facing upwards as the score.

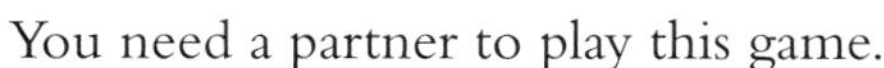

You need a partner to play this game.

Decide which of you wins a point for an 'even' score. The other person will win a point for an 'odd' score. Note that zero is always classed as an even number.

Roll both dice and find the *difference* between the two numbers.
Which of you has scored a point – 'odds' or 'evens'?
Play for 20 throws. Record your scores.
Who is the overall winner?

---

1 Based on your experience of playing game 1, do you think this is a fair game?

2 Where would you place 'odds' chance of winning on this probability scale?

3 Find out the results for other groups in your class. Are the results similar to yours?

– certain to win

– impossible to win

4 If you take their results into account, will you want to change your answer to question 2?

5 To work out whether game 1 is a fair game you can make a table showing all the possible outcomes.

a) How many even differences are there on the table? (Colour them in if you wish.)

b) How many odd differences are there?

c) What fraction of the differences are odd?

d) What is the probability that odd wins a point?

DIFFERENCES

Score on coloured dice \ Score on white dice	1	2	3	4	5	6
1	0					
2						
3						
4						
5						
6	5	4		2		0

Game 2 Products

You need 2 dice (or spinners or pencils) as before, and a partner.
As before, one person scores a point for 'odds' and the other for 'evens'.
Roll both dice and *multiply* the two numbers. (The answer is called the **product**.)
Play for 20 throws. Record your scores.
Who is the overall winner this time?

1 Do you think this is a fair game?

2 Where would you place the 'odds' chance of winning on the probability scale?

3 Make another table like the one above. This time, write the *product* in each square.

a) What is the largest product you can get?

b) What is the smallest product?

c) Count the squares with even products (colour them in if you like).

d) Count the squares with odd products.

e) What fraction of the possible outcomes are odd?

f) What fraction are even?

g) What is the probability that odd scores a point?

h) Is this a fair game?

i) Find the total for:
Probability that 'odds' wins + probability that 'evens' wins.

You can play the 'differences' game or the 'product' game with four-sided or eight-sided dice.

This net makes a tetrahedron which can be used as a four-sided dice. (A tetrahedron can be called a pyramid with a triangular base.)

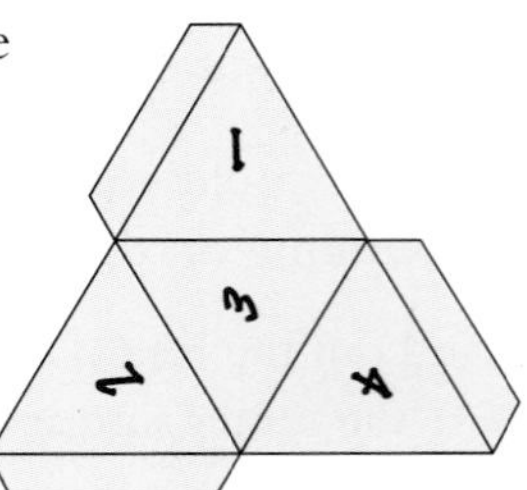

This net makes an octahedron which can be used as an eight-sided dice. Which kind of triangle must be used here?

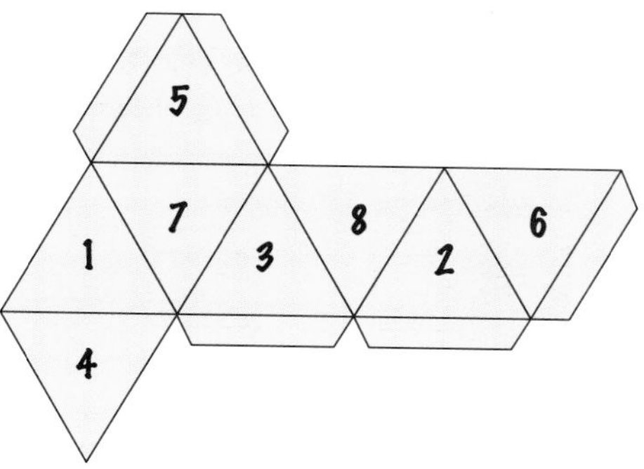

4 Tick the correct box for the answer to each calculation.
Use these results to explain why some games are not as fair as they seem.

Calculation	Answer Odd Even
odd + odd	✓
even + even	
odd + even	
odd – odd	
odd – even	
even – odd	
even – even	
odd × odd	
odd × even	
even × even	

Game 3 Fractions

You need 2 dice (or spinners or pencils) as before, and a partner.
One player is A and the other B. Roll both dice (or spinners or pencils).
Use the two numbers to make a fraction which is less than or equal to 1.
Write down the fraction you have made.
Scoring: if the fraction is reduced to its lowest terms (*cannot be cancelled*) player A scores a point. If the fraction *can* be cancelled player B wins a point.
Play the game 20 times. Record your scores. The winner is the person with the most points.

1 Based on your experience, decide whether this is a fair game or not. You can ask other groups in your class for their results and find the total points scored for each player, A and B. This may help you to decide better.

2 We can work out the probability of A (or B) winning the game by listing all the possible outcomes. The easiest way to do this is to make a table like this:

a) Copy and complete the table. Notice that the smaller of the two numbers must always be the numerator if your fraction is to have a value less than 1.

b) Colour in the squares showing fractions which cannot be cancelled. These are the outcomes for which player A scores a point.

c) What is the probability that player A scores a point?

d) What is the probability that player B scores a point?

e) Is this a 'fair' game?

GAME 3

Score on dice 2 \ Score on dice 1	1	2	3	4	5	6
1	$\frac{1}{1}$	$\frac{1}{2}$	$\frac{1}{3}$			
2		$\frac{2}{2}$	$\frac{2}{3}$			
3		$\frac{2}{3}$	$\frac{3}{3}$	$\frac{3}{4}$		
4		$\frac{2}{4}$	$\frac{3}{4}$	$\frac{4}{4}$		
5			$\frac{3}{5}$	$\frac{4}{5}$		
6						

Game 4 Proper or improper fractions

You need 2 dice (or spinners or pencils) as before, and a partner.
One player is A and the other B.
Roll the dice *one at a time*. The two numbers are to be used to make a fraction, but this time the first score must always be the numerator (so the score on the second dice is always the denominator). Write down all the fractions you have made.

- If the fraction is greater than 1 player A scores a point.
- If the fraction is less than 1 player B scores a point.
- If the fraction equals 1 both players score a point.

Play the game 20 times. Record your scores. Who scored the most points?
Did other groups in the class have similar scores to yours?

---

1 Do you think this is a fair game?

2 Copy and complete this table which lists all the possible outcomes:
Colour in the squares which show fractions which are greater than 1. Are these fractions called proper or improper fractions?
Use a different colour to show the squares in which the fraction is equal to 1.

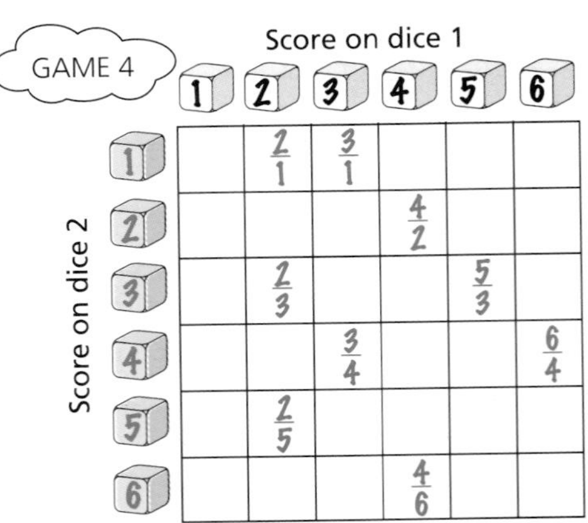
GAME 4

Score on dice 2 \ Score on dice 1	1	2	3	4	5	6
1		$\frac{2}{1}$	$\frac{3}{1}$			
2				$\frac{4}{2}$		
3		$\frac{2}{3}$			$\frac{5}{3}$	
4			$\frac{3}{4}$			$\frac{6}{4}$
5		$\frac{2}{5}$				
6				$\frac{4}{6}$		

3 What is the probability that you have:
a) a proper fraction
b) an improper fraction
c) a fraction equal to 1?

4 What is the probability that player A scores a point?

5 Is this a fair game? Explain your answer.

All the games in this section are examples of combined events.

6 There are six outcomes on dice 1 and six on dice 2, giving a total of 36 possible outcomes altogether.
a) How many possible outcomes would there be if you played game 4 with two four-sided dice?
b) How many if you used 2 eight-sided dice?

10.4 Payoffs

In this section we will see how probabilities can be used to design games involving chance and to calculate how much profit can be made.

Example

Jacob decides to set up a stall at the summer fair using the products game (game 2). He will ask people to pay 10p to play and if they get an odd number when they multiply the scores on two dice he will pay them a prize of 20p. If the product is an even number they will not win anything.

If 100 people are likely to play the game during the afternoon, work out:
a) how much money he should take in
b) how many people are likely to win a prize
c) how much he is likely to have to pay out in prize money
d) what his profit is likely to be.

Answer
a) $100 \times 10\text{p} = £10$
b) The probability of obtaining an odd number when you multiply the two dice scores is $\frac{1}{4}$. (Look back to page 96 if you have forgotten how this was worked out.)
So $\frac{1}{4}$ of the players (roughly) should win.
We expect $\frac{1}{4} \times 100 = 25$ winners.
c) He expects to pay out $25 \times 20\text{p} = £5$.
This is only an estimate and there may be more or less than 25 winners.
d) The profit he expects to make is $£10 - £5 = £5$

1 Sally has designed two spinners to use in a game at the summer fair. Each person who plays the game has to spin the arrow on both spinners. If both arrows point to the same colour the player wins a prize. If the colours are different they lose.

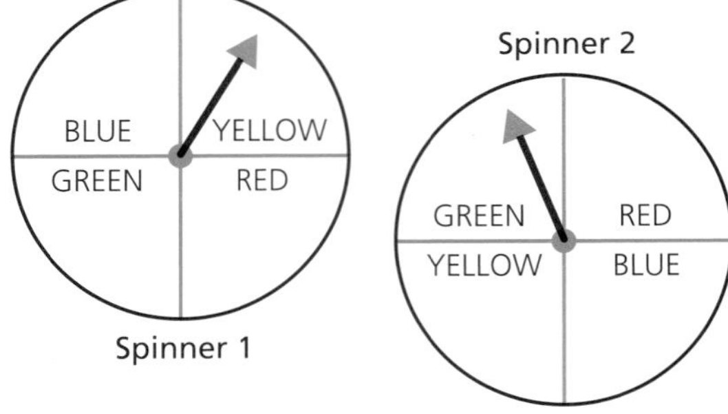

a) Use a diagram or find some other way of showing clearly all 16 possible outcomes. ✔
b) How many of these outcomes show both spinners pointing to the same colour?
c) What is the probability that a player wins a prize?
d) What is the probability that a player does *not* win a prize?
e) If 160 people play the game on the afternoon of the summer fair, roughly how many of them should win a prize? ✔
f) Sally charges people 10p to play the game and decides to pay the winners 25p. How much money will she take in if 160 people play? How much money (roughly) will she have to pay prize winners? Refer back to question e) to help you work this out.
g) How much profit should she make (roughly)?

2 Another game at the summer fair is the 'Human fruit machine'. Three people have to each sit in a booth. They cannot be seen by the players. The pupils in the booths cannot see who is playing either, nor can they see each other.

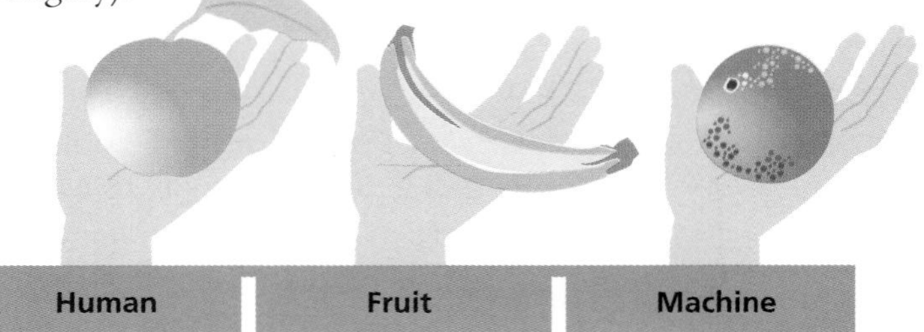

Each pupil in the fruit machine has an apple, a banana and an orange. When a person wishes to play the game they pay 10p. The supervisor then shouts 'PLAY' to the human fruit machine. The pupils inside each choose a fruit and hold it up. If the 3 fruits are the same the player wins a prize.

a) If there were only two booths, so that only two pieces of fruit were being shown how many possible outcomes would there be? (Don't forget there are still three fruits at each booth.) ✔
b) Write a list of all these outcomes.
c) Now consider the situation with three booths. How many possible outcomes are there? ✔
d) Try to list all these.
e) Can you work out a formula for calculating the total number of outcomes if two (or more) events take place at the same time?
f) What is the probability that a player wins a prize?
g) What is the probability that they do not win?
h) Can the game organiser afford to give winners a prize of 50p?

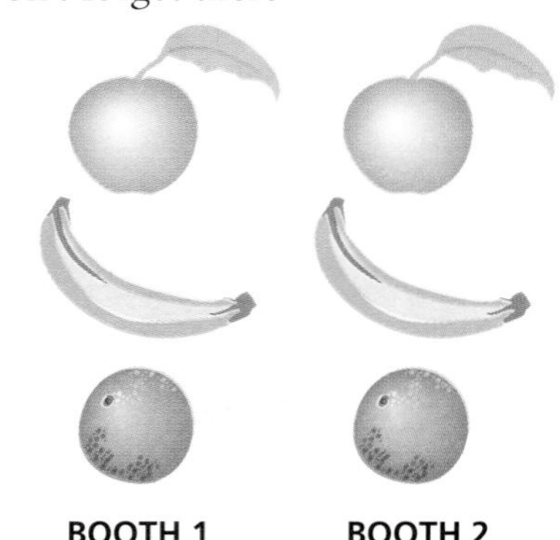

10.5 Spreadsheet simulation

These commands for the Excel spreadsheet will generate simulated results for the 'differences' game played with two six-sided dice.

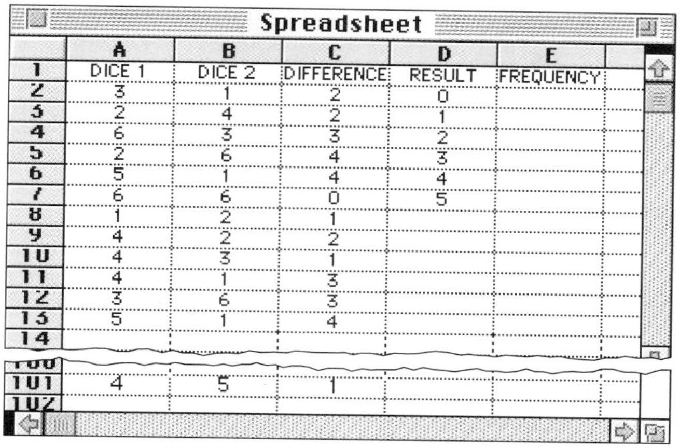

Spreadsheet

	A	B	C	D	E
1	DICE 1	DICE 2	DIFFERENCE	RESULT	FREQUENCY
2	3	1	2	0	
3	2	4	2	1	
4	6	3	3	2	
5	2	6	4	3	
6	5	1	4	4	
7	6	6	0	5	
8	1	2	1		
9	4	2	2		
10	4	3	1		
11	4	1	3		
12	3	6	3		
13	5	1	4		
14					
101	4	5	1		
102					

Step 1 Label all the columns as shown here. Enter the following command into cell A2.

=INT(RAND( )*6 + 1)

This command can then be copied into all the cells down to row 101 in columns A and B.

Step 2 Enter this command into cell C2:

=ABS(A2–B2)

Copy this down column C as far as row 101.

Step 3 Use only row 2 to row 7 inclusive in column D. Enter these numbers (which are the 6 possible results of the experiment):

0, 1, 2, 3, 4, 5

Step 4 Enter this command into cell E2:

=COUNTIF(C$2:C$101,D2)

Copy this into cells E3 down to E7. This will check down the values in column C and count the frequency of each result listed in column D. Column D and column E together form a frequency table which can be represented as a bar graph.

Shift F9 generates a new set of results and re-runs the simulation.

You can modify the commands (if you are careful) to change the simulation to one for four-sided or eight-sided dice:

At **Step 1**, change the '6'.

At **Step 3** work out all the possible values for the differences.

At **Step 4** the last number in the command may have to be changed.

ICT Extra!

Follow the instructions given here for producing a simulation of the 'differences' game. THEN try to change the instructions to simulate the results for the 'products' game.

11 STRAIGHT LINES

11.1 Using ratios

Nadine and Simon are preparing a concrete base for a garage. A friend has left them some instructions.

Instructions
For every shovel of cement, mix in 5 shovels of sand. Add a little water

These instructions can be simplified using the idea of **ratio**. The size of the units is unimportant but cement and sand should be mixed in the ratio 1 to 5. The ratio is usually written as 1 : 5.

Note
If you use buckets instead, it's the same – for every bucket of cement used, mix in 5 buckets of sand.

A ratio provides a means of comparing two related quantities.

1 How much sand should be mixed with the following amounts of cement?
a) 4 shovels ✓ b) 6 shovels c) 8 buckets

2 How much cement is needed for these amounts of sand?
a) 15 buckets b) 35 shovels c) 2.5 m^3.

3 A particular shade of green paint is made by mixing blue and yellow paint in the ratio 2 : 7.
a) Write some instructions for mixing the paint *without* using the idea of a ratio.
b) What difference does it make if the ratio is given as 7 : 2 ?

The idea of equivalence applies to ratios in the same way as to fractions.

4 Copy and complete these statements so that the ratios are equivalent:
a) 3 : 7 = 6 : ? ✓ b) 5 : 4 = 15 : ? c) 3 : 8 = 15 : ?
d) 7 : 2 = ? : 8 e) 3 : 11 = ? : 99 f) 9 : ? = 27 : 21
g) ? : 3 = 32 : 12 h) 64 : 72 = 8 : ? i) 3.5 : 7.5 = 7 : ?

5 Write each of these ratios in its simplest form:
a) 18 : 24 ✓ b) 25 : 35 c) 125 : 250
d) 32 : 40 e) 45 : 60 f) 81 : 90
g) 2.5 : 7.5 h) 0.05 : 0.2 i) 0.3 : 0.006

The simplification of some ratios may involve conversion of units.

For example:
£3.60 : 90p = 360p : 90p = 360 : 90 = 4 : 1
75 cm : 4 m = 75 cm : 400 cm = 75 : 400 = 3 : 16

The units may be cancelled when they are the same on both sides.

6 Simplify the following ratios as far as possible:

a) £7.50 : £15 ✓
b) £5.20 : £3.90
c) £4.80 : 32
d) 40 cm : 5 m
e) 30 mm : 60 cm
f) 750 g : 1 kg
g) 2.5 kg : 500 g
h) 0.7 mm : 28 cm
i) 9 inches : 1 ya
j) 5 minutes : 5 hours
k) 2 hours 25 minutes : 29 minutes
l) 450 ml : 9 litres

7 A map is drawn to a scale of one inch to one mile. Write the scale of the map in the form 1 : *n*.

8 What distance is represented by 1 cm on an Ordnance Survey map drawn to a scale of 1 : 50 000?
Two villages are 11 km apart. How far apart do they appear on the map?

9 One of the factors affecting the performance of an aircraft is the aspect ratio of its wings. This is the ratio of the span to the average chord and is usually written in the form *n* : 1.

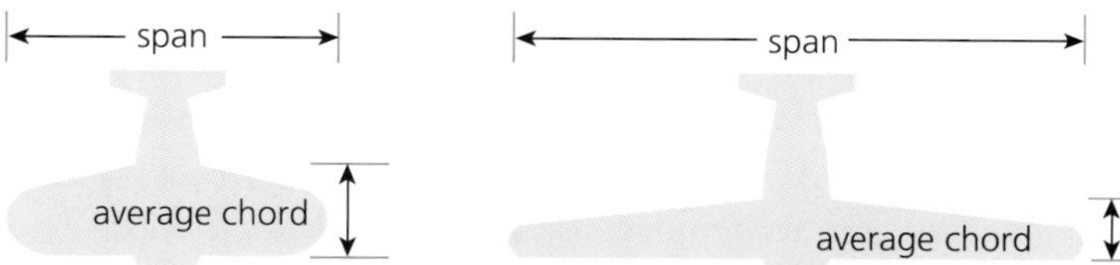

Low aspect ratio ($n \le 5$)
Fast and manoeuvrable

High aspect ratio ($n \ge 12$).
Slow, long range

Calculate the aspect ratio in the form *n* : 1 for each of these aircraft types.

Type	Wingspan (m)	Chord (m)	Max. speed (km/h)
Jet fighter	8.4	2.8	2500
Passenger plane	35	8	900
Glider	18	1.2	80

10 Concorde has a wing span of 25.5 m and can cruise at around 2200 km/h. What is the smallest possible value of its average chord if it is classed as fast and manoeuvrable?

11.2 Gradient

The idea of a gradient is extremely important in mathematics and has many applications at all levels of study. The gradient of a line is a measure of its slope, or steepness, and depends on the **ratio** of the vertical change to the horizontal. It is most commonly written as a fraction or a decimal but may also be expressed as a percentage.

Example
Find the gradients of AB, BC and AC.
What does this tell you?
Answer
From the diagram:

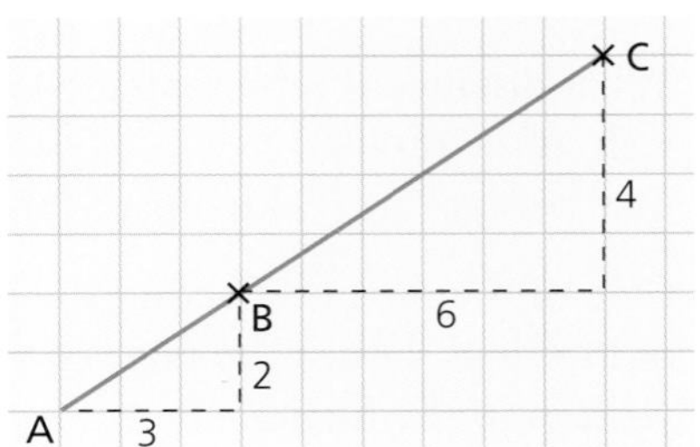

gradient of AB = $\frac{2}{3}$

gradient of BC = $\frac{4}{6} = \frac{2}{3}$

gradient of AC = $\frac{6}{9} = \frac{2}{3}$

The gradients of AB, BC and AC are **equivalent fractions**. In each case, the gradient may be given as $\frac{2}{3}$ in its simplest form and it follows that the gradient of a straight line is the same at all points.

1 Find the gradient of each of the lines shown in the diagram in its simplest form.

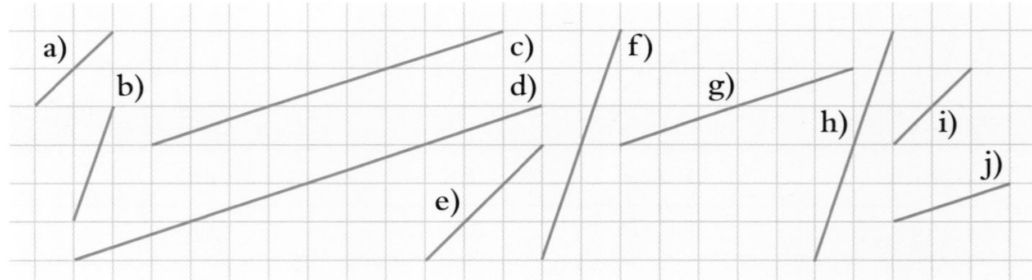

2 Describe the connection between lines that have the same gradient.

3 What is the gradient of a line that is:
a) horizontal
b) inclined at 45° to the horizontal?

4 Investigate how the gradient of a line changes as the angle that the line makes with the horizontal is increased. Change the angle in steps of 5°, each time, and put your results in a table. Plot the values as coordinates and describe what you find.

Angle	Gradient (1 S.F.)
5°	0.09

The gradient of a line joining two points may be calculated directly from the coordinates of the points.

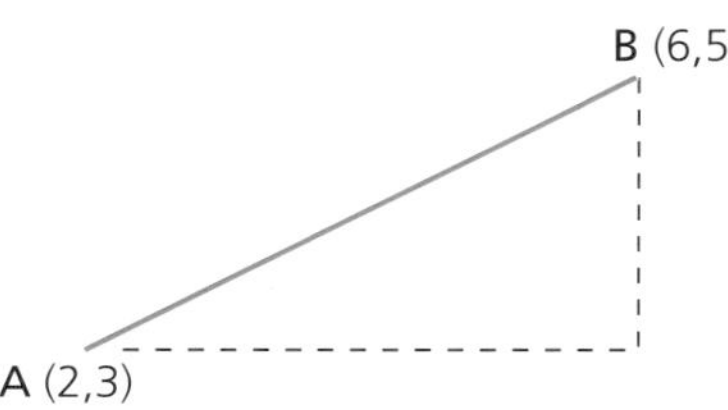

Example

What is the gradient of AB?

Answer

Gradient of AB $= \dfrac{5-3}{6-2} = \dfrac{2}{4} = \dfrac{1}{2}$

In general, if we use y_B to stand for the y coordinate at B, y_A for the y coordinate at A and so on, then the gradient of the line joining A to B is given by $\dfrac{y_B - y_A}{x_B - x_A}$.

5 Find the gradients of the lines joining the following pairs of points:

a) (4, 1) and (6, 3) ✓ **b)** (5, 2) and (6,10) **c)** (2, 5) and (11, 11)
d) (3, 8) and (18, 33) **e)** (15, 23) and (33, 27) **f)** (46, 32) and (67, 32)

6 To find the gradient of the line joining (12, 3) to (4, 1) one student calculates $\dfrac{3-1}{12-4}$ and another calculates $\dfrac{1-3}{4-12}$.
Does the order make any difference to the final result? Explain your answer.

7 The coordinates of four points are A (5, 2), B (3, 1), C (6, 2) and D (8, 3).
Find the gradients of the lines through:

a) A and B **b)** B and C **c)** D and A **d)** C and D

What shape is the figure ABCD? Explain your answer.
Plot the points on a diagram and compare its shape with your prediction.

All of the lines considered so far have sloped upwards from left to right. If, however, a line slopes downwards from left to right, then its gradient is taken to be negative.

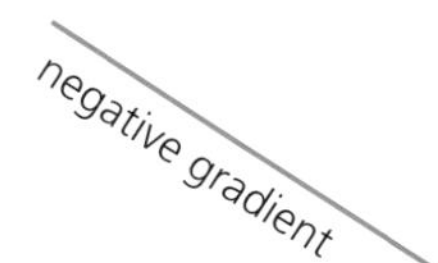

Example

Find the gradient of AB.

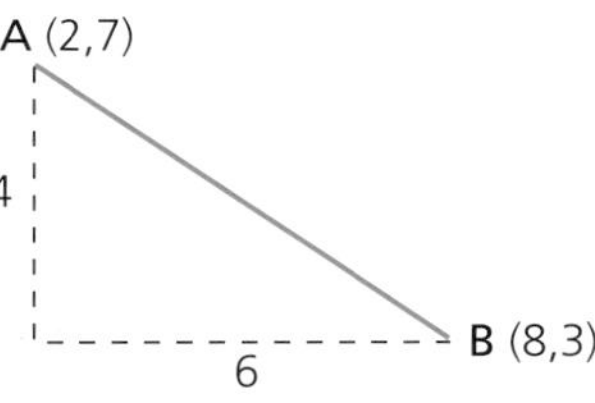

Answer

Gradient of AB $= -\dfrac{4}{6} = -\dfrac{2}{3}$

Note: using the coordinate formula, the sign of the gradient is found automatically.

Gradient $= \dfrac{3-7}{8-2} = -\dfrac{4}{6} = -\dfrac{2}{3}$

8 Find the gradients of these lines and match the parallel pairs:

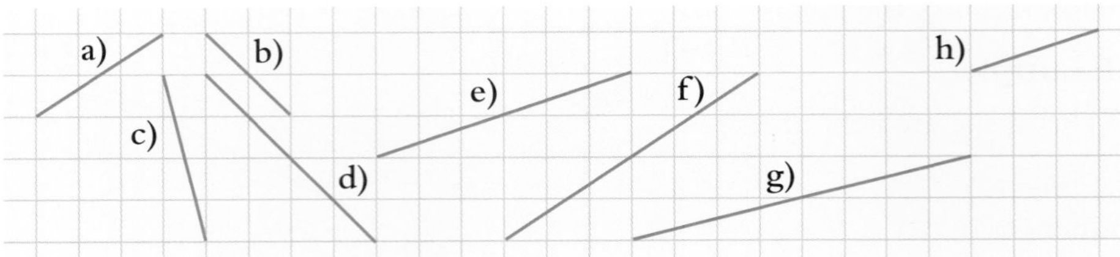

9 Calculate the gradients of the lines joining:

a) (5, 9) to (11, 6) ✓ b) (4, 7) to (0, 10)
c) (12, 3) to (2, 8) d) (47.8, 36.7) to (55.8, 32.7)
e) (79.4, 11.3) to (62.9, 16.3) f) (117.2, 68.2) to (216.8, 68.2)

10 Given the points P(3, 8), Q(11, 7), R(14, 6) and S(1, 2):

a) state which of the lines PQ, PS, RS, QR and QS has a negative gradient
b) explain how you made your decisions in part a).

11.3 Coordinates in four quadrants

The coordinate system may be extended to include negative values. For all points, the coordinates are given in the usual order as (x, y) and the formula for the gradient works equally well in all quadrants.

Example

Find the gradient of the line joining
a) B to D b) A to C.

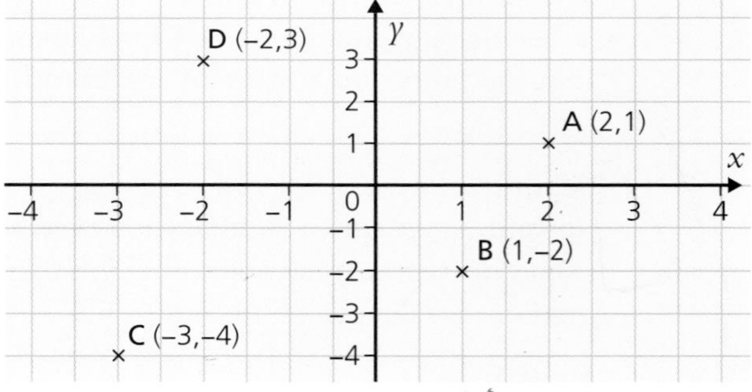

Answer

a) The gradient of the line joining B (1, –2) to D (–2, 3) is given by:

$$\frac{3-(-2)}{-2-1} = \frac{3+2}{-3} = -\frac{5}{3}.$$

b) The gradient of the line joining A (2, 1) to C (–3, –4) is given by:

$$\frac{1-(-4)}{2-(-3)} = \frac{1+4}{2+3} = 1$$

1 Find the coordinates of the labelled points on the diagram.

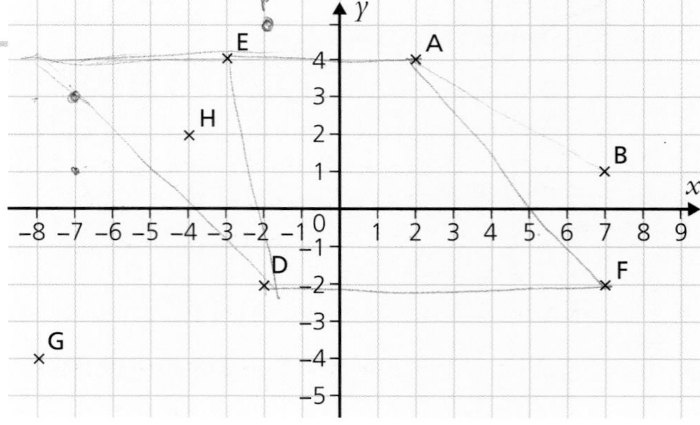

2 Using the diagram in question 1, calculate the gradient of:
a) AB ✓ b) AD c) AE d) AF e) DE
f) BH g) GH h) GD i) GB

3 What do your answers to 2(h) and 2(i) tell you about the points B, D and G?

4 The point C has coordinates (3, y). Find the value of y so that ABCD is a parallelogram.

5 Name another parallelogram that:
a) includes the point C b) does not include the point C.

6 What shape is AEFD?

7 The points P (−2, 5), Q (3,10) and R (x, 14) lie on a straight line. Find the value of x.

11.4 Equations of lines

One of the ways in which we can use our knowledge of equations at this stage is to describe the conditions that must be satisfied by all points that lie on a particular line. The use of equations allows us to communicate information to each other and also to devices such as computers and graphics calculators.

1 List the coordinates of the marked points on line (a).

2 If line (a) is continued in both directions, which of these points would it contain?

a) (3, 11)	b) (3, -27)
c) (4, 3)	d) (-3, 5)
e) (3, 99)	f) (3, -1.24)
g) (3, 0)	h) (0, 3)

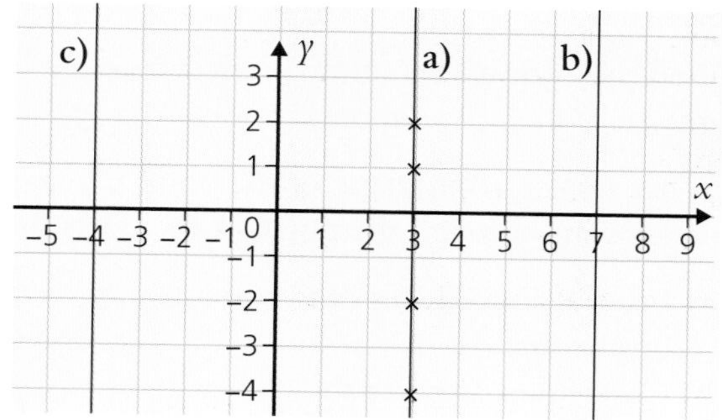

Example

Describe a condition that the coordinates of any point on line (a) must satisfy.

Answer
The condition may be described in any of the following ways:
- The first coordinate must be equal to 3
- The x-coordinate must be equal to 3
- The x number must be equal to 3
- $x = 3$.

The statement $x = 3$ is called the **equation of the line.**

3 Describe a condition that must be satisfied by the coordinates of all the points on line (b) in question 1. Give your answer as an equation.

4 What is the equation of line (c) in question 1?

5 Find the equation of the straight lines containing these points:
a) (7, 2), (7, 3), (7, −3) b) (−4, 0), (−4, −4), (−4, 16)
c) (8, 8), (8, 0), (8, −8) d) (0, −1), (0, 7), (0, 0)

6 Find the equations of the lines, parallel to the y-axis, that contain:
a) (3, 9) b) (−4, 0) c) (−7, 5) d) (2.8, −3.7)

7 Give the coordinates of the point where the line $x = -5$ meets the x-axis.

8 a) Write down the coordinates of any three points on line (p)
b) Describe, in words, the condition that a point lies on line (p).
c) What is the equation of line (p)? ✓
d) Find the equations of lines (q) and (r).

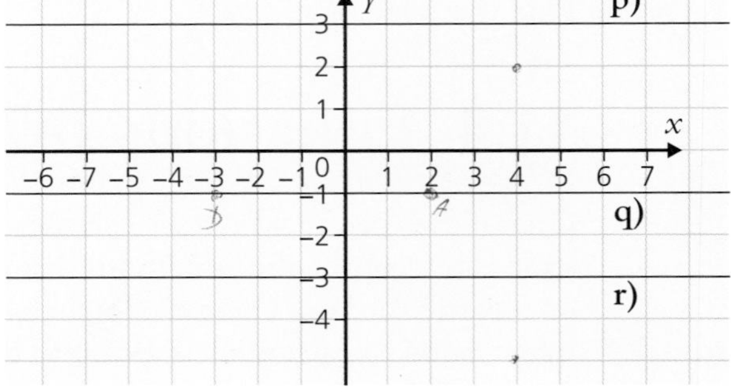

9 Find the coordinates of the point D such that A(2, −1), B(2, 8), C(−3, 8) and D form a rectangle.

Find the equation of the line through:
a) A and B b) C and D c) B and C d) A and D.

10 Find the coordinates of the point where the line through (4, 2) and (4, −5) intersects the line with equation $y = 3$.

11 What are the coordinates of the point where the line, parallel to the x-axis and passing through the point (4, 5), meets the line with equation $x = -2$?

12 a) List the coordinates of five points on the line AB.
b) Copy and complete these coordinates of points that lie on the line through A and B: (−3, ?), (4.5, ?), (2.6, ?), (?, 4.5), (?, −3).
c) Describe, in words, the condition that a point lies on this line. ✓
d) Re-write the condition given in c) as an equation.

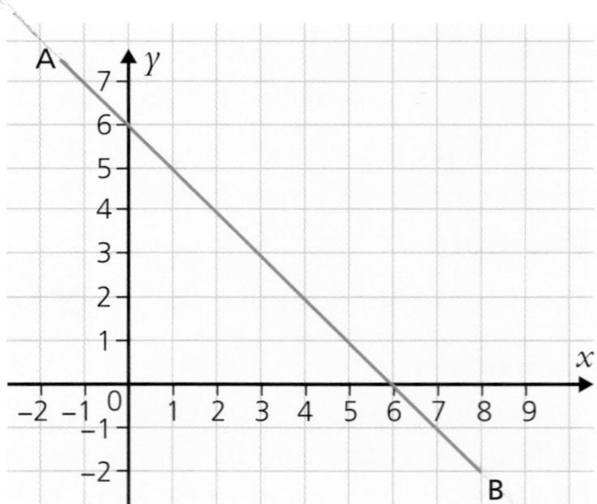

13 The equation of line (a) may be written as $x + y = 6$. Write the equations of the other lines in the same form.

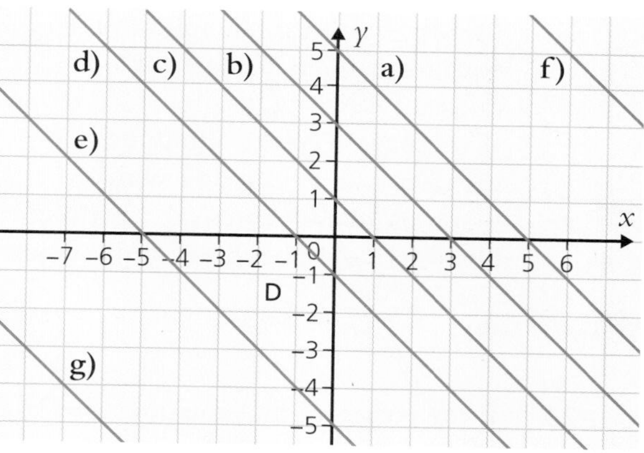

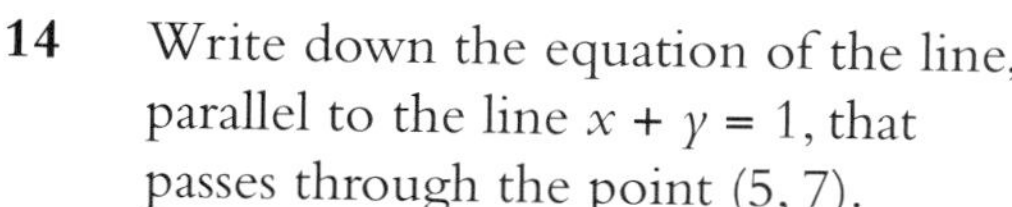

14 Write down the equation of the line, parallel to the line $x + y = 1$, that passes through the point (5, 7).

15 Draw a diagram to show the line with equation $x + y = 0$.

16 Three lines pass through the point with coordinates (9, –2). Line (a) is parallel to the x-axis, line (b) is parallel to the y-axis and line (c) is parallel to the line with equation $x + y = 99$. What are their equations?

17 a) Copy and complete the following coordinates of points that belong to the line through A and B:

(i) (5, ?) (ii) (0, ?) (iii) (12.5, ?)
(iv) (?, –4) (v) (?, –17.2) (vi) $(-\frac{2}{3}, ?)$

b) Describe, in words, the condition that must be satisfied by the coordinates of all points on the line.

c) Write down the equation of the line.

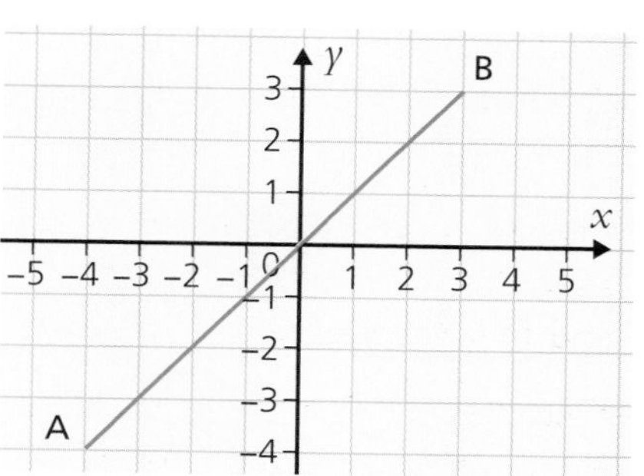

18 Draw a diagram to show the line with equation $y = -x$. Give the equation of the line in two alternative forms.

19 Copy and complete the following coordinates to satisfy the equation $y = 2x$:
(0, 0), (1, ?), (2, ?), (3, ?), (–1, ?), (?, 8), (?, –4), (?, –6)
Plot the points on a diagram and join them with a straight line. Label the line with its equation.
What is the **gradient** of the line?

20 Copy and complete the table so that the values of x and y satisfy the equation $y = 3x$.
Plot the x and y values as coordinates and join them with a straight line. Label the line with its equation.
What is the gradient of this line?

x	y
0	0
1	
2	6
3	
–1	
–2	–6
–3	

21 Investigate how the graph of the equation $y = mx$ changes for different values of m.
If you have access to a graphics calculator, or a computer with graph plotter, try to create a picture like the one shown here on the display.

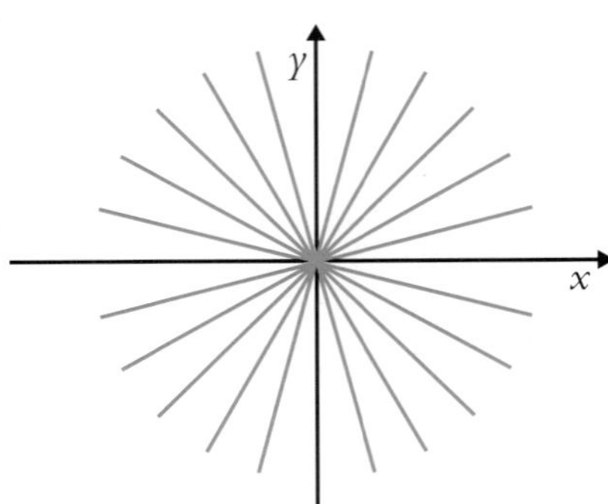

22 If the graphs of the equations $y = 7x$ and $y = -3x$ are drawn:
a) what point would lie on both lines?
b) what is the gradient of each line?

23 If a line has equation $y = mx$, what is its gradient?

24 Find the equation of each of these lines.

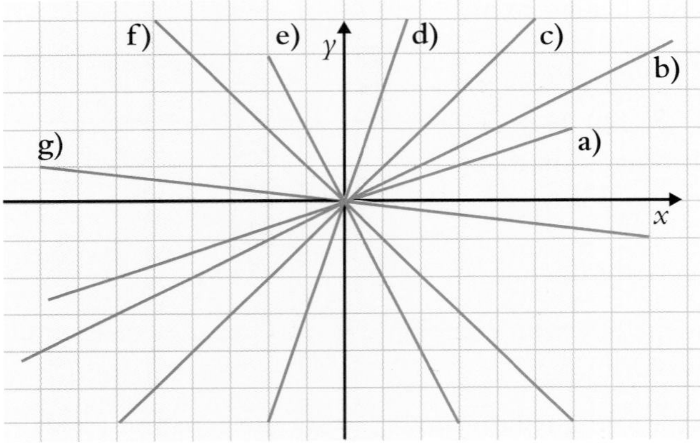

BEARINGS AND PLANS

12.1 Bearings

A **bearing** is an angle measured in a clockwise direction from North to describe the direction for a journey between two places.

A bearing can be any angle between 0° and 360° and is always written as a three-figure number.

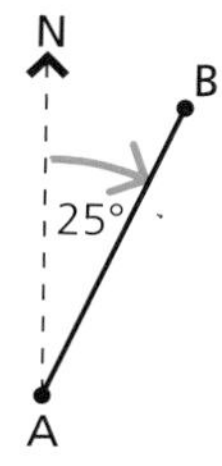

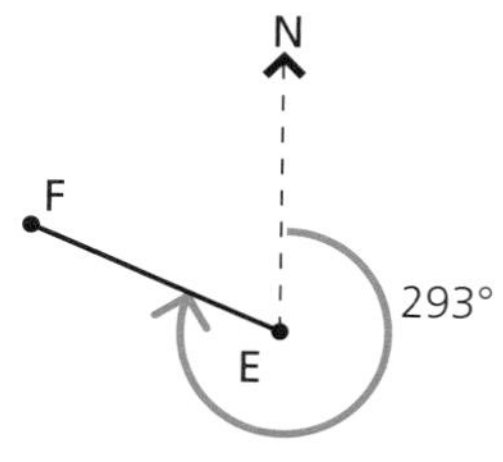

The bearing of B from A is 025°.

The bearing of D from C is 135°.

F is on a bearing of 293° from E.

If I travel due East my bearing is 090°. In order to return to my starting point I will have to go back on a course which is due west with a bearing of 270°.

This diagram shows the points of the compass.

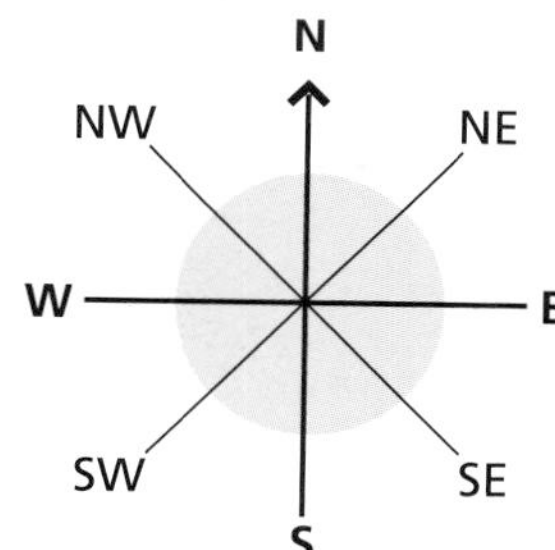

1 Pair up these compass points with their correct bearings:

Compass point

a) South
b) South West
c) West
d) North
e) North East
f) South East
g) North North East
h) South South East
i) East

Bearing	
270°	$022\frac{1}{2}°$
000°	090°
180°	125°
045°	$157\frac{1}{2}°$
225°	

Your first answer should be written as **a)** South = 180°

2 ✔ Find the bearings given by OA, OB, OC, OD, OE and OF.

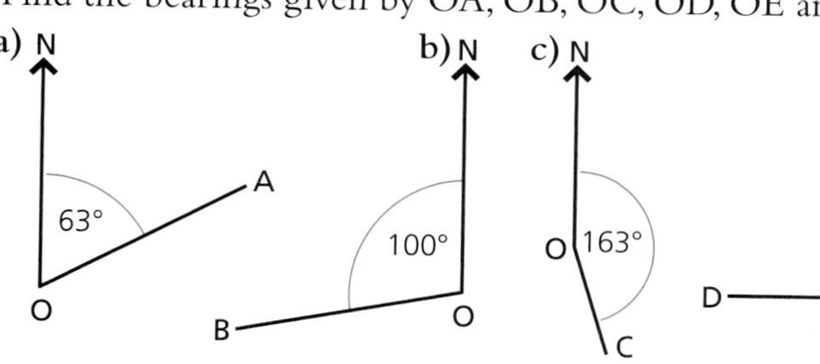

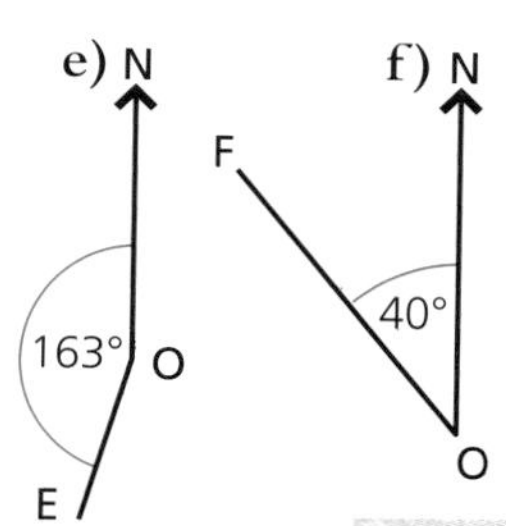

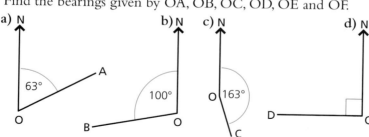

3 Draw a sketch to show the direction given by each bearing:
a) 030° b) 190° c) 295° d) 007° e) 125°

4 a) The bearing of OA is 041°.
The bearing of OB is 125°.
Find the size of ∠AOB. ✔

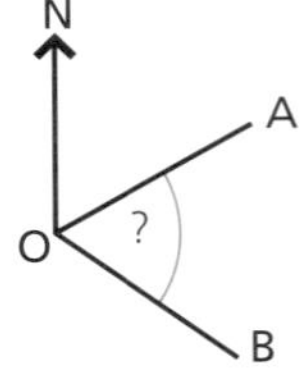

b) The bearing of OA is 165°.
The bearing of OB is 250°.
Find the size of ∠AOB. ✔

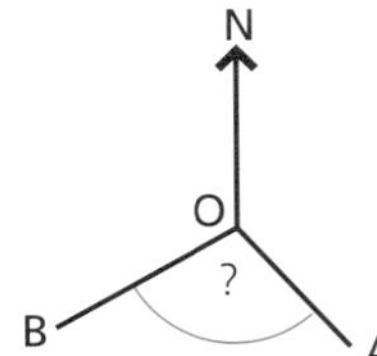

5 Find the bearings of OA ✔, OB, OC, OD and OE. Then calculate the value of x.

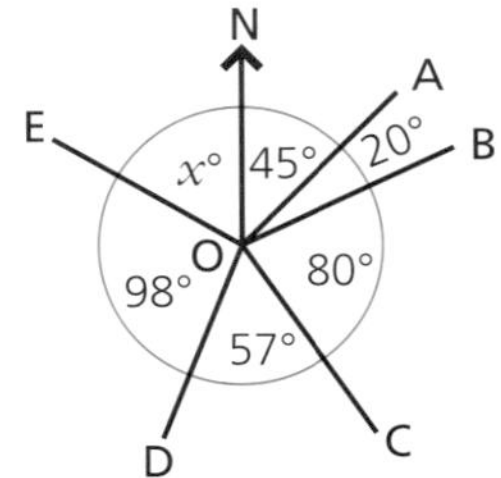

12.2 Return journeys

Example

If the bearing of A from O is 030°, what is the bearing of O from A (the **back bearing**)?

Answer
To find the answer first draw in another North line at A.

The two lines pointing North are parallel lines. This means that we can find that OAS is also 30° using alternate angles.

The bearing of O from A must be 180° + 30° = 210°.

Back bearings can always be calculated using alternate angles and parallel lines.

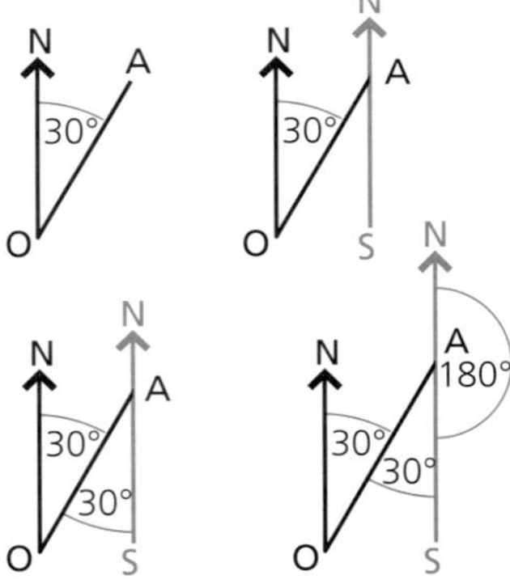

Example

If the bearing of B from O is 190°, what is the bearing of O from B?

Answer
Draw in another North line at B. Also extend the North line at O downwards (towards south).

You can now see that the alternate angles between the parallel lines are both 10° (shown marked in black on the next diagram). The bearing of O from B is therefore 010°.

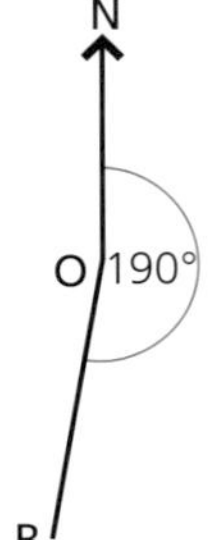

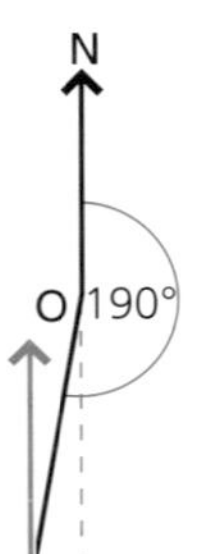

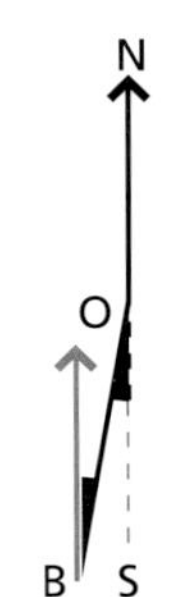

1 ✓ Look back at question 2 in the previous section (page 111). Make a copy of each sketch and use parallel lines and alternate angles to help you find the bearing of O from each of the points A to F.

2 ✓ Find the bearing of a) OX and b) XO for each of the following diagrams:

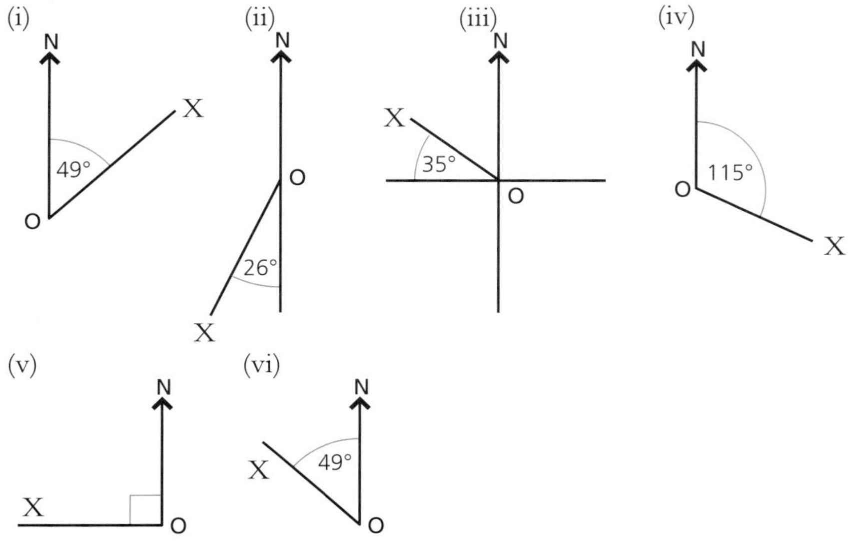

3 This map shows the area surrounding the Isle of Wight off the south coast of Britain.

A pilot flying a light aircraft flies from Southampton airport (Eastleigh) on a bearing of 010°.

a) If she returns by the same route what will her course (bearing) be on the return journey? ✓
b) Will she fly over the English Channel on her journey?
c) Give the bearing for a dinghy sailing from Ryde to Portsmouth.
d) What is the bearing for the return journey?
e) What is the bearing for a boat sailing from Lee-on-Solent to Calshot Castle?
f) What course should a sailor steer a dinghy sailing from Lymington to Cowes?
g) What is the bearing from St Catherine's Point to the Needles?
h) What is the course for the return journey?
i) What is the course for an aircraft flying from Portsmouth airport to Southampton airport?

12.3 Scale drawings and bearings

1 A ship sails from a harbour for 20 km on a bearing of 025° and then continues due East for 18 km. Make a scale drawing of this journey using 1 cm to represent 2 km. Here is a sketch to help you.

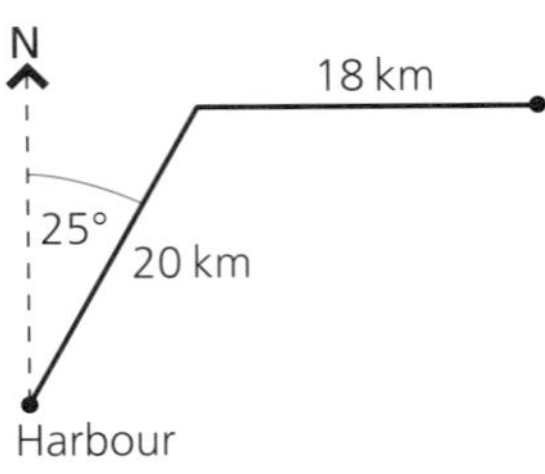

How far will the ship have to sail to get back to harbour by the shortest route? What will its bearing be? ✓

2 A ship sails from a harbour for 10 km on a bearing of 040° and then turns to travel due south for 14 km. Draw your own sketch, then make a proper scale drawing to find its distance back to harbour.

3 A surveyor wishes to estimate the width of a river. He takes two sightings of a tree on the opposite bank from positions marked A and B. The bearing of the tree from A is 035° and from B is 320°. Make a scale drawing and find the width of the river.

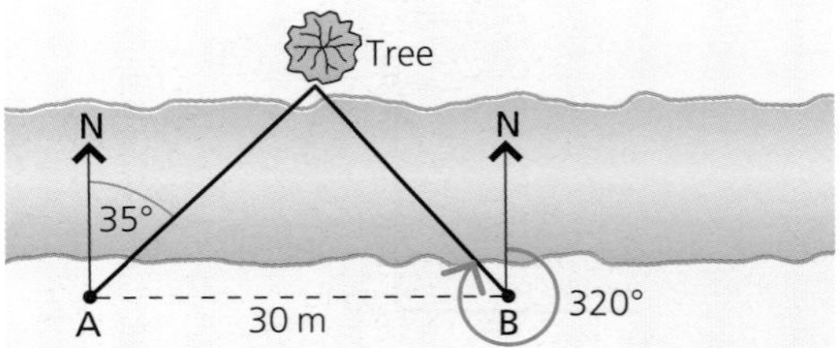

4 Debbie and Dave go for a hike across open moorland. They start at the hostel and walk on a bearing of 150° for 10 km. After a rest they walk a further 6 km on a bearing of 230°. Make a scale drawing using 1 cm to represent 1 km. Find their bearing for the return journey going directly back to the hostel, and the distance they have to walk.

5 A river pilot wishes to check the distance across a river estuary. He takes the bearing of a tower on the opposite bank from two positions A and B, 1 km apart. B is due South of A. From A the bearing of the tower is 095°. From B it is 048°.

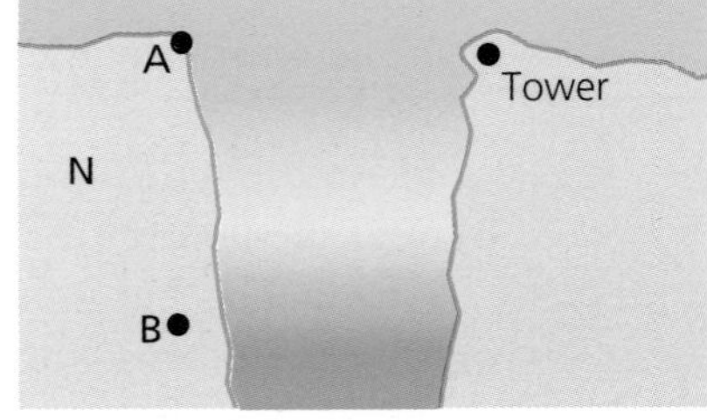

Use his sketch to help you make an accurate scale drawing and find the width of the river mouth.

12.4 Plans and elevations

A plan is an outline of an object or building viewed from above. It shows the outline shape of the building at floor level.

A plan can be used to show what size a building will be when it is finished and the positions of walls, windows and doors. A plan of an existing building may be used to help people find their way around, or to show an escape route in case of fire.

1 Here is a plan of a 'model' (or ideal) house which Prince Albert helped to design for the Great Exhibition of 1851. (This was the Victorian equivalent of the Ideal Home exhibition!)

The house was designed to accommodate four families, so presumably the two floors were identical and two families lived on each floor. These illustrations come from *A Vision of Britain* written by Prince Charles (Guild Publishing 1989).

This plan shows accommodation for two families. Two more would live upstairs.

a) How many bedrooms are provided for each family?
b) Which other rooms does a family have?
c) Do they have a bathroom?
d) What equipment was provided in the scullery?
e) Which feature is labelled 'E' on the plan?
f) The entrance to each apartment is through the area marked 'lobby'. Which room would you enter next?
g) Can the parents' bedroom be entered directly from the living room?
h) The approximate size of the living room in metres is:
(i) 6 m by 4 m (ii) 50 m by 30 m (iii) $4\frac{1}{2}$ m by 3 m

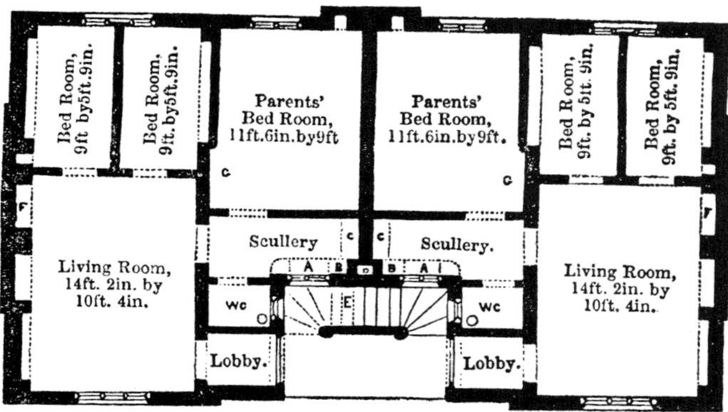

A side or front view of a building (or object) is called an elevation. A front view is called a front elevation. A side view is called a side elevation.

An elevation usually shows the height and shape of walls, doors and windows. It is easier to understand than a plan because it shows the building viewed straight on. Only one face (or side) is shown. There is no attempt to show perspective or other sides.

2 This diagram shows the front and side elevations of a house.

a) Find the area of the front of the house excluding the door, windows and roof. ✓
b) Find the area of the side of the house.
c) If paint costs £1.85 per square metre, find the cost of painting the front of the house and the two sides.
d) Find the cost of framing the windows on the front of the house at £2.90 per metre length.
e) What is the area of the ground floor of the house?

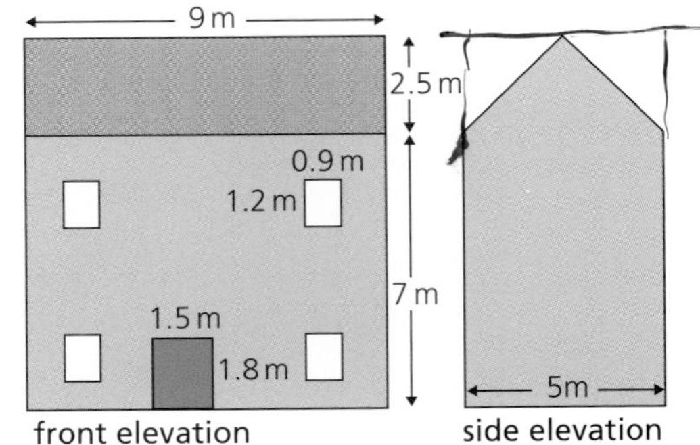

3 a) This diagram shows the plan of a first floor apartment. What is the area of the largest bedroom?
b) What is the total floor area of the apartment (excluding the stairs up to the entrance which are 1.2 m wide)?
c) What is the cost of carpeting the lounge at a cost of £21.25 per square metre?

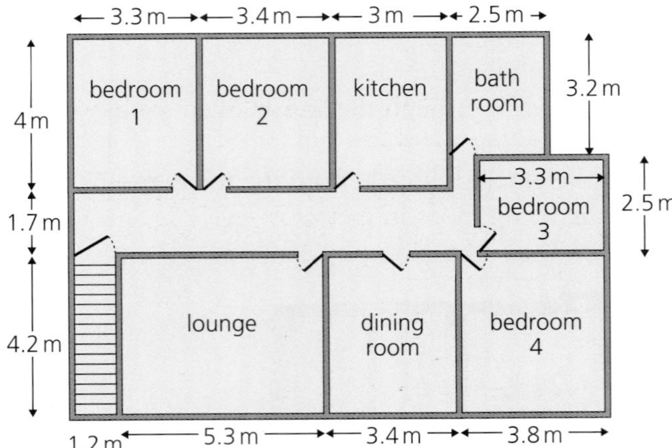

12.5 Plans and scale drawings

1 A room is 4 m wide and 3 m long.

a) Pair up the scale factor and the correct size drawing in the table below.

	Scale
A ✓	1 : 100
B	1 : 5
C	1 : 10
D	1 : 20
E	1 : 80
F	1 : 8
G	1 : 50

Size of drawing
40 cm by 30 cm
4 cm by 3 cm
20 cm by 15 cm
80 cm by 60 cm
8 cm by 6 cm
5 cm by 3.75 cm
50 cm by 37.5 cm

b) Here is a sketch of the room showing various features and their dimensions.

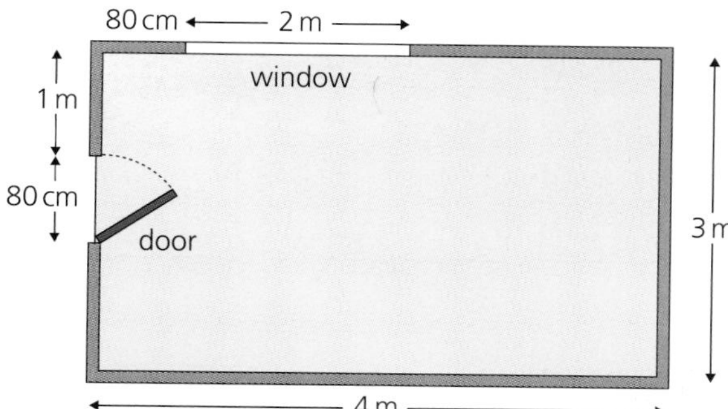

Make a correct scale drawing of the room using a scale of 1 : 20. Show the window and the door in their correct positions.

c) The room is used as an office for three people. Use graph paper to help you to draw and cut out plans of the following items of furniture:

3 desks	1.2 m by 0.8 m
2 filing cabinets	80 cm by 60 cm
1 table	1 m by 80 cm
3 chairs	50 cm by 50 cm

d) Arrange the furniture in the office, making sure that filing cabinets and desk drawers can be opened.

2 Here are some drawings of buildings. Match each building with the sketches of its correct plan and elevation.

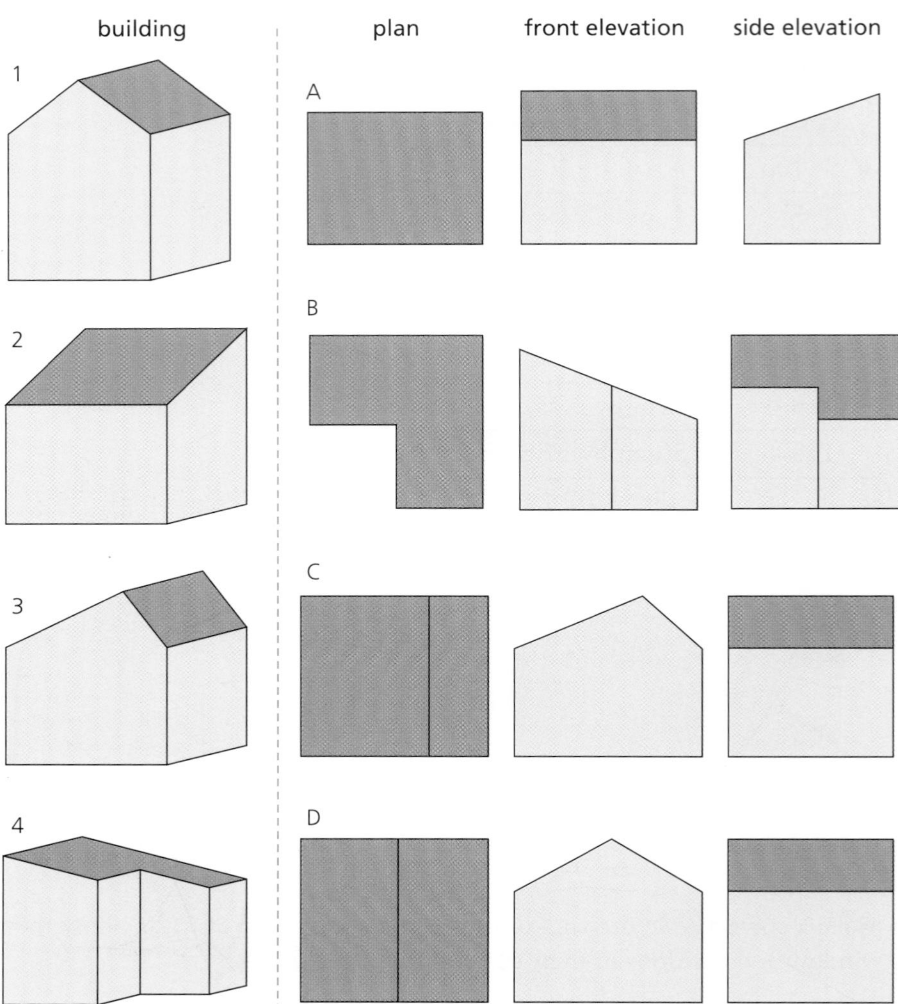

ALGEBRA AND GRAPHS (1)

13

13.1 Removing brackets

The use of brackets in an expression indicates which parts of a calculation are to be done first. This is important with regard to the value that the expression takes.

For example, $10 - 7 - 2 = 3 - 2 = 1$
but $10 - (7 - 2) = 10 - 5 = 5$

In this section we will explore the situations in which brackets can be removed to allow us to simplify algebraic expressions.

For example,
$9 - (5 - 2) = 6$ and $9 - 5 + 2 = 6$.
It follows that $9 - (5 - 2) = 9 - 5 + 2$

In the same way, removing the brackets, $11 - (8 - 5) = 11 - 8 + 5$.

---

1 Follow the pattern given in the examples to remove the brackets from these expressions. Check the results by calculation.
a) $10 - (7 - 2)$ **b)** $12 - (6 - 1)$ **c)** $20 - (16 - 5)$
d) $24 - (11 - 8)$ **e)** $42 - (32 - 10)$ **f)** $10 - (20 - 10)$

2 Find equivalent expressions to these by removing the brackets:
a) $p - (q - r)$ ✓ **b)** $x - (y - 2z)$ **c)** $3x - (2y - z)$
d) $x - (y - 3)$ **e)** $s - (3t - v)$ **f)** $a - (4b - 3c)$

3 Check that $10 - (3 + 4) = 10 - 3 - 4$. Follow the pattern to remove the brackets from each of the following. Check the results by calculation.
a) $20 - (5 + 4)$ **b)** $16 - (12 + 4)$ **c)** $25 - (3 + 7)$
d) $50 - (12 + 28)$ **e)** $100 - (15 + 35)$ **f)** $7 - (1.83 + 1.17)$

4 Remove the brackets from these expressions:
a) $x - (y + z)$ **b)** $2x - (3y + 5z)$ **c)** $4p - (7q + r)$

5 Find the patterns needed to remove the brackets from expressions such as $20 - (3 + 4 + 5)$ and $16 - (12 - 3 - 7)$. Use your results to write the following without brackets:
a) $p - (q + r + s)$ **b)** $p - (q - r - s)$ ✓
c) $p - (q - r + s)$ **d)** $p - (q + r - s)$

6 Copy and complete the following statements, by inserting the appropriate signs, to make them correct:
a) $32 + (7 - 5) = 32 \ldots 7 \ldots 5$ **b)** $24 + (11 - 3) = 24 \ldots 11 \ldots 3$
c) $16 + (10 - 7 - 1) = 16 \ldots 10 \ldots 7 \ldots 1$ **d)** $9 + (15 - 6 + 3) = 9 \ldots 15 \ldots 6 \ldots 3$
e) $p + (q - r) = p \ldots q \ldots r$ **f)** $p + (q - r + s) = p \ldots q \ldots r \ldots s$

7 Describe the process for removing the brackets from an expression depending on whether the sign outside the brackets is a '+' or a '–'. ✓

8 Remove the brackets from these expressions:

a) $3x + (2y - z)$ b) $5a - (3b + c)$ c) $2p + (q + 2r - s)$
d) $4s + (t - 3u - v)$ e) $q - (r - 2s + t)$ f) $a + (2b - c + d)$
g) $w + 2x - (y - z)$ h) $t + v + (3u - w)$ i) $x + y - (u + v)$

Example

In the diagram, all lines meet at right-angles.
Given that the total distance along the route BCD is v, find expressions in terms of v, w, x and y for:

a) CD b) BC c) DE

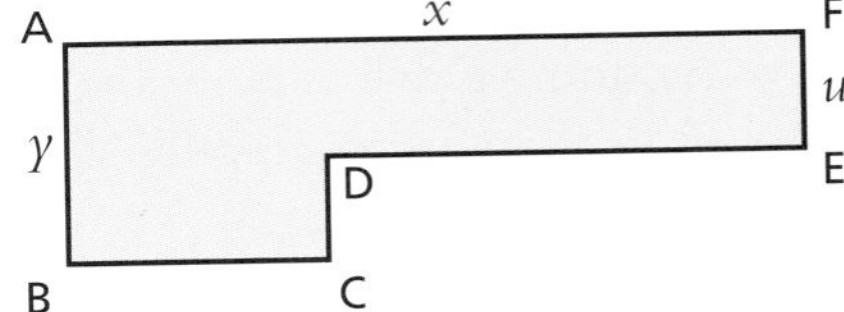

Answer

a) $CD = y - w$
b) $BC = v - CD = v - (y - w) = v - y + w.$
c) $DE = x - BC = x - (v - y + w) = x - v + y - w.$

9 All of the lines in this diagram meet at right-angles. Given that the total distance along the route PUT is d, copy and complete the following statements. The final form of ST should be given without brackets.

TU =
PU = d – (   ) =
ST = QR – PU =

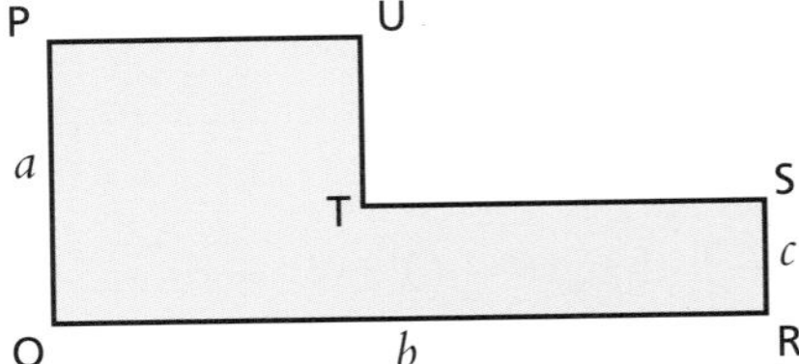

10 The profit £p that I can make by selling goods that cost £c depends on the selling price £s.

a) Write down a formula for p in terms of s and c.
b) Find a new formula for p given that the cost price has increased by £x.
c) If, instead, the cost price is reduced by £x find an expression for p that does not include brackets.

Removing brackets often allows us to simplify an expression.

Example

Simplify:

a) $8x - (5x - 4)$ b) $4x - 2y + 3 - (x - 2y + 4)$

Answer

a) $8x - (5x - 4) = 8x - 5x + 4 = 3x + 4$
b) $4x - 2y + 3 - (x - 2y + 4) = 4x - 2y + 3 - x + 2y - 4 = 3x - 1$

11 Remove the brackets and simplify:

a) $4x - (6 - 3x)$ ✓ b) $10x - (6x + 2)$ c) $7 - (5x + 3)$
d) $2x + 3 + (x - 2)$ e) $8 - x + (3x - 7)$ f) $x + 5y - (x + 4y)$
g) $2x - 3y + (5y - x)$ h) $2x - y + z - (x - y + z)$

12 Given that $p = 2x - 3y$, $q = x - 2y$, $r = 2y - x$, find and simplify expressions for:

a) $p + q$ ✓ b) $p - q$ c) $q + r$ d) $p - r$ e) $q - r$ f) $p - q + r$

Example

Find two expressions for the total area of this diagram and use the results to establish a rule for multiplying out brackets.

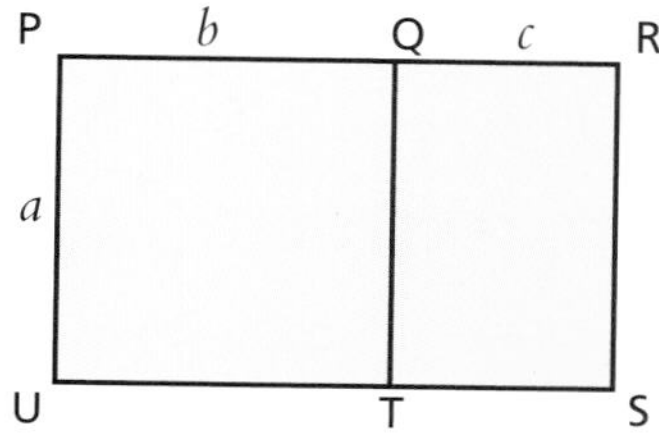

Answer

In appropriate units, the area may be found by:

(i) adding the areas of the rectangles PQTU and QRST giving $ab + ac$.
(ii) multiplying the distance PU by the distance PR giving $a(b + c)$.

Since the two expressions for the area must be equivalent, it follows that $a(b + c) = ab + ac$.

---

13 Use the diagrams below to extend the rule, given in the example, for multiplying out brackets.

a)
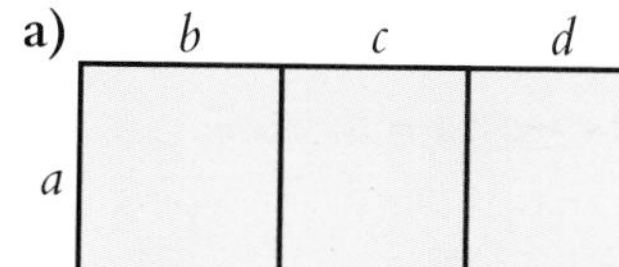

b)
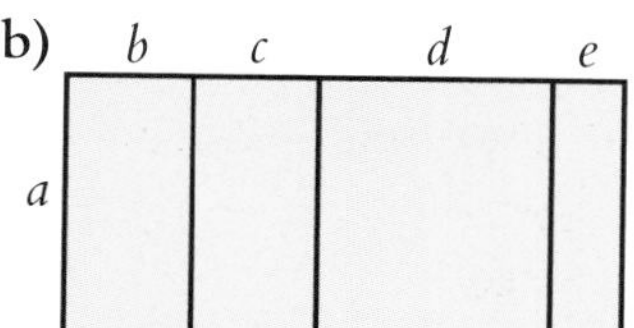

Example

Multiply out the brackets in these expressions:

a) $5(x + 3)$ b) $3(2x + 4)$ c) $2(3x - y)$ d) $x(x + 2y - z)$

Answer

a) $5(x + 3) = 5x + 15$ b) $3(2x + 4) = 6x + 12$
c) $2(3x - y) = 6x - 2y$ d) $x(x + 2y - z) = x^2 + 2xy - xz$

When the term outside the brackets is *positive*, the signs of the terms inside the brackets are unchanged when multiplying out.

14 Multiply out these brackets:

a) $4(x + 3)$ b) $7(x - 2)$ c) $5(2x - 3)$
d) $6(3x + y)$ e) $x(7x - y)$ f) $3x(2x + 3y)$

The process of multiplying out brackets is also known as 'expanding' the brackets.

15 Expand the brackets and simplify these expressions:

a) $2x + 3(x - 6)$ ✓ b) $3s - 2t + 4(t - s)$ c) $5(q - 2r) + 3r$
d) $8(x - 2) - 5x$ e) $8(x - 2) - 5x + 1$ f) $8(x - 2) - (5x + 1)$

Example

Expand and simplify the following where possible:

a) $-3(x + 4)$ b) $-2(3x - y)$ c) $4x - 3(2x - 5)$

Answer

a) $-3(x + 4) = -3x - 12$
b) $-2(3x - y) = -6x + 2y$
c) $4x - 3(2x - 5) = 4x - 6x + 15$
$= -2x + 15$ (This may be written as $15 - 2x$).

When the term outside the brackets is *negative*, all of the signs of terms inside the brackets are *changed* when multiplying out.

16 Expand:

a) $-6(x + 2)$ b) $-3(5 - 2x)$ c) $-2(4x - y + 2)$ ✓
d) $-5(2r - 3s)$ e) $-p(3 - 2q)$ f) $-ab(a - b)$

17 Expand and simplify:

a) $6x - 2(3x - y)$ ✓ b) $4 - x - 3(x - 5)$
c) $ab + a - a(1 - 3b)$ d) $2q - q(2 - r)$
e) $4(3x - 2) - 9(x - 3)$ f) $p(q - r) - q(p - r)$
g) $8(3x + 1) - 3(8x - 1)$ h) $2(3a + b) + 4(a - 2b) - 6(a - b)$

13.2 Factorising

The ability to *reverse* a process is a requirement of using mathematics at all levels (as is the ability to recognise and use equivalent forms). The reverse process of multiplying out brackets is known as **factorisation**.

When using algebra to solve a problem it may be necessary to introduce brackets into an expression, then expand the brackets to carry out some simplification, and even to factorise it again at a later stage. Finding the most appropriate form of an expression to work with at a particular stage is one of the skills that a mathematician needs to develop.

$$p(q + r) \underset{\text{factorise}}{\overset{\text{expand}}{\rightleftarrows}} pq + pr$$

The process of factorising $pq + pr$ involves:

(i) recognising that p is a common factor, i.e. a factor of each term
(ii) 'taking out' the common factor, i.e. writing p outside the brackets
(iii) completing the factor inside the brackets so that the expression is equivalent to $pq + pr$.

The statement $p(q + r) = pq + pr$ is true for *all* values of p, q and r. It is called an **identity**.

Example

Factorise: **a)** $5y + 10$ **b)** $5xy - 10x$

Answer

a) $5y + 10 = 5(y + 2)$ **b)** $5xy - 10x = 5x(y - 2)$

---

1 Copy and complete these identities:

a) $6x + 9 = 3(\ldots+\ldots)$ **b)** $4p + 8q = 4(\ldots+\ldots)$ **c)** $xy - yz = y(\ldots-\ldots)$
d) $12x - 6y = 6(\quad\quad)$ **e)** $8rs + 6rt = 2r(\quad\quad)$ **f)** $6ab - 6ac = \quad(b\quad\quad)$

2 Factorise these expressions. In each case 'take out' the largest common factor.

a) $5x + 15y$ **b)** $8p - 12q$ **c)** $6u + 9v - 3w$
d) $3ab + 7ac$ **e)** $5st + 10tu$ **f)** $22xy - 33yz$
g) $\pi rh - \pi rl$ **h)** $4\pi r - 6\pi a$ **i)** $2\pi rx - 3\pi rl$

3 Simplify these expressions and leave your answers in factorised form:

a) $6x + 7y - 4x + y$ **b)** $11p - 6\mathrm{r} - p + \mathrm{r}$
c) $7x + (5x - 6y)$ **d)** $3q - 5s - (2s - 11q)$
e) $8ab - a(2b + 3)$ **f)** $4xy + x(3 - 2y)$
g) $3(a + 2b) + 4(a + 2b)$ **h)** $9(2q - 3r) - 5(2q - 3r)$

13.3 Gradient intercept form

The point at which a straight line crosses the y-axis is known as the **y-intercept**. In this section the connection between the equation of a line and its gradient and y-intercept will be explored.

The values in the table satisfy the equation $y = 2x + 1$.

The (x, y) values shown in the table may be plotted as coordinates on a graph.

x	y
−3	−5
−2	−3
−1	−1
0	1
1	3
2	5
3	7

The x-axis must show values from −3 to 3 and the y-axis must include values from −5 to 7. However, the scale does not have to be the same on each axis.

From the graph we can see that the plotted points of $y = 2x + 1$ lie on a straight line with gradient 2 which intercepts the y-axis at 1.

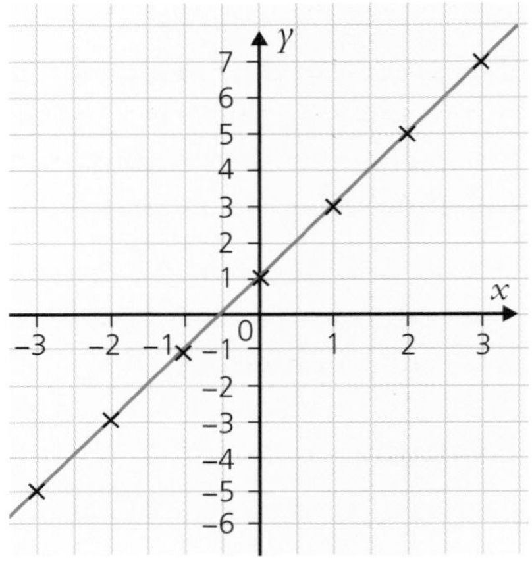

1 Copy the diagram above. Using values of x from −3 to 3 complete a table for the equation $y = 2x + 3$ and plot the (x, y) values as coordinates. Join the plotted points with a straight line and state the value of its gradient and y-intercept.

2 On the same diagram, draw the graphs of the following equations. In each case, state the value of the gradient and y-intercept.
a) $y = 2x + 4$ **b)** $y = 2x$ **c)** $y = 2x - 1$.

3 Find the equation of the straight line which has gradient 2 and crosses the y-axis at the point $(0, 5)$.

4 Copy and complete the table for the equation $y = 0.5x + 2$.

Using suitably labelled axes, draw the graph of the equation and find the value of the y-intercept and gradient.

x	y
−3	0.5
−2	
−1	1.5
0	
1	
2	
3	

5 Draw the graphs of $y = 0.5x$, $y = 0.5x + 1$ and $y = 0.5x - 1$. For each graph, state the value of its gradient and y-intercept.

6 Copy and complete the table for the equation $y = -x + 3$.

Draw the graph of the equation and state the value of its gradient and y-intercept.

Check that the x and y values also satisfy the equation $x + y = 3$. What extra information is easily obtained from the equation when it is written in the form $y = -x + 3$?

x	y
−3	
−2	5
−1	
0	
1	2
2	
3	
4	
5	−2
6	

7 Add the lines $y = -x$, $y = -x + 2$ and $y = -x - 1$ to the diagram. Explain how this can be done without having to work out a new table of values for each equation.

8 Find the value of the gradient and the y-intercept for the line shown in the diagram. Hence, write down the equation of the line.

List the cordinates of five points on the line and show that these coordinates satisfy the equation you have found.

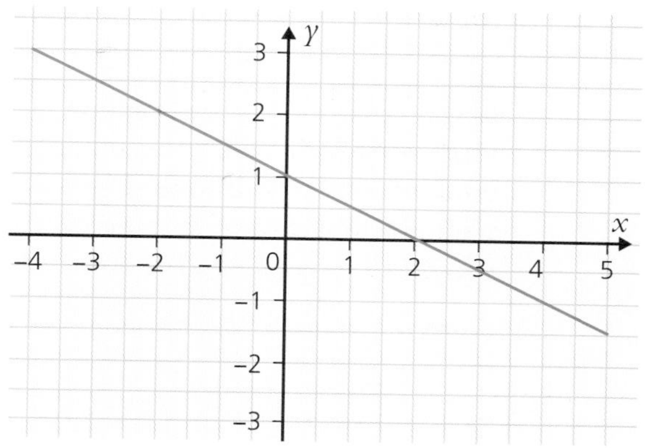

The graph of an equation of the form:

$$y = mx + c$$

is always a straight line. The value of m is equal to the gradient of the line and the value of c gives the y-intercept.

9 Write down the equation of the straight line passing through (0, 5) which has gradient:

a) 3 ✓ b) −1 c) −6 d) 4.9

10 Find the equation of the straight line, parallel to $y = 7x - 3$, which passes through the point with coordinates (0, −0.25).

11 Give the coordinates of the points where these lines cross the y-axis:

a) $y = 8x - 10$ b) $y = -3.7x + 6$ c) $y = 4.3x - 2.8$

12 Find the equations of the straight lines that pass through these pairs of points:

a) (0, 2) and (5, 7) ✓ b) (0, 3) and (3, 9) c) (0, −4) and (5, 26)
d) (7, 11) and (0, −3) e) (−8, 0) and (0, 8) f) (0, 2) and (3, −10)
g) (11, 0) and (0, 11) h) (0, a) and (a, 0) i) (0, 9) and (5, 9)

13 Find the coordinates of the labelled points in these diagrams:

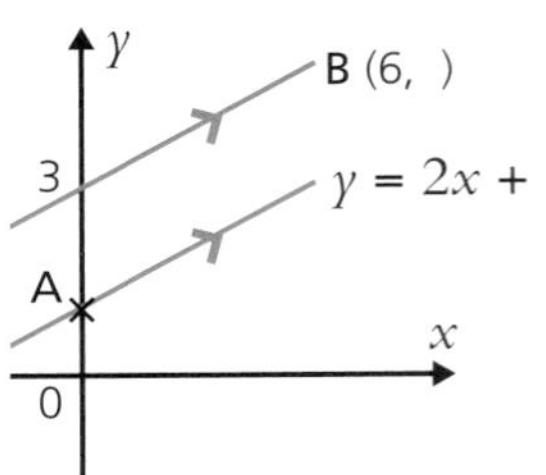

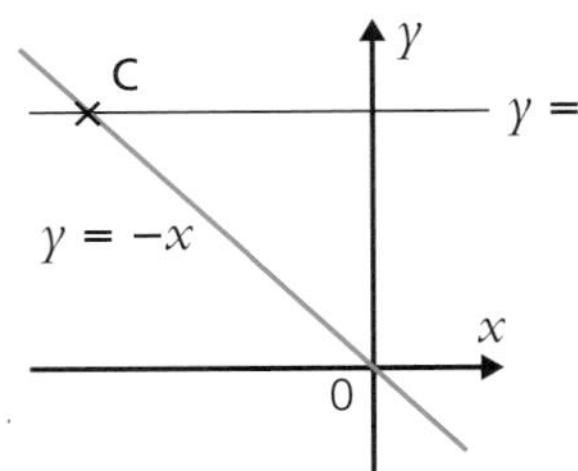

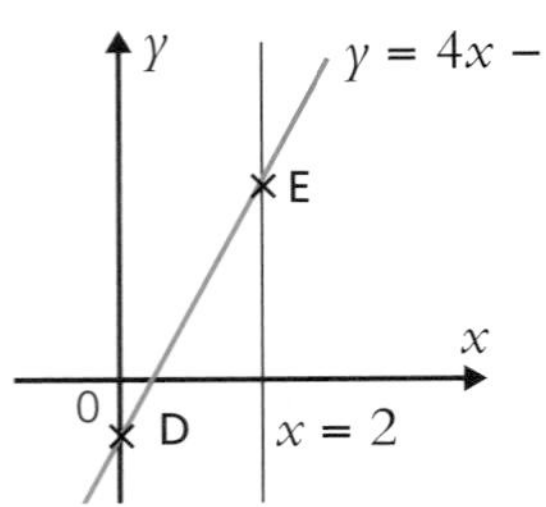

13.4 Using graphs to solve equations

Example

Use the diagram to solve the equation $0.9x + 1.6 = 7.3$. Care is needed when reading the scales.

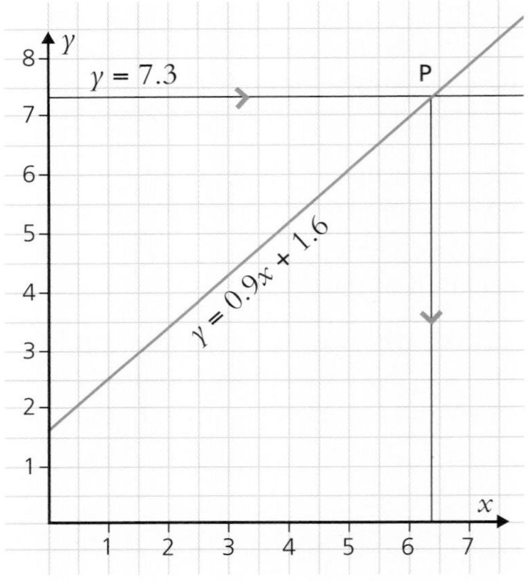

Answer

In the diagram, P is the point on the line $y = 0.9x + 1.6$ where the value of y is 7.3, and so the x-coordinate of P is the value needed to solve the equation.

From the graph, the solution is $x = 6.3$.

As a check: $0.9 \times 6.3 + 1.6 = 7.27$ which shows that the solution obtained is a slight under-estimate of the true solution.

---

1 Use the diagram to find solutions to these equations:
a) $0.9x + 1.6 = 4$ b) $0.9x + 1.6 = 7$ c) $0.9x + 1.6 = 2$

2 Check your solutions by calculation and, in each case, state whether the result is an under-estimate, an over-estimate, or an exact solution.

3 Find the value of $0.7x + 4.2$ when $x = 10$. Use your answer, together with the value of the y-intercept, to draw the graph of $y = 0.7x + 4.2$ for values of x from 0 to 10. Hence solve the following equations:
a) $0.7x + 4.2 = 6$ b) $0.7x + 4.2 = 10$ c) $0.7x + 4.2 = 7$
Show, by calculation, that one of the equations has an exact solution as a whole number.

4 Show that the equation $2.6x - 5.2 = 13$ has a solution between 0 and 10. (*Hint*: show that 0 is too small and 10 is too large.)
Draw the graphs of $y = 2.6x - 5.2$ and $y = 13$ for $0 \leq x \leq 10$ on the same axes and find the solution of $2.6x - 5.2 = 13$ as a whole number.
Show by calculation that the solution found is exact.

The equation $y = x^2$ is an example of a different form of equation known as a **quadratic**. In a quadratic expression in x, the highest power of x is 2 and its most general form is $ax^2 + bx + c$, where a, b, and c are constants. The following expressions are quadratics:

$2x^2 - 3$ ($a = 2$, $b = 0$ and $c = -3$)

$x^2 + 0.3x$ ($a = 1$, $b = 0.3$ and $c = 0$)

The graph of a quadratic is not a straight line but a special curve called a **parabola**.

When a > 0, the graph looks like this.

When a < 0, the graph looks like this.

---

5 Copy and complete the table for $y = x^2$.

x	y
−3	9
−2.8	7.84
−2.6	6.76
.	.
.	.
.	.
3	9

Plot the points and join them with a smooth curve.

Add the line $y = 5$ to your diagram and explain why there is more than one solution to the equation $x^2 = 5$. Find these solutions to 1 D.P.

Check your results by calculation and state whether your solution is too large or too small. How could you obtain the result to greater accuracy?

CHARTS, GRAPHS, HISTOGRAMS

14.1 Different sorts of data

In data handling work, there are three main ways of obtaining data (or results) for analysis. They are:

1 By classifying
- What colour is your hair?
- Is this puppy male or female?
- Which blood group is she?

These questions will all have **categorical** (or qualitative) data as results, e.g. black hair, female, and so on (see Unit 6 section 6.2).

2 By counting
- How many children are there in a family?
- How many students were absent each day?
- How many videos did you watch in a week?

These questions will have **discrete** data as results, e.g. 5 children, 3 videos, etc. Results are whole numbers of things.

3 By measuring
- How tall are you?
- How far from school do you live?
- How long does it take to get here?

These questions all give **continuous** data as results. Results may involve fractions or decimals, e.g. 157.3 cm, 8.2 km, $5\frac{1}{2}$ minutes, etc. Even if you decide to write an answer correct to the nearest whole number, you do have the choice of being more accurate if you wish.

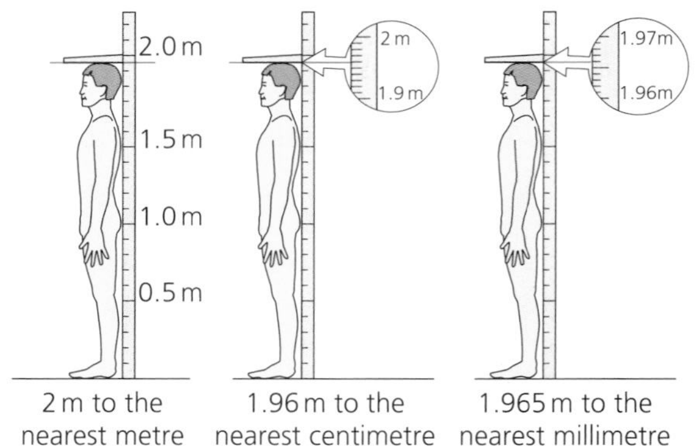

The questions being asked above are all about **variables**.

A variable is any attribute which changes from one person to another or one situation to another and which can be classified, counted or measured.

Variables can be either numerical or non-numerical.

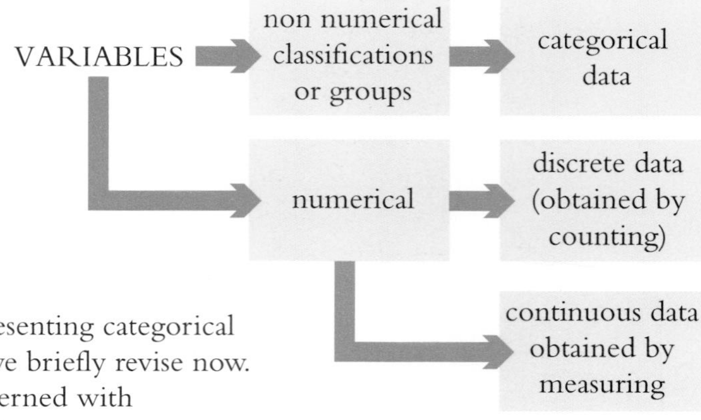

Unit 6 dealt with ways of representing categorical data and discrete data, which we briefly revise now. Most of this Unit will be concerned with continuous data obtained by taking measurements.

1 Match up each of the variables listed on the left-hand side with the correct type of data chosen from categorical, discrete or continuous. The first one has been done for you:

a) number of rooms in a house → discrete
b) time taken to walk to the library
c) hand used for writing
d) length of stride
e) time taken to run 100 metres
f) colour of eyes
g) number of heartbeats per minute
h) length of foot measured in cm
i) size of shoe
j) area of the country in which you live
k) temperature
l) number of rings inside a tree trunk
m) number of books in your school bag
n) weight
o) 'star sign' (or sign of the zodiac)
p) age
q) number of days absent due to illness
r) time spent doing homework
s) number of pets
t) day of the week on which you were born

continuous
discrete
categorical
continuous
discrete
categorical
continuous
continuous
categorical
continuous
discrete
continuous
discrete
categorical
continuous
discrete
continuous
discrete
discrete
categorical

14.2 Pie charts and bar charts

A **pie chart** (see Unit 6, section 6.3) is ideal for illustrating categorical data. It shows the proportions in each category or group.

1 a) Which category of road users contributed most to the total number of people killed?
b) Apart from 'others', which is the smallest category?
c) If there were 4658 people killed altogether in road accidents that year, was the number of pedestrians killed less than 1000 or more?
d) Can you easily tell exactly how many pedestrians there were?
e) If the actual number of motor cyclists killed was 548, explain how to work out the angle on the pie chart for that group.

Number of people killed on the roads in the UK (1991)

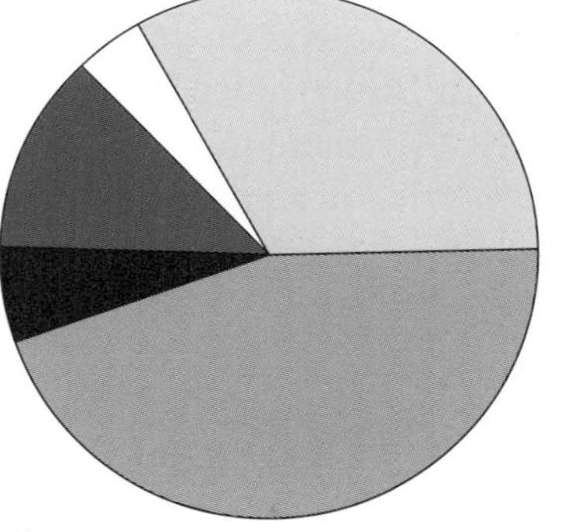

pedestrians, others, on motor cycles, on pedal cycles, in cars and taxis

Source: Annual Abstract of Statistics 1993

A **bar chart** may be used to illustrate categorical data. The height of each bar is used to show the frequency. If the actual frequencies need to be known, then a bar chart is preferable to a pie chart (see Unit 6).

Bar charts are also drawn to illustrate discrete data. There should be gaps between the bars which should be as narrow as possible. (Compare this to a histogram shown in a later section.)

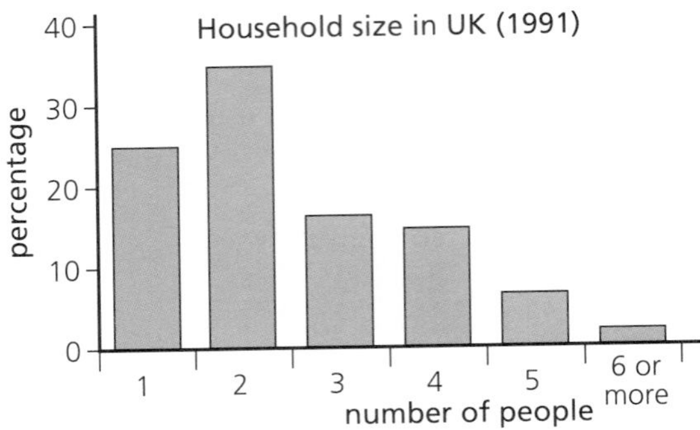

A **bar line graph** shows more clearly the fact that only the integer (whole number) values are possible.

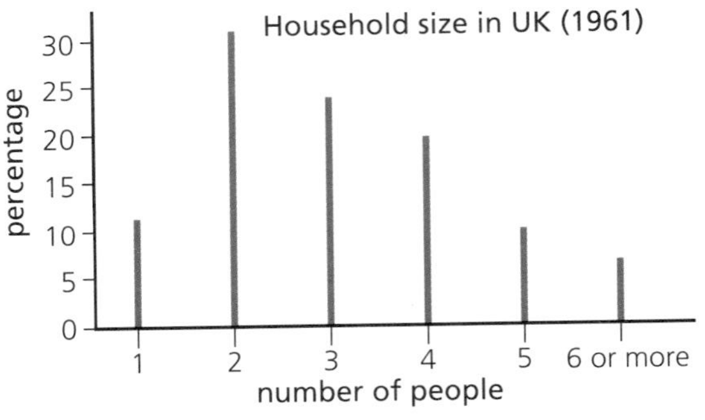

Source for both these diagrams: *Social trends* 1994.

2 a) Which was the modal household size in 1991? (Remind yourself of the meaning of modal in Unit 6, section 6.1.) ✓
b) Which was the modal household size in 1961?
c) What percentage of households in 1991 had 6 or more people?
d) Were there more six (or more) person households in 1991 or 1961?
e) What percentage of households were single person households in 1991?
f) Were there more single person households in 1991 or 1961?
g) Can you think of any reasons why more people are living alone?

14.3 Histograms and continuous data

A **histogram** is drawn to illustrate continuous data. The data may need to be grouped into class intervals. There are no gaps between the groups or class intervals, and there should be no gaps between the blocks on the histogram.

1 Here are two histograms drawn to show the ages of the mothers of babies born in 1971 and 1991.

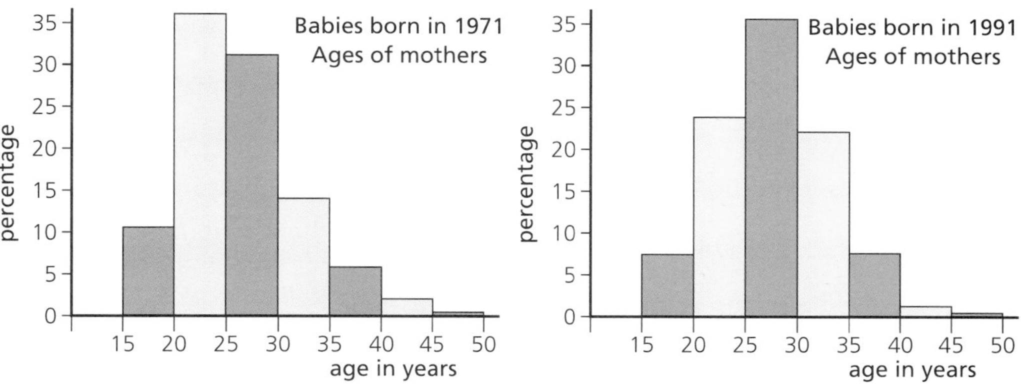

Source: *Social trends* 1994

a) Which is the modal age group for mothers giving birth in 1971?
b) Which is the modal age group for mothers giving birth in 1991?
c) Which age groups have decreased (as a percentage of the total) between 1971 and 1991?
d) Which age groups have increased?
e) Are women tending to have babies at a younger age than they used to, or at an older age?

Experiment

How good are you at estimating angles? Without using a protractor try to guess the size of each of these angles:

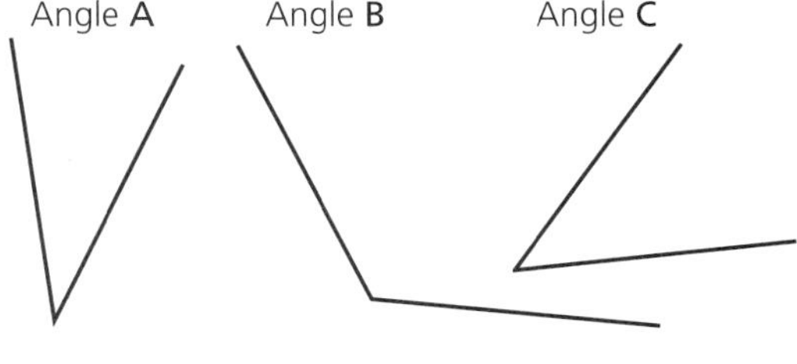

- Write down your guess for each angle in degrees.
- Collect together the results for the whole class, for each angle.

Here are the guesses for angle C for all the pupils in Nirmal's class:

Angle C: guesses in degrees

40	57	20	42	50	61	30	52	35	45
51	48	31	48	62	38	35	47	53	45
29	45	55	54	60	39	28	45	53	55

It is clear that there is a wide range of answers, but we need to organise the guesses into a table to get a better picture.

- What is the smallest guess? What is the largest?

So we need a table which will show results in that range.
If we group the results in 10s we will have 5 groups. What are they?
If we group the results in 5s we will have 9 groups.
How many groups will there be if we group in 2s?

Guess in degrees	Tally	Frequency
$20 \le x < 25$		
$25 \le x < 30$		
$30 \le x < 35$	||	
$35 \le x < 40$		
$40 \le x < 45$	|	
$45 \le x < 50$		
$50 \le x < 55$	|	
$55 \le x < 60$		
$60 \le x < 65$	|	

Nirmal's class decide to use groups of 5s. They make a table like this, in which x stands for the guess:

Nirmal has recorded the first 5 results.

This group is for results of 60° and over but less than 65°

a) Copy this table. Finish writing in the tally marks, then write in the frequencies.

b) Here is the histogram which Nirmal drew.
Check that the frequencies shown on the histogram agree with those on your frequency table.

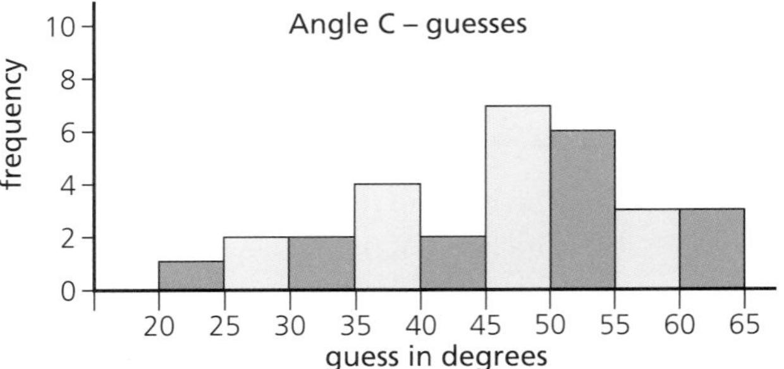

c) Make a frequency table for the guesses made by your class for *each* of the angles A, B and C.
(This work can be shared out among your class, by splitting the class into 3 groups who each work with one angle.)

d) Draw histograms for your results.

e) Which angle were people best at estimating?

f) Do you think people find it easier to estimate large angles or small angles? Explain your answer.

---

2 As part of a biology lesson, Joe's class are asked to measure their temperatures using clinical thermometers. The results are in °C.

36.9	37.0	36.5	36.6	36.9	36.5	36.9	36.2	36.4	37.0
36.7	36.2	36.4	36.5	36.8	36.6	36.7	36.5	36.3	36.7
37.0	36.4	36.9	36.4	36.7	36.4	37.1	36.8	36.6	36.6

a) Draw up a table organising the temperatures into groups or class intervals each of 0.2 degrees. The groups should start at 36.2, then 36.4, 36.6, etc.

Temperature	Tally	Frequency
$36.2 \le t < 36.4$		
$36.4 \le t < 36.6$		
$36.6 \le 6 < 36.8$		

b) Use tally marks to record the temperatures on the frequency table. Fill in the frequency column. ✓

c) Draw a histogram for the temperatures.
d) Which is the modal group for these temperatures?
e) Find the value of the 'normal' body temperature. How did the temperatures of this group of students compare with that?

ICT Extra!

Look at some data from Internet sources such as the Office for Health Statistics or the DFEE website for educational performance tables. Here are some websites for you to try:

www.ons.gov.uk
www.detr.gov.uk
www.stats.demon.nl
www.hea.org.uk/research/index.html

Organise your data into a suitable graph.

14.4 Discrete data and frequencies

In this section we will be looking at discrete data, i.e. data such as number of children per family, goals scored,etc.

Where data cover a wide range of results they will need to be grouped into class intervals. This will also make any patterns in the data easier to see.

The numbers of goals scored by teams in a netball tournament are given below:
35, 3, 18, 15, 58, 36, 19, 20, 40, 38, 29, 52, 6, 18, 27, 39

Here data have been grouped into class intervals (or groups) of 10.

Be careful to choose sensible groupings which should always be multiples of 2, 5 or 10. (It is more difficult to work with groups of 3s or 7s.) Here is the frequency diagram for these data.

Number of goals	Tally	Frequency
0–9	||	2
10–19	||||	4
20–29	|||	3
30–39	||||	4
40–49	|	
50–59	||	2

Goals scored in a netball tournament

frequency

0 1 2 3 4

0–9 10–19 20–29 30–39 40–49 50–59

goals scored

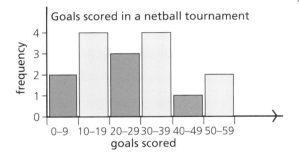

Notice that this graph is not a histogram because the horizontal axis cannot show a continuous scale, as these are not continuous measurements.

1 Here are the number of absences (in days) for students in a particular form, during one term.

6, 9, 0, 1, 0, 5, 3, 15, 0, 4
2, 3, 5, 5, 1, 1, 10, 0, 3, 0
12, 4, 3, 0, 0, 10, 5, 13, 2, 7

a) Decide on a suitable way of grouping the data. ✓
b) Use tally marks to organise the results into a frequency table.
c) Draw a frequency diagram to illustrate the data.
d) Look at the raw data again. Which single value is the mode? Which result has the second highest frequency? Does the graph show this or hide it?
e) Why is five days such a popular result?

14.5 Scatter graphs

Scatter graphs are used to investigate relationships between two variables (for example, height and weight). The data must be collected in pairs and may be either discrete or continuous.

Experiment

For each person in your group, measure their height in centimetres and their armspan (also in centimetres). Measuring the armspan is most easily done when the person stretches out their arms against a wall or a black-board. The purpose of the experiment is to find out whether armspan measurement is related to a person's height.

Here are the results for Edina's group:

Name	Height	Armspan
Edina	158 cm	157 cm
Deborah	148 cm	149 cm
Michael	146 cm	145 cm
Joe	175 cm	174 cm
Lisa	169 cm	169 cm
Nirmal	178 cm	179 cm
Denise	171 cm	170 cm
Ramesh	174 cm	176 cm
Sally	166 cm	159 cm
Donna	173 cm	174 cm

It is easier to see whether two quantities are related if a graph is drawn.

If height is shown on the x-axis and armspan on the y-axis, each person's result can be plotted as a point. So Edina is (158, 157). This graph shows the results for Edina's group, and is called a **scatter graph**.

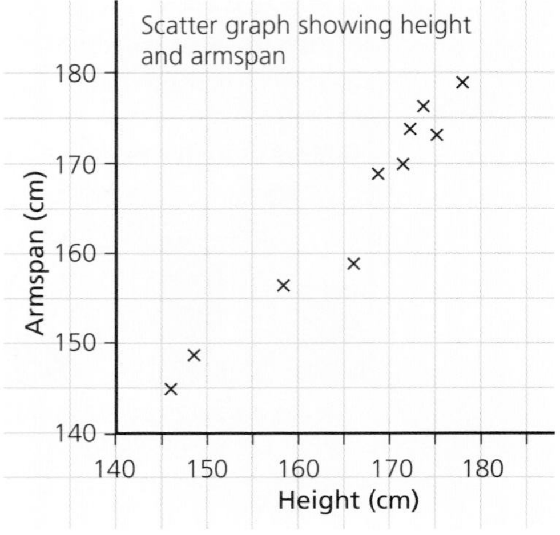

It clearly shows that the tallest people in the group have the longest armspan, while the shorter students have smaller armspans. You may have noticed that the two sets of measurements – height and armspan – have very similar values.

1 a) Was there anyone in the group who had their height equal to their armspan?

b) What line could you draw on the graph to show armspan = height?

This is the scatter graph with the armspan = height line drawn in.

c) What can we say about people whose points lie above this line? What about those below the line? In this particular example $y = x$ seemed to be an appropriate line to draw but in most cases it will not be.

d) Draw a scatter graph to show your results for height and armspan.

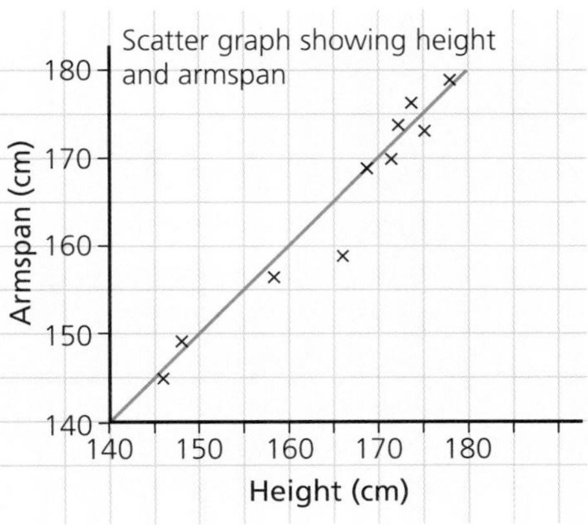

2 Katy had to draw a scatter diagram as part of her work in GCSE Geography. For each part of Sheffield, the city in which she lives, her class found out the unemployment rate and the percentage of households owning a car. Here is the graph she drew:

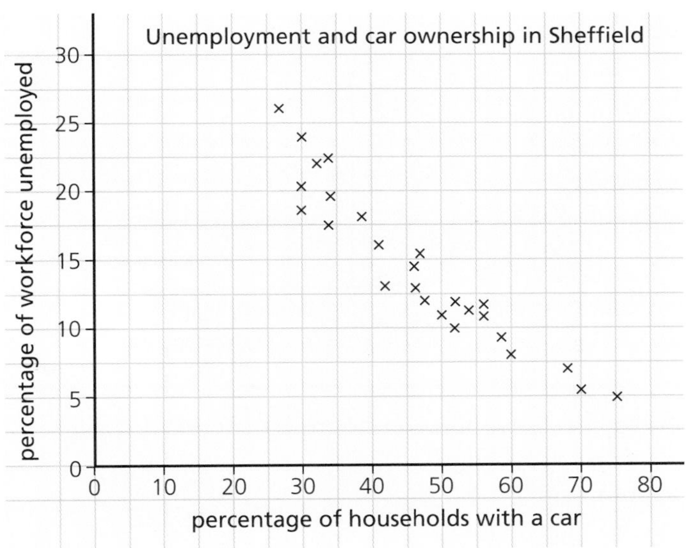

Do not join the points with a jagged line. A later unit will show how to draw a line of 'best fit'.

a) Does there appear to be a relationship between unemployment and car ownership?

b) In areas with high unemployment is car ownership high or low?

c) In areas with low unemployment is car ownership high or low?

d) Explain in your own words what the scatter graph shows.

e) Give an estimate of what percentage of households you would expect to own a car in areas where unemployment is 10%.

14.6 Different kinds of relationships

Here are three examples of scatter graphs.

Positive correlation: where two values increase together, there is a positive relationship between them. The closer the points are to a straight line, the stronger the relationship is. In this example there is a strong relationship often referred to as a high positive correlation.

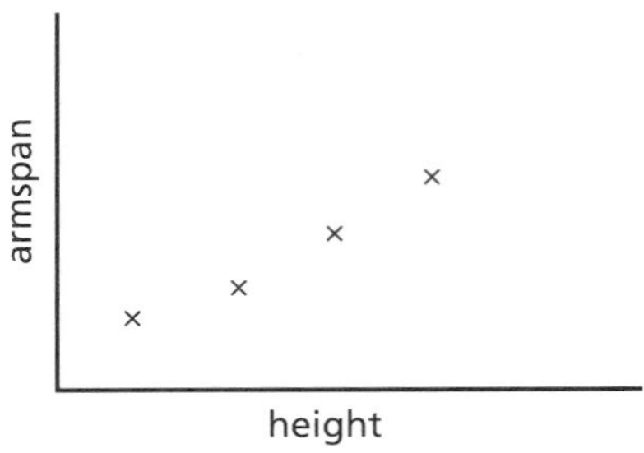

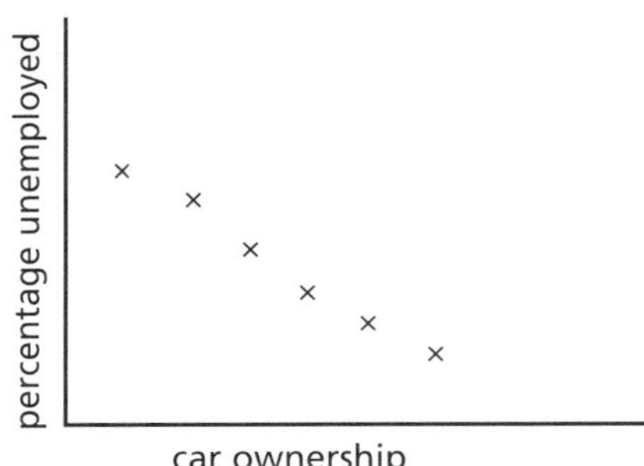

Negative correlation: where one value increases while the other decreases, the relationship is negative. In this example the relationship is a strong one, and we call it a high negative correlation.

Zero correlation: if the points on a scatter graph are widely scattered there is no relationship between the two sets of measurements (or possibly a very weak relationship).

The correlation here is either very low or zero.

1 For each pair of measurements listed here, say whether there would be a positive, a negative or a zero relationship:

a) age of child and height in cm
b) age of adult and height in cm
c) distance run and time taken
d) number of people immunised and number of people catching that disease
e) height from which you drop a tennis ball and the height it bounces
f) age of child and amount of pocket money
g) temperature and sales of ice cream
h) time spent watching TV and time spent doing homework
i) age of child and distance travelled to school
j) the numbers obtained on a black dice and a red dice when they are tossed together.

2 Nicky decided to investigate whether there is any relationship between leg length and running speed. He asked the boys in his maths group to help in his investigation. Each boy had to run round a course marked with cones on the school field. Nicky used a stop watch to measure the time each took to run round the course and also found their inside leg measurements in centimetres.

Here are his results:

Name	Running time	Inside leg
Joe	30.67 s	90 cm
Ramesh	40.25 s	70 cm
Nirmal	31.55 s	85 cm
James	35.45 s	82 cm
Ben	32.68 s	85 cm
Andy	36.75 s	80 cm
Tom	34.42 s	81 cm
Richard	35.41 s	81 cm
Ruben	38.95 s	80 cm
William	39.68 s	80 cm

a) Draw a scatter graph for these results. Show inside leg length on the horizontal axis and running time on the vertical axis.

b) Is there a relationship between leg length and running time?

c) Is this relationship positive or negative?

d) Did the boys with longer legs run faster or slower than the others?

3 Joe is a keen swimmer. He believes that larger people have larger lungs and will be able to hold their breath for longer (enabling them to swim under water longer). He asked some of his friends to time how long they could hold their breath and compared this to their chest measurements.

Chest measurement in inches	Time for holding breath in seconds
38	31
36	40
37	42
37	42
40	40
40	49
36	52
36	57
40	58
38	60
36	70
38	67

a) Plot these points on a scatter diagram. Show chest measurement on the horizontal axis, and time for holding breath on the vertical axis.

b) Is there a relationship between chest measurement and the length of time these students can hold their breath?

c) Can you predict how long someone with a chest measurement of 39 inches can hold their breath?

15 RATIO, PERCENTAGE, PROPORTION

15.1 Division in a given ratio

Example

Sophie and Helen are on a job-share scheme in which Sophie works 25 hours each week and Helen works 15 hours. At the end of the year they are given a bonus payment of £4328 and they agree to share the money according to the number of hours worked.

How much should they each receive?

Answer

The money is to be shared in the ratio 25 : 15 = 5 : 3.

Alternatively, for every £8 shared out, Sophie receives £5 and so, altogether, Sophie must receive $\frac{5}{8}$ of £4328.

$\frac{5}{8}$ means 5 parts out of 8.

In the same way, Helen's share is $\frac{3}{8}$ of £4328.

£4328 ÷ 8 = £541 (i.e. $\frac{1}{8}$ of £4328 = £541)

Therefore Sophie receives 5 × £541 = £2705
and Helen receives 3 × £541 = £1623.
Check: 2705 + 1623 = 4328

---

1 Ian and Luke share a cash prize of £210 in the ratio 3 : 4.
 a) What fraction of the prize do they each receive?
 b) Calculate the value of each person's share and check that the total is £210.

2 In normal winter conditions, it is recommended that anti-freeze is mixed with the water in a car's cooling system in the ratio 1 : 3.
How much anti-freeze is needed for a system which has a total capacity of 8 litres?

3 A particular shade of pink paint is made by mixing white and red paint in the ratio 5 : 1. How much of each colour is needed in order to make the following amounts?

a) 6 litres b) 3 litres c) 12 gallons ✓
d) 24 tins e) 72 litres f) 7.2 litres

4 A fizzy orange drink is made using lemonade and fresh orange juice in the ratio 4 : 1. What fraction of the fizzy orange is lemonade?
How much fresh orange is needed to make these amounts of fizzy orange?

a) 10 glasses b) 15 litres c) 1.5 litres

The idea of a ratio is easily extended to compare several amounts.

Example

A builder makes concrete for a driveway by mixing cement, sand and gravel in the ratio 1 : 2 : 3.

a) What fraction of the mixture is cement?
b) How much of each component does the builder need to make 3 tonnes of concrete?

Answer

a) $\frac{1}{6}$ (one part in six of the mixture is cement)

b) $\frac{1}{6}$ of 3 = $\frac{1}{6} \times 3 = \frac{1}{2}$ = 0.5 (this is the same as 3 ÷ 6)

Therefore 0.5 tonne of cement is needed.
2 × 0.5 tonnes = 1 tonne of sand is needed
3 × 0.5 tonnes = 1.5 tonnes of gravel is needed

Check: 0.5 + 1 + 1.5 = 3

---

5 A school enters its students for GCSE mathematics at Foundation, Intermediate and Higher tiers in the ratio 1 : 4 : 2. If 154 students take the examinations, how many are in each tier? ✓

6 The angles of a triangle are in the ratio 2 : 2 : 5. What are its angles? What is the special name given to this kind of triangle?

7 A sum of money £x is to be shared between three people A, B and C in the ratio 3 : 4 : 5.

a) What fraction of the amount does A receive?
b) Find the value of x if A receives £900.
c) How much do B and C receive?

8 Find the value of x given that when £x is shared in the ratio 2 : 3 : 4 : 5 the smallest share is £1428.57.

15.2 Ratio and percentage

Example

The mathematics department in a school spends money on books and equipment in the ratio 4 : 1. Express the amount spent on books as a percentage of the total.

Answer

Step 1 Express the given amount as a *fraction* of the total.

Amount spent on books is $\frac{4}{5}$ of total.

Step 2 Convert the fraction to a percentage by multiplying by 100.

$\frac{4}{5} \times 100 = 80\%$

80% of the money is spent on books.

Note: if the ratio given in the example was, say, 11 : 3 then the calculation would become $\frac{11}{14} \times 100$.

This may be worked out as 11 [÷] 14 [×] 100, using a calculator, giving the amount spent on books as 78.6% to one decimal place.

---

1 Harry and Sally split the bill for a meal in the ratio 3 : 2. What percentage of the bill does Harry pay?

2 At the local disco, the ratio of girls to boys is 5 : 4. Calculate the percentage of girls at the disco to one decimal place.

3 If the time I spend at work, rest, play and sleep is in the ratio 8 : 3 : 2 : 7, what percentage of my time is spent:
a) at work? b) at play?

4 An aluminium alloy is made of aluminium, copper and silicon in the ratio 16 : 2 : 1. Calculate the percentage of copper in the alloy to 3 significant figures.

5 Air is largely made up of nitrogen and oxygen together with relatively small amounts of other gases such as argon. The ratio of nitrogen, oxygen and argon in air is approximately 87 : 23 : 1.

Express the amount of each gas in air as a percentage to 1 decimal place.
Check your answers by adding the percentages.

15.3 Percentage change

The two-step process given in the last section is easily adapted so that an amount (A) can be expressed as a percentage of an amount (B) using: $\frac{A}{B} \times 100\%$.

In some situations, the choice of values for A and B may be clear.

Example

Express 23 as a percentage of 35.

Answer

The required percentage is given by $\frac{23}{35} \times 100\% = 65.7\%$ (to 1 D.P.)

(Using a calculator this is worked out as 23 [÷] 35 [×] 100.)

Example

I score 48 marks out of a possible 62 in a test. What is my score as a percentage?

Answer

My percentage is given by $\frac{48}{62} \times 100\% = 77\%$ (to the nearest 1%).

A very useful result concerns the idea of percentage change. In general, this is given by:

$$\textbf{percentage change} = \frac{\textbf{change in value}}{\textbf{original value}} \times 100\%$$

It is often possible to adapt this result to suit a particular situation. For example:

$$\text{percentage gain in height} = \frac{\text{gain in height}}{\text{original height}} \times 100\%$$

$$\text{percentage profit} = \frac{\text{profit}}{\text{cost price}} \times 100\%$$

In this case, 'profit' may be thought of as the change in value and 'cost price' as the original value.

---

1 Find expressions for each of these:

a) percentage loss ✓

b) percentage wage increase

c) percentage height gained

d) percentage depreciation

e) percentage weight loss

f) percentage extra contents

g) percentage service charge

h) percentage discount

2 Select one of the expressions given in question 1 and describe a situation in which it might be applied.

3 What information would be needed to calculate the percentage of pupils who achieved grades A* to C in mathematics at your school last year?

4 Express the first amount as a percentage of the second in each of the following:

a) 3 litres, 5 litres b) 2 kg, 20 kg c) 9 m, 50 m
d) 30 p, 120 p e) 40 p, £5 f) 75 p, £1.50
g) 5 cm, 2 m h) 60 cm, 3 m i) 120 cm, 6 m
j) 9 mm, 25 cm k) 0.3 mm, 4 cm l) 15 mm, 12 cm
m) 50 m, 1 km n) 24 m, 3 km o) 780 m, 0.78 km

5 When Paula last measured her height she was 1.43 m tall. She is now 1.48 m tall. What is her percentage gain in height?

6 a) Consider the statement:
'New cars tend to depreciate most rapidly during their first few years.'
Do you agree? Give reasons for your answer.
b) In comparing the depreciation of different makes of car, why might it be more sensible to use percentages rather than simply the loss in value?
c) A car costing £10 950 when new is valued at £8600 one year later. Calculate the percentage depreciation over the year to one decimal place.
d) If the car depreciates a further 15% in the second year, what is the value of the car, to the nearest £10, when it is two years old?

7 The table below shows the numbers of male and female students starting sixth form courses, at one school, over a three-year period.

Year	Males	Females	Total
1994	28	19	
1995	34	25	
1996	36	31	

a) Copy and complete the table.
b) What percentage of the students starting in 1994 were male?
c) What percentage of the students starting in 1995 were female?
d) Express the increase in the number of males from 1994 to 1996 as a percentage of the 1994 figure.
e) Repeat part **d)** for the females.
f) What do your answers to parts **d)** and **e)** show?

8 The manager of a local garage offers a cash bonus to the sales team if they increase the number of car sales by 8% over the year.
Last year the number of cars sold was 763 and the number sold this year is 827. Does the sales team qualify for its bonus? Explain your reasoning.

15.4 More than 100%!

In many situations it is *not* sensible to consider percentages greater than 100%, such as examination scores or the depreciation in the value of a car. However, in any situation where it is meaningful to have more than the whole amount, the percentage may be greater than 100%.

Example

At a fund-raising event a car is crammed with balloons, of various shapes and sizes, and the object is to guess the number of balloons correctly in order to win a prize.

The most extreme estimates made during the course of the day were 55 and 400. Calculate the percentage error in each case given that the actual number of balloons used was 187.

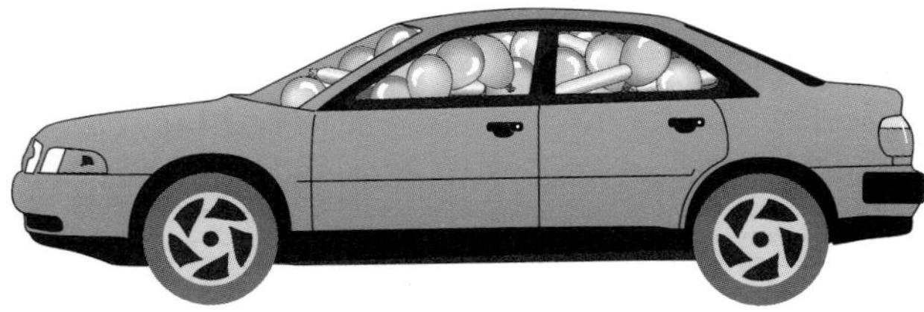

Answer

The percentage error is given by $\frac{\text{error}}{\text{true value}} \times 100\%$

For the lowest estimate, percentage error $= \frac{187 - 55}{187} \times 100\% = 70.6\%$

For the highest estimate, percentage error $= \frac{400 - 187}{187} \times 100\% = 113.9\%$

(*Note*: in the second case the error is 213 which, itself, is greater than the true value and so the percentage error is greater than 100%.)

---

1 A dealer buys a number of shares for a total cost of £750. Calculate the dealer's percentage profit if the shares are later sold for:
a) £900 b) £1500 c) £2000 d) £2500

2 Baby Fred weighed 4.2 kg when he was born. By the time of his first birthday he weighed 15.3 kg. Find his percentage weight gain over the year.

3 When Paul and Lisa first bought their house in 1969 it was worth £3500. By the end of the property boom in 1989 it was valued at £48 000. Calculate the percentage increase in the value of the house.

4 For each of the following, express the first amount as a percentage of the second:
a) 60, 50 **b)** 60, 40 **c)** 60, 30
d) 4.3, 2.5 **e)** 0.27, 0.25 **f)** 0.76, 0.19
g) 2.4 m, 1.6 m **h)** 0.8 m, 64 cm **i)** 45 cm, 0.18 m

5 Express A as a percentage of B in each of these situations:
a) A is the same size as B **b)** A is twice as big as B
c) A is one and a half times B **d)** B is one quarter of A
e) If B is increased by 20% then the result is the same as A
f) 37% more than B is the same as A **g)** A is 6% more than B

6 A garage bill is split between parts and labour in the ratio 2 : 5.
a) Express the cost of parts as a percentage of the labour charge.
b) Give the labour charge as a percentage of the total bill.
c) What is the total bill as a percentage of the charge for parts?

15.5 Proportion

The values in the table show how the weight W(g), of a length of wire varies in relation to its length l(cm).

l	5	10	15	30	
W	11	22	33		99

W and l are regarded as **variables**, which means that they can take different values, e.g. when l takes the value 5, W is 11 and when l is 15, W is 33.

However, the fractions $\frac{5}{11}$, $\frac{10}{22}$ and $\frac{15}{33}$ are equivalent and, in general, the ratio of l to W is constant, i.e. it has a fixed value. Whenever two variables remain in constant ratio to each other they are said to be **proportional** or to vary in **direct proportion**.

---

1 Copy and complete: a) $\frac{5}{11} = \frac{30}{?}$ b) $\frac{10}{22} = \frac{30}{?}$ c) $\frac{15}{33} = \frac{?}{99}$

2 Using the idea of equivalent fractions state the missing values of l and W in the table.

3 Find the value of: a) W when l is 90 b) l when W is 88

Example

Find the missing values in these tables given that q is proportional to p in each case.

a)

p	7.3	14.6
q	6	

b)

p	11	12.3
q	55	

Answer

a) $\frac{7.3}{6} = \frac{14.6}{?}$ The missing value is 12.

b) $\frac{11}{55} = \frac{12.3}{?}$ The missing value is 61.5.

(*Note*: when working with equivalent fractions, sometimes it is easier to compare the values horizontally and sometimes it is easier to compare them vertically.)

---

4 Find the missing values in these tables by the simplest method given that, in each case, the variables are proportional:

a)

p	4.1	16.4
q	5	

b)

m	3.2	5.9
l	9.6	

c)

t		12.4
d	2.7	3.1

d)

h	10.3	
v	6.7	67

5 Find the missing values in each of these tables given that y is proportional to x in each case.

a)

x	3	9	15	30	
y	8		40		88

b)

x	5	10		30	
y		16	24		96

c)

x	4		20	40	
y		1.9		7.6	15.2

d)

x	7	11	15		
y	28			80	100

e)

x	3	8	11		
y		40		70	85

f)

x	0.21	0.73	0.87		
y			8.7	9.6	17

g)

x	23				72
y		0.38	0.49	0.6	0.72

6 The cost of using an electrical appliance is proportional to the length of time it is in use. Given that the cost for 18 hours is £1.50, use the table below to find:

a) the cost for 6 hours

b) the time used if the cost = £7.50

Time (h)	18	6	
Cost (£)	1.5		7.5

In some situations, we need to *recognise* that the variables referred to in a problem will be proportional to each other.

7 Given that 50 cm^3 of gold weighs 950 g, find the weight of 200 cm^3 of gold. A gold ring weighs 9.5 g, what volume of gold does it contain?

8 A car travelling at a steady speed on a motorway covers a distance of 7 miles in 6 minutes.

a) How long will it take to travel a further 14 miles?

b) How far will it travel in 15 minutes?

9 With the tap turned on full it takes 30 seconds to fill a bucket.

a) How long will it take to fill 8 buckets?

b) How many buckets may be filled in 7 minutes?

Depending on the numbers involved, it may be convenient to change one of the variables to unity (one) first. This approach to proportion problems is known as the **unitary method**.

Example

A rug costing £96 covers an area of 3 m^2.
How much should
be charged for a rug of similar quality that
covers 17 m^2?

(continued)

Answer

$1\,m^2$ costs £96 ÷ 3 = £32

Therefore $17\,m^2$ costs £32 × 17 = £544

In this case it is helpful to consider the cost of a unit area first.

(*Note*: an estimate of the cost could be made by considering, for example, the cost of $18\,m^2$ at £100 (≈ 96) for $3\,m^2$. This gives an over-estimate of 6 × £100 = £600, which is in line with the answer obtained.)

---

10 A recipe for making 12 scones requires 240 g of self-raising flour.
a) How much self-raising flour is needed for each scone?
b) If 10 scones are to be made, how much self-raising flour is needed?

11 Use the unitary method to work out how much milk is needed to make 25 buns from a recipe that requires 600 ml of milk for 20 buns.

12 Ken bought 16 m of wire for £7.20. He later realised that he needed an extra 3 m to complete his task. How much should he expect to pay for the extra wire?

13 While on holiday in France, Simon exchanges a £50 travellers cheque for 375 francs. How many francs would be obtained for the following amounts at the same rate?
a) £37 b) £93 c) £216.80

When dealing with money, the value of a single unit of one currency in terms of another is known as the **exchange rate**.

Example

a) Find the value of £75 in Japanese yen given that the exchange rate is £1 = 161.68 yen.
b) Convert 4578 yen back to sterling.

Answer

a) £1 = 161.68 yen
so £75 = 161.68 × 75 yen = 12 126 yen

The exchange rate provides us with a scale factor for converting from £ to yen.

b) £ $\underset{\xleftarrow{\div 161.68}}{\xrightarrow{\times 161.68}}$ yen

4578 ÷ 161.68 = 28.315 ...
so 4578 yen = £28.32 to the nearest penny

The process may be reversed to convert from yen to £. Alternatively, 1 yen = £(1 ÷ 161.68), so 4578 yen = £(1 ÷ 161.68 × 4578) which gives the same result.

ICT Extra!

Currency conversions
Can you work out how to use a spreadsheet to convert pounds sterling into Japanese yen?
Find out the exchange rate for any currency you like and design an exchange rate spreadsheet.

14 Given that the exchange rate from sterling to Italian lira is £1 = 2440 L, find the number of lira equivalent to the following amounts:
a) £53 b) £78.50 c) £475 d) £1280

15 A camera in Germany costs 336 DM. What is the equivalent cost in sterling if the exchange rate is given by £1 = 2.2435 DM?

16 A tourist on holiday in the US sees a personal CD player for sale at $109 which is identical to one on sale at home for £89.99. Given that the exchange rate is £1 = $1.5547, which CD player is the better buy? Show your method clearly.

Decisions about which option represents best value, in the same currency, can also be made by considering unit amounts.

Example

The same make of breakfast cereal is sold in two different sized boxes.
Which box represents the better value?

Answer
One approach is to compare the cost per gram of cereal in each case.
For the small box, the cost in pence per gram is 189 ÷ 500 = 0.378
For the large box, the cost in pence per gram is 239 ÷ 750 = 0.318 (to 3 D.P.)
So cereal in the large box costs less per gram and so the large box gives the better value.
(*Note*: there are other ways of making the comparison. In this case, for example, you might prefer to compare the cost of 250 g of cereal in each box.)

---

17 In the example above, the number of grams of cereal per penny in the large box is given by 750 ÷ 239 = 3.14 (to 2 D.P.). Find the corresponding value for the small box and explain how this may be used to confirm the conclusion that the large box gives the best value.

18 A supermarket sells packets of crisps in packs of 12 and 20. If the pack of 20 costs £3.25 and the pack of 12 costs £1.89, which pack gives the best value? How much would need to be charged for the pack of 12 so that the unit cost is the same as for the pack of 20?

19 Which box gives the best value?

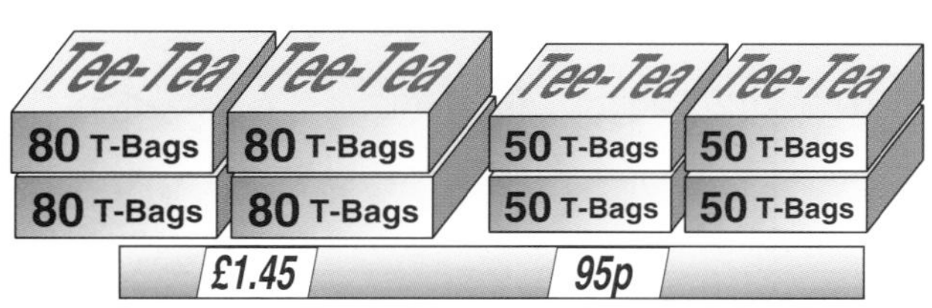

16 POLYGONS AND CIRCLES

16.1 Quadrilaterals

A quadrilateral is a figure with 4 sides.

1 Match up each quadrilateral with its name.

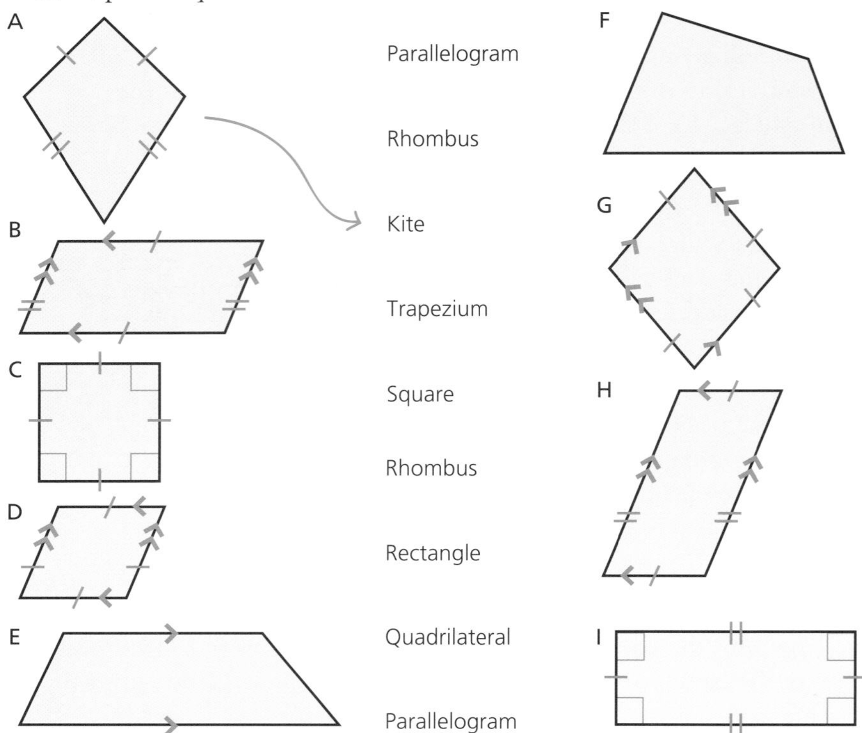

2 Which of these shapes has:

a) 4 axes of symmetry
b) 2 axes of symmetry
c) 1 axis of symmetry
d) 0 axes of symmetry?

3 Which properties belong to each quadrilateral? See if you can match them up. (The number in brackets after each quadrilateral is the number of properties you need to find; and properties can be used more than once.)

A all 4 sides equal
B opposite sides equal
C adjacent sides equal
D all angles right angles
E 2 pairs of opposite angles equal
F 2 pairs of opposite sides parallel
G one pair of opposite sides parallel
H one pair of opposite angles equal

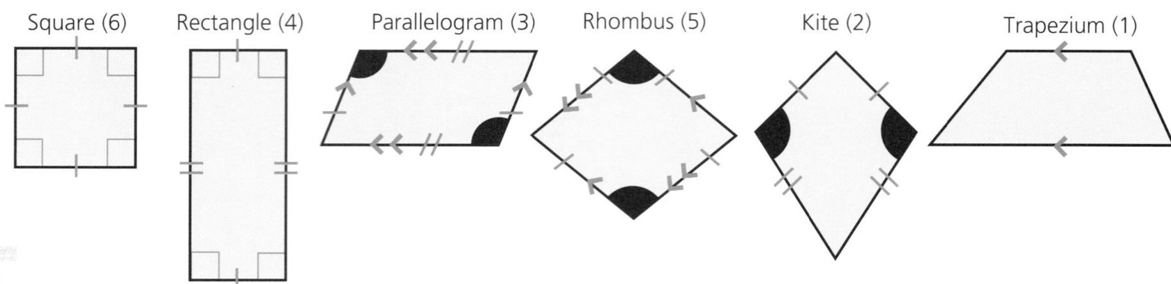

4 Use the flow diagrams to identify the mystery quadrilaterals.

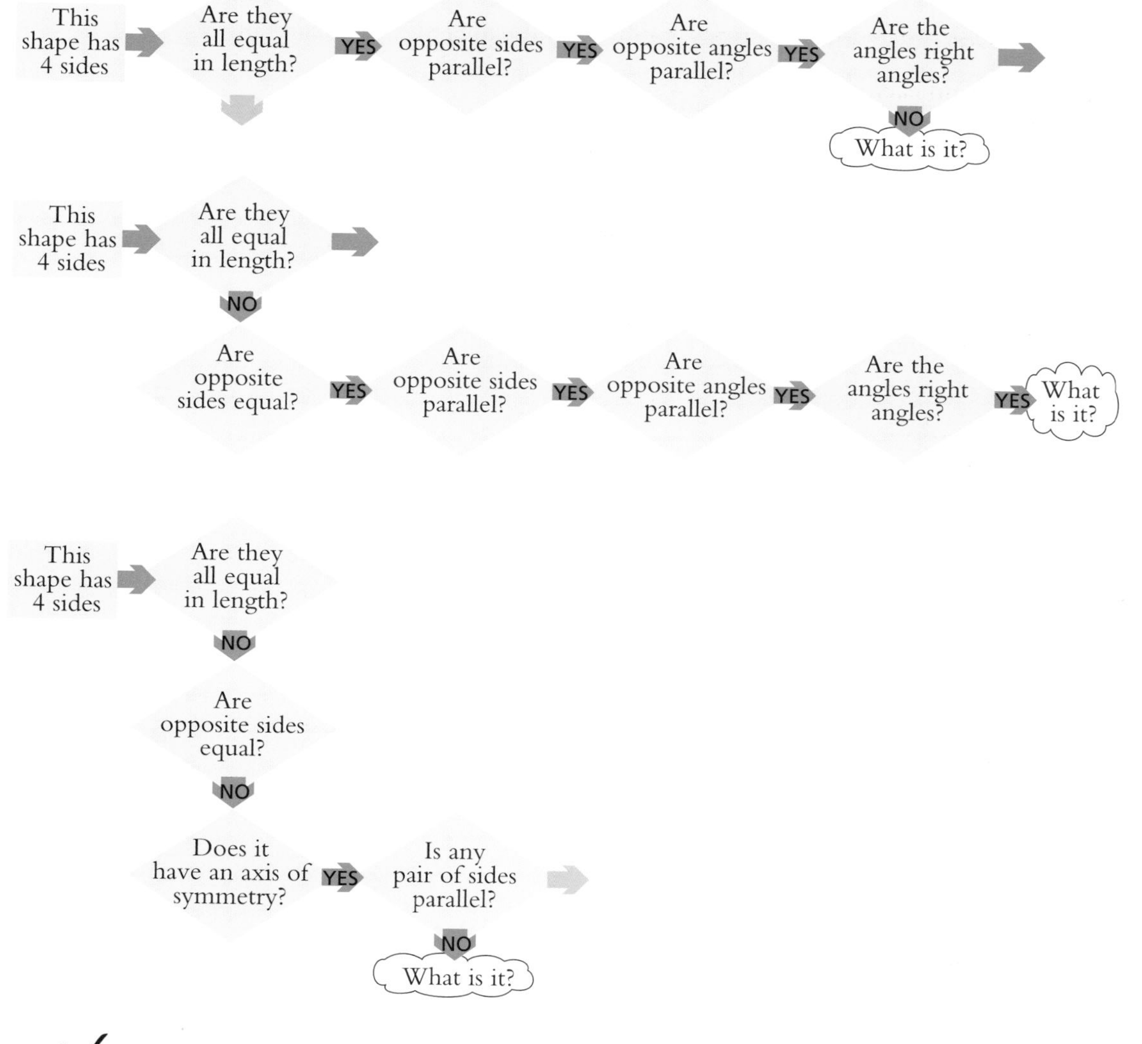

5 ✓ Name one pair of alternate angles in this diagram. Name a pair of corresponding angles. What does this show about angles in a parallelogram?

16.2 Areas of quadrilaterals

1 Use these diagrams to explain how to find the area of a parallelogram.
The area of a parallelogram = ?
Write a formula for area A in terms of b and h.

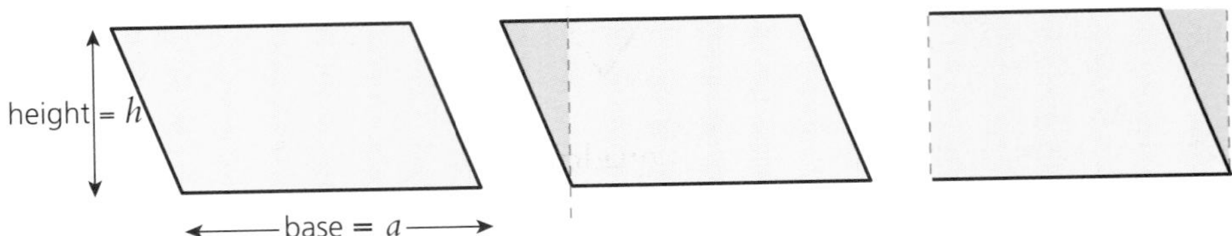

2 Use these diagrams to explain how to find the area of a kite.
The area of a kite = ?

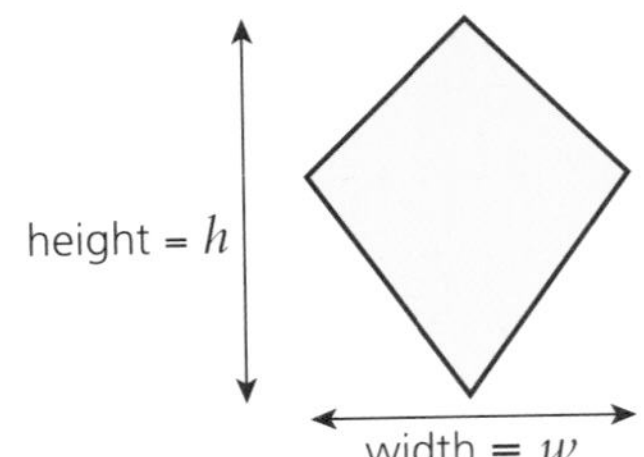

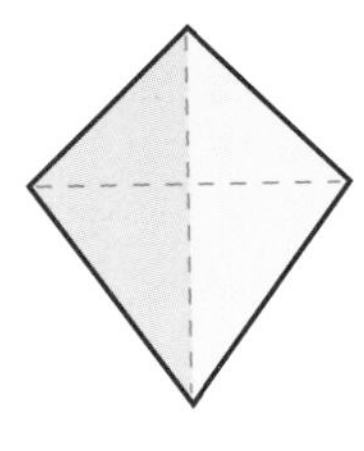

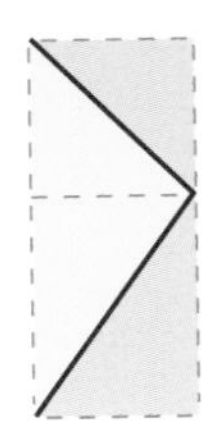

Write a formula for area A in terms of w and h.

3 **a)** Use this diagram to find the area of the trapezium.
Area of triangle A = ?
Area of triangle B = ?
Explain why the area of a trapezium

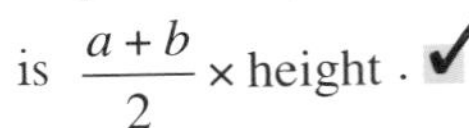

is $\frac{a+b}{2} \times$ height.

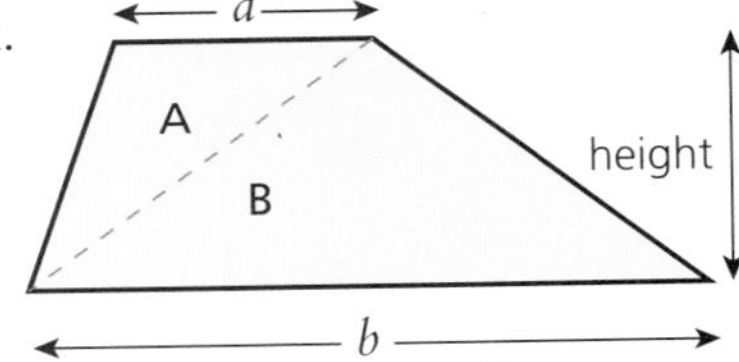

b) Here is another way of finding the same result. The diagram shows how an identical trapezium can be rotated through 180° and placed next to the first one.
Find the area of the parallelogram made by the two trapeziums, then find the area of one trapezium.

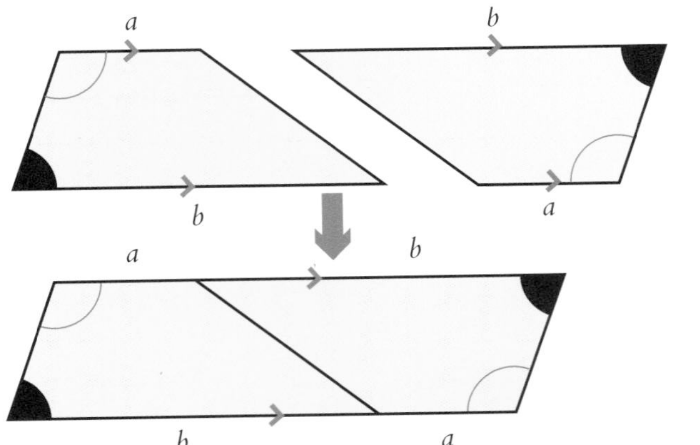

4 Find the area of each quadrilateral. ✓

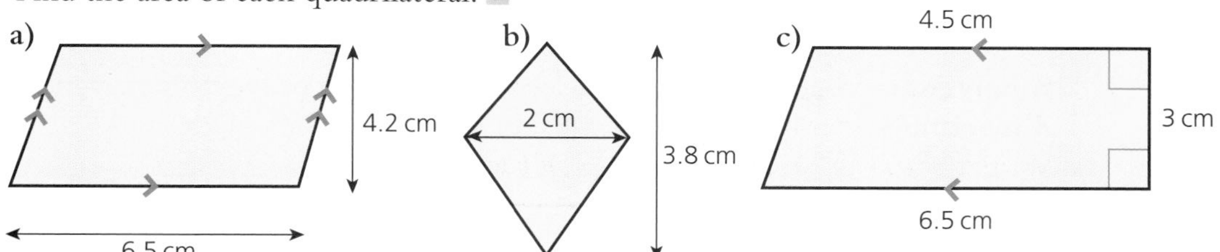

5 Find the area and perimeter of each quadrilateral.

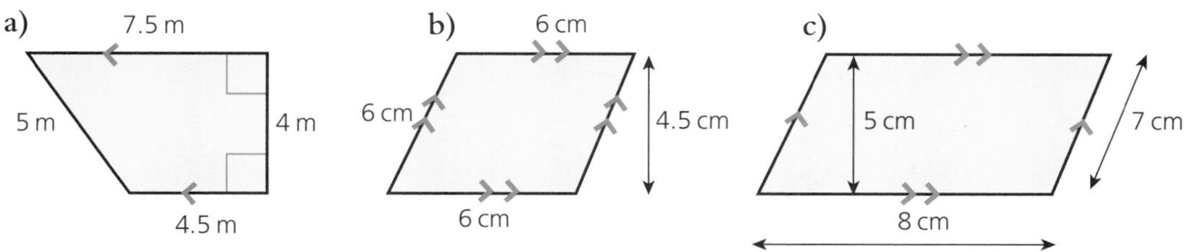

6 Make an accurate drawing of each quadrilateral so that you can find the measurements you need to calculate the area and perimeter. ✓

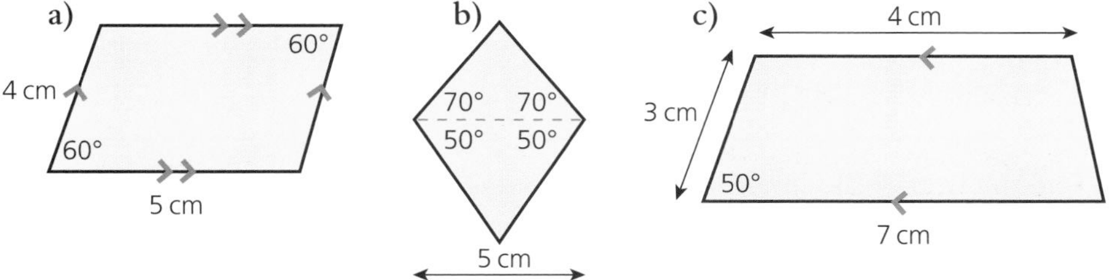

7 Right or wrong? Tick the box if the property is correct. Put a cross if it is wrong. You may need to make a careful drawing of each shape to help you.

Shape	Diagonals equal	Diagonals perpendicular	Diagonals bisect each other	Both diagonals bisect angles
Square				
Rectangle				
Rhombus				
Kite				
Parallelogram				

16.3 Polygons

A **polygon** is a figure with many angles and sides. It can be regular or irregular. A regular polygon has all its sides equal in length and all its angles equal.

1 Copy and complete the table.

Polygon	Number of sides
Quadrilateral	
Octagon	
Hexagon	
Heptagon	
Pentagon	
Triangle	
Decagon	
Nonagon	

You may need to know the sum of the interior angles of a polygon. The next question shows you how to find this.

2 To find the sum of the interior angles in a polygon, first divide the polygon into the *minimum* number of triangles. This is most easily done if you work from one vertex, like this:

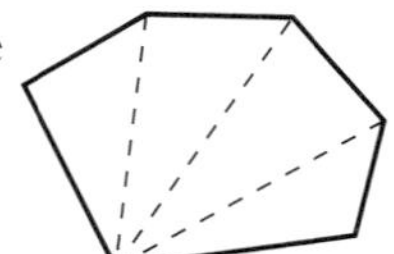

a) How many sides has this polygon?
b) Can you find a different way of splitting the hexagon? Can you make fewer triangles? (It is easy to make more triangles, but you will find that some of the vertices of the triangles are in the centre of the hexagon and not at the corners.)
c) What is the minimum number of triangles you can split it into?
d) What is the sum of the angles in one triangle?

i) 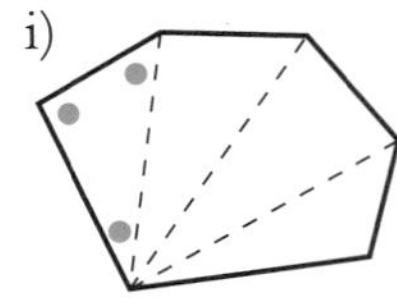 ii) 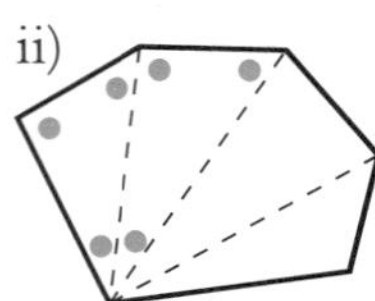 iii) 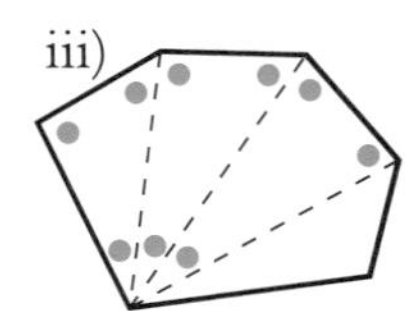 iv) 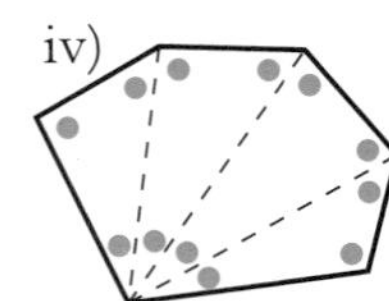

e) What is the sum of the angles in four triangles?
f) What is the sum of the angles in a hexagon? ✓
g) Is this true for any hexagon?
h) What is the size of each angle in a *regular* hexagon? ✓

i) Draw some diagrams of your own like these to help you fill in the table below:

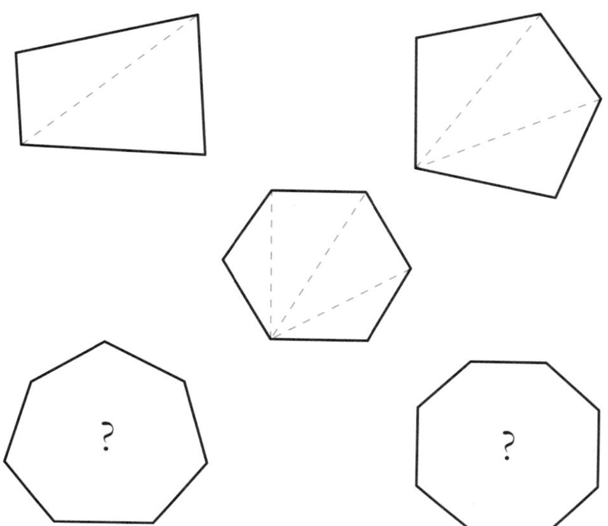

Polygon	Number of sides	Number of triangles	Total of interior angles
Quadrilateral			
Pentagon			
Hexagon			
Heptagon			
Octagon			

j) Can you see a rule linking the number of sides and the number of triangles? Copy and complete this sentence:
The number of triangles is always ... the number of sides. ✓

3 a) Into how many triangles can you divide a dodecagon (12-sided polygon)?
b) What is the total of the interior angles of a dodecagon?

4 Find the fifth angle of an irregular pentagon when each of the other angles is 120°.

5 If three angles of a quadrilateral are 40°, 100° and 150°, find the fourth angle.

6 If the angles of a hexagon are $x°$, $(x + 10)°$, $(x + 20)°$, $(x + 30)°$, $(x + 40)°$ and $(x + 50)°$, find x.

7 Follow these instructions to investigate the exterior angles of a polygon.

a) Mark a point on your page. Label it 'A'.
Draw a line 3 cm long going from A.
Turn clockwise through 45°.
Draw another line 3 cm long, then turn through another 45° clockwise.
Repeat until you return to A.

b) What shape have you drawn?

c) How many times did you have to turn through 45° (the exterior angle)?

These are exterior angles
45°
45°
A

d) What is the sum of the angles inside the shape (interior angles)?

e) What is the total for an interior plus an exterior angle?

f) How many lines of symmetry has this shape?

g) What is its order of rotational symmetry?

h) What is 8 × 45°? What does this tell you about the sum of the exterior angles in this case?

8 What shapes would you make if you followed the instructions for question 7 but turned through:

a) 60° b) 90° c) 120° d) 72°?

Make a drawing if you are not sure of the answer.

9 Fill in this table.

Regular polygon	Exterior angle	Interior angle
Equilateral triangle		
Square		
Pentagon		
Hexagon		
Octagon		
Nonagon (9 sides)		
Decagon (10 sides)		
Dodecagon (12 sides)		

10 The centre of this star is a regular pentagon. Calculate the sizes of the angles marked by letters.

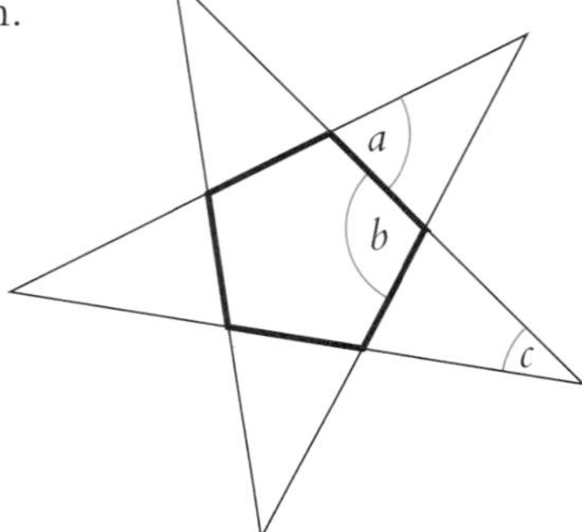

11 Calculate the missing angles for these irregular polygons.

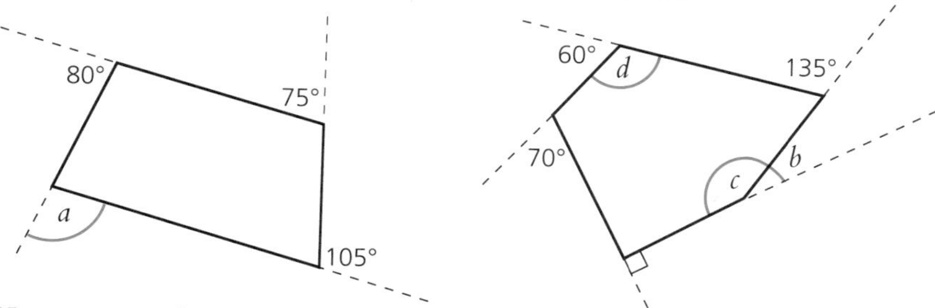

12 How many sides must this regular polygon have?

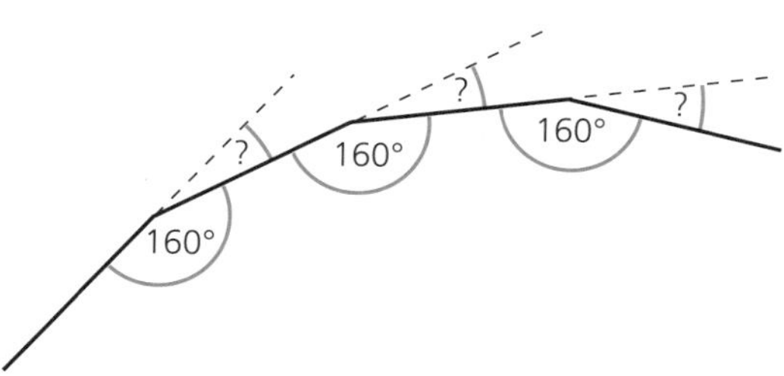

13 This flow diagram shows you how to find the number of sides of a regular polygon if you know the interior angle.

a) Explain how to calculate step 1 and step 2.

b) Explain how you would find the *total* of the interior angles.

You know the interior angle

Step 1 Find the exterior angle

Step 2 Find the number of sides

16.4 Circles

The **circumference** of a circle can be found by multiplying the diameter by π (called 'pi'). The value of π can be calculated to hundreds of decimal places, but as a rough approximation we can take it as just over 3.

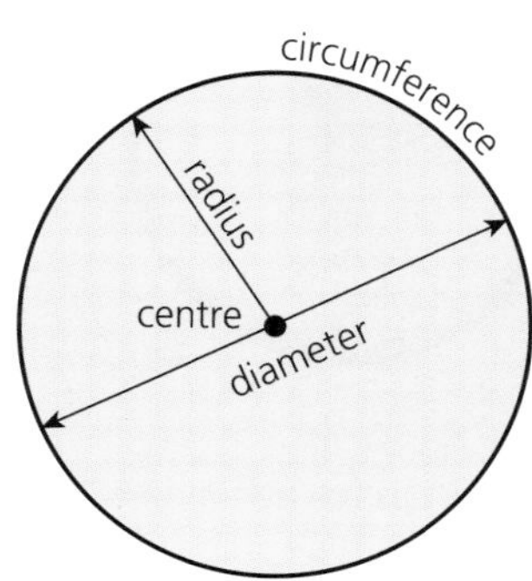

Circumference = diameter × π.

Try to work out the answers to questions 1 to 7 without using your calculator. Use $\pi \approx 3$ to work out approximate distances.

In this case circumference $\approx$ 3 × diameter.

1 Give a method for finding the approximate circumference if you know the radius. ✔

2 Find the circumference (approximately) for each of these circles taking π to be 3.

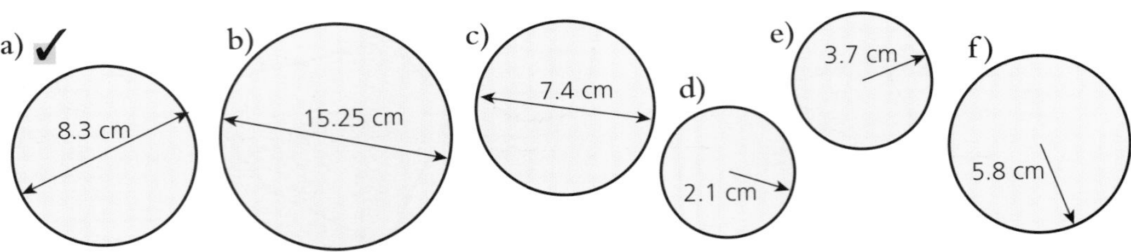

3 What size must the label be for this can of spaghetti?

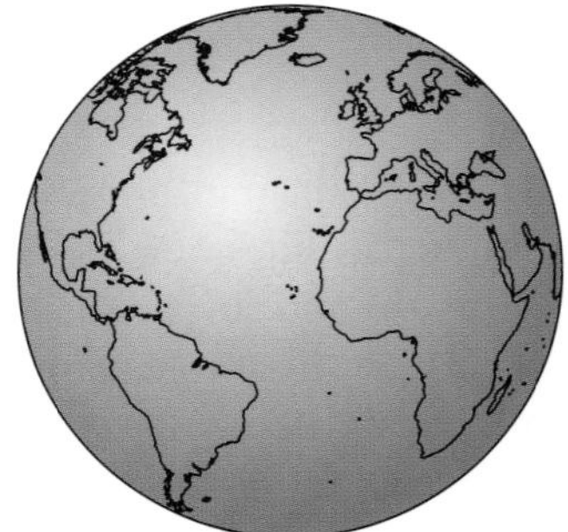

4 The circumference of the Earth is 40 106 km. What is the diameter? What is the radius?

5 The circumference of this bicycle wheel is 198 cm. What is the approximate length of a spoke?

6 These circles are made from fine wire. Which design uses the most wire?

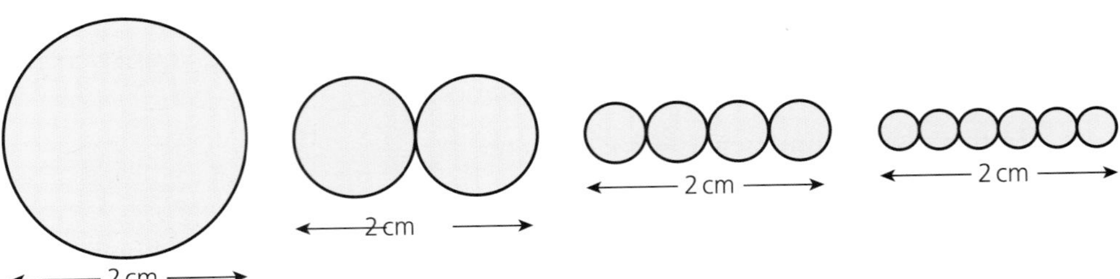

7 Which of these curves uses the most wire?

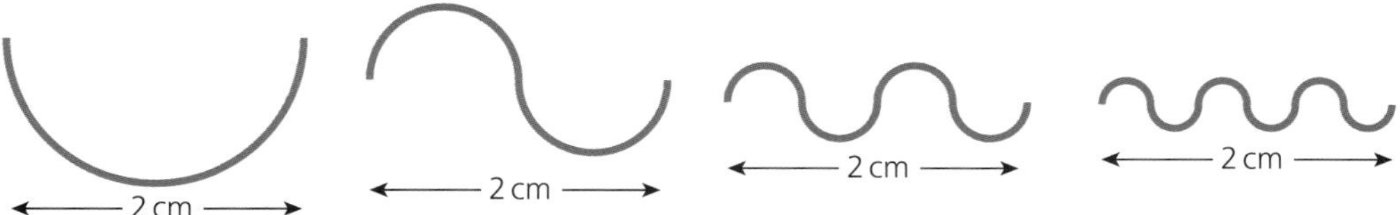

Multiplying the diameter by 3 gives an approximate answer for the circumference. A better answer is given by using a more accurate value for π, which to 7 decimal places is 3.141 592 7. (This is the value you obtain by pressing the π key on an 8-figure calculator.)

In question 3 the spaghetti tin has a diameter of 7 cm.
Circumference = π × 7 cm.
Using a calculator, circumference = 21.991 149 cm
Correct to one decimal place, the circumference is 22.0 cm.

Use the π value on your calculator to find more accurate answers for these problems. Give each answer correct to 1 decimal place.

8 Find the circumference of each of these circles:

a) ✓

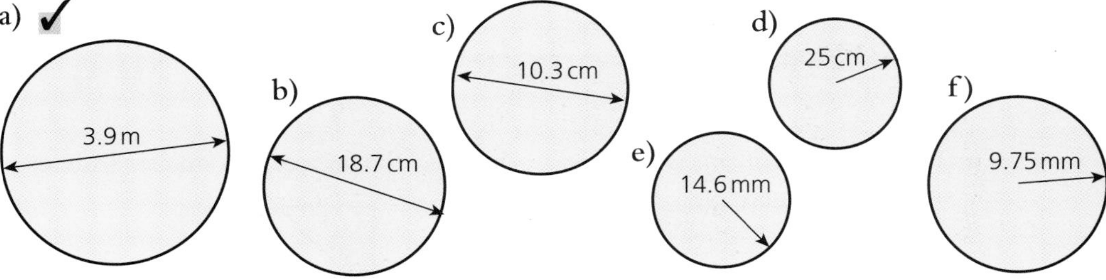

9 Find the perimeter of each of these shapes:

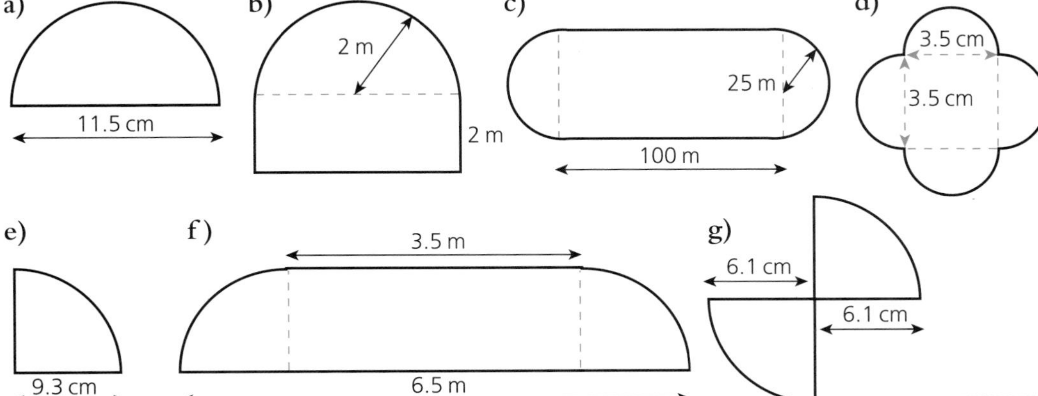

10 a) A car tyre has a radius of 28 cm.
What is the circumference of the wheel?

b) The car is driven on a journey of 4.4 kilometres.
(i) How many centimetres is this?
(ii) How many times did the wheel turn on that journey (to 3 S.F.)?

11 Some cotton thread is wound onto a reel with a radius of 35 mm.

a) What length of cotton fits round one turn of the reel?

b) How many turns of the reel are needed to wind 100 m of cotton onto the reel?

12 A running track has two semicircular ends of radius 63 metres and two straight lengths.
The perimeter of the track is 1000 metres. Find the length of each straight (correct to the nearest metre).

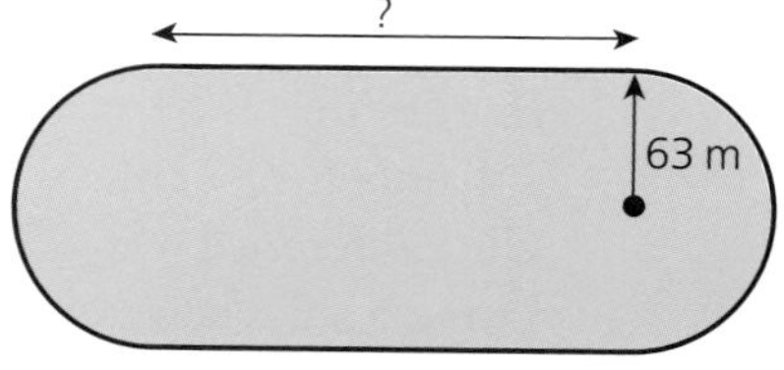

13 The circumference of a water pipe is 25.6 cm.
What is its diameter?

14 A circular table cloth has a circumference of 345.6 cm.

a) Is the cloth large enough to fit on a round table which is 50 cm in diameter?

b) If so, what length of the table cloth would hang down on each side?

16.5 Areas of circles, complex shapes

1 a) Find the area of this square:

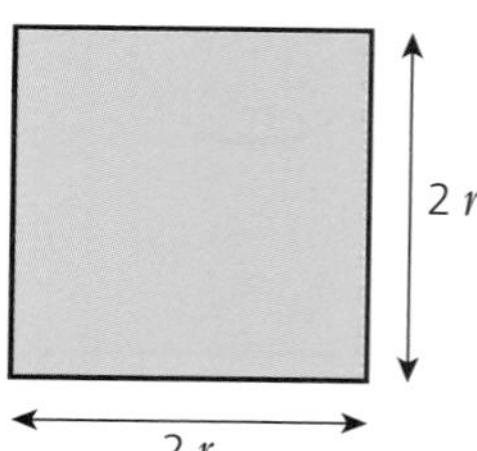

b) Find the area of the smaller square.

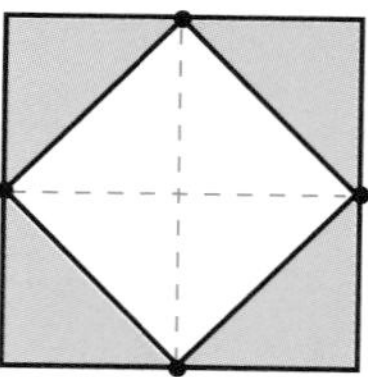

c) What does this tell you about the area of a circle?

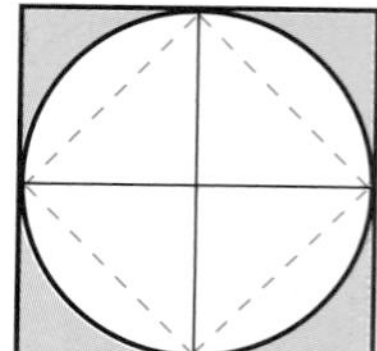

2 Draw a circle on a spare piece of paper. Cut it into sections and arrange these to form a 'wobbly' rectangle. like this:

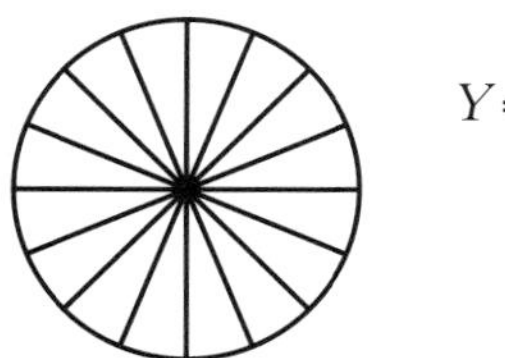

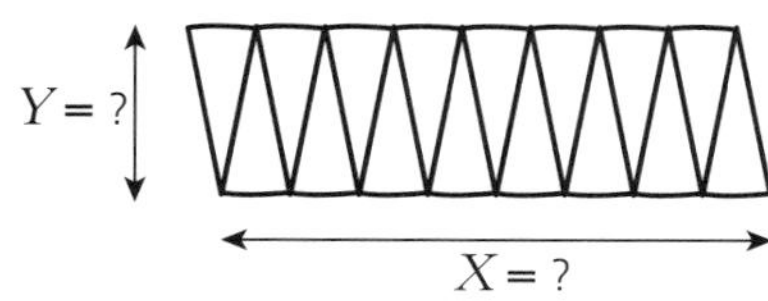

a) What is the distance marked X? b) What is the distance marked Y?

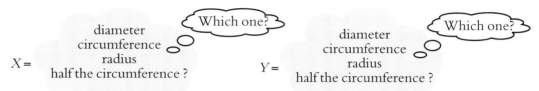

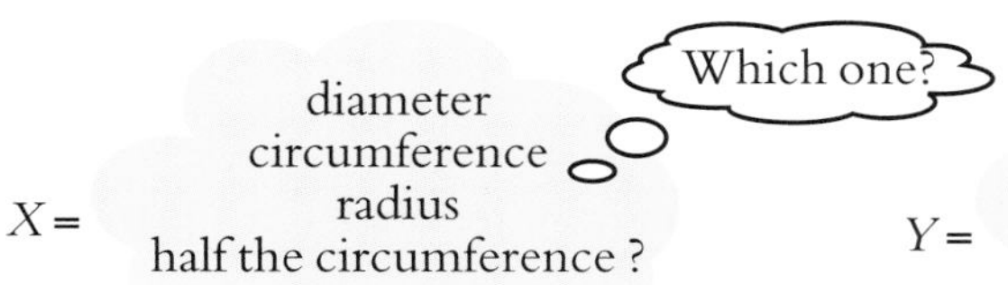

c) So what is the area of the circle?

d) Explain why the area of a circle can be found by:
$A = \pi r^2$

Example

a) A circle has radius of 6.5 cm. Find its area to 1 decimal place.

b) A circle has a diameter of 11.8 cm. Find its area to 1 decimal place.

Answer

a) Using the formula $A = \pi r^2$,
Area $= \pi \times 6.5 \times 6.5 = 132.732\,29$
$= 132.7\text{ cm}^2$ (to 1 D.P.)

b) First we need to find the radius:

$$\text{Radius} = \frac{\text{diameter}}{2} = \frac{11.8}{2} = 5.9$$

Using the formula $A = \pi r^2$,
Area $= \pi \times 5.9 \times 5.9 = 109.358\,84$
$= 109.4\text{ cm}^2$ (to 1 D.P.)

---

3 Find the areas of these circles. Give your answers correct to 1 decimal place.

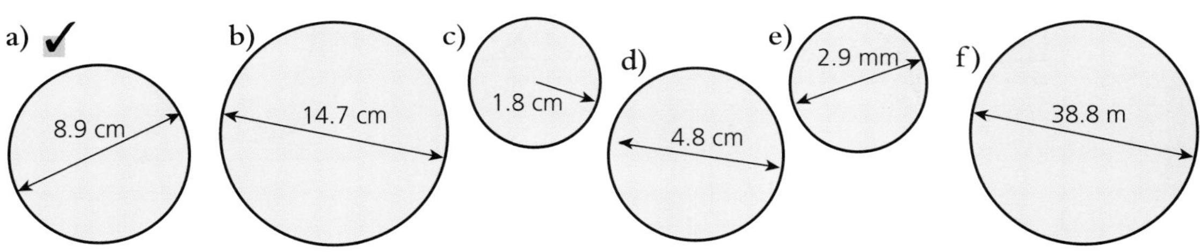

Example

Find the area of the shaded section.

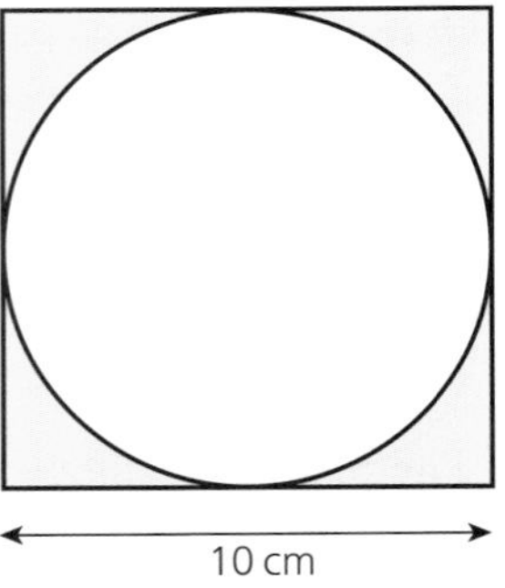

Answer

Use the π button on your calculator. Give your final answer correct to 1 decimal place.

Shaded area = area of square – area of circle

$= 10 \times 10 - \pi \times 5 \times 5$

$= 100 - 78.54 = 21.46$

$= 21.5 \text{ cm}^2$ (to 1 D.P.)

Use the π button on your calculator to find the areas in these problems. Give your final answers correct to 1 decimal place.

4 Find the areas of these shapes. They are all made from rectangles or squares and circles or semicircles. ✓

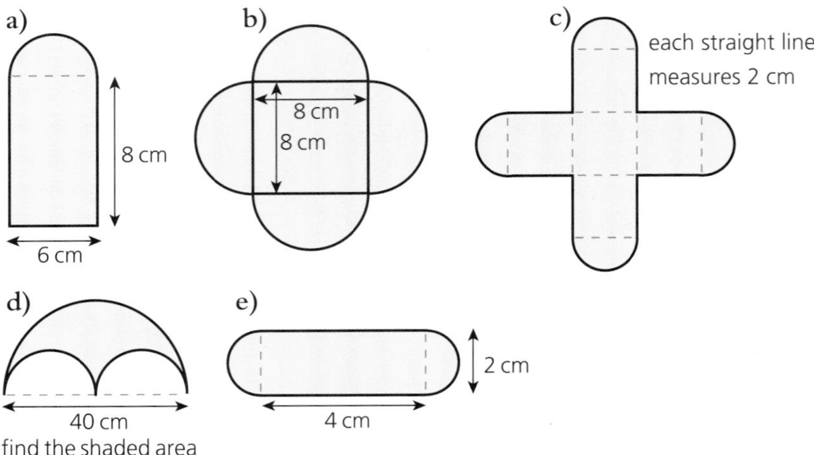

5 Our local baker makes sponge cakes in two sizes. One measures 7 inches in diameter, the other measures 10 inches. (They are both the same depth). He says he needs twice the amount of cake mixture for the larger cake compared to the smaller one. Is this right? Explain your answer.

6 Find the shaded area in each of these diagrams.

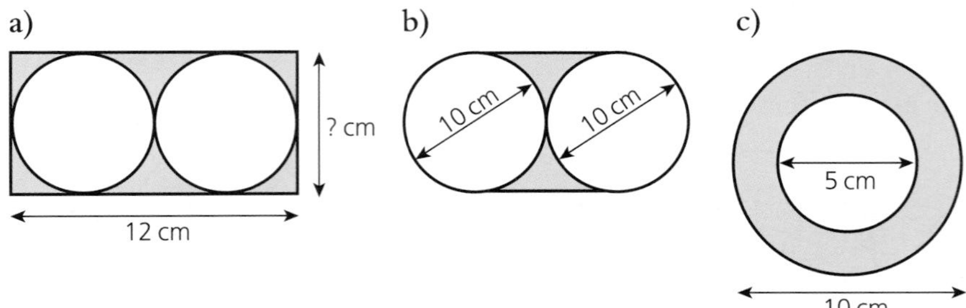

16.6 Drawing polygons using LOGO

If LOGO is available on your school's computers, you can draw regular polygons using a simple LOGO procedure.

```
POLY 5
REPEAT 5 [FD 50 RT 72]
```

The procedure above will draw a regular pentagon.

1 Can you guess what shape the next procedure will draw?

```
POLY 6
REPEAT 6 [FD 50 RT 60]
```

2 The procedure must tell the turtle:

a) the number of repeats

b) the length of a side

c) the exterior angle of the polygon, which is the amount the turtle must turn at each vertex (or corner).

Can you identify those three parts of the procedure?

3 Copy and complete a procedure for drawing:

a) an octagon

```
POLY 8
REPEAT ... [FD 50 RT ...]
```

b) a square

```
POLY ...
REPEAT ... [FD 50 RT 90]
```

c) an equilateral triangle.

```
POLY ...
REPEAT ... [FD ... RT ...]
```

Try these out for yourself.
Experiment with LOGO to see if you can draw other regular polygons.
Try changing the size of the polygons you have drawn.
Can you find a way to repeat your polygon to make a tessellation?

The commands listed here will perhaps be useful:

CLEAN	This clears the screen but does not change the position of the turtle.
LIFT	The turtle will not draw a line when it moves, following this command.
DROP	Puts the turtle down again, to draw.
PICTURE	Prints out the current graphics screen.
CS	Clears screen and puts turtle in the centre pointing upwards.

ICT Extra!

Follow the instructions given here to draw regular polygons. Can you work out how to change the number of sides in your polygon? Which polygons can be used to make a tessellation?

REVIEW 2

Unit 9 Signs, equations, sequences

1 Work out without using a calculator:

a) -4×5 b) 6×-3 c) -4×-10
d) 5×-8 e) -6×-11 f) -2×4.5
g) $-21 \div 3$ h) $-15 \div -5$ i) $12 \div -6$
j) $24 \div -8$ k) $-9 \div 2$ l) $32 \div -10$

2 Find the missing values:

a) $-4 \times \ldots = 20$ b) $\ldots \times 6 = -30$ c) $\ldots \times -12 = 60$
d) $18 \div \ldots = -2$ e) $\ldots \div -11 = 3$ f) $\ldots \div 7 = -70$

3 Work out:

a) $10 \times (-6 + 4)$ b) $-3 \times (2 - 7)$ c) $(-3 + 11) \times (-3 -2)$
d) $15 \div (-7 + 2)$ e) $(-9 -3) \div -6$ f) $(2 - 16) \div (-9 + 2)$

4 Given that $p = -6.5$ and $q = -4.25$, use a calculator to find the value of the following expressions:

a) $p + q$ b) pq c) pq^2
d) $p - 3q$ e) $p - (q - 7.8)$ f) $3.2(2q - p)$
g) $p - \frac{q}{5}$ h) $\frac{p - q}{5}$ i) $\frac{\sqrt{2p - 4q}}{p - 2q}$

5 Use flow diagrams to solve these equations:

a) $4x - 7 = 11$ b) $3(x + 11) = 60$ c) $7(x + 8) = 14$
d) $\frac{x}{3} - 12 = 4$ e) $\frac{2x}{3} = 20$ f) $\frac{3x - 5}{4} = 10$
g) $\sqrt{x} + 3 = 7$ h) $\sqrt{x - 5} = 5$ i) $\sqrt{2x + 1} = 11$
j) $(x - 4)^3 = 8$ k) $(3x + 2)^3 = -64$ l) $x^2 - 14 = 35$

6 Solve the following equations giving your answers to 3 S.F.:

a) $17x = 11$ b) $0.49x = 8.24$ c) $3.58(x - 2.7) = 20$
d) $\frac{x}{387} = 0.26$ e) $\frac{x - 5.62}{0.359} = 16$ f) $\sqrt{\frac{x}{17.8}} = 0.92$

7 List the first 5 terms of the sequence in which the nth term is given by:

a) $n + 1$ b) $3n - 1$ c) $10 - n$
d) n^2 e) n^3 f) $1 - n^2$

8 Find the 20th term of the sequence given by $u_n = \frac{n + 4}{3}$.

Unit 10 Probability (2)

9 For each part of this question, decide whether the correct answer is A, B, C or D:

a) The mean of 37, 34, 27, 19 and 13 is:

A 14 B 26 C 27 D 37

b) Ten numbers have a mean of 261. The sum of the ten numbers is:

A 26.1 B 61 C 261 D 2610

c) Find the median of the following numbers:

13, 14, 13, 17, 15, 12, 11, 14, 13, 15

A 14 B $13\frac{1}{2}$ C 13 D $12\frac{1}{2}$

d) The marks of ten students in a test were:

13 17 19 14 17 18 15 17 14 18

What is the modal score?

A 19 B 14 C 17 D 17.5

e) A car park contains 100 cars of which 34 are black and 28 are red. What is the probability that if a car is selected at random it is neither black nor red?

A $\frac{38}{50}$ B $\frac{19}{50}$ C $\frac{17}{25}$ D $\frac{17}{50}$

f) If two ordinary six-sided dice are thrown together, what is the probability of scoring a total of 5?

A $\frac{1}{9}$ B $\frac{5}{36}$ C $\frac{1}{6}$ D $\frac{1}{18}$

10 Apart from $\frac{2}{3}$, all the fractions used by the ancient Egyptians had a numerator of 1 with a denominator of any number. Find the probability that an Egyptian fraction between $\frac{1}{10}$ and $\frac{1}{20}$ inclusive chosen at random can be expressed as a terminating decimal. (Denominators 10, 11, 12, ... 19, 20 only)
(For example, $\frac{1}{4} = 0.25$ which is a terminating decimal, whereas $\frac{1}{9} = 0.\dot{1}$ which is a recurring decimal.)

11 A card is picked at random from a pack of 52 playing cards. Find the probability that it is:

a) the Queen of hearts
b) a King
c) a 'court' card (King, Queen or Jack)
d) a Jack or a ten.

12 There are 8 tomatoes in a paper bag. Only five are ripe. A tomato is taken from the bag. What is the probability that it is not ripe?

13 A letter is chosen from the word 'mathematics'. Find the probability that it is:

a) an 'h' b) an 'm' or a 't' c) a vowel d) a consonant.

14 Two cards are dealt from a well shuffled pack of playing cards. What is the probability that:

a) the first card is an ace
b) the second card is also an ace. (Remember that the first card has not been put back.)

Unit 11 Straight lines

15 Simplify these ratios as far as possible:

a) 8 : 12　b) 25 : 35　c) 100 : 10
d) £30 : £15　e) £3.50 : £14　f) £5 : 50p
g) 10 cm : 20 mm　h) 25 cm : 5 m　i) 4 kg : 250 g

16 Write these ratios in the form 1 : *n*:

a) 25 : 75　b) 10 : 1000　c) 30 : 150　d) 0.5 : 20
e) 2.5 : 10　f) 0.3 : 6　g) $\frac{1}{4}$: 11　h) $\frac{1}{3}$: 9
i) $\frac{2}{3}$: 10　j) 20 : 10　k) 50 : 30　l) 25 : 18

17 Find the gradients of these lines:

a)

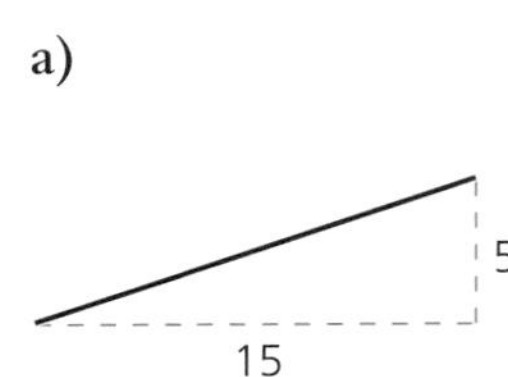

b)

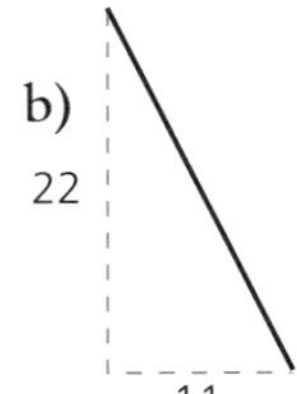

18 Find the gradients of the lines joining these pairs of points:

a) (3, 7) and (5, 19)　b) (–2, 3) and (3, 18)　c) (11, 8) and (7, 0)

19 a) Find the coordinates of each of the labelled points.

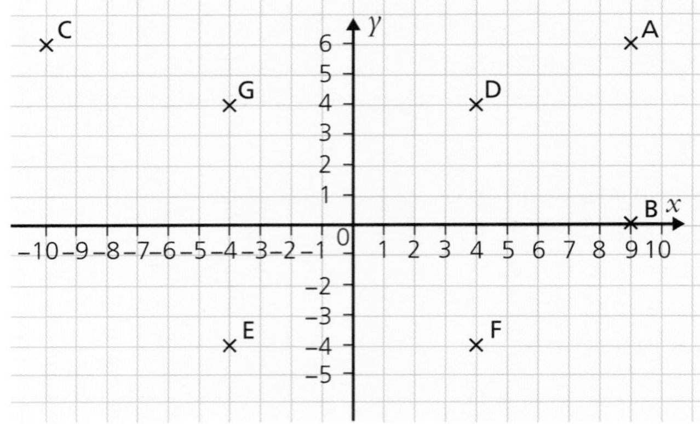

b) Give the equations of the lines through the following pairs of points:

(i) A and B　(ii) A and C
(iii) D and G　(iv) D and F
(v) E and F　(vi) D and E
(vii) F and G

Unit 12 Bearings and plans

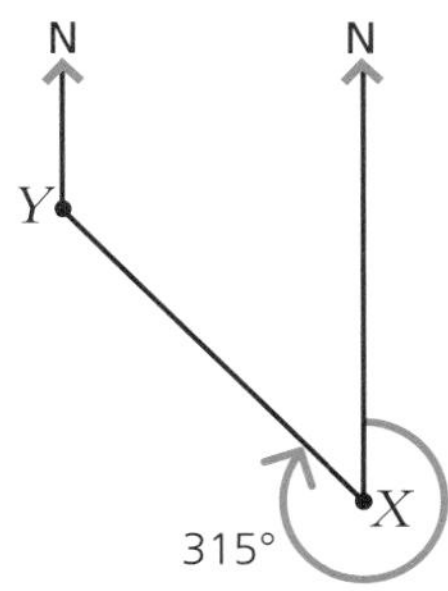

20 a) Without drawing this diagram to scale, calculate the bearing of X from Y.
A boat leaves a harbour on a course of 120° and sails 100 km in this direction until it reaches point B.

b) Use a scale of 1 cm to 10 km to make a scale drawing of this journey.

c) How far is B east of the harbour?

d) How far is B south of the harbour?

e) What is the bearing of the harbour from B?

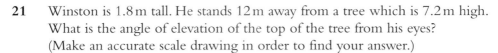

21 Winston is 1.8 m tall. He stands 12 m away from a tree which is 7.2 m high. What is the angle of elevation of the top of the tree from his eyes? (Make an accurate scale drawing in order to find your answer.)

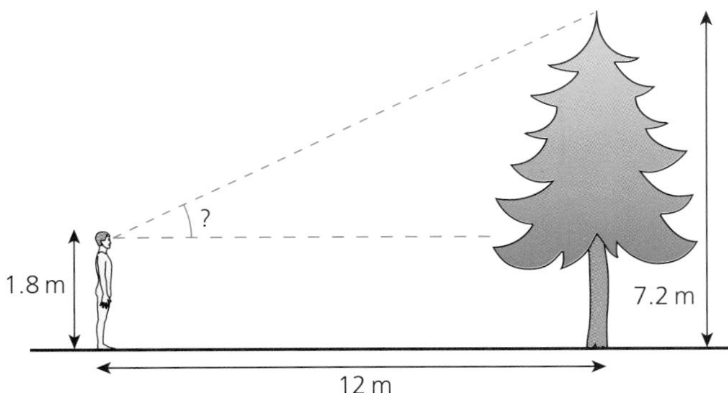

22 A ship is on a bearing of 093° from a lighthouse. What is the bearing of the lighthouse from the ship?

23 Two boats (A and B) are both 10 km from the harbour H. B is on a bearing of 235° from A. Calculate or find by scale drawing:

a) the bearing of H from A

b) the bearing of B from H.

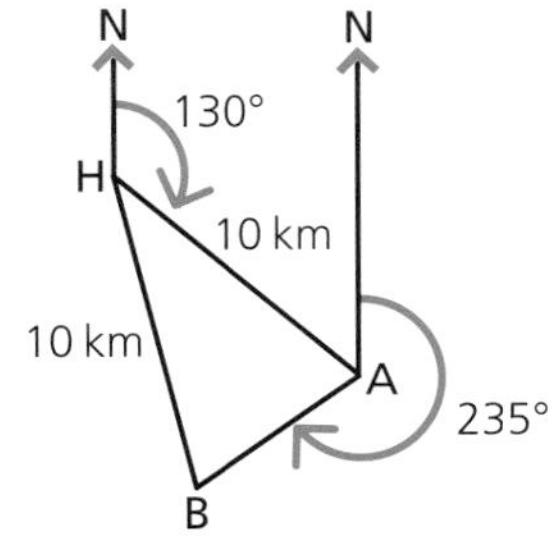

24 Here is a sketch of a 'lean-to' shed. The door measures 1.75 m by 1 m and is positioned centrally at the front.

a) Draw the plan, front elevation and side elevation of the shed, using a scale of 1 : 100.

b) What is the area of the wall at the far end of the shed?

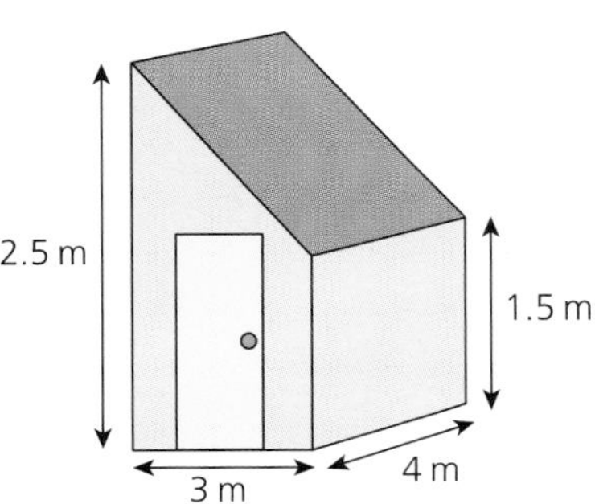

Unit 13 Algebra and graphs (1)

25 Remove the brackets from these expressions:
a) $x + (y + z)$ b) $x + (y - z)$ c) $3x - (2y + z)$
d) $2x - (y - 4z)$ e) $-(x - 2y + 3z)$ f) $(x + 2y) - z$

26 Remove the brackets and simplify:
a) $p + (2p - q)$ b) $2p - (p - 3q)$ c) $p - 3q + (p - 2q)$
d) $5p + 3q - (2p - 3q)$ e) $4p - 3 - (q - 7)$ f) $7p + 3 - (2p + 8)$

27 Expand:
a) $3(x + 2)$ b) $4(y - 5)$ c) $2(x + 2y - 5)$
d) $x(x + 3)$ e) $x(x + y)$ f) $3x(x - 2y)$

28 Expand and simplify:
a) $3(x + 4) + 2(x + 3)$ b) $5(x + 2) - 3(x + 3)$
c) $5(x + 1) - 4(x - 2)$ d) $x(2x + 3y) + 4xy$
e) $2x(3y - 1) + 4y(3 - x)$ f) $x(x + 4) + 3x(x - 5)$

29 Copy and complete:
a) $12x + 8y = 4(\ldots + 2y)$ b) $9x - 6xy = 3(3x - \ldots)$
c) $10y + 15xy = \ldots (2 + \ldots)$ d) $x^2 + 3xy - 5x = x(x + \ldots - \ldots)$

30 Factorise:
a) $9x + 12y$ b) $25x - 15$ c) $12x + 16y$
d) $14xy - 7x + 21y$ e) $x^2y + 3xy - y$ f) $x^2y - xy + xy^2$

31 Find the gradients of the lines with these equations:
a) $y = x + 5$ b) $y = 2x - 7$ c) $y = -3x + 11$

32 Give the coordinates of the points where these lines cross the y-axis:
a) $y = 4x + 3$ b) $y = 2x - 9$ c) $y = 3.8x + 0.7$

33 Find the equations of the straight lines passing through these pairs of points:
a) (0, 0) and (6, 12) b) (0, 3) and (5, 18) c) (0, 7) and (7, 0).

34 A line passing through the point (0, 5) is parallel to the line $y = 8x + 1$. What is its equation?

35 Copy and complete the following coordinates of points that lie on the line with equation $x + y = 10$:
a) (4, …) b) (… , 7) c) (4.5, …)
d) (−2, …) e) (… , −6) f) (a, …)

Unit 14 Charts, graphs, histograms

36 Decide whether each of the following is a discrete or a continuous variable:
a) the daily temperature at noon
b) the lifetime of a battery
c) the number of coins in a purse
d) the weights of bags of apples
e) the number of apples in each bag
f) the number of pairs of shoes sold in a day
g) the number of phone calls to a police station each day
h) the quantity of washing-up liquid in a bottle measured in ml.

37 The speed of vehicles passing a police checkpoint was measured in miles per hour. Here are the results summarised as a frequency table.

Speed (m.p.h.)	Frequency
$30 \le x < 35$	1
$35 \le x < 40$	4
$40 \le x < 45$	9
$45 \le x < 50$	17
$50 \le x < 55$	23
$55 \le x < 60$	31
$60 \le x < 65$	8
$65 \le x < 70$	4
$70 \le x < 75$	6
$75 \le x < 80$	2

a) How many vehicles passed the police checkpoint during the speed check?
b) What is the probability that a vehicle chosen at random would be breaking the speed limit of 60 m.p.h.?
c) Draw a histogram to illustrate these results.

38 The table gives the heights of 12 mothers together with the height of their child at age 18.

Height of mother (cm)	152	168	155	160	160	170	155	150	163	159	160	152
Height of child (cm)	157	175	157	163	173	173	165	150	180	175	170	168

a) Draw a scatter graph showing mother's height on the x-axis and child's height on the y-axis.
b) Does there seem to be a correlation between mother's height and child's height? If so, is the correlation positive or negative?

Unit 15 Ratio, percentage, proportion

39 Joe made some purple paint by mixing red and blue paint in the ratio 5 : 3. How much of each colour would be needed to make the following amounts of the same shade of purple?

a) 24 litres b) 40 litres c) 16 gallons
d) 12 gallons e) 10 gallons f) 36 litres.

40 The angles of a quadrilateral are in the ratio 1:2:3:4. Find the size of each angle.

41 A pie chart shows the proportion of votes received by three candidates A, B and C in a local election. The angles for candidates A and B are 72° and 108° respectively.

a) What is the angle for candidate C?
b) Express the angles for A, B and C as a ratio in its simplest terms.
c) What fraction of the vote did each candidate receive?
d) What percentage of the vote did each candidate receive?

42 Express the first amount as a percentage of the second in each of the following:

a) 35, 50 b) 16, 40 c) 11, 25
d) 17 km, 20 km e) 20 cm, 2 m f) £1.10, £2.50.
g) 67, 50 h) £76, £40 i) 8.5 kg, 1.7 kg

43 Martin scored 38 marks out of 55 on the first of his mathematics exam papers and 25 out of 45 on the second paper.

a) Find Martin's percentage score on each paper.
b) On which paper did Martin perform best?
c) What is his overall percentage?

44 Julie's pay increase took her monthly salary from £1240 to £1550.

a) Express her new salary as a percentage of her old salary.
b) What is Julie's percentage increase in pay?

45 A recipe for 12 popovers requires 150 g of plain flour. How much flour would be needed to make 18 popovers?

46 A hardware store sells two brands of white emulsion paint of similar quality. Find the cost per litre of each brand to the nearest penny. Which brand represents the best value?

Brand A

Brand B

Unit 16 Polygons and circles

47 a) Find the sizes of the other angles in this parallelogram:

b) Find the sizes of the angles in this rhombus.

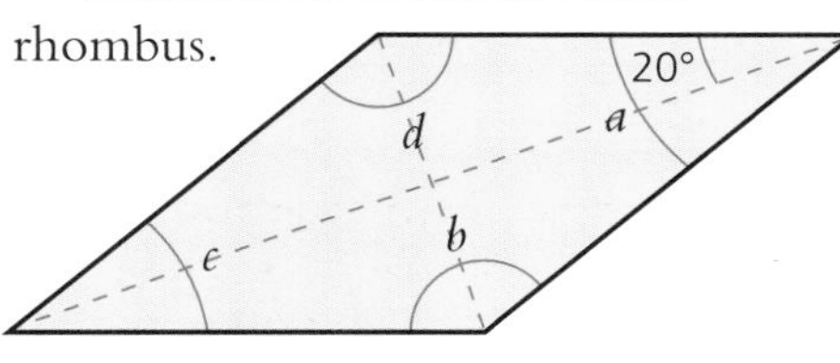

48 A square birthday cake is cut from one outside edge to the centre of the cake (marked O in the diagram).

a) Copy the diagram and show how the cake can be cut into 4 identical pieces.
b) If the first cut is always made to the centre, will it always be possible to cut 4 identical pieces? Investigate what happens if you move the first cut round but still cut to O.

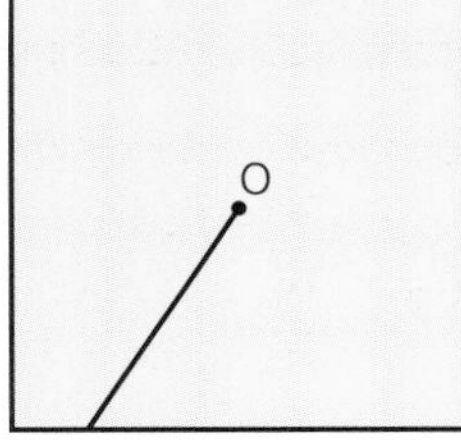

49 a) Each angle of a regular polygon is 162°. How many sides does it have?
b) One angle of a pentagon is 160°. If the other angles are equal, how large are they?
c) Is it possible for a regular polygon to have exterior angles equal to:
(i) 24° (ii) 28° (iii) 36°?
d) Is it possible for a regular polygon to have interior angles equal to:
(i) 170° (ii) 168° (iii) 164°?
State the number of sides for those polygons which do exist.

50 Find the values of a, b, c, d and e.

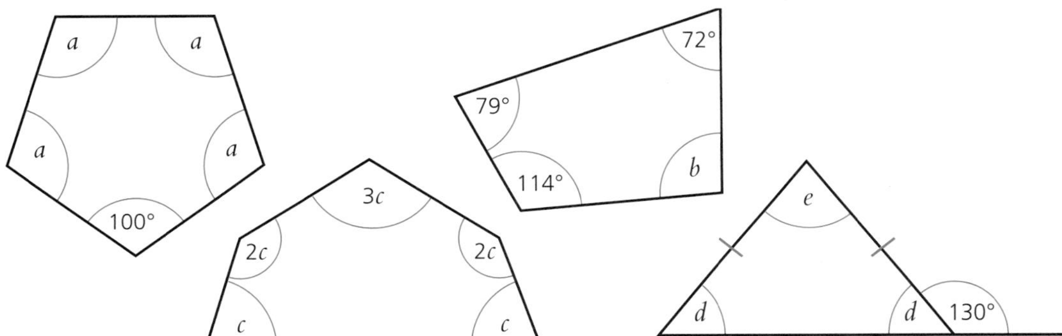

51 a) The tyre of a car wheel has a diameter of 30 cm. How many times will the wheel rotate on a journey of 5 km?

b) Circular badges are cut from a plastic sheet measuring 84 cm by 24 cm. If each badge has a radius of 4 cm, how many can be cut from one sheet?

c) Find the total area of the badges cut out.

d) Find the area of plastic wasted.

52 Find the area of each of these ornamental flowerbeds planted outside our local zoo.

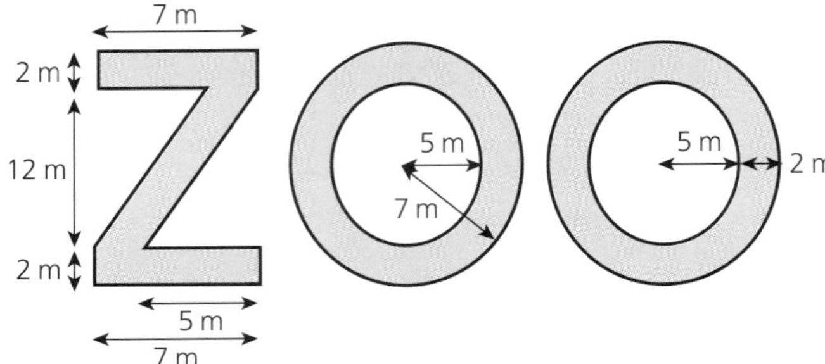

NUMBERS AND EQUATIONS

17.1 A change of scale

The diagram shows how the number 10 is affected when it is multiplied by different values. An important point is that some of these values, often called **scale factors**, have an **enlarging** effect, i.e., the result is larger than the starting value: and some have a **reducing** effect, i.e. the result is smaller than the starting value.

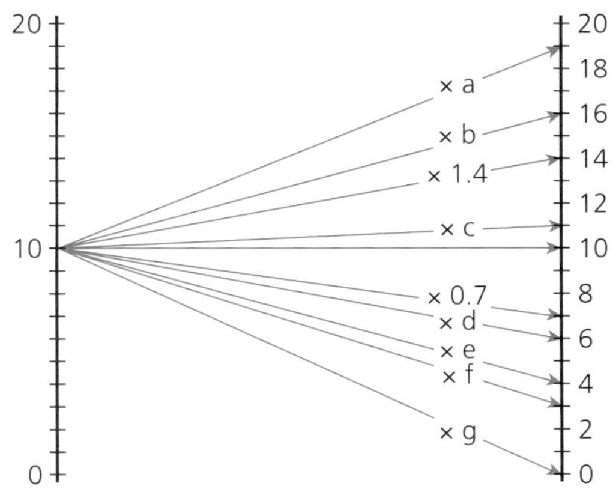

1 Find the values of the scale factors *a*, *b*, *c*, *d*, *e*, *f* and *g*.

2 What scale factor produces no change?

3 Describe what is special about the scale factors that have an enlarging effect. ✓

4 Describe what is special about the scale factors that have a reducing effect.

5 Describe the effect of multiplying by each of the following scale factors either as a reduction or an enlargement:

a) 3 **b)** 0.3 **c)** 1.6 **d)** 1.1
e) 0.9 **f)** 0.02 **g)** 2.03 **h)** 0.099

6 For each of the following statements decide which of the symbols < or > is needed to complete it correctly:

a) 18.6 × 0.78 ... 18.6 ✓ **b)** 4.2 × 1.04 ... 4.2 **c)** 6.5 × 0.79 ... 6.5
d) 7.6 × 1.46 ... 7.6 **e)** 0.78 × 1.2 ... 0.78 **f)** 0.78 × 1.2 ... 1.2
g) 1.16 × 0.83 ... 1.16 **h)** 1.16 × 0.83 ... 0.83 **i)** 0.39 × 0.72 ... 0.72

Statements such as those in question 6 can give us information that we can use to check answers.

■ 0.63 × 8.72 = 9.4936 must be **wrong** because multiplying by 0.63 has a reducing effect, i.e. the answer must be less than 8.72.

■ 3.8 × 0.24 = 0.212 must be **wrong** because multiplying by 3.8 has an enlarging effect, i.e. the answer must be bigger than 0.24.

---

7 Use the approach given in the example to explain what is **wrong** with each of the following statements:

a) 8.37 × 0.25 = 9.0925 **b)** 2.36 × 1.4 = 2.304
c) 17.8 × 0.9 = 18.02 **d)** 0.84 × 0.92 = 0.8728
e) 0.431 × 1.8 = 0.2938 **f)** 0.431 × 1.8 = 2.9308
g) 1.57 × 0.62 = 0.5734 **h)** 1.57 × 0.62 = 1.5734

8 Without using a calculator, decide which of the following statements must be false:

a) $4.23 \times 1.15 = 4.8645$ b) $6.47 \times 1.23 = 5.9581$
c) $0.96 \times 0.82 = 0.8772$ d) $0.96 \times 0.82 = 0.7872$
e) $0.93 \times 1.16 = 1.0788$ f) $0.93 \times 1.16 = 0.9788$

The inequalities produced when considering the effect of multiplying by scale factors may be shown on a number line.

$1.89 \times 0.72 < 1.89$ (taking 0.72 as the scale factor)

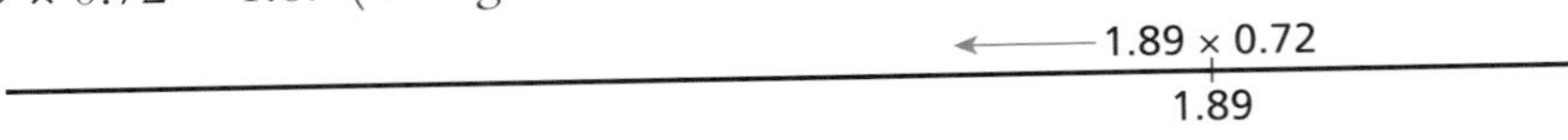

and $1.89 \times 0.72 > 0.72$ (taking 1.89 as the scale factor)

1.89 × 0.72

0.72

Combining the statements gives $0.72 < 1.89 \times 0.72 < 1.89$

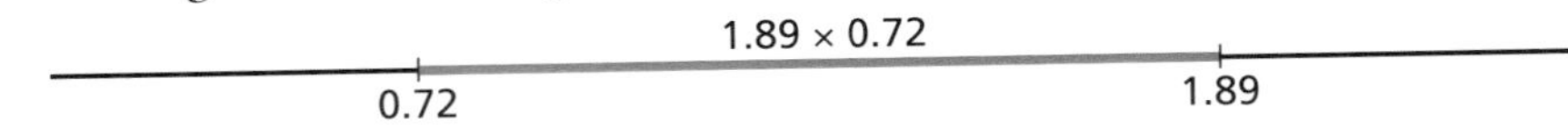

So we now know that the answer must lie between 0.72 and 1.89.

9 Write down two inequalities that must be satisfied by 0.876×1.25. Combine the two inequalities into a single statement and illustrate using a number line.

10 Repeat the process given in question 9 for these calculations:

a) 1.03×0.91 b) 0.38×1.46 c) 0.074×2.39 d) 1.876×0.423

Information concerning the effect of division, by numbers of various sizes, can be found by making a statement about multiplication and reversing the process.

10 → [× 1.6] → 16 10 ← [÷ 1.6] ← 16

Multiplication by 1.6 has an enlarging effect. Dividing by 1.6 has a reducing effect.

11 Follow the steps given in the example replacing the 1.6 with a number of your choice:

a) greater than 1 b) between 0 and 1.

12 Describe the effect of dividing by a number n if:

a) $n > 1$ b) $0 < n < 1$ c) $n = 1$

13 Without using a calculator, decide which of the symbols < or > is needed to complete each of the following statements correctly.

a) 16.8 ÷ 0.72 ... 16.8 b) 12.3 ÷ 1.24 ... 12.3 c) 0.24 ÷ 0.81 ... 0.24
d) 0.14 ÷ 1.5 ... 0.14 e) 57 ÷ 0.96 ... 57 f) 0.08 ÷ 1.09 ... 0.08

14 Without using a calculator, find the statements that must be false:

a) $2.318 \div 0.61 = 3.8$
b) $4.146\,75 \div 0.873 = 4.75$
c) $23.998\,2 \div 1.38 = 24.39$
d) $57.540\,4 \div 0.97 = 59.32$
e) $154.35 \div 1.05 = 147$
f) $0.007\,948\,8 \div 1.08 = 0.073\,6$

15 Find the false statements without using a calculator:

a) $6.89 \times 0.97 \div 1.3 > 6.89$
b) $0.073 \div 0.86 \times 1.04 > 0.073$
c) $0.003\,4 \div 1.29 \times 0.78 < 0.003\,4$
d) $0.005\,4 \times 0.073 \div 2.75 < 0.054$
e) $\dfrac{17.8}{0.989} \times 1.03 > 178$
f) $\dfrac{0.0683}{1.012} \times 834 < 834$

17.2 Non-calculator methods

When carrying out calculations without a calculator it is useful to be aware that there may be different ways of working towards the result. We can then choose the simplest method to suit a particular situation.
For example,

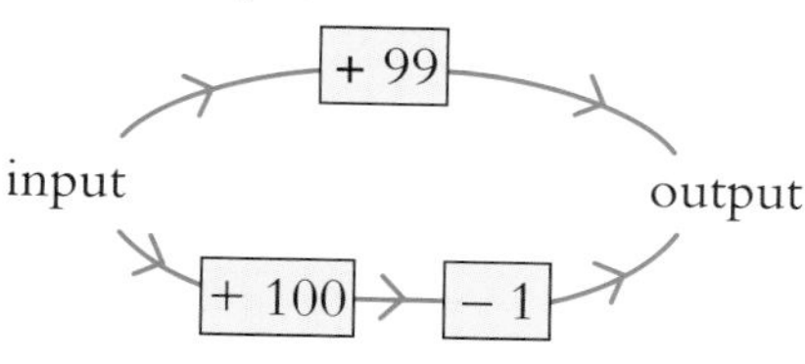

The diagram illustrates that adding 99 to any number can be achieved by adding 100 and then subtracting 1.

1 Copy and complete the diagrams below to show different ways of working.

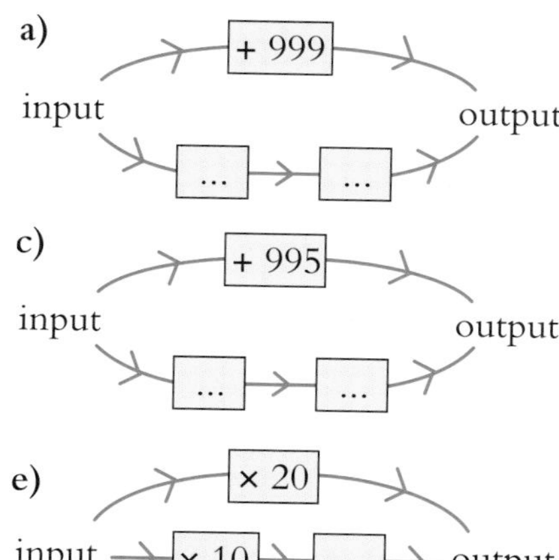

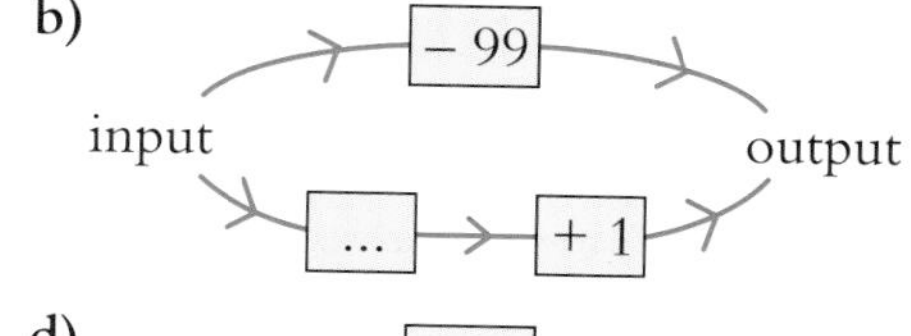

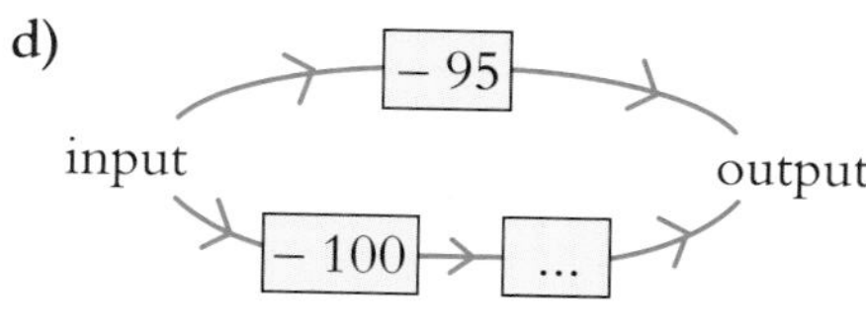

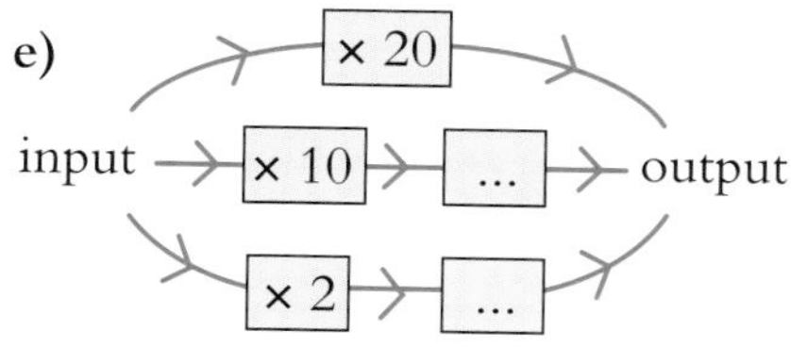

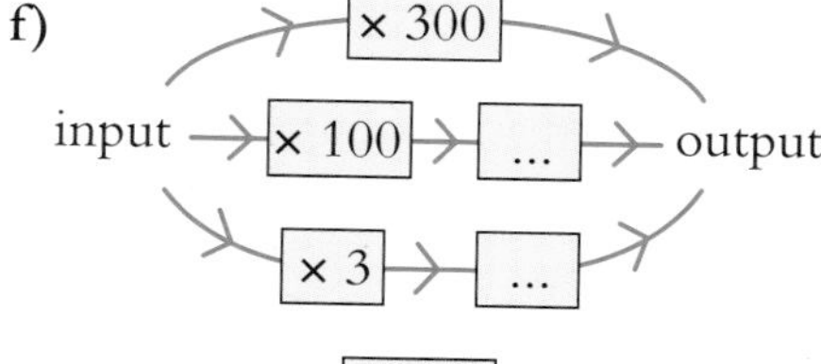

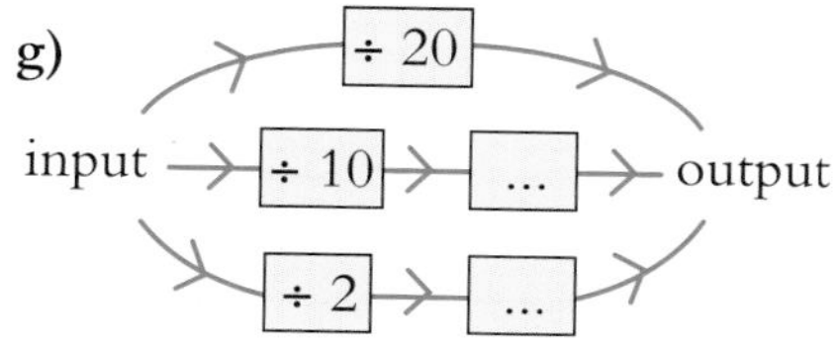

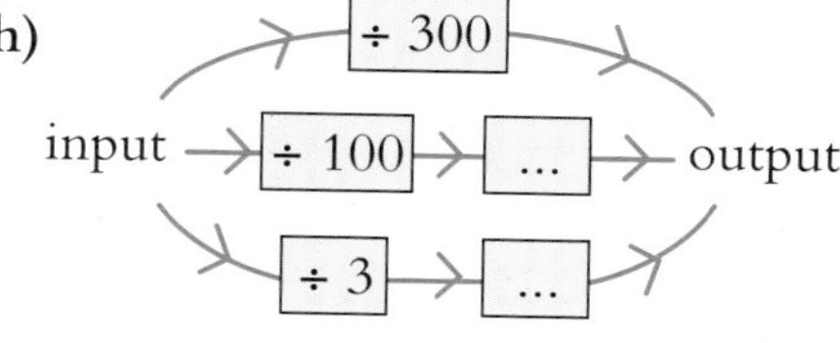

The answers to questions 2 to 6 can be worked out mentally if the simplest approach is chosen in each case.

2 Add 99 to each of these:
a) 73 b) 48 c) 165 d) 387 e) 712 f) 1846

3 Subtract 99 from each of these:
a) 147 b) 238 c) 652 d) 498 e) 8463 f) 9721

4 Add 9.9 to each of these:
a) 7.4 ✓ b) 16.8 c) 38.5 d) 154.8 e) 8.73 f) 186.54

5 Multiply these by 200:
a) 43 b) 0.81 c) 0.073 ✓ d) 3.25 e) 670 f) 0.0045

6 Divide these by 30:
a) 600 b) 180 c) 27 000 d) 183 e) 252
f) 1.65 g) 4.12 h) 0.75 i) 0.02

In some situations, the use of brackets can suggest an alternative method.

Example

Work out 276 × 99.

Answer

Since 99 = (100 − 1), it follows that 276 × 99 = 276(100 − 1)
= 27 600 − 276
= 27 324

$$\begin{array}{r} 27\,600 \\ -\ 276 \\ \hline 27\,324 \end{array}$$

---

7 Work out without using a calculator:
a) 561 × 99 b) 99 × 638 c) 432 × 98
d) 374 × 998 e) 0.87 × 99 f) 6.39 × 99
g) 320 × 9.9 h) 62.1 × 9.9 i) 684 × 0.99

The idea of *equivalent fractions* can also suggest alternative methods.

For example, for any value of n,

$$\frac{n}{5} = \frac{2n}{10}$$

which shows that dividing by 5 is the same as doubling and dividing by 10.
Thus 3.42 ÷ 5 = 6.84 ÷ 10 = 0.684.

---

8 Work out without using a calculator:
a) 62 ÷ 5 b) 134 ÷ 5 c) 0.83 ÷ 5
d) 4.7 ÷ 50 e) 0.721 ÷ 50 f) 64 ÷ 25

17.3 Balancing equations

The purpose of this section is to adapt the flow-diagram method, used in Unit 9, to be able to solve different types of equations.

The equation $3x + 2 = 14$ can be solved by first presenting the information it contains in the form of a flow diagram:

$x \rightarrow \boxed{\times 3} \rightarrow \boxed{+ 2} \rightarrow 14$

and then reversing the process...

$x \xleftarrow{4} \boxed{\div 3} \xleftarrow{12} \boxed{- 2} \leftarrow 14$

This gives the solution $x = 4$.

An alternative approach is to apply the reverse process to both sides of the equation at the same time. The effect is to simplify the equation at every stage until the solution is reached.

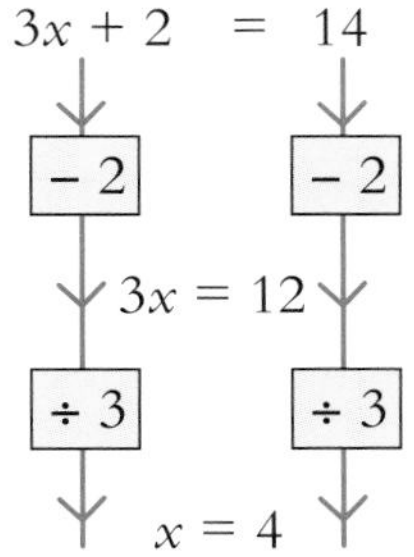

$3x + 2 = 14$

$\downarrow \boxed{-2}$ $\quad \downarrow \boxed{-2}$

$3x = 12$

$\downarrow \boxed{\div 3}$ $\quad \downarrow \boxed{\div 3}$

$x = 4$

It is important to balance what we do on both sides of the equation.

Once you can recognise the steps of the reverse process, one at a time, you can write the solution simply as:

$$\begin{aligned} 3x + 2 &= 14 \\ 3x &= 12 \\ x &= 4 \end{aligned}$$

---

1 Copy and complete the solutions of the equations given below:

a) $4x - 5 = 19$
$4x =$
$x =$

b) $3(x + 7) = 33$
$x + 7 =$

c) $\frac{x - 5}{3} = 2.5$
$x - 5 =$

2 Copy and complete these solutions:

a) $\frac{x}{3} - 7 = 2.3$

$\frac{x}{3} =$

$x =$

b) $\frac{4x}{3} - 5 = 7$

$\frac{4x}{3} =$

$4x =$

c) $\frac{4x - 5}{3} = 7$

$4x - 5 =$

$4x =$

d) $\frac{3x + 7}{4} - 21 =$

$\frac{3x + 7}{4} =$

$3x + 7 =$

e) $3\sqrt{x} + 1 = 16$

$3\sqrt{x} =$

$\sqrt{x} =$

$x =$

f) $3\sqrt{x + 1} = 21$

$\sqrt{x + 1} =$

$x + 1 =$

g) $\sqrt[3]{\frac{2x - 5}{3}} = 2$

$\frac{2x - 5}{3} =$

$2x - 5 =$

h) $\frac{\sqrt[3]{x} + 12.8}{2} + 7 = 14.4$

$\frac{\sqrt[3]{x} + 12.8}{2} =$

$\sqrt[3]{x} + 12.8 =$

3 Solve these equations. As a check, the answer should be a whole number in each case.

a) $4x + 7.1 = 19.1$ b) $3(x - 7) - 5.2 = 6.8$ c) $\frac{x}{2.5} - 2.9 = 1.1$

d) $\frac{x - 3.7}{1.1} + 17 = 20$ e) $\sqrt{\frac{7x}{3} - 12} = 4$ f) $\frac{\sqrt{x + 9.25}}{3} = 1.5$

4 Solve the following equations, giving your answers to 3 significant figures:

a) $8.7x - 4.5 = 11.3$ b) $9.04(x + 3.7) = 50$ c) $\frac{\sqrt{x}}{3} - 12.8 = 0$

d) $\frac{3\sqrt{x} + 7}{5} = 6$ e) $\frac{7x}{3} - 11 = 4$ f) $\sqrt{\frac{x}{3}} - 2 = 1.7$

g) $\sqrt{\frac{x + 3}{5}} = 2.9$ h) $\frac{7}{9}(x - 3) = 8$

All of the equations considered so far in this section could have been solved by the flow-diagram method, since the unknown value only appears once in each case. However, the balancing method is usually needed whenever the unknown value occurs more than once.

Example

a) Solve $5x - 7 = 3x + 8$ b) Solve $3(2x - 4) = 9 - 4x$

Answer

a)
$$5x - 7 = 3x + 8$$
$$2x - 7 = 8$$
$$2x = 15$$
$$x = 7.5$$

By subtracting $3x$ from both sides, the equation simplifies to one in which x only appears once.

b) $3(2x - 4) = 9 - 4x$
$6x - 12 = 9 - 4x$
$10x - 12 = 9$
$10x = 21$
$x = 2.1$

A good first step is to remove the brackets. Try to keep the number of xs positive so add $4x$ to both sides rather than subtract $6x$.

5 Solve these equations. In each case the unknown value is a whole number.

a) $6x + 11 = 5x + 27$ ✓
b) $8x - 3 = x + 18$
c) $4.8x - 7.3 = 2.8x + 2.7$
d) $3.6x - 6.1 = 5.9 - 2.4x$
e) $2(x - 5) = x + 2$
f) $5(x - 3) = 3(7 + x)$
g) $4(3y + 10) = 9y + 64$
h) $3(5y - 2) + 2y = 16y + 1$

6 Solve these equations. Each unknown value is a *negative* whole number.

a) $4x + 8 = 3x + 2$ ✓
b) $11x + 10 = 10x + 7$
c) $8x - 3 = 6x - 11$
d) $2x + 15 = 3 - x$
e) $8 - (3 - 2x) = x + 1$
f) $12 - (4 - 5x) = x$

In questions 5 and 6 you were given information that may have helped you realise when an error was made. We don't normally have such information available, however, so we need some other way to check our solutions. The simplest way is to substitute the answer back into the original equation to see if it works.

To check the solution given in example **a)** we substitute $x = 7.5$ in both sides of the equation separately.

LHS $5x - 7 = 5 \times 7.5 - 7 = 37.5 - 7 = 30.5$
RHS $3x + 8 = 3 \times 7.5 + 8 = 22.5 + 8 = 30.5$; LHS = RHS

7 Find the solutions to these equations and check by substitution:

a) $5x - 2 = 3x + 4$
b) $9x + 5 = 7x + 1$
c) $3(x - 4) + 7 = x + 5$
d) $11 - (7 - x) = 2 - x$
e) $4x + 3 = 2x + 6$
f) $5(x - 4) = 3(x - 2) - 5$
g) $5x + 2 - (x - 3) = 2x + 10$
h) $6(x - 1) - (x - 1) = 1$

18 HYPOTHESES

18.1 Testing a hypothesis

A hypothesis is a clear statement of a theory that may be tested by observation. It may take the form of a prediction about what will happen or an opinion about an issue.

Here is a hypothesis:
'Most people prefer to drink coffee in the morning and tea in the afternoon.'
All statistical investigations should start either with a hypothesis or a question to be answered.

---

1 Here are the stages in testing a hypothesis.
Can you arrange them in the right order? ✓

Analyse the data ?
Collect the data ?
Decide which data to collect ?
Interpret the results ?
State the hypothesis 1
Report your findings with reference to the original hypothesis ?

2 For each of the following questions write down:
a) a hypothesis which can be tested
b) what data will need to be collected
c) how you could collect the data.
(i) Do cats prefer 'BRAND X' cat food?
(ii) Do girls learn to talk at a younger age than boys?
(iii) Does 'BRAND Y' washing-up liquid really wash more dishes?
(iv) Is it easier for male or for female students to find part-time work?

One way of testing a hypothesis is to conduct an **experiment**.

In an experiment you control the changes in one variable and keep all the other factors constant so that they cannot interfere with the results of the experiment. It is useful to draw a diagram to show the processes involved in an experiment.

This diagram represents an experiment in which one tray of lettuce seeds is kept at 10 °C and the other at 25 °C. The hypothesis is that the seeds kept at 25° C will grow faster.

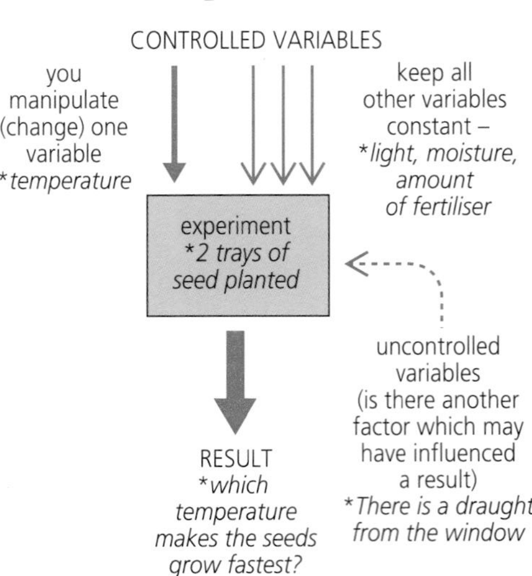

CONTROLLED VARIABLES
you manipulate (change) one variable
*temperature
keep all other variables constant –
*light, moisture, amount of fertiliser
experiment
*2 trays of seed planted
uncontrolled variables (is there another factor which may have influenced a result)
*There is a draught from the window
RESULT
*which temperature makes the seeds grow fastest?

3 Imagine you are going to conduct an experiment. You wish to test the hypothesis that passers-by are more likely to help a girl who drops her school bag, and all its contents, than a boy.

a) Which is the variable you will manipulate or change? ✓

b) Which other variables might influence what happens in the experiment?

c) Which of these variables can you try to keep constant?

d) Draw a diagram like this:

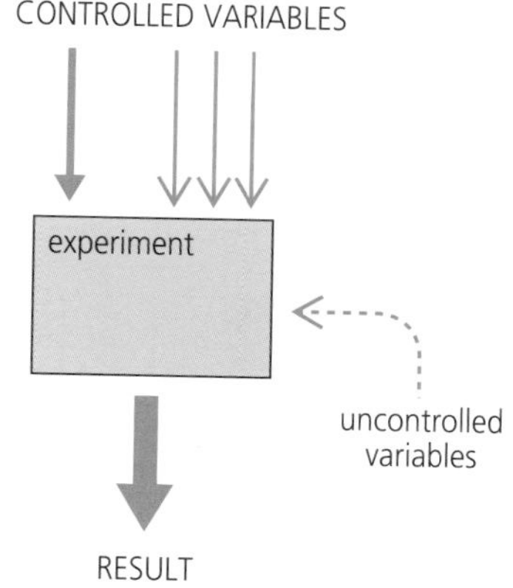

Where on the diagram will you write these words or phrases?

- Does the passer-by help to pick up the dropped items?
- Girl or boy chosen to drop bag
- All experiments conducted outdoors on a dry sunny day
- All experiments conducted near a phone box
- What do other passers-by say?
- What do other passers-by do?
- Passers-by alone or in a group
- Passers-by male or female

At the end of an experiment it may not always be easy to make a decision about whether your hypothesis is true or not. Statisticians use quite complicated methods for reaching decisions about the hypotheses they test.

Suppose you wished to test the hypothesis that:

'School pupils prefer to wear school uniform to school, rather than their other clothes.'

You might ask 100 pupils for their views, being careful to include boys and girls representing all years in the school.

If 80 or 90 pupils agreed with the statement you would have to accept the hypothesis. If, on the other hand, only 20 or 30 agreed, you would be able to reject the hypothesis.

The problem arises for results in the middle, at around 50%. A statistician will be able to use various tests to decide whether a result does support a hypothesis or not. As a 'rule of thumb' your results only support the hypothesis if 60 or more people (out of 100) agree with it.

All the possible results for a sample of 100 people can be represented on a diagram.

Sample of 100

reject hypothesis　you can't tell　accept hypothesis

0 10 20 30 40 50 60 70 80 90 100

number of people who agree

The situation has to be re-assessed if you change the size of the sample.

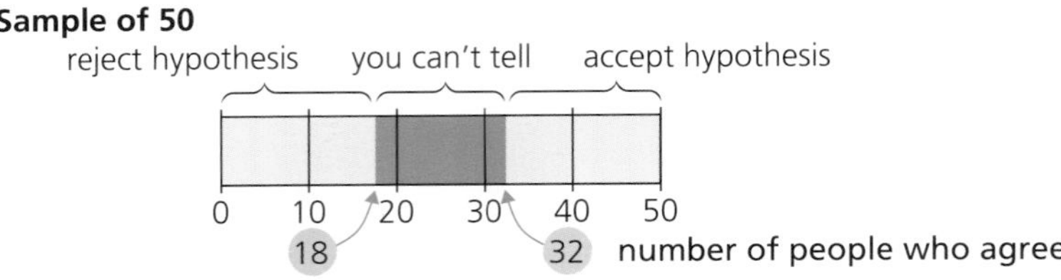

With smaller samples the 'grey area' in the middle has to be recalculated. In fact your results have to be more extreme in order to reach a definite decision, with a smaller sample.

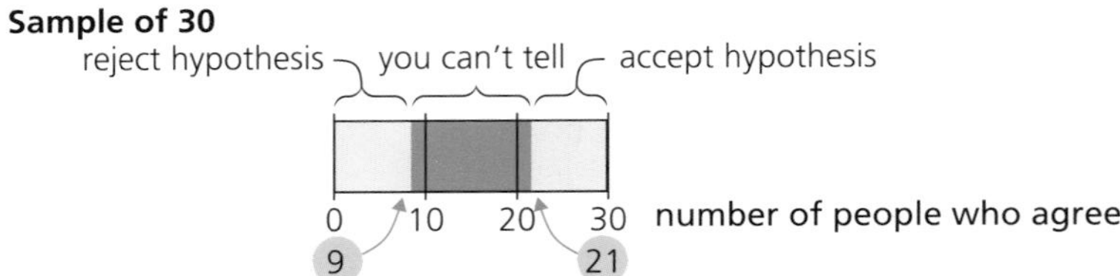

These guidelines only work in situations where there are only two answers to choose from, such as 'agree' or 'disagree'.

Experiment

In this experiment you will test people's reaction times.

Across the bottom of these two pages is a 'reaction ruler', which is specially marked so that you can use it to measure a person's reaction time.

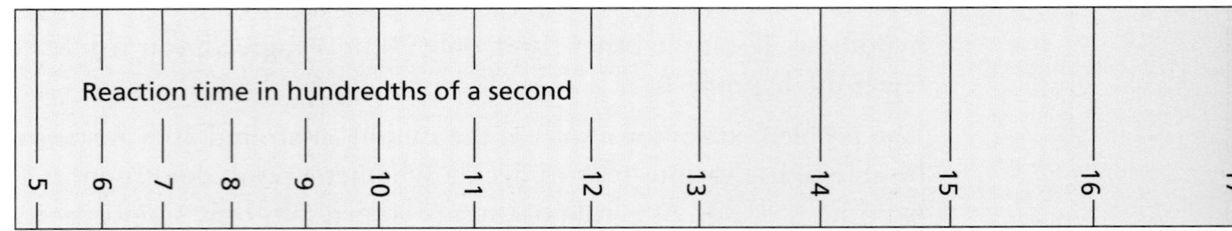

Here is how you use the ruler.

The tester holds the top of the ruler. He or she will drop the ruler without warning.

The person being tested is ready to catch the ruler between thumb and first finger. (They must not actually touch the ruler until it is dropped.) The distance the ruler falls is converted to a reaction time.

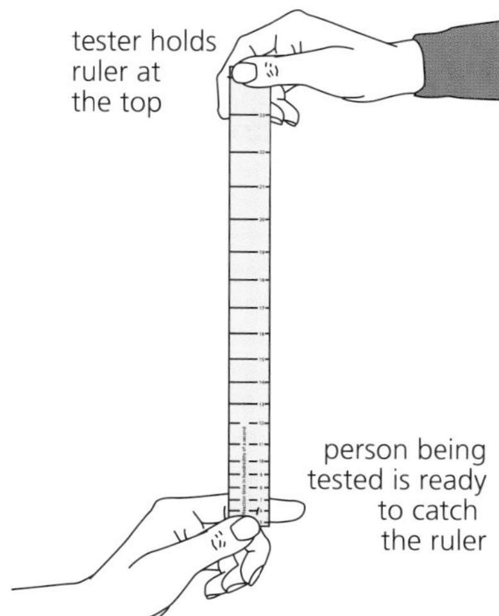

You can make your own reaction ruler. The distance the ruler falls due to gravity in each $\frac{1}{100}$ second can be worked out using this formula:
$d = 5t^2$

1 Write down a hypothesis regarding people's reaction times according to which hand they use to catch the ruler. ✓

2 Write down a hypothesis regarding people's reaction times according to whether they have had practice.

3 Say what is wrong with each of these experiments:

a) Joe asks people to catch the reaction ruler first using their right hand, then using their left hand. He then compares results for right hands with results for left hands.

b) Sally asks people to catch the reaction ruler first using the hand they use for writing (dominant hand), then using their other hand (non-dominant hand). She then compares results for 'writing' and 'non-writing' hands.

4 Say how Sally's experiment can be improved to take account of the 'practice effect' (people may improve with practice).

5 State a suitable hypothesis to test using a reaction ruler. Then run your own experiment to test your hypothesis.

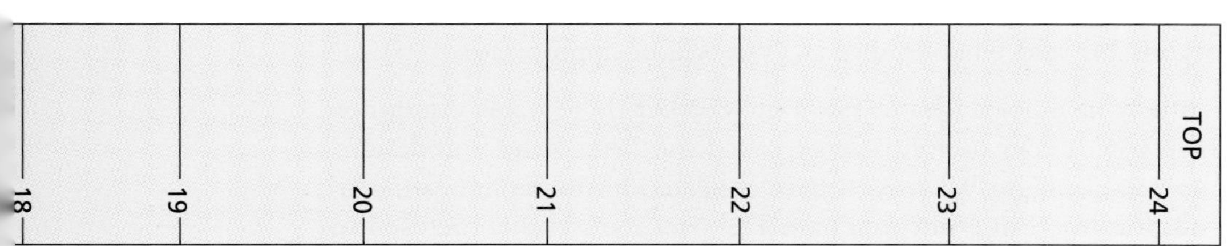

18.2 Surveys and questionnaires

Other ways of testing a hypothesis may involve collecting information by conducting a survey or a questionnaire.

Unlike an experiment, there is no attempt to control or manipulate any aspect of the situation. Your role is to collect measurements or ask specified questions.

1 Lee has done a survey at the local supermarket. He has recorded every customer going in between 11 am and 11.15 am on a Thursday. Here are his results.

Supermarket customers – Thursday		
Age	Female	Male
under 5	3	5
5–16	0	0
17–30	14	14
31–60	15	3
over 60	9	8

Pam has done the same survey on a Saturday morning at the same time. Here are her results.

Supermarket customers – Saturday		
Age	Female	Male
under 5	9	8
5–16	12	13
17–30	16	20
31–60	26	18
over 60	5	6

a) What are the main differences between Lee's results on Thursday and Pam's results on Saturday?

b) Why are the two sets of results so different?

c) Which groups of people cannot go shopping on a Thursday morning? Which people are more likely to go shopping on a Saturday?

d) Can you think of any other factors like this which could affect the results of a survey?

Questionnaire

You need to plan your questionnaire before you start. Think carefully about what kind of results you will obtain. Will the answers people write be words or numbers (i.e. will the data be qualitative or quantitative)?

How will you process the results? Will you enter them into a data base?

Think about which graphs will be suitable for your data (you may want to refer back to Unit 14), and what kind of analysis will be appropriate.

At this stage, it may be a good idea to find out whether there is any computer software to help you. A very useful package, called *Pin Point*, helps you design and print your questionnaire. When you have collected in the replies, you can enter the results into the Pin Point data base. The package can then be used to analyse the results and to produce graphs.

Create a database to store the information you have collected from your survey. Experiment with different ways of presenting this information graphically. Try out pie charts and bar graphs etc. and decide which format is the most effective.

Guidelines for designing a questionnaire

- **Plan your questionnaire before you start. Ask the questions you need. Miss out the questions you don't need.**
- **Keep it simple. Use simple words in short sentences.**
- **Avoid questions which suggest the 'right' answer (called leading questions).**
- **Ask one question at a time.**
- **Avoid negatives – they can confuse.**
- **Make sure your questions have a clear meaning. They must be unambiguous. Do not ask vague questions.**
- **Avoid embarrassing questions or questions which people will not wish to answer.**
- **If you provide boxes for people to tick, make sure every possible answer is provided.**
- **Pre-test your questionnaire.**
- **Do not ask people to remember events which happened some time ago.**
- **Always be polite and thank people for taking part in your survey.**

2 Read these questionnaire questions. Decide what is wrong with each one.

a) Have you brushed your teeth today? ✔

b) Do you suffer from headaches or dizziness?

c) Do you think smoking should not be allowed in public places?

e) What did you watch on TV last Friday evening?

f) Are you afraid of animals?

g) Which films have you seen recently?

h) Do you prefer not to use a non-medicated shampoo?

i) Do you think that cosmetics should be tested on animals; as the animals may experience pain and discomfort?

j) How often do you eat meat? (i) once a week (ii) two or three times a week (iii) more than three times a week.

k) What did you have to eat for dinner yesterday?

l) What is your opinion about this statement:
'Students should not have to do homework if they work hard in school.'
Do you:
strongly agree   agree   don't know   disagree

Selecting your sample – It is important to design your survey in such a way as to avoid **bias** in the results. When bias occurs you get a false impression of the situation due to an error in the way you have set up your survey or experiment. You need to make sure your sample is representative of the group you wish to make a decision about.

Try to ask a broad range of people, both male and female, representing different age groups and social backgrounds. This can sometimes be difficult to organise.

If you do conduct a survey in a shopping centre, say, at 10 o'clock in the morning, you are unlikely to interview people with full-time jobs. Your sample in that situation is likely to consist mainly of elderly people and other groups who do not work.

Bear in mind also that people with different social backgrounds may go shopping in different kinds of shops and supermarkets.

If you conduct a survey in school, make sure that all year groups are represented.

Your sample should be of a size that you can manage; 50 to 100 people should be sufficient.

---

3 Design an experiment or questionnaire survey to test a hypothesis.

a) What is your hypothesis?

b) Collect your results (and results from other people in the class) and put them into a table. Are your results: (i) qualitative (ii) quantitative?

c) Present your results in the form of a suitable chart or graph. Why did you choose it?

d) What conclusions can you draw from your questionnaire? Did it support your hypothesis?

FACTORS AND INEQUALITIES

19.1 Scale factors and percentages

The idea of using scale factors to represent an enlargement or a reduction may be applied to the calculation of a percentage increase or decrease. The scale factor approach has a number of advantages and is particularly well suited to the use of a calculator.

For example:

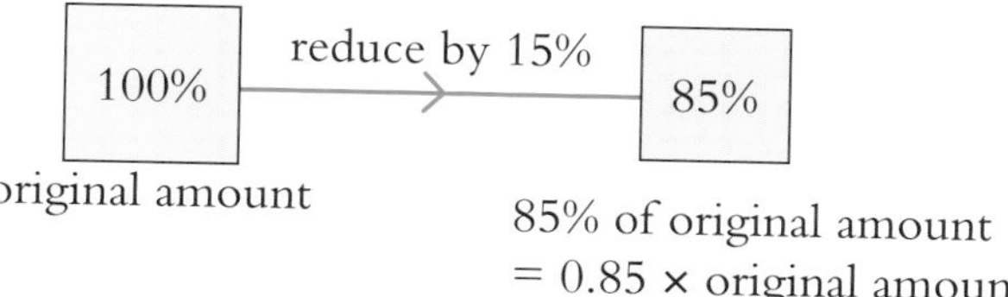

85% of original amount
= 0.85 × original amount

We see that multiplying by a scale factor of 0.85 has the effect of reducing an amount by 15%.

At this point it is worth comparing two methods and considering what each has to offer.

Example

A pair of running shoes priced at £89.99 is to be reduced by 15% (to the nearest penny) in a sale. Calculate the sale price.

Answer

Method (1)

15% of £89.99 = 0.15 × £89.99
= £13.498 5
= £13.50
(to the nearest penny).
Sale price = £89.99 − £13.50
= £76.49

Method (2)

85% of £89.99 = 0.85 × £89.99
= £76.491 5
= £76.49
(to the nearest penny).
Sale price = £76.49

Method (1) is most useful in the situation where we need to know the actual reduction (£13.50 in this case).

Method (2) has the advantage in the situation where we need to reduce several amounts by the same percentage and we can use the same scale factor each time. This can be made particularly efficient by making use of the calculator's constant multiplier facility.

---

1 Find the scale factors that may be used to calculate the following percentage reductions:

a) 25% ✓ b) 35% c) 20% d) 12%
e) 16% f) 21% g) 9% h) 0.6%

2 Reduce each of the following amounts by 17% as efficiently as possible. State your answers in the correct units:

a) £72 b) £356 c) £148 d) £6742
e) 68.4 kg f) 92.8 kg g) 0.86 m h) 0.072 m²

3 In a clearance sale, all items are to be reduced in price by 25% to the nearest penny. Make efficient use of your calculator to find the sale price for each of the following.

a) £96.99 b) £87.49 c) £214.99 d) £63.49
e) £88.49 f) £11.99 g) £750 h) £16.50

4 Reduce each of these amounts by the percentage shown. Give your answers to 3 significant figures:

a) 36; 9% ✓ b) 127; 28% c) 683; 22% d) 936; 7%
e) 429; 5.4% f) 81.6; 4.7% g) 0.74; 8.1% h) 0.029; 0.3%

Each of the scale factors used in questions 1 to 4 was chosen to have a reducing effect and so had a value less than 1. We can *increase* an amount by a given percentage by choosing an appropriate scale factor greater than 1. For example:

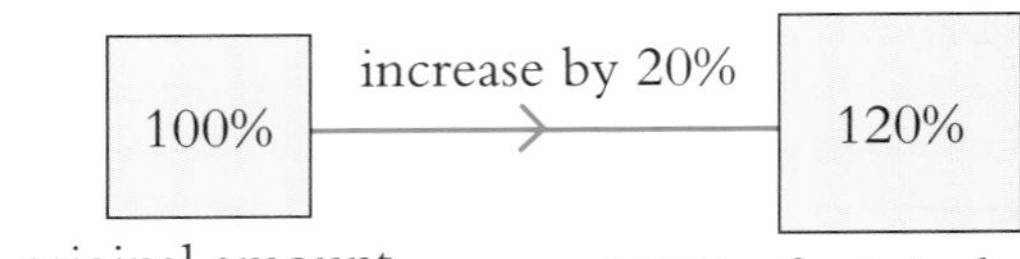

120% of original amount
= 1.2 × original amount

Note
$120\% = \frac{120}{100}$
$= 120 \div 100$
$= 1.2$

We may now compare two methods for increasing an amount by a percentage.

Example

A computer is advertised at a price of £998 + VAT. How much would a customer have to pay if the rate of VAT is 17.5%?

Answer

Method (1)

17.5% of £998 = 0.175 × £998
= £174.65
Total price = £998 + £174.65
The customer pays £1172.65

Method (2)

The customer pays 117.5% of £998
= 1.175 × £998
= £1172.65

If the actual increase, in this case £174.65 (given by the VAT) is required, then method (1) is most useful. Method (2) has the corresponding advantages to the scale factor method for reducing by a percentage.

---

5 Find the scale factors corresponding to the following percentage increases:

a) 30% b) 60% c) 40% d) 70%
e) 15% f) 21% g) 33% h) 75%
i) 12.5% j) 9% k) 4.2% l) 0.7%
m) 100% n) 120% ✓ o) 215% p) 530%

6 The prices displayed in a particular store do not include VAT. Find, as efficiently as possible, the total price including VAT at 17.5% on these displayed amounts. Give your answers to the nearest penny where appropriate.

a) £475 ✓ b) £67.50 c) £1.28 d) £6.89
e) £49.99 f) £3.75 g) 87p h) £978.99

7 Increase each of these amounts by the percentage shown, giving your answers to 3 significant figures:

a) 46; 8% b) 92; 6.4% c) 29; 11.2% d) 87.6; 7.5%
e) 1.47; 0.39% f) 654; 0.8% g) 0.86; 72% h) 6.52; 100%
i) 36; 320% ✓ j) 1.73; 276% k) 0.48; 417% l) 421; 150%

8 A school which has 972 pupils is expecting to increase its population by 3.4% next year. If its population exceeds 1000 then it will qualify for a special grant for new buildings. Show by calculation whether or not the school is expected to qualify.

9 The end of year profits for a firm are £247 870. The target for next year is to increase profits by 4%. What is the minimum profit that can be made in order to meet the target?

10 At an athletics meeting a javelin thrower beats his personal best distance of 87.54 m by 2%. What is his new personal best distance?

11 An advert in a newspaper offers jewellery for sale to people who want to make money by working from home. The claim is that a necklace costing £11.99 can be re-sold for a 500% profit. How much would the necklace need to be sold for to justify the claim?

12 The promoters of a night-club claim that average Saturday night attendance figures have increased by 9% since the introduction of live music. If the previous average attendance was 980, what do the promoters claim it is now, to the nearest 10 people?

19.2 Reversing the process

The idea of reversing a process has already been seen to be useful in a number of situations. It is useful again here whenever we know the final figure, after a percentage change, but need to know the original amount. However, there is a possible trap that we need to be aware of as shown by the diagram.

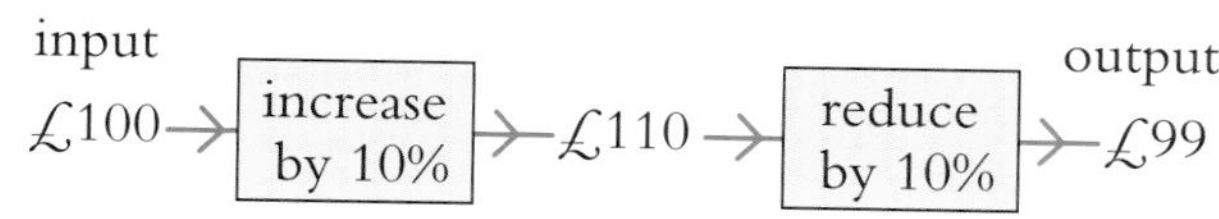

The input and output values are *not* the same, which shows that reducing the new figure by 10% *doesn't* cancel the original 10% increase.

1 Explain *why* the two percentage changes shown in the diagram don't cancel.

The scale factor approach for calculation of percentage changes provides a solution to the problem as shown below.

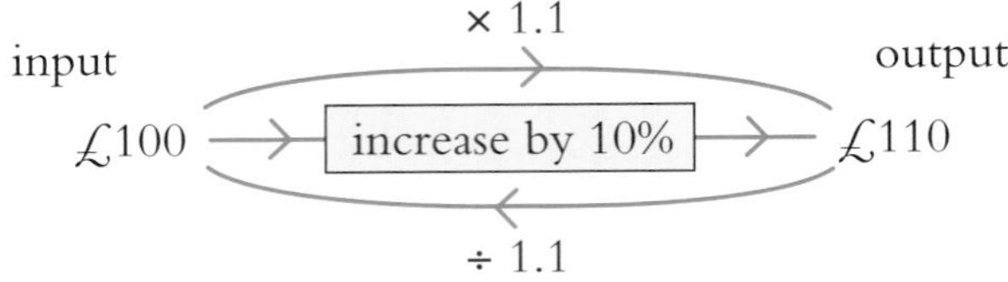

2 a) Check that dividing by 1.1 undoes the process of adding 10% shown in the diagram.
b) Laura's salary payment of £836.88 this month includes a 10% bonus. What is her monthly salary without any bonus?
c) Bank charges of 10% have been added to my overdraft so that I now owe the bank £1 270.50. How much did I owe before the charges were added?

3 a) Describe the calculation needed to undo a reduction of 10%.
b) Paul's car has lost 10% of its value since he bought it. If it is now worth £4275, how much did Paul pay for the car?
c) My estimate of the cost of replacing some carpets was 10% short of the true cost. If my estimate was £450, how much did I have to pay?

4 Copy and complete the diagram below to show how to *undo* the effect of a percentage change.

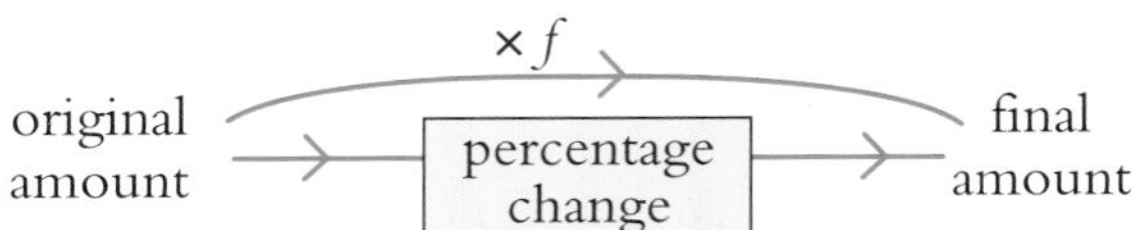

5 Describe the process for *undoing* each of these percentage changes:
a) 15% increase ✓ b) 7% decrease c) 6% increase
d) 5.8% increase e) 1.2% decrease f) 24.5% decrease
g) 17.5% increase h) 0.8% increase i) 0.9% decrease

6 Each of the following amounts contains VAT at 17.5%. Calculate the corresponding amounts before VAT was added.
a) £42.30 b) £98.70 c) £1410
d) £4 288.75 e) £293.75 f) £9 987.50
g) £16 450 h) £47

7 Anyone in business registered for VAT can claim back any VAT that they have paid. How much could be claimed back on each of the amounts given in the previous question?

8 The amount of VAT that can be claimed back on £47 works out at exactly £7.
a) Use this information to write down, as a fraction, the amount that can be claimed back on each £1.
b) Using your answer to part **a)** as a scale factor, check your answers to question 7.

19.3 Solving inequalities

The balancing approach to solving equations may also be used to solve inequalities. The solution itself usually takes the form of an inequality since it is often impossible to list all of the possible values.

Example

Solve $3x + 2 < 14$ and show the solution on a number line.

The steps involved in the solution are the same as those for solving the equation $3x + 2 = 14$.

Answer

$3x + 2 < 14$

$3x < 12$

$x < 4$ This means that any value of x which is less than 4 is a solution.

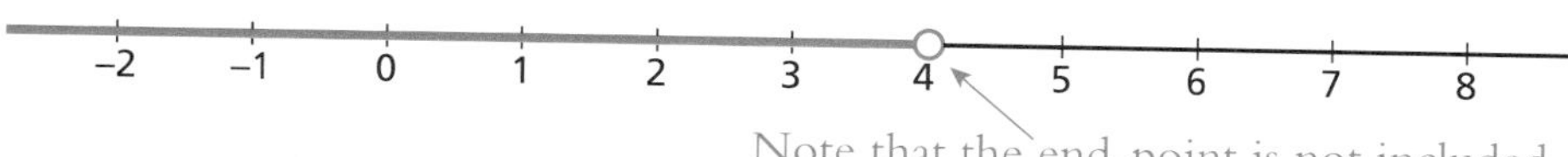

Note that the end-point is not included

Example

Solve $x + 7 \geq 6 - x$ and show the solution on a number line.

Answer

$x + 7 \geq 6 - x$ Add x to both sides. As usual try to keep the number of x's positive.

$2x + 7 \geq 6$

$2x \geq -1$

$x \geq -\frac{1}{2}$ *Note:* $-\frac{1}{2}$ *is included as a solution.*

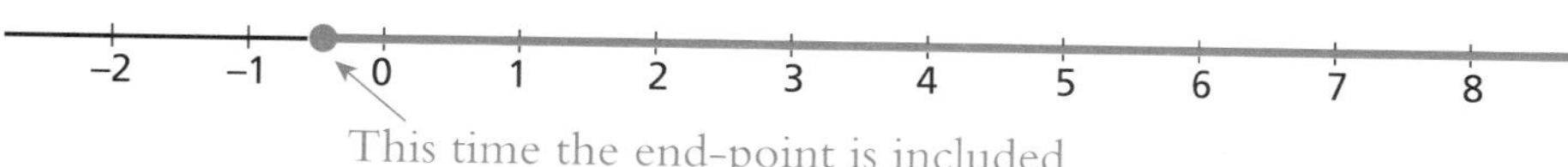

This time the end-point is included

---

1 Solve these inequalities and show each solution on a number line:

a) $x + 5 < 7$ b) $x - 3 > 7.2$ c) $x + 6 > -1$ d) $x - 5.8 < -4$

e) $2x - 3 \geq 11$ f) $5x + 7 \leq 2$ g) $3x + 5 < 7$ h) $4x + 3 > 17$

2 Find the values of x that satisfy each of the following:

a) $7x + 3 < 4x + 15$ ✓ b) $8x - 7 \geq 3x + 8$ c) $7.5x - 4.3 > 3.5x + 3.7$

d) $x + 9 < 15 - 2x$ e) $3(x - 4) \leq 9$ f) $11 - (5 - x) > 7.2$

3 Find the *smallest* value of x that satisfies each of these inequalities:

a) $\frac{x}{3} - 5 \geq 2$ b) $\frac{2x - 3}{5} \geq 2.4$

The inequalities solved so far have led to solutions that are represented on the number line by a line of infinite length. However, in some situations the solution may be bounded at both ends, i.e. it may be represented by a line *segment*.

Example

This is like solving two inequalities at the same time.

Solve $3 < 2x - 5 \le 8$ and show the solution on a number line.

Answer

$3 < 2x - 5 \le 8$ — First add 5 to each part.

$8 < 2x \le 13$ — Then divide throughout by 2.

$4 < x \le 6.5$

Example

Solve $x^2 < 16$ and show the solution on a number line.

It's tempting to take the square root of both sides and conclude that $x < 4$ but this is not always true, e.g. $-5 < 4$ but $(-5)^2 = 25 > 16$.

Answer

The solution is given by:

$-4 < x < 4$

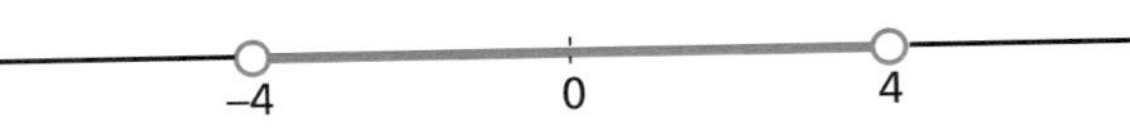

4 Solve these inequalities and show each solution on a number line:

a) $6 < x + 2 < 9$ b) $5 \le x - 3 < 8$ c) $8 \le 2x \le 12$

d) $6 < 3x \le 15$ e) $2 < \frac{x}{3} < 4$ f) $1.5 \le \frac{x}{4} < 2.5$

g) $3 < 2x - 1 < 7$ h) $5 \le 3x + 2 < 11$ i) $-5 < x - 3 < 0$

j) $-10 \le x + 2 \le -4$ k) $-2 < \frac{x}{4} \le -0.5$ l) $-3 \le \frac{x+1}{2} < 0$

m) $x^2 < 9$ n) $x^2 \le 25$ o) $x^2 - 3 < 46$

p) $x^2 + 7 \le 43$

If, for example, we know that x can only take whole number values, then it may be possible to list all of the values in the solution.

Example

List all of the values of x such that $3 < x + 5 \le 8$ given that x is an **integer**.

Answer

$3 < x + 5 \le 8$ — Subtract 5 from each part.

$-2 < x \le 3$

The possible values are:

$-1, 0, 1, 2, 3$.

Note that integers are whole numbers that may be positive, negative or zero.

5 List the integer values that satisfy the following inequalities:

a) $2 \le x \le 7$ b) $4 < x \le 10$ c) $-3 \le x < 3$

d) $-6 \le x \le -2$ e) $2.5 < x < 5.8$ f) $3.7 < x < 8.3$

g) $\sqrt{5} < x < \sqrt{11}$ ✓ h) $\sqrt{19} < x < \sqrt{29}$ i) $-4.2 < x < 2.3$

j) $-7.6 < x < -4.9$

6 Find the integral values that satisfy these:

a) $4 \le x + 1 \le 11$ ✓ b) $8 < 2x < 12$ c) $15 < 2x < 19$

d) $-12 \le 3x < 9$ e) $-7 < 4x < 5$ f) $-19 < 5x + 1 < 11$

20.1 Enlargements

A **transformation** is a mathematical description of a change in the position, shape or size of an object.

An **enlargement** is a type of transformation in which the size of an object is changed although the shape of the object remains the same.

This diagram shows an enlargement.

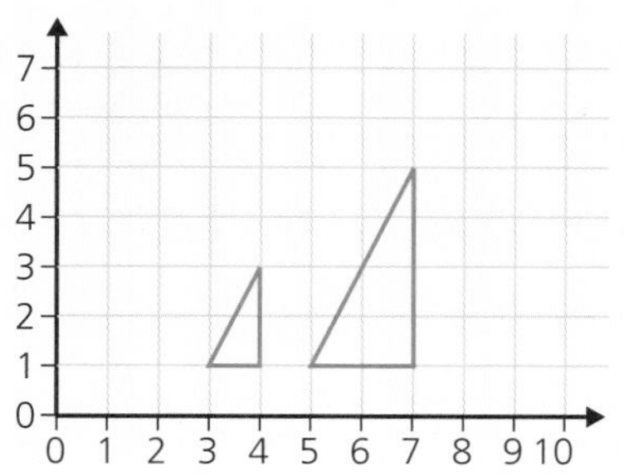

1 How many times longer are the sides of the large triangle, compared to the smaller one?

This value is called the **scale factor**.

In addition to the scale factor we have to consider the **centre of enlargement.** To find the centre of enlargement, draw lines joining the corresponding vertices on the two triangles.

Extend these lines back to the point where they cross.

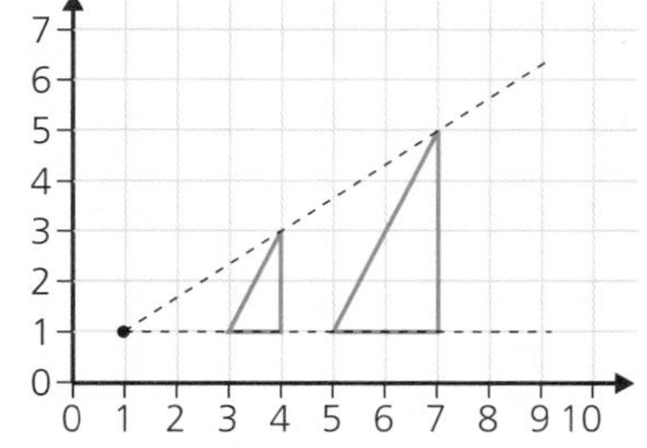

When you describe an enlargement you should give the scale factor and the centre of the enlargement.

2 What are the coordinates of the centre of enlargement here? ✓

3 For each of the following diagrams (see next page for **d)** to **f)**) the coloured triangle has been enlarged. Write down:
(i) the scale factor (ii) the coordinates of the centre of enlargement.

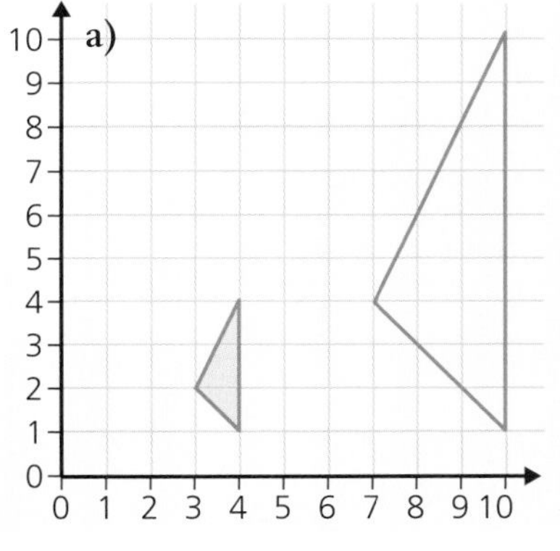

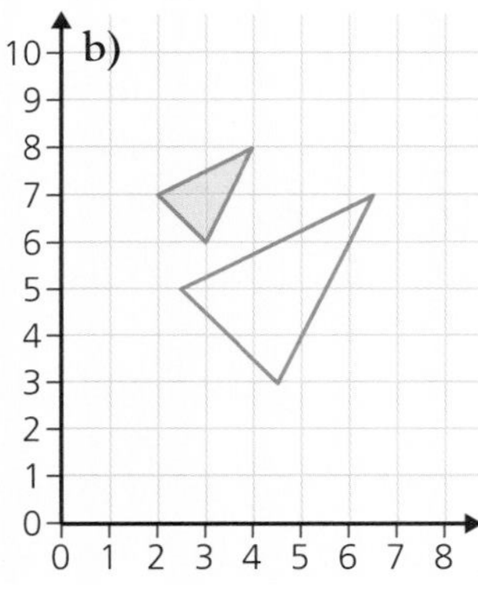

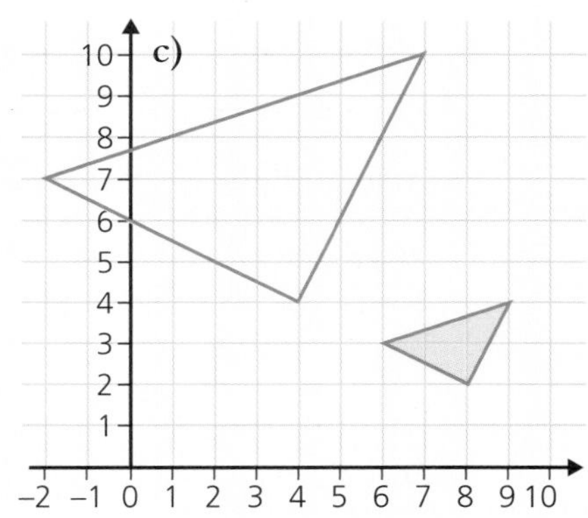

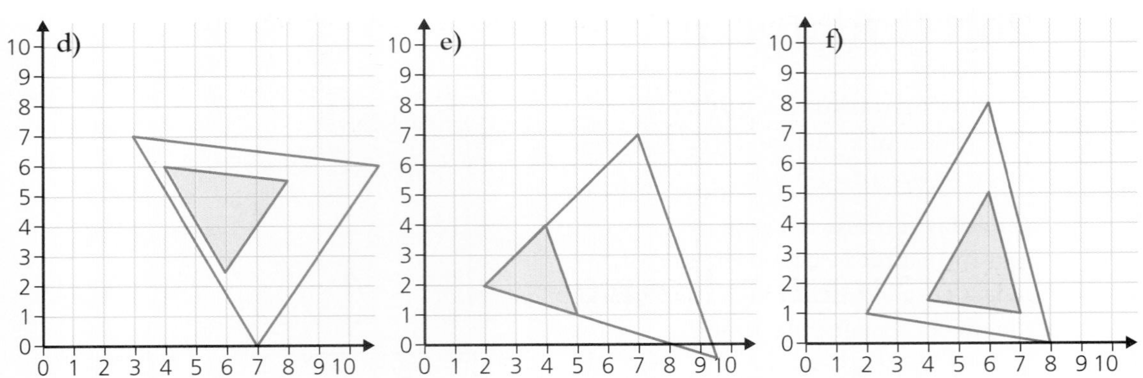

4 ✓ a) What is the scale factor for the enlargement shown here?
b) What is the centre of enlargement?
c) Measure the distance from A to the centre of enlargement. Compare this to the distance from A′ to the centre of enlargement. What do you notice?

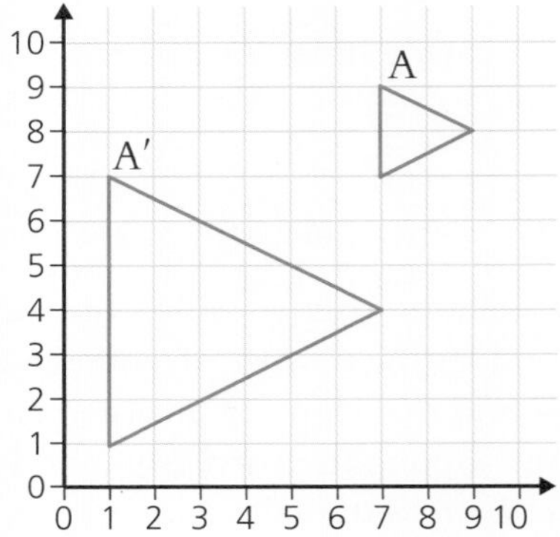

5 a) What is the scale factor for the enlargement shown here?

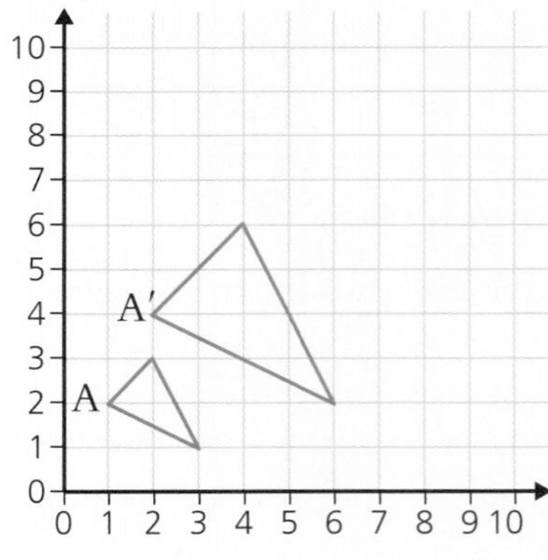

b) What is the centre of enlargement?
c) How does the distance from the centre of enlargement to A′ compare to the distance to A?
d) Write down the coordinates of the larger triangle, set out like this next to those of the smaller one:

(1, 2) → (2, 4)
(2, 3) →
(3, 1) →

→ means 'maps on to'

e) What do you notice about the coordinates of the larger triangle?
f) Would this work for questions 3 and 4? What is special about question 5?

6 Draw some x and y axes extending from 0 to 10 and plot the following points:
A = (2, 3) B = (4, 4) C = (5, 1) D = (3, 1)
Join the points to form a quadrilateral. Enlarge this using a scale factor of 2 and a centre of enlargement at (0, 1).
Write down the coordinates A′, B′, C′ and D′ of the enlarged quadrilateral.
a) State a rule connecting the points A, B, C, D and A′, B′, C′ and D′.

b) Plot the same points A, B, C, D on a new diagram but this time extend your x-axis from 0 to 15 and your y-axis from −2 to 10. Enlarge the quadrilateral using a scale factor of 3 and a centre of enlargement at (1, 2). Write down the coordinates of the enlarged quadrilateral.

c) Does the rule you found in **a)** connecting the points A, B, C, D and A′, B′, C′ and D′ still work in this sutuation?

20.2 Similar figures

If an object is enlarged, the original object and its enlargement are **similar figures**.

Similar figures are the same shape, but are different sizes.

This implies that all the corresponding angles are equal.
It also implies that corresponding lengths are in the same ratio; so that if one side has been doubled in length, so too are all the other sides.

The following diagrams each show two figures A and B which are similar figures.

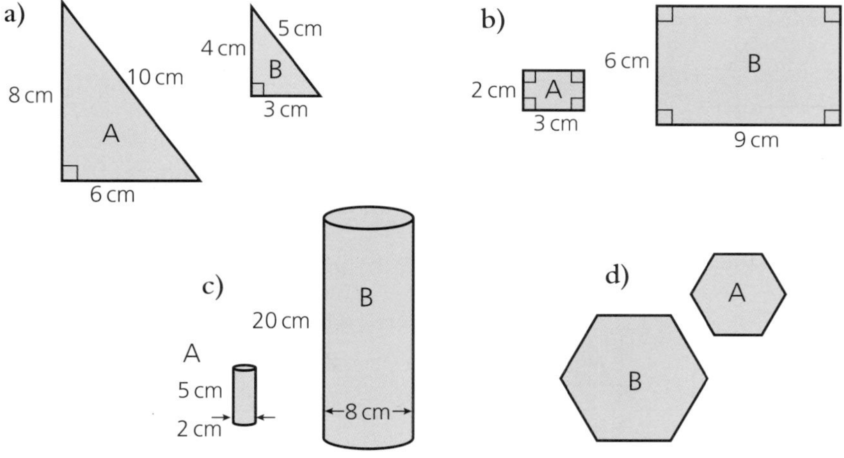

1 Decide whether the following diagrams show pairs of similar figures or not.

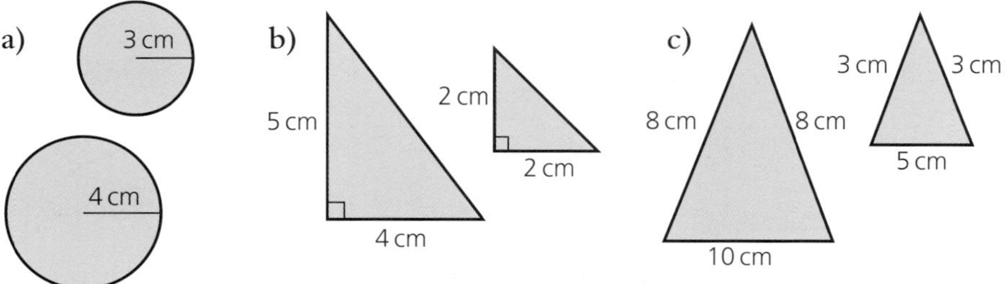

(continued on next page)

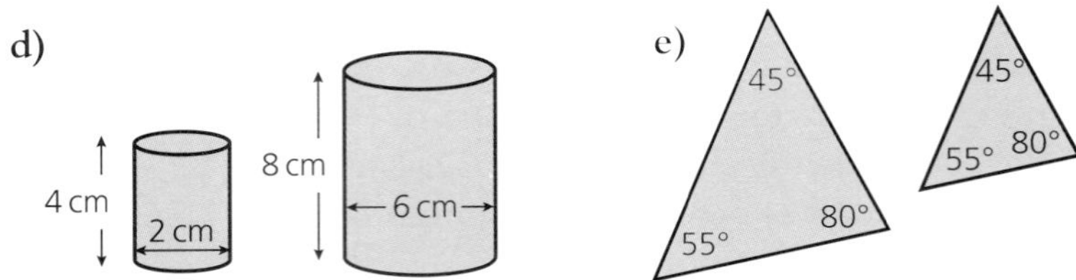

2 Find the lengths of each line marked by a letter, given that each pair of figures is similar. ✓

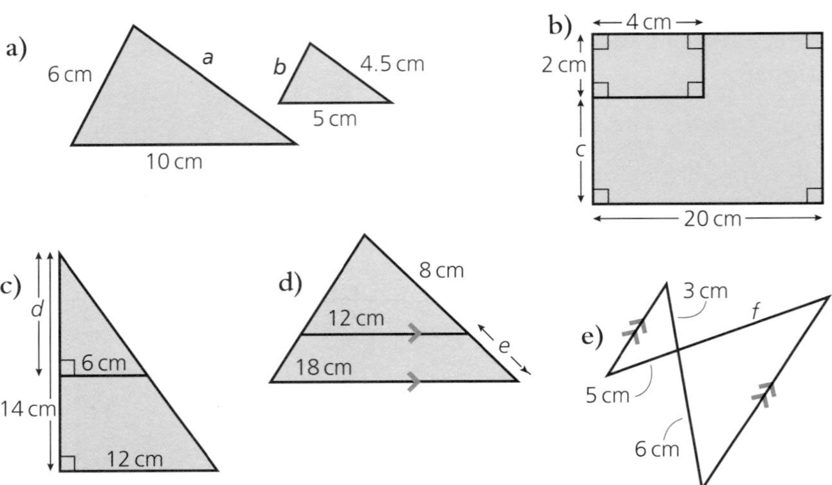

3 Explain why the following diagrams do show pairs of similar figures. In some cases you will have to look for angles which match.

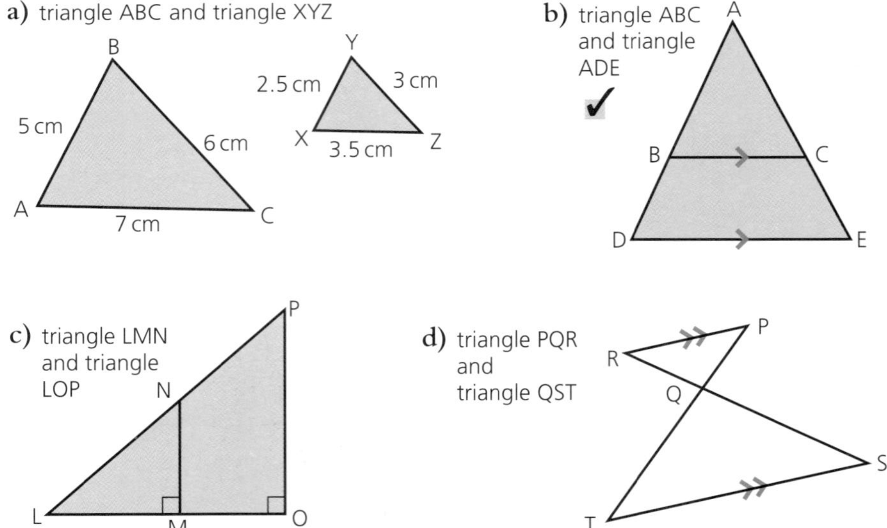

20.3 Fractional enlargements

If the scale factor is less than 1, the image is smaller than the original. So, if the scale factor is $\frac{1}{2}$, the length of each side of the image will be half as long as on the original. (Note that we still use the term 'enlargement' even though the image is smaller than the original.)

1 This diagram shows the shaded shape enlarged by a scale factor of $\frac{1}{2}$.

a) What are the coordinates of the centre of enlargement? ✓

b) What has happened to the distance of the image from the centre of enlargement?

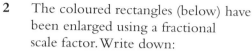

2 The coloured rectangles (below) have been enlarged using a fractional scale factor. Write down:

(i) the scale factor

(ii) the coordinates of the centre of enlargement.

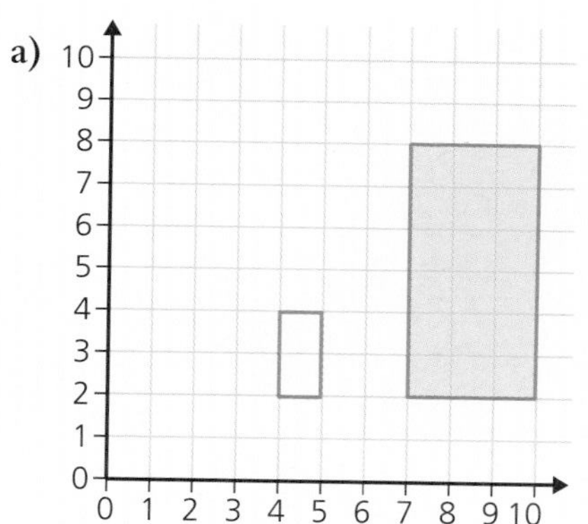

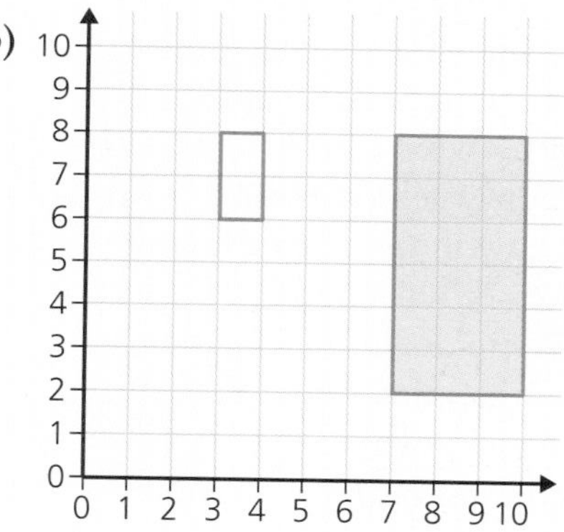

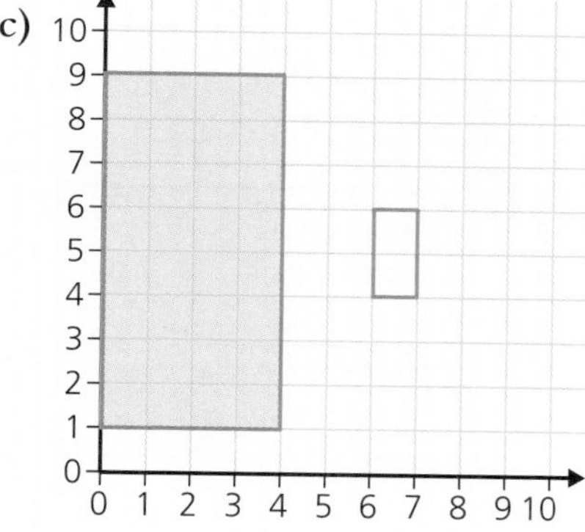

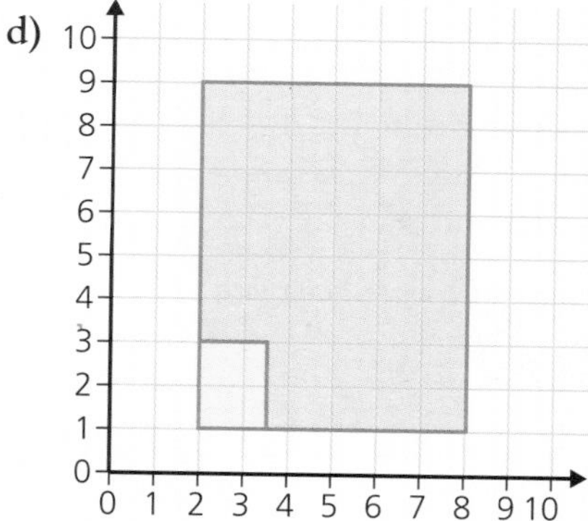

3 Draw a diagram like this showing the triangle ABC.

a) Draw the triangle A′B′C′ which results from an enlargement scale factor $\frac{1}{2}$ with the point (1, 3) as the centre of enlargement.

b) On the same diagram show the triangle XYZ which results from an enlargement of ABC using a scale factor 3 with (0, 0) as the centre of enlargement.

c) Now show the triangle PQR which results from an enlargement of ABC using a scale factor of 3 with the point (0, 2) as the centre of enlargement.

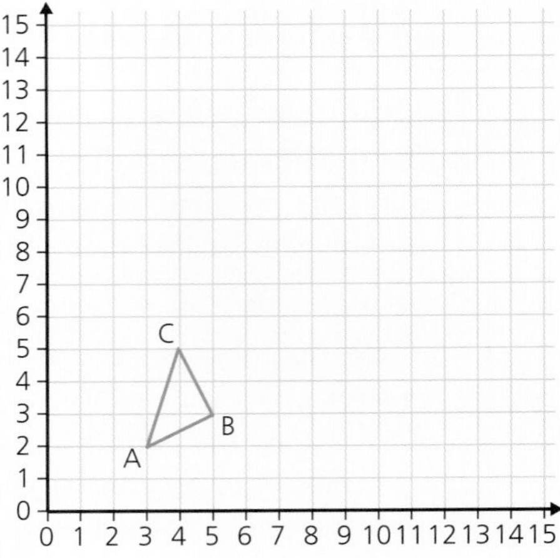

20.4 Reflections

A **reflection** is a transformation in which a figure or object is flipped over and moved to the other side of the mirror line (or axis of reflection).

1 Each of the following diagrams shows a reflection of the triangle ABC onto A′B′C′:

a) Copy each diagram.

b) Draw in the mirror line or axis of reflection.

c) Write down the equation of the mirror line. ✔

d) Write down the coordinates for A, B and C with the transformed coordinates A′, B′ and C′ next to each one.

e) Write down a rule for working out the coordinates A′, B′ and C′ each time. ✔

(See next page for (iii) and (iv))

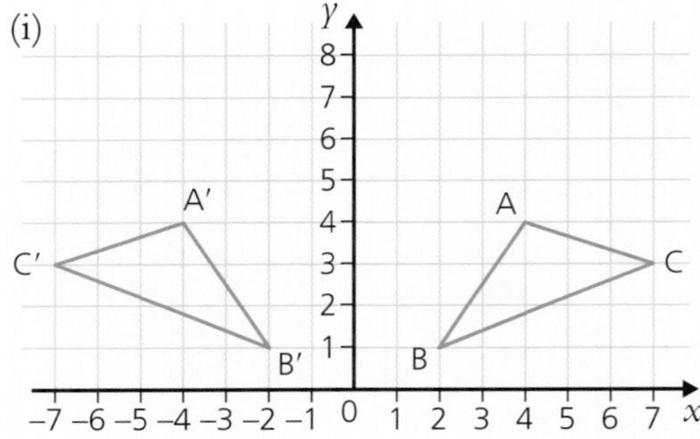

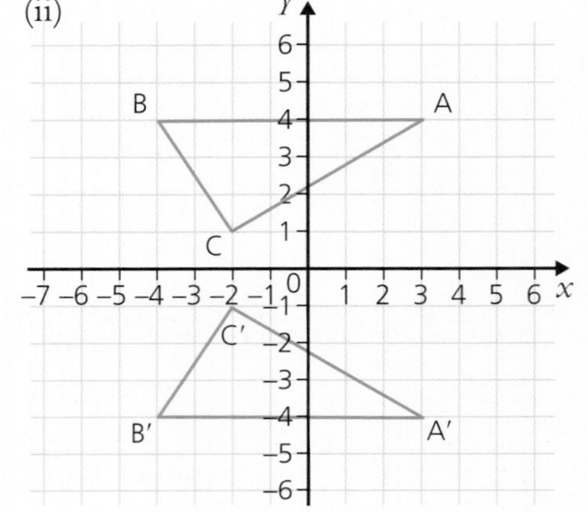

(iii) (iv)

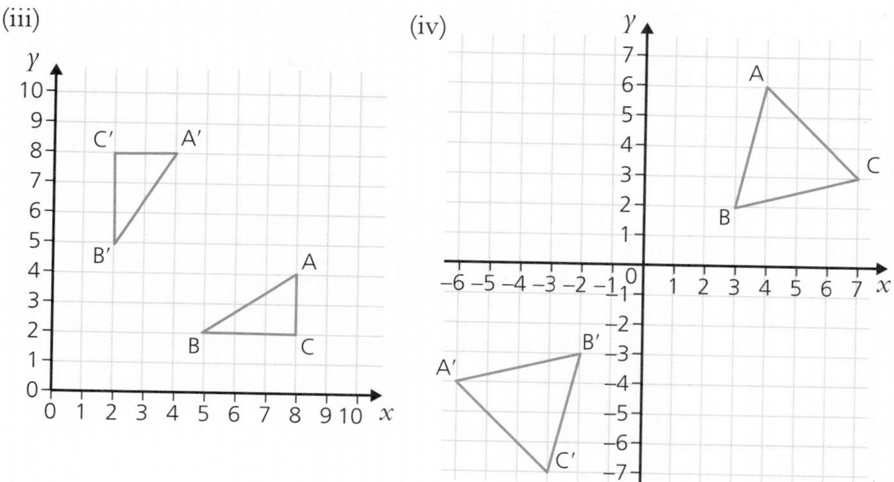

2 Explain why triangle A is not a reflection of triangle B in the given mirror line. ✓

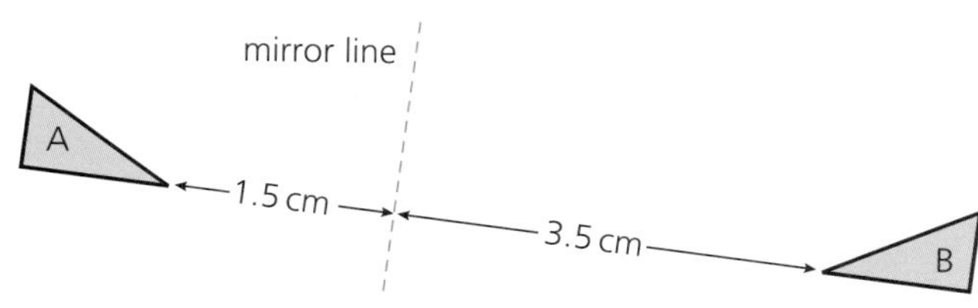

3 Explain why rectangle A is not a reflection of rectangle B in the given mirror line.

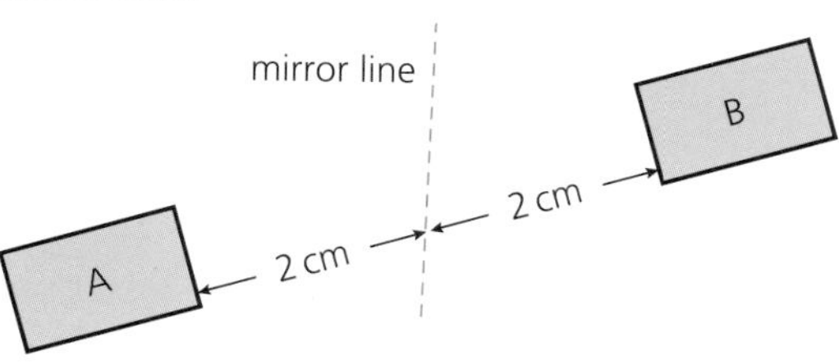

4 Draw x and y axes both extending from −5 to +5.
Plot the points A (2, 1), B (2, 3), C (5, 3), D (5, 1).
Reflect the rectangle ABCD in the line $y = -x$.
Write down the coordinates of the image A′B′C′D′.

ICT Extra!

Use LOGO to draw a figure and its reflection.
Can you produce a reflection in the line $y = x$?
Try to draw the diagram for question 1 part (iii). Then try a figure of your own choice. There are some useful Logo commands on page 161 which may help you.

20.5 Rotations and translations

A **rotation** is a transformation in which a figure or object is rotated about a point called the **centre of rotation.** All the lines in the figure are turned through the same angle.

1 The following diagrams each show a rotation about the origin (0, 0).

Copy each diagram and write down the number of degrees the triangle has rotated in an *anticlockwise* direction.

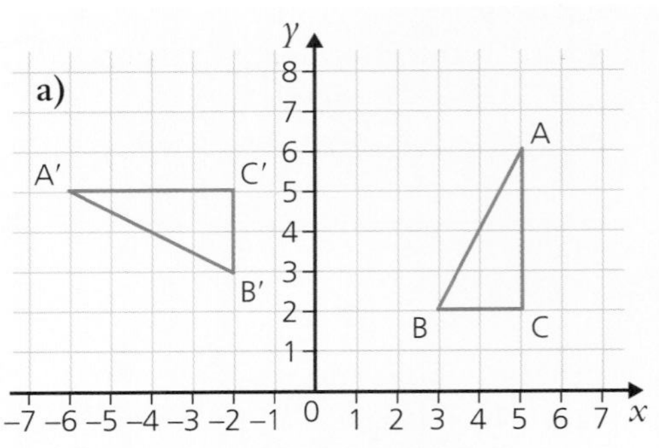

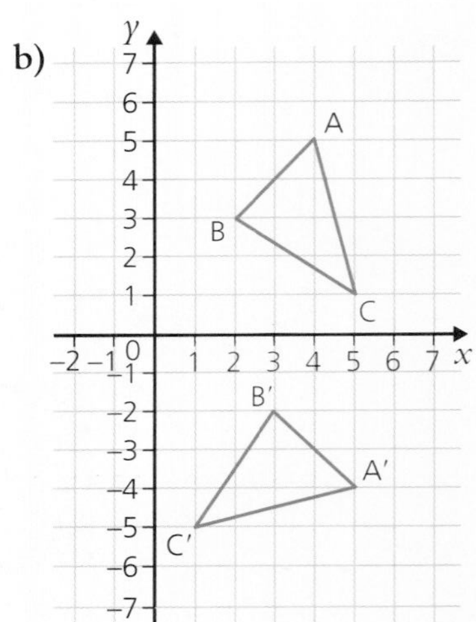

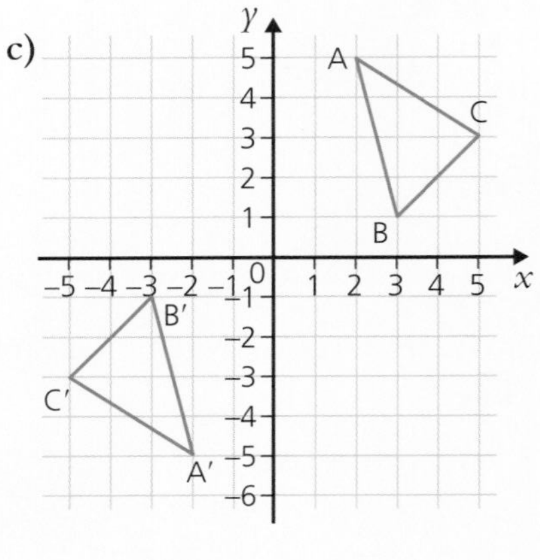

2 Draw x and y axes both extending from −5 to +5.
Plot the points A (2, 1), B (4, 2) and C (4, 4). Rotate the triangle ABC through 180° with the centre of rotation at (1, 0).

3 Explain why A is *not* the centre of rotation.

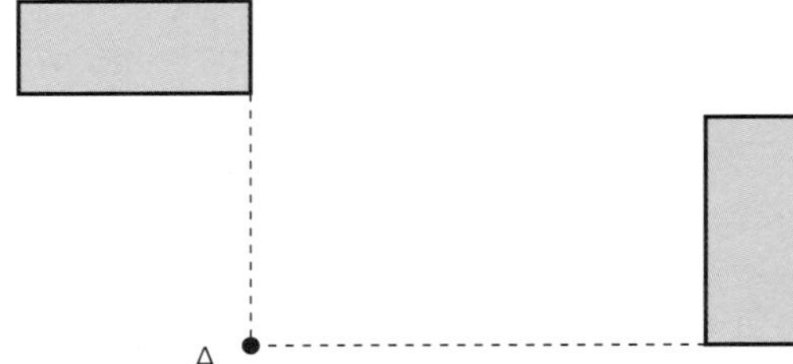

A **translation** involves sliding the figure across the page. The size of the figure is not changed, nor is it rotated or turned over.

4 This diagram shows a **translation**. The triangle ABC has been translated 5 units in the x direction and 2 units in the y direction.

a) Write in the coordinates missing from these statements:

A (1, 4) → A′ (6, 6)

B (,) → B′ (,)

C (,) → C′ (,)

b) Explain how the coordinates A′, B′ and C′ can be worked out from the coordinates of A, B and C.

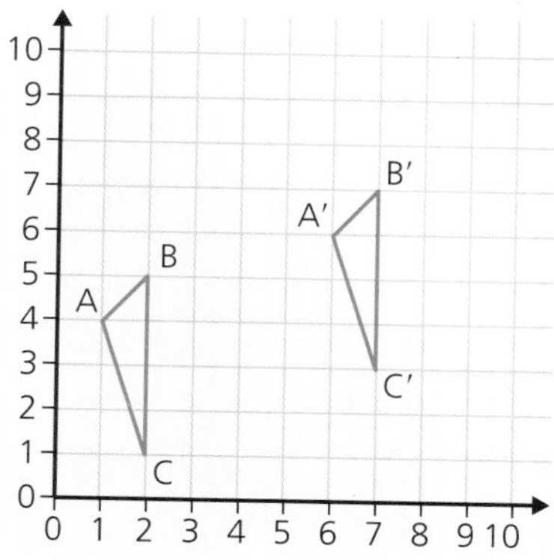

5 Draw x and y axes extending from 0 to 10. Plot the points A (7, 8), B (7, 3) and C (10, 5). Translate the triangle ABC by moving −4 units in the x direction and −3 units in the y direction. Write down the coordinates A′ B′ C′ of your new triangle.

6 Say which single transformation will map:

a) B onto A b) C onto A
c) A onto C d) A onto D
e) D onto A f) A onto E
g) A onto F h) A onto G
i) A onto H j) C onto B
k) C onto F l) G onto D.

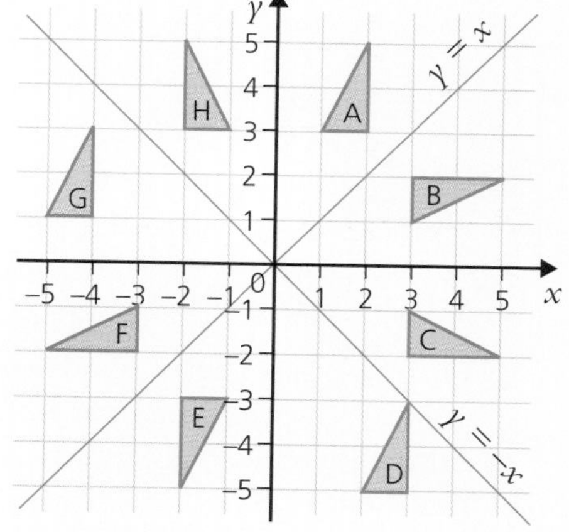

7 Which transformation will map:

a) A onto B b) A onto C
c) A onto D d) C onto B
e) D onto C.

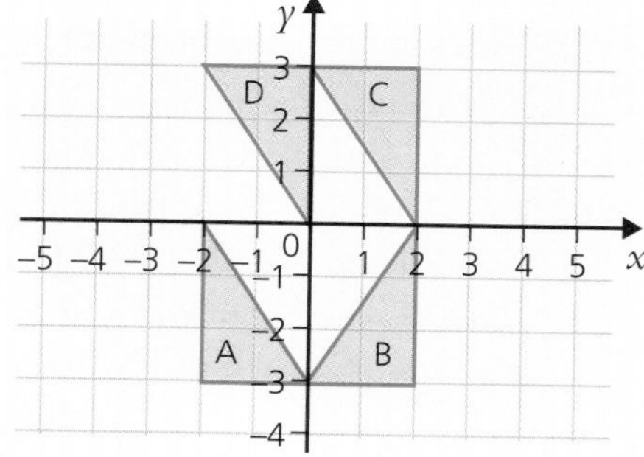

Congruent figures are the same shape and the same size. Reflections, rotations and translations are all examples of transformations which do not affect the shape or size of a figure.

8 In the following diagrams triangles A and B are congruent. Describe accurately the transformation which has been used to map triangle A onto triangle B.

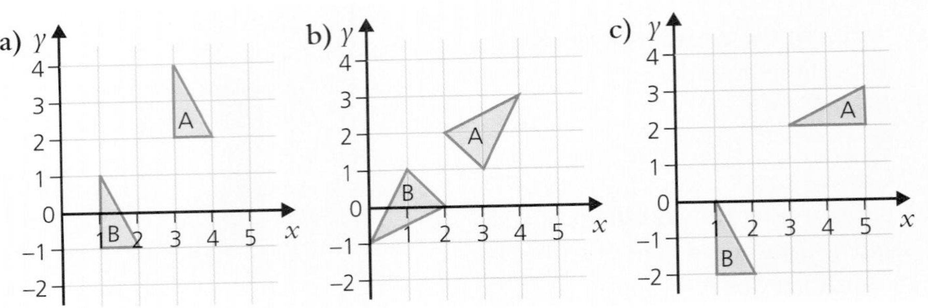

20.6 Combined transformations

A series of two or more transformations (for example, a translation followed by a rotation) is described as a **combined transformation**.

1 ✓ a) On graph paper draw x and y axes extending from −10 to +10. Plot the points A (2, 4), B (8, 4) and C (8, 7) to form triangle ABC.
b) Reflect triangle ABC in the x-axis and draw its image $A_1B_1C_1$.
c) Now reflect triangle $A_1B_1C_1$ in the y-axis to form triangle $A_2B_2C_2$. Write down the coordinates of $A_2B_2C_2$.
d) Which single transformation would map ABC directly on to $A_2B_2C_2$?

2 a) On graph paper draw x and y axes extending from −4 to +12. Plot the points P (2, 2), Q (3, 2) and R (2, 4) to form triangle PQR.
b) Enlarge triangle PQR using a scale factor of 3 and centre (0, 2) to give triangle $P_1Q_1R_1$.
c) Now translate triangle $P_1Q_1R_1$ by moving it 2 units in the x direction and 2 units in the y direction. Draw its image and label it $P_2Q_2R_2$.
d) Which single transformation will map PQR directly on to $P_2Q_2R_2$?

3 a) On graph paper draw x and y axes extending from −10 to +10. Draw the triangle L (4, 2), M (8, 2), N (4, 8).
b) Reflect the triangle LMN in the line $x = 2$ and show its image as $L_1M_1N_1$.
c) Now reflect triangle $L_1M_1N_1$ in the line $y = -2$. Label its image $L_2M_2N_2$.
d) What are the coordinates of $L_2M_2N_2$? Which single transformation will map $L_2M_2N_2$ back to LMN?

SIMULTANEOUS EQUATIONS

21.1 The graphical approach

The diagram below shows the graphs of the equations $y = x + 3$ and $x + y = 7$. The point at which the graphs intersect is of particular interest since it gives us information about *both* equations.

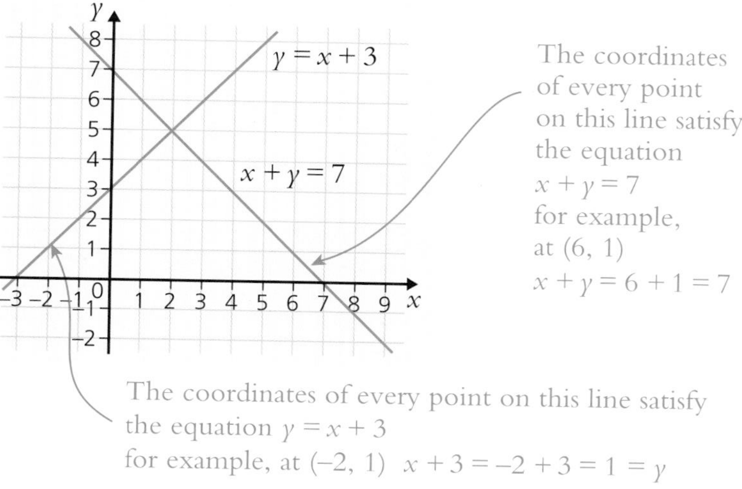

y
x
y = x + 3
x + y = 7
The coordinates of every point on this line satisfy the equation x + y = 7 for example, at (6, 1) x + y = 6 + 1 = 7
The coordinates of every point on this line satisfy the equation y = x + 3 for example, at (–2, 1) x + 3 = –2 + 3 = 1 = y

The coordinates of the point where the lines intersect must satisfy both equations at the same time, i.e. simultaneously, since the point lies on both lines.

Each equation taken separately has an infinite number of solutions because for *any* given value of x, a value of y may be found to balance the equation. However, only the values $x = 2$ and $y = 5$ will make both equations work.

(Check: at (2, 5) $x + 3 = 2 + 3 = 5 = y$ and $x + y = 2 + 5 = 7$.)

In general, a pair of equations in x and y may be solved simultaneously by drawing the graphs of the equations and finding the x and y values at the point of intersection.

1 Use the diagram to find the simultaneous solution of the equations $2y + x = 14$ and $y = x - 5$. Check by substituting into both equations.

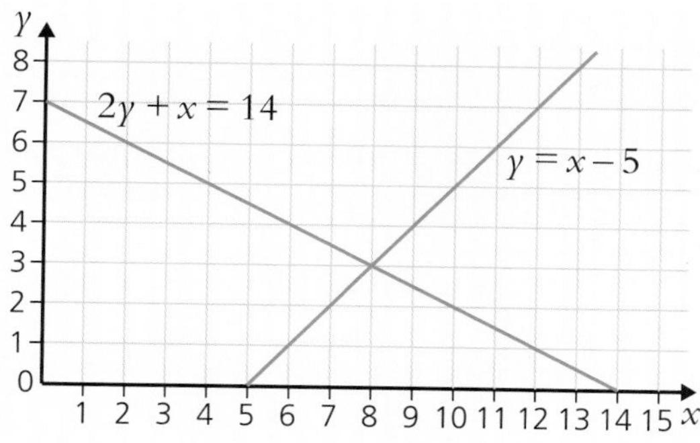

2 For each of the points A, B and C in the diagram, write a pair of equations and find their simultaneous solution. Check by substitution.

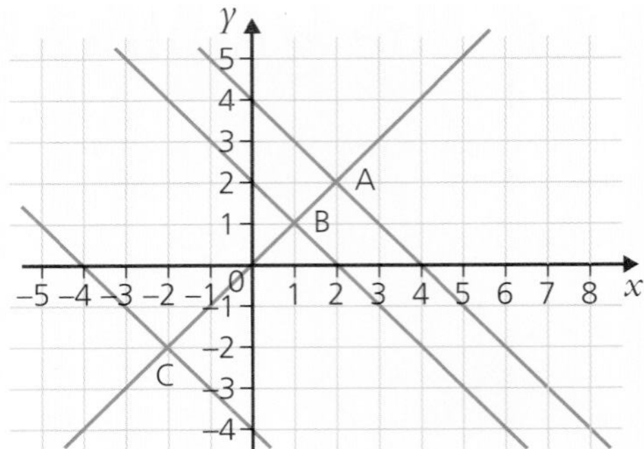

3 Repeat question 2 for this diagram.

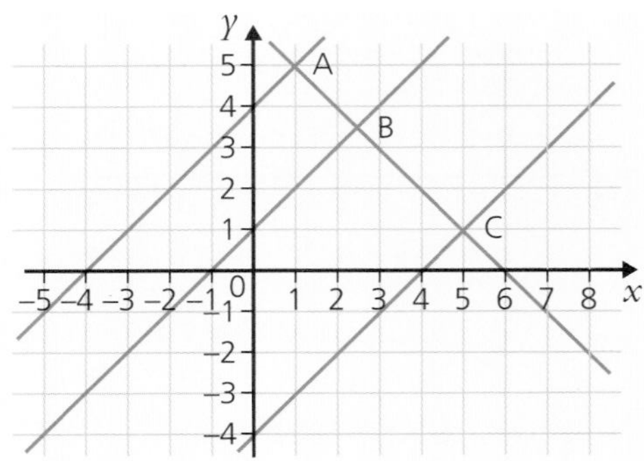

Once either the x or y value of the simultaneous solution is known, the other value may be found by substitution.

Example

Solve the simultaneous equations $y = 2x + 1$ and $y = x + 4$.

Answer

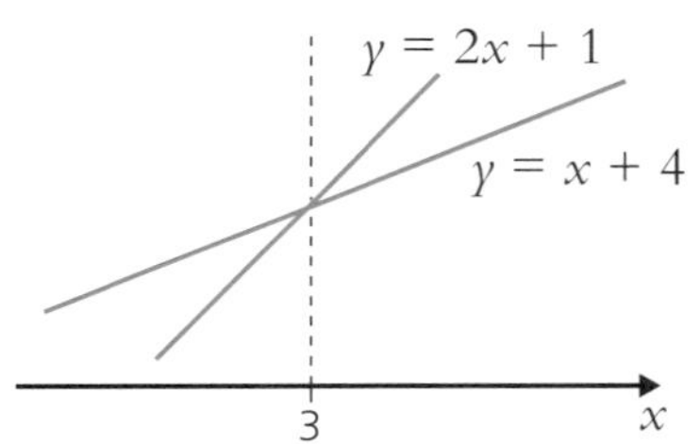

From the diagram, part of the solution of the simultaneous equations:

$$y = 2x + 1 \quad (1)$$

and $y = x + 4 \quad (2)$

is given by $x = 3$.

Substituting for x in (1) gives

$$y = 2 \times 3 + 1 = 7$$

(*Note*: substituting for x in (2) gives the same result for y.)

Therefore the simultaneous solution of the equations is $x = 3$ and $y = 7$.

---

4 By selecting the appropriate diagram from those given opposite, in each case, find the simultaneous solution of these pairs of equations. Check your answers by substitution and show your working.

a) $y = x + 2$
$x + y = 12$

b) $y = x + 5$
$y = 3x - 3$

c) $y = x + 1$
$x + y = 4$

d) $y = 2x - 3$
$2x + y = 15$

e) $4y = x + 3$
$x + 2y = 18$

f) $x + y = 1$
$2x + y = -2$

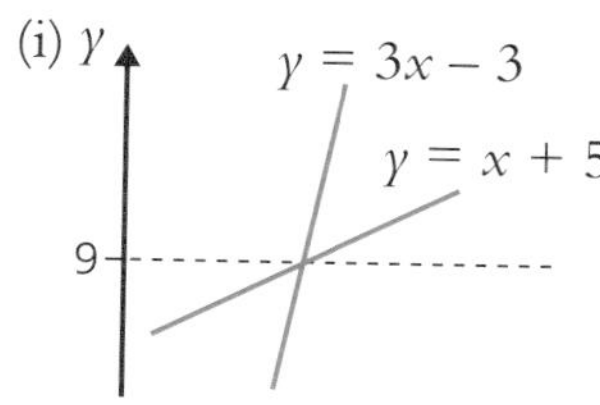

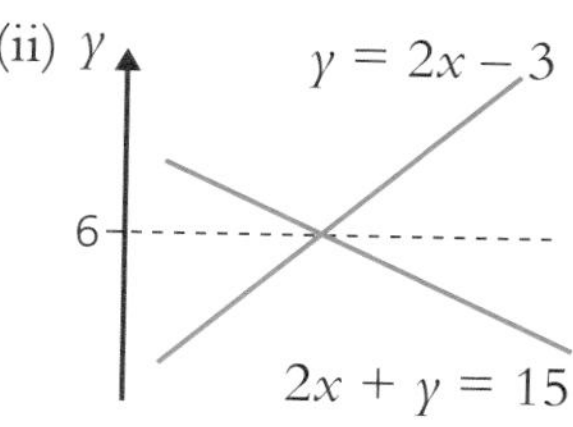

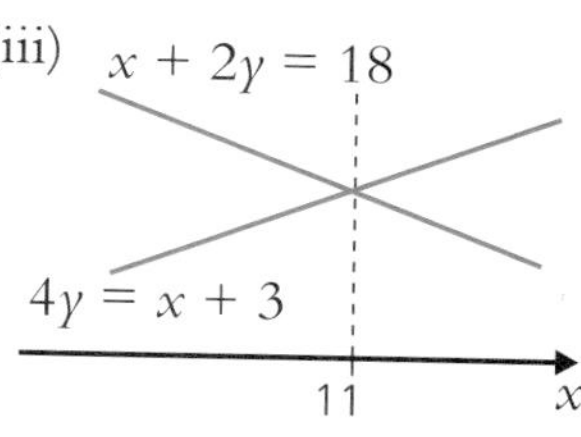

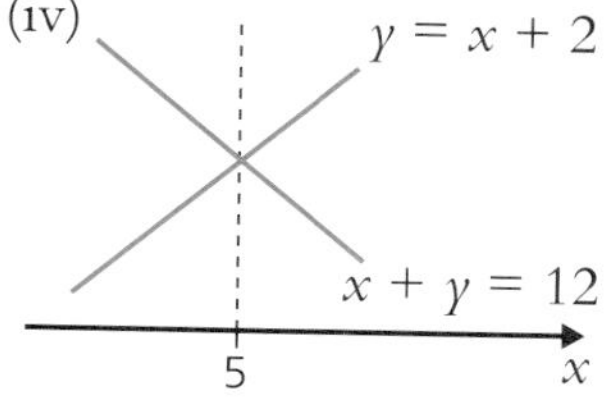

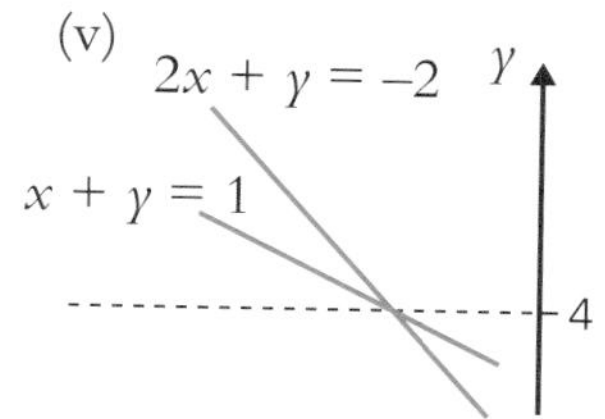

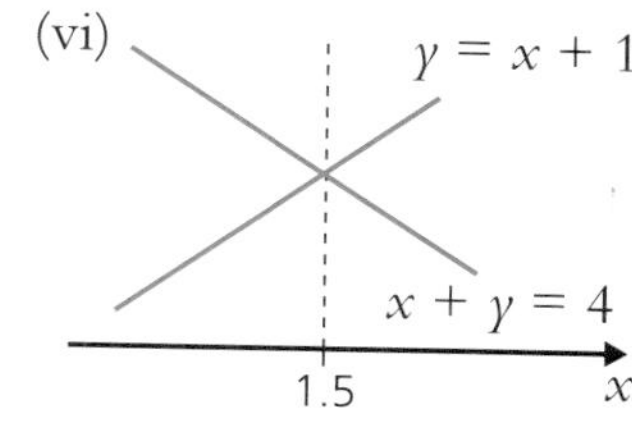

The ability to recognise that a particular equation will produce a straight line is useful because, in this case, we need only find the coordinates of *two* of its points to be able to draw the graph. Such equations are known as **linear** equations and include any that may be written in the form $y = mx + c$.

For example,

$4x + 5y = 9$ and $x - 2y = -5$ are linear

but $y = x^2 + 1$ and $2x + y^2 = 3$ are not.

5 Which of the following equations are linear?

a) $y - 3x = 8$ b) $x^2 + y^2 = 25$ c) $y = \frac{x}{3}$ d) $y = \frac{3}{x}$

Once an equation is recognised as linear we can proceed by selecting values for x or y that allow the coordinates to be found as simply as possible.

Example

Draw the graph of $2x + 3y = 12$.

Answer

The equation $2x + 3y = 12$ is a linear equation.

Taking $x = 0$ gives $3y = 12$ and so $y = 4$, i.e. the point (0, 4) lies on the graph.

Taking $y = 0$ gives $x = 6$ and so the point (6, 0) must lie on the graph.

It follows that the graph of the equation $2x + 3y = 12$ may be drawn as shown below.

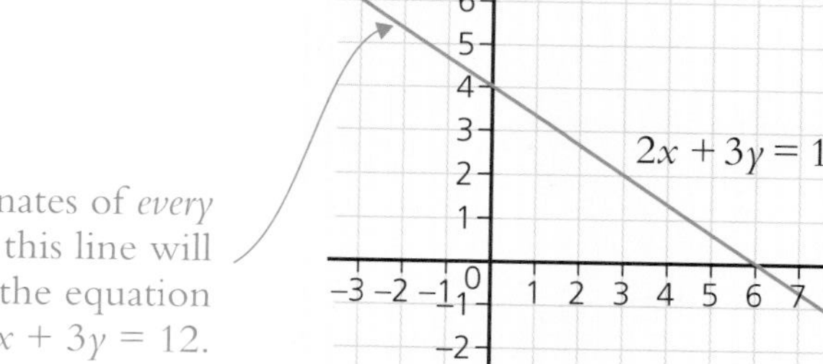

The coordinates of *every* point on this line will satisfy the equation $2x + 3y = 12$.

6 Solve the following pairs of simultaneous equations by drawing their graphs. (Label the x and y axes from -5 to 5.)

a) $x + y = 4$, $y = x - 2$
b) $x + y = -1$, $y = x - 5$
c) $x + 2y = 0$, $y = x + 6$
d) $y = x$, $y = 2x + 3$
e) $2x + y = 8$, $y = 2x - 2$
f) $x + 2y = 0$, $2y = x - 6$

7 Find the solutions of these simultaneous equations correct to 1 decimal place by drawing their graphs on axes labelled from -2 to 6.

a) $x + 3y = 9$, $y = x - 2$
b) $3x + 2y = 6$, $y = x + 1$
c) $2x + y = 11$, $y = x$

21.2 The elimination method

An alternative approach to solving simultaneous equations is to use algebra. The idea is to combine the information from both equations in such a way that we are left with a single equation with only one unknown value.

The **coefficient** of a letter in an expression is the number it is multiplied by. For example, in the expression $5x - 7y$, the coefficient of x is 5 and the coefficient of y is -7.

Using the **elimination method**, we subtract one equation from the other to eliminate terms that have the same coefficients.

Example

Solve the simultaneous equations $x + 3y = 13$ and $x + y = 7$.

Answer

$x + 3y = 13$ (1)
$x + y = 7$ (2)

It's a good idea to label the equations.

(1) − (2) gives:
$2y = 6$
Therefore $y = 3$.

The coefficient of x is the same in both equations and so we subtract one equation from the other to eliminate x.

Substituting for y in (2) gives
$x + 3 = 7$
Therefore $x = 4$.

Once the value of a letter is found, we use this information to find the value of the other letter

Check:
substituting for x and y in (1) gives:
$x + 3y = 4 + 3 \times 3 = 13$.

We should always check that the values found make both equations work

The solution is $x = 4$, $y = 3$.

1 Solve these simultaneous equations:

a) $x + 5y = 21$, $x + 3y = 13$
b) $x + 7y = 25$, $x + 2y = 10$
c) $2x + 3y = 16$, $2x + y = 12$
d) $3x + 8y = 27$, $3x + 5y = 18$
e) $5x + 3y = 28$, $4x + 3y = 23$
f) $11x + 2y = 43$, $6x + 2y = 28$
g) $7x + 4y = 10$, $3x + 4y = 2$
h) $9x + 5y = 12$, $6x + 5y = 3$
i) $11x + 7y = 6$, $11x + 9y = 14$
j) $8x + 3y = 13$, $10x + 3y = 11$

The coefficients of all the letters in question 1 are positive, but the elimination method works in the same way if the coefficients of the terms to be eliminated are both negative.

Example

Solve the simultaneous equations $5x - 3y = 8$ and $2x - 3y = -1$.

Answer

$5x - 3y = 11$ (1)
$2x - 3y = -1$ (2)

The coefficient of y is the same in both equations so we subtract to eliminate y.

(1) − (2) gives

$3x = 12$

Note that $11 - -1 = 11 + 1 = 12$.

Therefore $x = 4$.

Substituting for x in (1) gives:

$20 - 3y = 11$

$3y = 9$

Therefore $y = 3$.

Check in (2): $2 \times 4 - 3 \times 3 = -1$.

The solution is $x = 4$, $y = 3$.

Simultaneous equations are not always expressed in terms of the letters x and y. Very often, when equations are used to solve problems, the choice of letters is influenced by the quantity represented. For example, we might use the letter c to stand for a cost or the letter d to stand for a distance.

---

2 Solve these equations:

a) $5h - 4t = 14$, $4h - 4t = 8$
b) $4u - 3v = 30$, $u - 3v = 3$
c) $7n - 3w = 23$, $4n - 3w = 8$
d) $3a - 5b = 36$, $a - 5b = 22$
e) $10x - 3y = 40$, $8x - 3y = 26$
f) $50w - 11m = 445$, $25w - 11m = 195$
g) $6p - 5q = 70$, $p - 5q = 20$
h) $3m - 16n = 1$, $m - 16n = 11$
i) $5r - 2s = 20$, $3r - 2s = 28$
j) $4u - 5v = 9$, $u - 5v = -9$
k) $3h - 4t = -11$, $h - 4t = -17$
l) $6c - 3d = 21$, $2c - 3d = 13$

To eliminate terms which have opposite signs, the equations must be added.

Example

Solve the equations $2x + 3y = 23$ and $x - 3y = -11$.

Answer

$2x + 3y = 23$ (1) Adding these equations will eliminate the
$x - 3y = -11$ (2) terms containing the letter y.

(1) + (2) gives $3y + -3y = 3y - 3y = 0$
$3x = 12$ $23 + -11 = 23 - 11 = 12$

Therefore $x = 4$.

Substituting for x in (1) gives:

$8 + 3y = 23$
$3y = 15$

Therefore $y = 5$.

Check in (2): $4 - 3 \times 5 = -11$

The solution is $x = 4$, $y = 5$.

---

3 Solve these simultaneous equations:

a) $3a + 2b = 34$
$2a - 2b = 6$

b) $2s - 5t = 5$
$3s + 5t = 45$

c) $q - 4p = 27$
$q + 4p = -5$

In some situations it may be necessary to multiply both sides of one of the equations by some number in order to match the coefficients of one of the letters.

Example

Solve the equations $7x - 6y = 29$ and $2x + 3y = 13$.

Answer

$7x - 6y = 29$ (1) As it stands, the coefficients in the two equations don't
$2x + 3y = 13$ (2) match, but if both sides of equation (2) are multiplied by 2 then y may be eliminated.

Equation (2) × 2 gives:

$4x + 6y = 26$ (3)

Equation (1) + equation (3) gives:

$11x = 55$ To find y we substitute into the simplest equation.
$x = 5$

Substituting for x in equation (2) gives:

$10 + 3y = 13$
$3y = 3$
$y = 1$

Check: substituting for x and y in (1) gives $7x - 6y = 35 - 6 = 29$.

The required solution is $x = 5$ and $y = 1$.

In questions 4, 5 and 6 there is no need to complete the solutions

4 Eliminate y from these equations to produce an equation in x.

a) $3x - 8y = 11$, $x + 4y = 9$ ✓
b) $8x + 9y = 17$, $2x + 3y = 4$
c) $11x + 7y = 5$, $x - y = 3$
d) $7x - 12y = 10$, $x + 4y = 9$
e) $9x - 12y = 11$, $2x - 6y = 5$
f) $18x + 5y = -2$, $3x + y = 8$

5 Multiply each of these simultaneous equations by an appropriate number in order to eliminate y and produce an equation in x.

a) $5x + 3y = 11$, $3x + 2y = 5$
b) $7x + 2y = 8$, $2x - 3y = 1$
c) $11x - 4y = 10$, $4x - 6y = 3$

6 Eliminate x from these equations to produce an equation in y.

a) $4x + 3y = 15$, $2x + y = 6$
b) $3x - 5y = 4$, $12x + y = 10$
c) $3x + y = 5$, $2x + 3y = 1$

7 Solve these simultaneous equations:

a) $x + 2y = 15$, $3x + y = 15$
b) $4p + 3q = 26$, $2p + q = 12$
c) $3a + 5b = 31$, $2a - b = -1$
d) $7m - 3n = 19$, $2m + n = 11$
e) $8u - 4v = 0$, $3u - 2v = -6$
f) $3h - d = 110$, $5h - 2d = 120$
g) $2c + 3d = 95$, $3c + 2d = 105$
h) $3g + 4h = 73$, $2g - 3h = -8$
i) $5x - 3y = 55$, $3x - 5y = -15$

21.3 Solving problems

A first step in solving some problems is to re-write the given information in the form of simultaneous equations. The solution of these equations may then be interpreted in terms of the original problem.

> Kathy,
>
> Please order some theatre tickets for me for the 6.30 p.m. performance on Wednesday. The cost for adults is £10 each but the kids get in for $\frac{1}{2}$ price.
>
> I've collected £310 to cover the cost of the tickets – we need 39 altogether.
>
> Thanks, Pete

Example

How many tickets will Kathy need to order for adults, and how many for children?

Answer

Let a stand for the number of adult tickets and let c stand for the number of tickets for children.

Re-writing the information we obtain:

$a + c = 39$ (1) The total number of tickets needed is 39

$10a + 5c = 310$ (2) The cost of a tickets at £10 each, for example, is £10a. Note: units aren't needed in the equation.

Each term in equation (2) contains a factor of 5 and so the equation may be simplified by dividing both sides by 5, giving:

$2a + c = 62$ (3)

Subtracting equation (1) from equation (3) gives: $a = 23$.

Substituting for a in (1) gives $c = 16$.

Check:
$23 \times £10 + 16 \times £5$
$= £230 + £80 = £310$.

Kathy will need to order 23 adult tickets and 16 tickets for children.

---

1 Gaynor orders some calculators for re-sale to pupils at the school. Model A is a basic 4-function calculator which is sold for £4 and model B is a scientific calculator priced at £8. Altogether, 140 calculators are sold for a total of £1020.

a) Using a to stand for the number of model A calculators and b to stand for the number of model B calculators, write an equation for the number of calculators sold.

b) Write a second equation in terms of a and b using the information about prices.

c) Solve the equations simultaneously to find the number of each model sold.

d) Gaynor orders the two types of calculator from different companies to get the best prices. How much, in total, does she need to collect for each model?

2 The perimeter of this rectangle is 30 cm and its length is 6 cm more than its width.

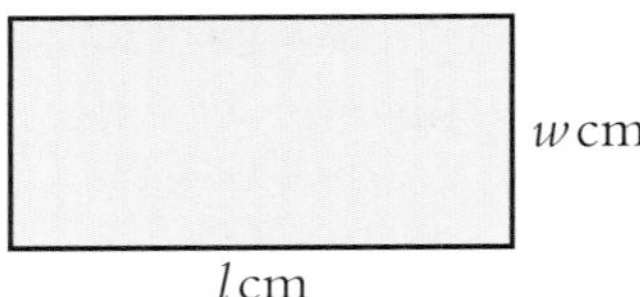

a) Use this information to form a pair of simultaneous equations.

b) Solve the equations and find the area of the rectangle.

3 A car hire company charges a basic amount per day and then adds an extra amount based on the mileage.
Lisa hires a car for one day. She travels 150 miles and is charged £30.
Adam hires the same model of car for three days and travels 400 miles. He is charged £85.

a) Using £b to stand for the basic charge and £m to stand for the extra charge per mile, re-write the given information in the form of two simultaneous equations.

b) Solve the equations to find the basic charge and amount per mile.

c) How much should Vicky expect to pay to hire the same kind of vehicle for two days to cover a journey of 450 miles?

4 Find the coordinates of the point where the graphs of $7x - y = 1$ and $x + 3y = 41$ intersect.

5 In the diagram, the height of a building is represented by h m and the total distance from B to C is made up of x m across a road and 3 m for the verge.
One equation connecting x and h is:
$h = 0.6(15 + x)$

a) Find a second equation connecting x and h. ✓

b) Solve the equations simultaneously to find the height of the building and the distance across the road.

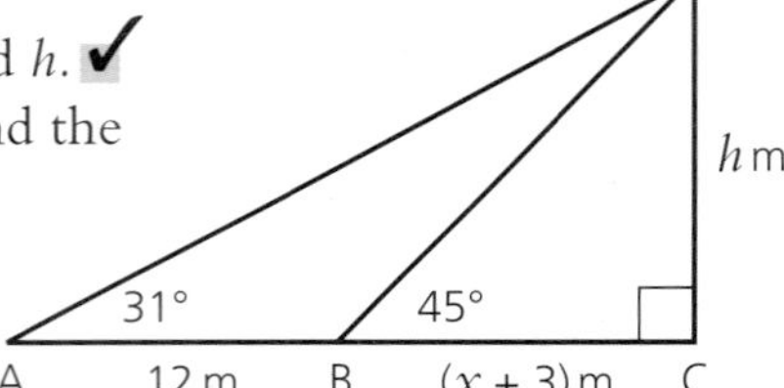

FREQUENCY TABLES

22.1 Frequency tables and medians

The data from surveys and experiments are often organised into frequency tables (Unit 14). We may need to find the median and mean of such data.

Investigation

Cereal manufacturers try to entice customers by offering sets of 'Free gifts' in their products. Why is it necessary to buy so many packets to collect a full set? Suppose there are 6 different models to collect. How many packets of cereal will you need to buy in order to collect a complete set?

In this investigation we will simulate this situation.

You need either:

an ordinary six-sided dice
or a six-sided spinner
or a hexagonal pencil with each side numbered 1 to 6.

For the simulation, each number on your dice, spinner or pencil stands for a different gift in the set.

In order to simulate this situation we have to assume two things:

- there are equal numbers of all six gifts in the country as a whole (and in each region)
- the gifts occur randomly in the cereal packets, so that it is 'just luck' as to which one you get.

Do you think these assumptions are realistic?

---

1 a) *Guess* how many packets of cereal you would need to buy in order to collect a complete set of models.

b) Make a table to record your experiment like this:

Gift number	Tally
1	
2	
3	
4	
5	
6	
Total number of packets	

c) Throw your dice (alternatively spin the spinner or roll the pencil). Record your score each time using a tally mark.
Stop the simulation when you have scored every number *at least once*. Some numbers will have been scored more than once.

d) Count the number of times you had to repeat the experiment. This stands for the number of packets of cereal you had to buy.

e) Find out how many packets other members of your class had to buy. Make a frequency table of the class results.

f) What is your answer now to the question:
'How many packets of cereal do I need to buy?'
Is there any one number which is a sensible answer?

2 Here are the results of the simulation for Sanjey's class.

a) How do these results compare to those for your class?
b) What is the largest number of packets needed among Sanjey's class? What is the smallest number of packets?
c) What is the range?
d) What is the mode for the number of packets needed?
e) How many students took part in the simulation?
f) Write down all 32 results in a list. Find the median.
g) Find the mean.
h) Which result, mode, median or mean, do you think is the most representative?

Number of packets	Frequency
6	0
7	1
8	3
9	3
10	4
11	2
12	5
13	2
14	2
15	2
16	3
17	1
18	0
19	1
20	1
25	1
38	1

22.2 Cumulative frequency tables

There is an easier way to find the median for a frequency table.

As the results in a frequency table are organised in numerical order, there is no need to write them out again in a full list.

What we need is a count of how many results there are, and a way of finding the middle result (or in this case with an even number, the middle two results).

Here are the results for Sanjey's class again. Next to each frequency we have written the **cumulative frequency** or running total. This keeps a count of how many results there have been so far.

Add on each frequency as you go down

Number of packets	Frequency	Cumulative frequency
6	0	0
7	1	1
8	3 (3+1=4)	4
9	3 (4+3=7)	7
10	4 (7+4=11)	11
11	2	13
12	5	18
13	2	20
14	2	22
15	2	24
16	3	27
17	1	28
18	0	28
19	1	29
20	1	30
25	1	31
38	1	32

1 ✓ a) Where does it tell you how many results there are altogether?
b) Can you work out how to find the 16th and 17th results?
c) What is the median number of packets?
Does this agree with your answer to question 2 f) in the previous section?

2 ✓ For the assessment of GCSE art at Sam's school at least six pieces of work are required. Last year the numbers of pieces of work produced by the students in one group were as follows:
a) Copy the table and work out the cumulative frequencies.
b) How many students were there in the group?
c) What was the median number of pieces of work?

Number of pieces of work	Frequency
6	5
7	4
8	6
9	3
10	0
11	2
12	1

3 This table shows the number of pupils per class in each class of a school.
a) Copy the table, including an extra column for cumulative frequencies.
b) How many classes are there?
c) What is the median number of pupils?

Number of pupils	Frequency
27	2
28	3
29	3
30	8
31	5
32	5
33	4

4 Find the median and mode for each of these surveys.

a) Shoe sizes of girls in the athletics team

Shoe size	Frequency
5	2
$5\frac{1}{2}$	3
6	4
$6\frac{1}{2}$	3
7	6
$7\frac{1}{2}$	4
8	0
9	1

b) Number of people living in students' households in class 11X

Number of people	Frequency
2	2
3	5
4	12
5	3
6	3
7	1
8	2
10	1

c) Number of days absent for students in 11Y last week

Number of days absent	Frequency
0	17
1	6
2	2
3	3
4	0
5	2

d) Number of GCSEs obtained by students enrolling on a college course
Set out your table going down the page.

Number of GCSEs	5	6	7	8	9	10
Frequency	8	7	6	9	2	1

22.3 Frequency tables and means

If you wish to find the mean for data organised as a frequency table, there is no need to write out a long list of results.

To find the mean you need to know:

- the total for all the results
- the number of results there are.

Both these quantities can be found directly from the frequency table.

Here again are the results for the 'Free gifts' simulation run by students in Sanjey's class:

In order to find the total number of packets bought you need to multiply each result by its frequency.

(*Note*: 'x' is used to stand for the measurement or variable in the problem, 'f' stands for frequency.)

Number of packets (x)	Frequency (f)	Packets × frequency ($x \times f$)
6	0	$6 \times 0 = 0$
7	1	$7 \times 1 = 7$
8	3	$8 \times 3 = 24$
9	3	$9 \times 3 = 27$
10	4	$10 \times 4 = 40$
11	2	
12	5	
13	2	
14	2	
15	2	
16	3	
17	1	
18	0	
19	1	
20	1	
25	1	
38	1	
	TOTAL	TOTAL

1 ✓ a) Copy the table and complete the missing calculations.
b) Which total tells you how many packets of cereal were bought altogether?
c) Which total tells you how many students there were in the class?
d) How can you find the mean number of packets from these results?
e) What is the mean?
f) Is this lower or higher than the median?
g) Which is more representative?

2 Look back at the data sets in question **3** and parts **b)**, **c)** and **d)** of question **4**.
(i) Find the mean for each set of results.
(ii) Say whether the mean is higher or lower than the median.

3 Find the mean, median and mode for the results of your class's 'Free gifts' simulation. How do they compare to the results for Sanjey's class?

From experience, it has been found that if you repeat this experiment many times the results will always be slightly different, but the mean is usually similar at around 13.

22.4 Calculator means

Most scientific and programmable calculators have statistical functions programmed into them. Look for these symbols on your calculator:

$\bar{x}$ mean (sometimes called x bar)

$\sum x$ total of results (Σ is the Greek letter 'sigma' and means 'summation of')

n number of results

Note that

$$\text{mean } \bar{x} = \frac{\text{total of results}}{\text{number of results}} = \frac{\sum x}{n}$$

1 If you use the numbers 1, 2 and 3, what answers should you get for $\bar{x}$, $\sum x$ and n?

These symbols are usually the second function for a button, and to use them you will need to find the 'second function button' on your calculator. Look in the top left hand corner for:

SHIFT or INV or 2ndF

Next you need to find out how to access these statistical functions by getting your calculator into *statistics mode*. This is shown as SD or STAT on the numerical display. Some calculators have a MODE button and a list of modes under the display.

There are so many different kinds of calculators that we cannot give full instructions for all of them here. The following instructions are for a scientific calculator. (Programmable calculators may work differently. Many graphics calculators now work by 'menus'. Please refer to your own calculator manual.)

Then follow the four steps listed here.

Step 1 Get your calculator into statistics mode possibly using MODE (works for most Casio calculators).
SD will appear on the display.

Step 2 Clear the statistics memory.
(For a Casio calculator press SHIFT then AC)

Step 3 Enter the data.
(For a Casio calculator key in the number then M+)

Step 4 Read off the results.

You will find that $\bar{x}$, n and $\sum x$ are usually the second (or even third) functions on various keys on your calculator (try using the shift key, and refer to your calculator manual if necessary).

2 Now use your calculator to find the values of $\overline{x}$, n and $\sum x$ for the numbers 1, 2, and 3. Did you obtain the values you expected in question 1?

3 Find the mean of each of these data sets using your calculator. Don't forget to *clear the memory* each time.

a) The weights of 5 boys are:
63 kg, 67 kg, 58 kg, 52 kg, 70 kg ✓
If your answer here is 39.5, you are wrong! You forgot to clear the memory!

b) The temperature each day in a winter week in Dover was (in °C):
7, 5, 1, 3, 10, 8, 5 ✓

c) The playing times of six films on video are:
1 hr 50 min, 2 hr 10 min, 2 hr 40 min, 2 hr 5 min, 1 hr 57 min, 2 hr 50 min
(*Hint*: change all these times to minutes.)

d) Times taken for students to swim 25 m (in seconds):
21, 27, 25, 23, 24, 25, 27, 29

e) Heights in metres of 10 girls are:
1.60, 1.63, 1.74, 1.73, 1.59, 1.48, 1.69, 1.75, 1.80, 1.66

Step 3 has to be modified to find the mean of data in the form of a frequency table. For the GCSE art exam at Sam's school (question 2 page 211) students entered these numbers of pieces of work:

Number of pieces of work (x)	6	7	8	9	10	11	12
Frequency (f)	5	4	6	3	0	2	1

This is how to enter the data into your calculator. Use steps 1 and 2 as before. *Don't forget to clear the memory.*

Mean $\overline{x} = \dfrac{\sum fx}{\sum f}$

Step 3 Enter the data like this:

6 [×] 5 [M+]
7 [×] 4 [M+]
8 [×] 4 [M+]
9 [×] 6 [M+]
10 [×] 0 [M+]
11 [×] 2 [M+]
12 [×] 1 [M+]

Note: do not press = at any time.
Always enter the data in the order
x [×] f
results [×] frequency
not the other way round.

This method works for most scientific calculators but please check your calculator manual.

Step 4 Read off your results as before. The button [n] gives you the total number of results, which is Σf for a frequency table. Likewise the button [Σx] gives you the total for Σfx, if frequencies have been used.

4 Use your calculator to find the mean for the number of pieces of work entered for GCSE art.

5 Sam's class used a reaction-timer ruler to find their reaction times using their writing hands and their other hands. Use your calculator to find the mean and the range for both sets of results. Comment on the difference.

Reaction times in $\frac{1}{100}$ second	Frequencies	
	Writing hand	Other hand
12	1	0
13	0	0
14	1	0
15	0	0
16	3	1
17	2	2
18	5	0
19	4	3
20	3	2
21	0	2
22	1	2
23	0	6
24	0	2

6 Gopal did a survey of the number of passengers (including the driver) in cars travelling into town at 8.30 am and later at 10 am the same morning. Find the mean and range for both sets of results and comment on the differences.

Number of passengers	Frequencies	
	8.30 am	10 am
1	9	3
2	4	4
3	2	5
4	3	2
5	0	0
6	2	0
7	1	0

Sometimes we need to find the mean of *grouped data.*

Example

This table shows the pulse rates for a group of 30 students. Find the mean pulse rate.

Pulse rates counted in beats per minute	
Number of beats	Frequency
60–64	1
65–69	3
70–74	6
75–79	11
80–84	5
85–89	2
90–94	2

Answer

Because the results have been grouped as class intervals, we no longer know the results for individual students. This means that we do not know the exact value for calculating the mean.

(continued)

We can estimate the mean quite closely by taking the *middle* of each class interval as the value of 'x'. So for instance, the middle value for class 60–64 is 62. Each of these values is then multiplied by the frequency as before.

Pulse rates counted in beats per minute			
Number of beats	**Frequency f**	**Middle of class interval x**	**Frequency × middle fx**
60–64	1	62	62
65–69	3	67	201
70–74	6	72	432
75–79	11	77	847
80–84	5	82	410
85–89	2	87	174
90–94	2	92	184
TOTAL	30		2310

Here the mean, $\bar{x} = \dfrac{\text{total for } f \times x}{\text{total for } f} = \dfrac{\sum fx}{\sum x}$ $\quad \bar{x} = \dfrac{2310}{30}$ = 77 beats per minute.

You can use your scientific calculator to calculate the mean for grouped data. Use the same method as described earlier but enter the middle of the class interval as 'x'. Steps 1 and 2 are the same as before. (Clear the memory!)

Step 3 Entering the data

62 [×] 1 [M+]

67 [×] 3 [M+]

72 [×] 6 [M+]

77 [×] 11 [M+]

82 [×] 5 [M+]

87 [×] 2 [M+]

92 [×] 2 [M+]

Don't forget that the calculator requires you to enter result × frequency, or $x \times f$, not the other way round.

This method will work for most scientific calculators. Find out how to do this on your calculator by referring to the manual if necessary.

Try this out on your calculator.

Check that you obtain:

$n = 30$

$\Sigma x = 2310$

$\bar{x} = 77$

Use both the 'paper and pencil' method and the calculator method to find the mean for each set of results. Your answer should be the same using both methods.

7 ✓ Jed measured the temperature (t, in °C) of 32 students as part of his biology coursework. Find the middle temperature in each class interval and use this to find the mean.

Temperature in °C	Frequency
$36.0 \leq t < 36.2$	1
$36.2 \leq t < 36.4$	0
$36.4 \leq t < 36.6$	1
$36.6 \leq t < 36.8$	6
$36.8 \leq t < 37.0$	12
$37.0 \leq t < 37.2$	7
$37.2 \leq t < 37.4$	2
$37.4 \leq t < 37.6$	1

8 The following gives the heights (h in cm) of a group of year 11 girls. Copy the table and complete the calculations to find the mean.

Height in cm	Frequency f	Middle of class interval (x)	Middle × frequency (fx)
$140 \leq h < 145$	1	142.5	
$145 \leq h < 150$	0		
$150 \leq h < 155$	4		
$155 \leq h < 160$	7		
$160 \leq h < 165$	9		
$165 \leq h < 170$	12		
$170 \leq h < 175$	5		
$175 \leq h < 180$	3		

9 This table gives the weights (w in kg) of 25 children. Find their mean weight.

Weight in kg	Frequency
$20 \leq w < 30$	1
$30 \leq w < 40$	7
$40 \leq w < 50$	12
$50 \leq w < 60$	4
$60 \leq w < 70$	1

10 The daily rainfall (r) in mm was recorded over a one month period and the results summarised in this table. Find the mean daily rainfall for that month.

Rainfall in mm	No. of days
$0 \leq r < 10$	8
$10 \leq r < 20$	6
$20 \leq r < 30$	6
$30 \leq r < 40$	2
$40 \leq r < 50$	5
$50 \leq r < 60$	4

ICT Extra!

Ask the people in your class how long they each spent watching TV yesterday. Summarise your results on a frequency table. Use the statistical functions on your calculator to calculate the mean of those times.

23 PATTERNS AND PRIMES

23.1 Further sequences

Consider the sequence:
7, 11, 15, 19, 23, ...

One way to describe the sequence is to say that it starts with 7 and then goes up in 4s.

Another way is to give the formula for the *n*th term as $u_n = 4n + 3$.

The attraction of the first method is that it is very easy to understand, but it has the disadvantage that it isn't very helpful for answering questions about the sequence such as:

- What is the value of the 250th term?
- Which term of the sequence has the value 131?
- How many terms of the sequence are less than 403?

Questions such as these are easily answered when the formula for the *n*th term is known – the *details* will be given later. In general, the use of algebra enables us to describe patterns that may occur, during an investigation for example, in such a way that new results can then be found.

---

1 The first three terms of a sequence take the form
$(3 \times 1) + 2$
$(3 \times 2) + 2$
$(3 \times 3) + 2$.
a) Write the next three terms of this sequence in the same way.
b) Write an expression for the 50th term.
c) Find a formula for the *n*th term.
d) Find the value of the 100th term of the sequence 5, 8, 11, 14, ...

2 The first three terms of a sequence are $(5 \times 1) + 4$, $(5 \times 2) + 4$ and $(5 \times 3) + 4$.
a) Write down the next two terms of the sequence.
b) Write the 37th term of the sequence in the same way.
c) Find a formula for the *n*th term.
d) Find the value of the 50th term of the sequence 9, 14, 19, 24, ...

3 The first four terms of a sequence are 11, 15, 19 and 23.
a) Follow the pattern of the sequences given in the first two questions to re-write these terms in the form $(4 \times ...) + ...$
b) Find a formula for the *n*th term of the sequence.
c) Find the value of the 60th term.

When faced with an unfamiliar sequence it is a good idea to work out the **differences** of consecutive terms, i.e. terms that follow on from each other.

These can often give us the information that we need in order to calculate later terms and may also help us to find a formula for the *n*th term.

Example

Find the next term of the sequence 8, 11, 14, 17, 20, ...

Answer

Sequence	8		11		14		17		20
Differences		3		3		3		3	

All of the differences have the same value, i.e. 3. It follows that the next term in the sequence will be 23.

Check that the formula for the *n*th term in this case is $u_n = 3n + 2$.

---

4 Find the first five terms of the sequence given by $u_n = 4n + 1$ and work out the differences of consecutive terms.

5 Repeat question 4 using the formula $u_n = 4n - 3$.

6 Find the differences of consecutive terms when the *n*th term is given by:
a) $u_n = 6n + 1$ b) $u_n = 5n - 2$ c) $u_n = \frac{1}{2}n + 1$

If the terms of a sequence become progressively smaller then the differences are taken to be *negative*.

Example

Find the next term of the sequence 10, 5, 0, –5, –10, ...

Answer

Sequence	10		5		0		–5		–10
Differences		–5		–5		–5		–5	

So the next term in the sequence is –15.

Check that the *n*th term of the sequence is given by $u_n = 15 - 5n$.

---

7 Predict the value of the differences when the *n*th term is given by the following formulae. Check by finding the first three terms and the corresponding differences in each case.
a) $u_n = 12 - 2n$ b) $u_n = 20 - 4n$ c) $u_n = 10 - 3n$
d) $u_n = 8 - 0.5n$ e) $u_n = 1 - 0.1n$ f) $u_n = -5 - 2n$

8 The *n*th term of a sequence is given by $u_n = 4n + k$ for some value of k. If one of the terms of this sequence is 61, what is the value of:
a) the next term
b) the previous term?

If the formula for the nth term of a sequence takes the form $u_n = an + b$, where a and b have fixed values, then the value of a is given by the differences of consecutive terms. Once the value of a is known, the value of b may be calculated using the value of any term.

Example

a) The first 4 terms of a sequence are 7, 12, 17 and 22. Find a formula for the nth term.

b) The tenth term of a sequence is 49. Find a formula for the nth term if the next two terms are 46 and 43.

Answer

a) The differences have a fixed value of 5 and so $u_n = 5n + b$ for some value of b.
The first term is given by $u_1 = 5 \times 1 + b = 7$ and so $b = 2$.
It follows that the formula for the nth term is $u_n = 5n + 2$.
(*Check*: $5 \times 2 + 2 = 12$, $5 \times 3 + 2 = 17$ and $5 \times 4 + 2 = 22$.)

b) The value of the difference is -3 each time and so $u_n = -3n + b$ for some value of b. However this would normally be written as $u_n = b - 3n$.
The tenth term is given by $u_{10} = b - 3 \times 10 = 49$ and so $b = 79$.
The nth term may now be given as $u_n = 79 - 3n$.
(*Check*: $79 - 3 \times 11 = 46$ and $79 - 3 \times 12 = 43$.)

---

9 Find a formula for the nth term of these sequences. In each case, the values shown are the *first* four terms.

a) 5, 7, 9, 11 ✓
b) 11, 16, 21, 26
c) 41, 47, 53, 59
d) 32, 47, 62, 77
e) 1, 3, 5,7
f) −1, 2, 5, 8
g) 3.7, 4.2, 4.7, 5.2
h) 0.85, 0.87, 0.89, 0.91
i) 10, 8, 6, 4 ✓
j) 15, 12, 9, 6
k) 50, 46, 42, 40
l) 100, 90, 80, 70
m) 3, −2, −7, −12
n) −8, −11, −14, −17
o) 10, 9.5, 9, 8.5
p) 1, 0.9, 0.8, 0.7

10 The 20th term of a sequence is 129 and the next two terms are 136 and 143.

a) Find a formula for the nth term.
b) Find the value of the first term.

11 The 10th term of a sequence is −35 and the next two terms are −39 and −43.

a) Find a formula for the nth term
b) Find the value of the 50th term.

We are now in a position to consider again the example given at the start of the chapter and to solve the problems that were left unanswered at that stage.

In the sequence 7, 11, 15, 19, 23, ... the terms have a fixed difference of 4.
This tells us that the nth term is given by $u_n = 4n + b$ for some value of b.
The first term is given by $u_1 = 4 \times 1 + b = 7$ and so $b = 3$.
We now see how the formula $u_n = 4n + 3$ was established.

■ *What is the value of the 250th term?*
The 250th term is given by $u_{250} = 4 \times 250 + 3 = 1003$.

■ *Which term of the sequence has the value 131?*
We solve this problem by setting the nth term equal to 131 and solving the equation:

$$4n + 3 = 131$$
$$4n = 128$$
$$n = 32$$

The 32nd term of the sequence has the value 131.

■ *How many terms of the sequence are less than 403?*
The approach is similar to the previous problem but this time the information is expressed as an inequality.

$$4n + 3 < 403$$
$$4n < 400$$
$$n < 100$$

It follows that 99 terms are less than 403 (the 100th term is *equal* to 403).

---

12 The first four terms of a sequence are 10, 14, 18 and 22.
a) Find a formula for the nth term.
b) Find the value of the 50th term.
c) Which term of the sequence has the value 106?
d) How many terms of the sequence are less than 170?

13 The first four terms of a sequence are 100, 93, 86 and 79.
a) Find a formula for the nth term
b) Which term has the value 37?
c) Which term has the value –26?
d) How many of the terms are positive?

14 The 15th term of a sequence is 41 and the next two terms are 43 and 45.
a) Find a formula for the nth term.
b) Find the value of the first term.
c) How many terms are less than 100?
d) How many terms are less than 200?
e) How many terms have a value in between 100 and 200?

15 The tenth term of a sequence is 7 and the previous two terms are 11 and 15.
a) Find a formula for the nth term.
b) Find the value of the first term.
c) How many of the terms are positive?
d) What is the value of the first negative term?

The approach used to answer the questions given above may also be applied to the solution of problems involving patterns presented in a visual form.

Example

These diagrams show patterns made with matchsticks.

a) Draw a diagram to show Pattern 4.

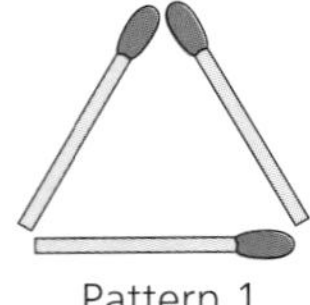
Pattern 1

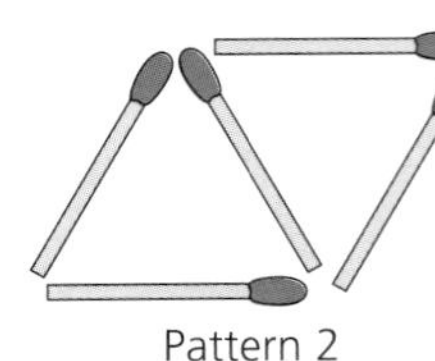
Pattern 2

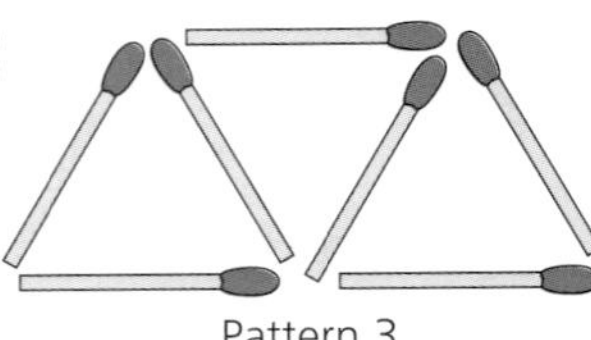
Pattern 3

b) How many matchsticks will be needed for Pattern 10?

c) Find a formula for Pattern n and explain why it works.

d) Which pattern needs 35 matches?

Answer

a) Continuing in the same way, Pattern 4 is given by:

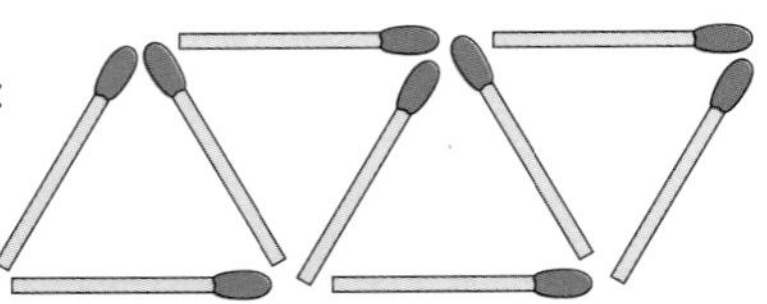

b) The number of matches needed forms the sequence 3, 5, 7, 9....
Continuing the pattern gives
.... 11, 13, 15, 17, 19, 21
and so Pattern 10 needs 21 matches.

c) The difference of consecutive terms is 2 in each case and so Pattern n will require $2n + b$ matches. Pattern 1 contains 3 matches and so $2 \times 1 + b = 3$, giving $b = 1$. It follows that Pattern n requires $2n + 1$ matches.
The formula works because 2 matches are needed to make every new triangle, apart from the first triangle which needs 1 extra match.

d) Using the formula $2n + 1 = 35$
$2n = 34$
$n = 17$
The pattern requiring 35 matches is Pattern 17.

---

16 The diagram shows patterns of squares made from matchsticks.

a) Find how many matchsticks will be needed for Pattern 6.

b) Find a formula for Pattern n and explain why it works.

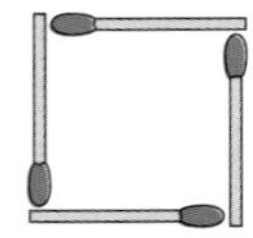
Pattern 1

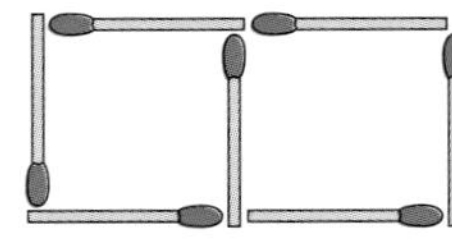
Pattern 2

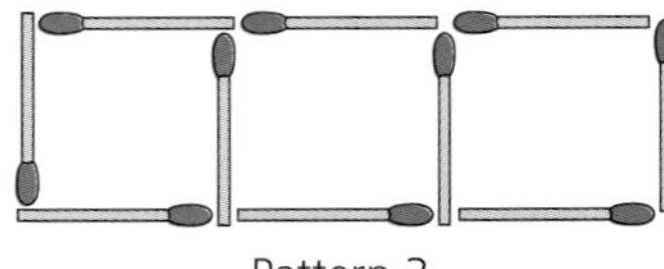
Pattern 3

c) How many matchsticks would be needed for Pattern 50?

d) Which pattern needs 250 matches?

17 When David looked at the triangle patterns given in the example he tried a different way of finding the formula for Pattern n. He argued that Pattern n is made up of n triangles and that the first of these needs 3 matches, but the remaining $(n - 1)$ triangles only need 2 matches each. He concluded that the formula for Pattern n must be $3 + 2(n - 1)$. Is this correct? Explain.

18 Adapt the approach given in the previous question to find an alternative formula for Pattern n of the square patterns. Show that the two formulae are equivalent.

Not all sequences have a fixed difference between consecutive terms. However, in some cases the **second differences** are constant.

Example

Find the second differences of the sequence 8, 11, 16, 23, 32.

Answer

Sequence	8		11		16		23		32
1st differences		3		5		7		9	
2nd differences			2		2		2		

The second differences have a constant value of 2.

---

19 Find the first five terms of the sequences given by each of the following and calculate the value of the second differences. Comment on what you find.

a) $u_n = 2n + 1$ **b)** $u_n = n^2$ **c)** $u_n = n^3$

d) $u_n = n^2 + 2$ **e)** $u_n = 3(n + 2)$ **f)** $u_n = n(n + 1)$

20 **a)** Calculate the second differences for the sequence 3, 8, 15, 24...

b) Which of the following could be the formula for the nth term for some value of a? Explain how you were able to decide.

(i) $u_n = a(n - 1)$ (ii) $u_n = (n + 1)^2 - a$ (iii) $u_n = n^3 + 2n - a$

c) Find the value of a to complete the formula selected in part **b)** and show that it gives the correct values for the first four terms.

23.2 Prime factors

A whole number such as 210 may be written as the product of 15 and 14, i.e. 210 = 15 × 14. The numbers 15 and 14 are said to be **factors** of 210.

However, neither of these factors is a **prime** number and so they, in turn can be expressed as the product of smaller factors. The process may be represented on a diagram.

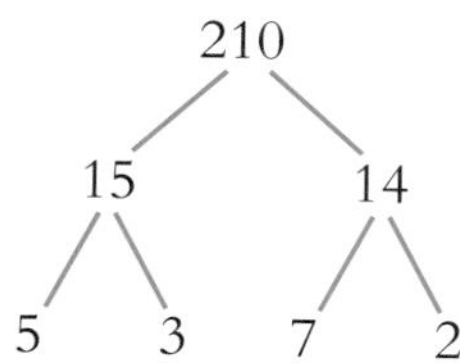

Each of the numbers 2, 3, 5 and 7 is not only a factor of 210 but is a prime number. We say that 2, 3, 5 and 7 are the **prime factors** of 210.

210 may be written as a product of its prime factors, i.e. 210 = 2 × 3 × 5 × 7.

These diagrams show that even though we may start the process in a different way, we obtain the same prime factors at the end.

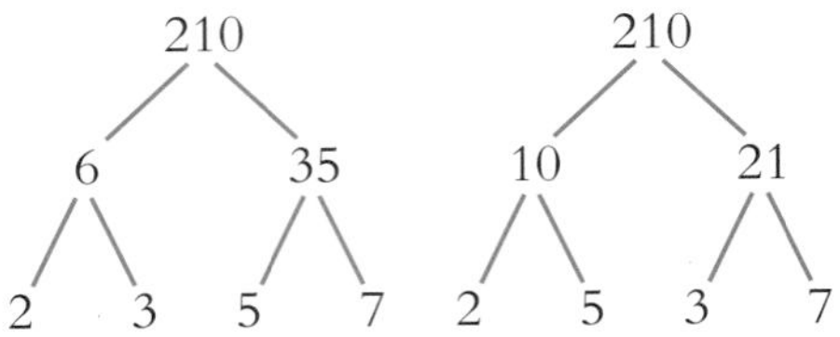

(*Note*: it may be tempting to extend the diagrams by using the number 1 as a factor. However, 1 is *not* a prime number and if its use is allowed in these diagrams then they could be continued forever without providing any new information.)

---

1 Copy and complete these diagrams.

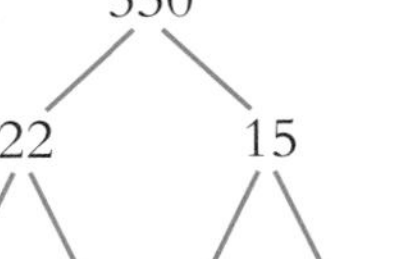

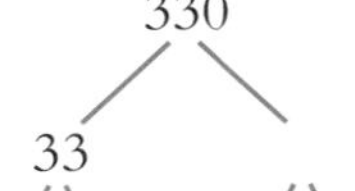

2 Write 330 as a product of its prime factors.

3 Copy and complete these factor tree diagrams. Use the results to write 715 and 910 as products of their prime factors.

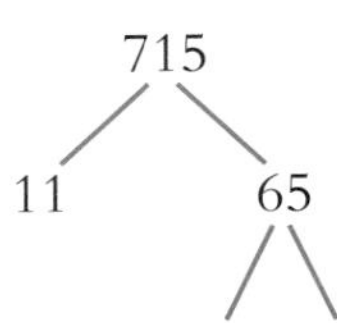

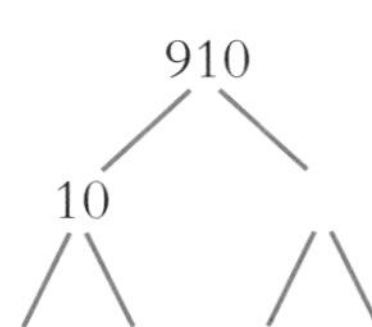

The diagram below shows the prime factors of 360.

As a product of its prime factors, 360 may be written as:

$$2 \times 2 \times 2 \times 3 \times 3 \times 5$$

However, since some of the prime factors are repeated we can make use of index notation (i.e. using powers) to obtain:

$$360 = 2^3 \times 3^2 \times 5$$

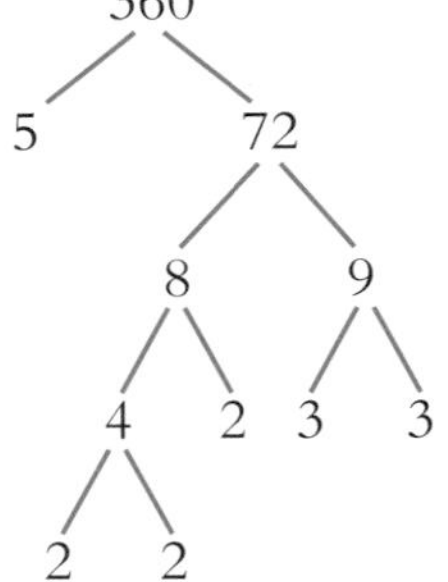

---

4 Use factor tree diagrams to find the prime factors of each of the following. Express each number as a product of its prime factors using index notation.

a) 108	b) 225	c) 56	d) 64
e) 200	f) 2000	g) 245	h) 2450
i) 500	j) 5000	k) 324	l) 628

The results of writing numbers as products of their prime factors may be combined to give new information.

Example

Use these results to answer the following questions.

$360 = 2^3 \times 3^2 \times 5$ $\quad$ $54 = 2 \times 3^3$ $\quad$ $12\,600 = 2^3 \times 3^2 \times 5^2 \times 7$

■ *What is 3600 as a product of its prime factors?*
$3600 = 360 \times 10 = (2^3 \times 3^2 \times 5) \times 2 \times 5 = 2^4 \times 3^2 \times 5^2$
Note: 2 may be considered as 2^1 and 5 as 5^1. Powers of the same number are added when we multiply.

■ *How can we recognise that 3600 is a perfect square?*
All of the powers of its prime factors are even.
It follows that 3600 may be written as the product of two numbers with identical prime factors, i.e. $3600 = (2^2 \times 3 \times 5) \times (2^2 \times 3 \times 5)$

■ *What is the smallest whole number that we can multiply 12 600 by to make a perfect square?*
Two of the prime factors of 12 600 are raised to an odd power. If we multiply by 2×7 then all of the powers will be even. It follows that 14 is the required number. (*Note*: $12\,600 \times 14 = 176\,400 = 420^2$).

■ *Is 360 divisible by 54?*
No. 54 contains a higher power of 3 than 360.

■ *Is 12 600 divisible by 360?*
Yes. 12 600 contains all of the factors of 360.
(*Note*: $12\,600 \div 360 = (2^3 \times 3^2 \times 5^2 \times 7) \div (2^3 \times 3^2 \times 5) = 5 \times 7 = 35$.)

---

5 Use these results to answer the following questions:
$162 = 2 \times 3^4$ $504 = 2^3 \times 3^2 \times 7$ $2268 = 2^2 \times 7 \times 3^4$

a) What is 162×504 as a product of its prime factors? ✓
b) Is 504 divisible by 162? Explain your answer.
c) Is 2268 divisible by 162? Explain.
d) What is the smallest whole number that 162 can be multiplied by to make a perfect square?
e) What is the smallest whole number that 2268 can be multiplied by to make a perfect square?
f) What whole numbers could 504 be divided by to make a perfect square?
g) Find the value of $\sqrt{2268 \div 7}$ without using a calculator.
h) What is the smallest whole number that 2268 may be multiplied by so that the result is divisible by 504?
i) What is 162^2 as a product of its prime factors?
j) What is 162^3 as a product of its prime factors?
k) What is 504×21 as a product of its prime factors?
l) Find the value of $\sqrt[3]{504 \times 21}$ without using a calculator.
m) Cancel the fraction $\frac{504}{2268}$ as far as possible.
n) Write the ratio 162 : 504 in its simplest terms.

6 Write 90 and 150 as products of their prime factors.
a) Express the ratio 150 : 90 in its simplest terms.
b) What is the smallest number that is divisible by both 90 and 150?
c) Find the smallest whole number that 90 may be multiplied by to make a perfect square.
d) Find the value of $\sqrt[3]{2 \times 90 \times 150}$ without using a calculator.

The factor tree approach to finding the prime factors of a number is useful when the numbers are not too large and don't contain too many factors. For larger numbers it may be easier to adopt a systematic approach involving repeated division.

Example

Write 358 875 as a product of its prime factors.

Answer

We start by dividing by the smallest prime number that we recognise as a factor.

358 875 ÷ 3	358 875 is not divisible by 2 but the digit sum shows that it is divisible by 3.
119 625 ÷ 3	119 625 is also divisible by 3.
39 875 ÷ 5	39 875 isn't divisible by 3 but it is divisible by 5.
7975 ÷ 5	7975 and 1595 are both divisible by 5.
1595 ÷ 5	
319 ÷ 11	319 is not divisible by 5 or 7 but it is divisible by 11.
29	29 is a prime number.

Using this method, the prime factors are cancelled one by one until the remaining factor is prime, which then shows that the prime factors have all been found. Thus 358 875 = $3^2 \times 5^3 \times 11 \times 29$.

---

7 Use the method given in the example to write the following numbers as a product of their prime factors:

a) 3800 ✓ b) 3906 c) 11 660
d) 3875 e) 4862 f) 33 275
g) 141 151 h) 75 647 i) 808 201

The systematic approach to finding the prime factors of a number can be adapted to check if any given whole number is prime.

Suppose that we want to check if 101 is prime. We need only check for possible prime factors which are less than $\sqrt{101}$.

---

8 a) List the prime numbers less than $\sqrt{101}$.
b) Use the numbers in your list to check if 101 is prime.
c) Explain why we need only consider possible prime factors.
d) Explain why there is no need to consider numbers greater than $\sqrt{101}$.

9 Check to see if 307 is prime. Explain your reasoning.

AREAS AND VOLUMES

24.1 Areas of quadrilaterals

The first two sections revise work previously covered in Unit 16. Please refer back to that unit for examples and formulae.

1 Find the areas of the following shapes by splitting them into rectangles and triangles. ✓

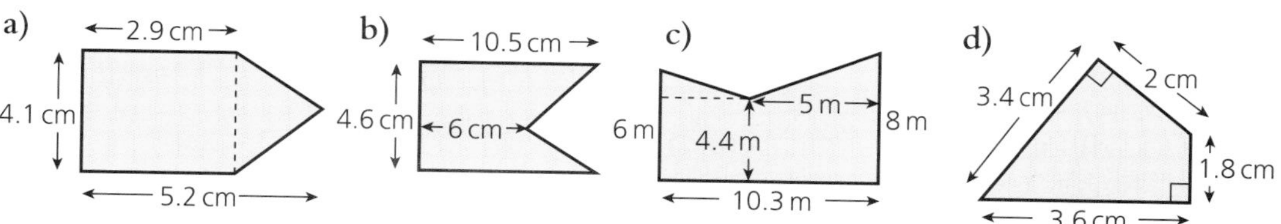

2 A kite 80 cm long and 55 cm wide is cut from a rectangular piece of cloth 1 m by 60 cm.

a) Draw a diagram of the cloth with the kite cut out.

b) Find the area of the cloth left.

3 Find the area of the trapezium below. ✓

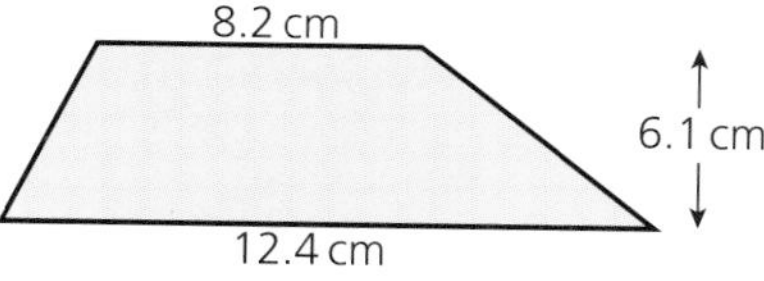

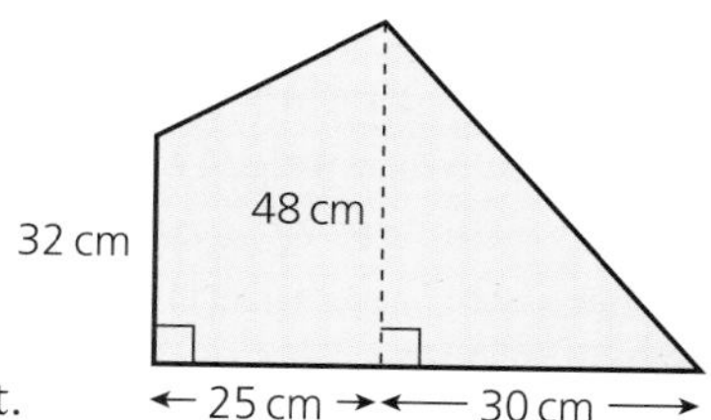

4 Find the area of the quadrilateral on the right.

5 A rectangular field is 240 m long and 150 m wide. Calculate its area in square metres. If 1 hectare equals 10 000 square metres, what is the area of the field in hectares?

6 How many square tiles measuring 20 cm each side are needed to cover a floor 3.8 m by 2.8 m?

7 A piece of wire 14 cm long is to be bent to form a rectangle. In how many ways can this be done so that each side is a whole number of centimetres?

a) Draw all the different possible rectangles which can be made, and calculate the area of each one.

b) Is it possible to obtain a larger area if you lift the restriction on the sides being a whole number of centimetres? Sketch any possible solutions.

8 Find the missing dimensions:

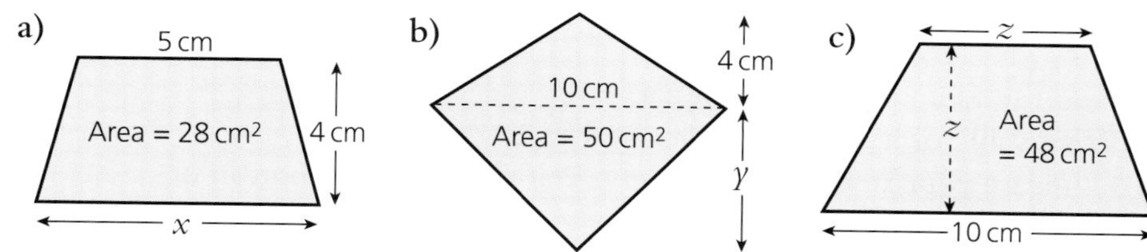

24.2 Circles

1 ✓ A bicycle wheel is 70 cm in diameter. If the wheel makes 500 complete turns, how far has the bicycle travelled (approximately)? Is it:

a) 2200 m b) 1100 m c) 350 m d) 220 m e) 110 m

2 ✓ O is the centre of this circle which has a radius of 3 cm.

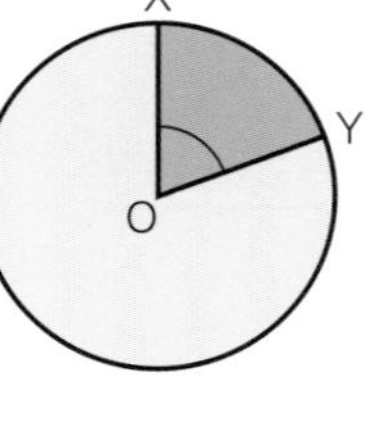

a) Find the circumference of the circle.

b) What fraction of the circle is covered by the sector XOY if the angle at the centre, ∠XOY, is 60°?

c) Find the length of the arc XY.

d) Find the area of the sector XOY.

3 This shape is one quarter of a circle, with a radius of 14 cm. Find:

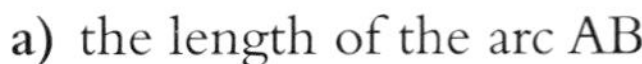

a) the length of the arc AB

b) the perimeter of the figure

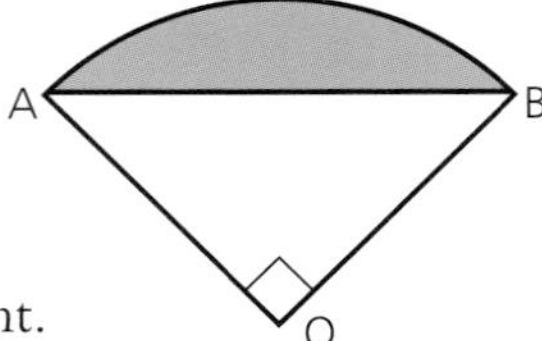

c) the area of the figure

d) the area of AOB

e) the area of the shaded segment.

4 This circle has a radius of 12 cm. ABCD is a square drawn inside the circle. O is the centre of the circle.

a) What is the size of ∠AOB?

b) What is the area of triangle AOB?

c) What is the area of the square?

d) What is the length of AB?

5 For this shape, find:

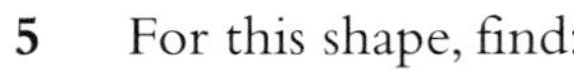

a) the perimeter

b) the total area.

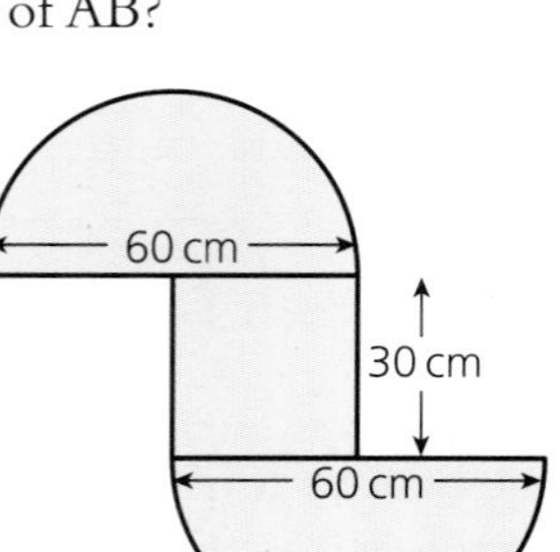

6 Nirmal wishes to find the area of a circular pond in the park. He is unable to measure the diameter or the radius but he is able to measure the circumference. He finds that the circumference is 220 m.

a) What is the diameter of the pond? (Use $\pi = \frac{22}{7}$.) ✓

b) What is the radius of the pond?

c) What is the area?

7 a) Find the value of $\frac{22}{7}$ as a decimal.

b) What value of π does your calculator give?

c) Compare your answer to question 6 a) if you use the π button on the calculator.

24.3 Volumes of cuboids

The volume of a cuboid is found by
V = length × width × height

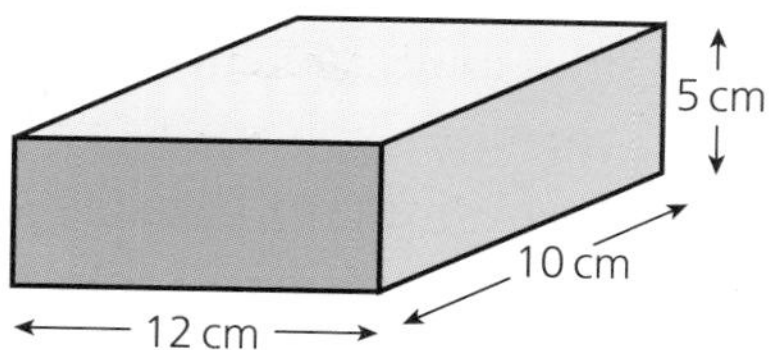

In this case:
$V = 12 \times 10 \times 5 = 600\,\text{cm}^3$

The volumes required in the following questions can be found directly using this formula. Some problems may require you to split a complex shape into smaller cuboids.

1 Wooden play blocks exactly fill a rectangular box with inside measurements 80 cm by 70 cm by 35 cm. The blocks are cubes with sides of 5 cm.
a) What is the volume of the box? ✓
b) What is the volume of a block?
c) How many blocks are there?

2 Find the volumes of these wooden steps:

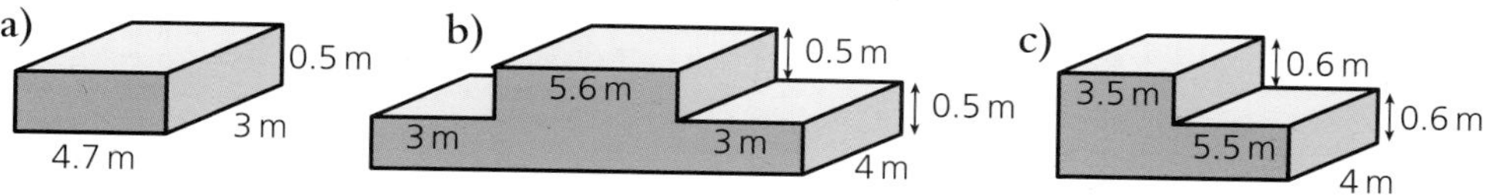

3 One brick measures 24 cm by 12 cm by 8 cm. How many bricks are needed to build a wall 12 cm thick, 30 m long and 1.6 m high? (Ignore the thickness of the cement.)

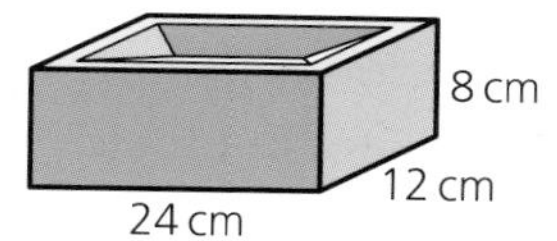

4 a) A square piece of cardboard with sides of 20 cm has a small square of side 4 cm cut out of each corner. The remaining flaps are turned up to make a box 4 cm deep. Find the volume of the box.
b) What is the surface area of the outside of this box?

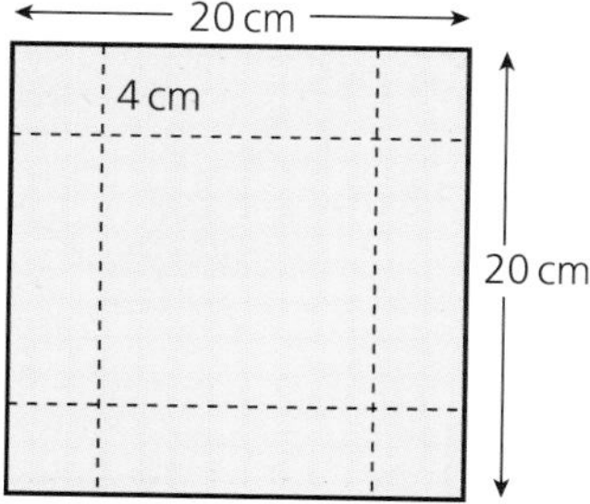

5 a) A rectangular tank is 2 m long, 1.6 m wide and 1.5 m high. Calculate its capacity in cubic metres. What is this in cubic centimetres?
b) 2400 litres of water are poured into the tank. How much is this in cubic centimetres?
c) Find the area of the base of the tank in square centimetres.
d) Use this calculation to help you to find the depth of the water.

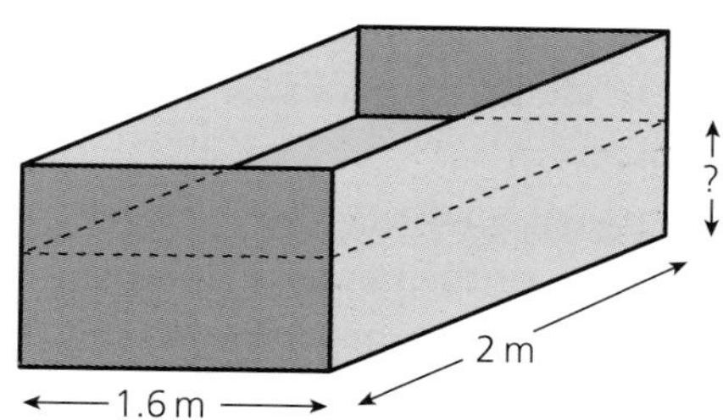

24.4 Volumes of prisms

A cuboid is a special kind of prism.

A **prism** is any solid which can be cut into slices which are all the same shape. This is called having a **uniform cross-section**.

These are all examples of prisms:

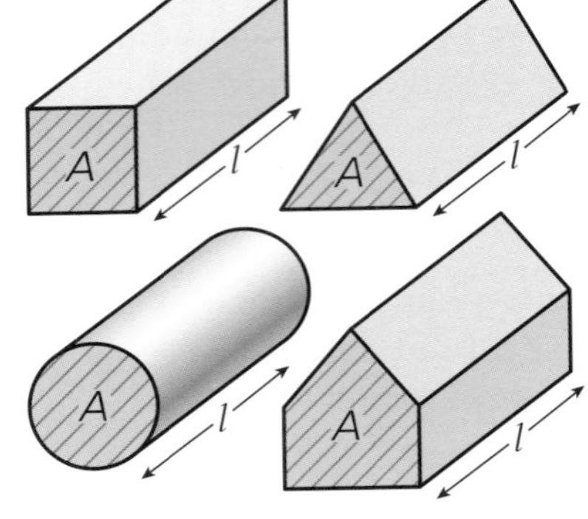

The volume of any prism can be found by multiplying the area A of the end face by the length l:
$V = A \times l$

Example

Find the volume of this triangular prism:

Answer

Volume = area of end face × length

Area of triangle = $\frac{1}{2}$ base × height

$= \frac{1}{2} \times 9 \times 8$

$= 36\text{ cm}^2$

Volume of prism = 36×20

$= 720\text{ cm}^3$

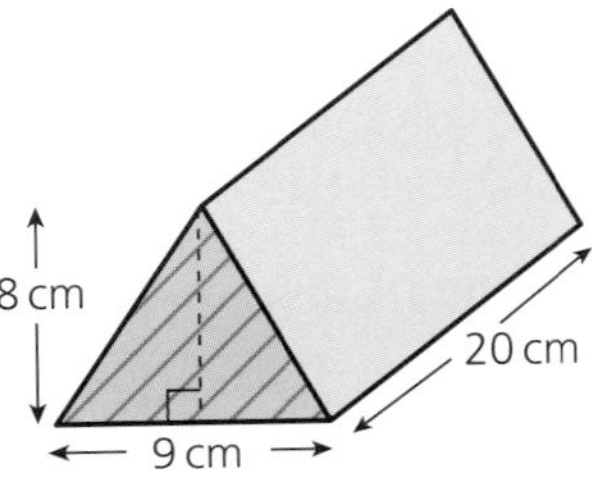

1 Find the volumes of these prisms:

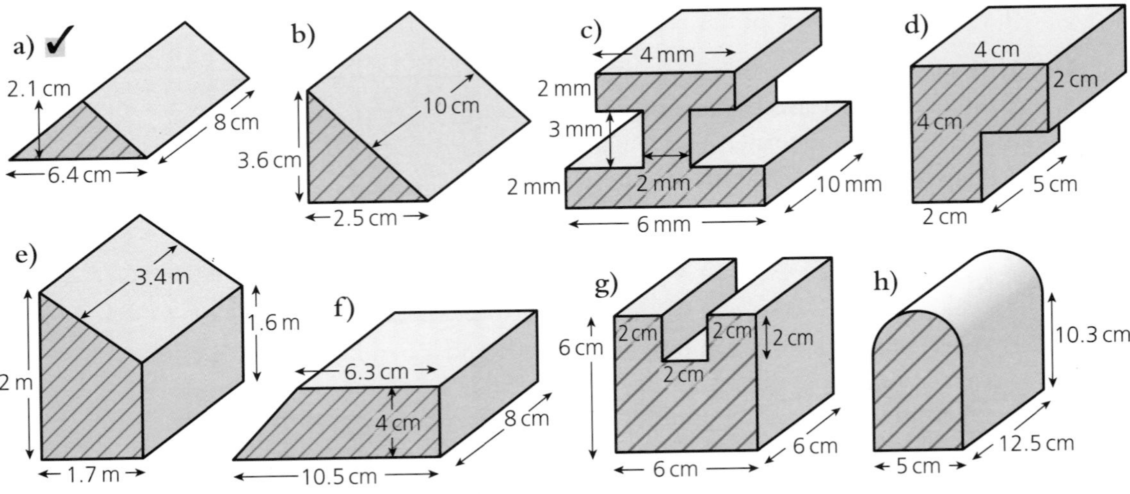

2 A new pencil is a hexagonal prism, 15 cm long.
The volume of the pencil is 5.4 cm^3.
Find the area of the hexagonal end.

15 cm

3 This swimming pool is 1 m deep at the shallow end and 3 m at the deep end. The bottom of the pool slopes uniformly down to the deep end. Find the volume of water in the pool.

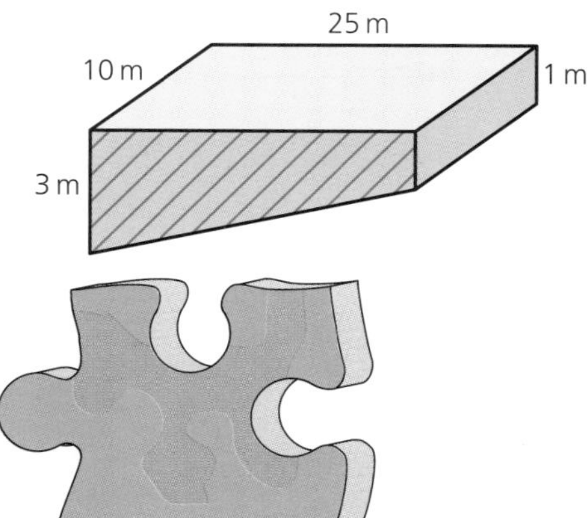

4 This piece of a jigsaw puzzle has a volume of 420 mm³. The puzzle is made out of wood 1.2 mm thick. Find the area of one side of this piece.

5 A cubical storage box has sides of 40 cm. Find the side of a cubical box which will hold twice as much.

24.5 Volumes of cylinders

A **cylinder** is another example of a prism. Its volume is found by multiplying the area of the circular end by the length (or height).

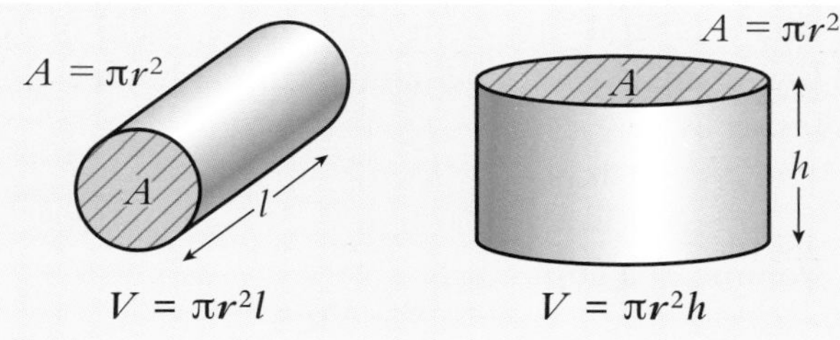

Example

Find the volumes of these cylinders (to 2 D.P.):

a)

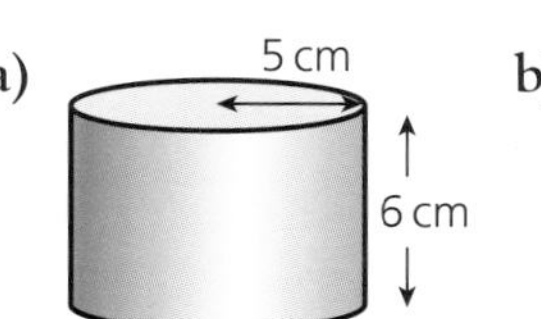

b)

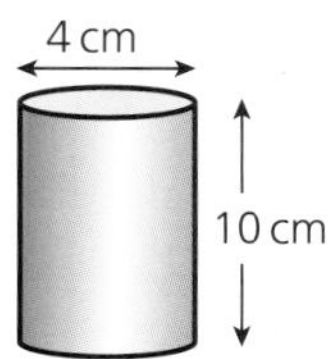

Answer

a) Using $V = \pi r^2 h$,

$V = \pi \times 5 \times 5 \times 6$ (using π on the calculator)

$V = 471.24\,\text{cm}^3$ (to 2 D.P.)

b) The diameter is given as 4 cm, so $r = 2$ cm.

Using $V = \pi r^2 h$,

$V = \pi \times 2 \times 2 \times 10$

$V = 125.66\,\text{cm}^3$ (to 2 D.P.)

1 ✔ Find the volumes of these cylinders (use π on your calculator):

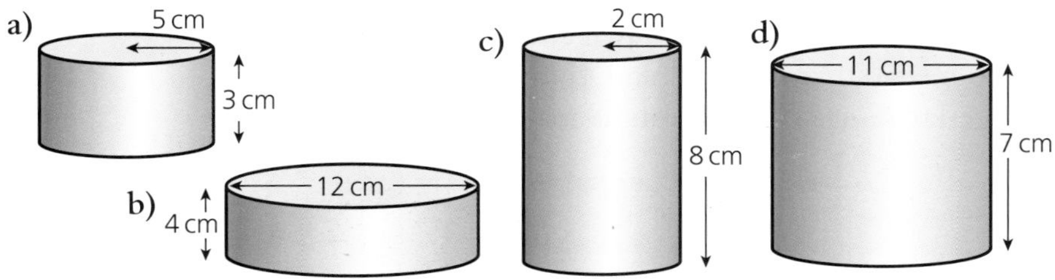

2 These tins are filled with soup. Which tin holds more soup?

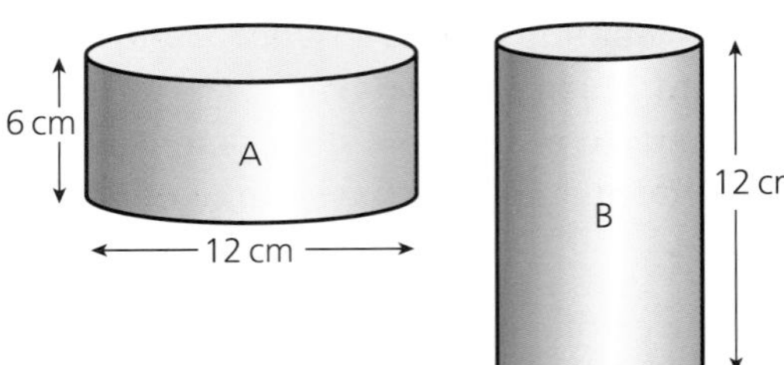

3 Find the area of the paper label which is wrapped round the sides of this tin.

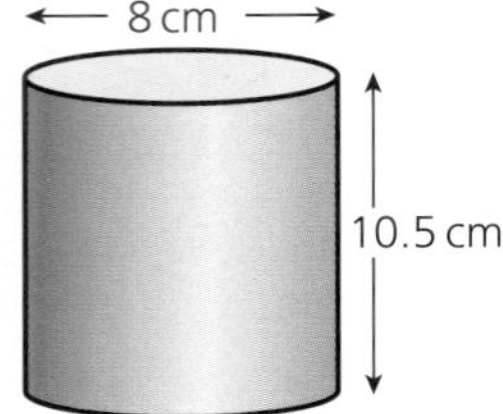

Example

A two litre bottle of lemonade is to be poured out into cylindrical cups 6 cm high with a radius of 3 cm. How many cups can be filled from the bottle?

Answer

1 litre = 1000 cm^3

so 2 litres = 2000 cm^3

Volume of a cup = $\pi r^2 h$

= $\pi \times 3 \times 3 \times 6$

= 169.65 cm^3

Number of cups = 2000 ÷ 169.65

= 11.8 cups

The actual number of cups which can be filled is 11 cups.

4 Find the capacity in litres of a cylindrical tank with a diameter of 35 cm and a height of 48 cm.

5 How many cylindrical cups each 7 cm tall and with a diameter 8 cm can be filled from a cask containing 20 litres of fruit juice? ✓

6 A 3 litre bottle of pop is to be served in cylindrical paper cups 10 cm tall and with a radius of 2 cm. How many cups can be filled from the bottle?

7 An ingot of metal 20 cm long, 5 cm wide and 3 cm high is to be melted down and cast into medals 0.25 cm thick and 4 cm in diameter. How many medals can be made?

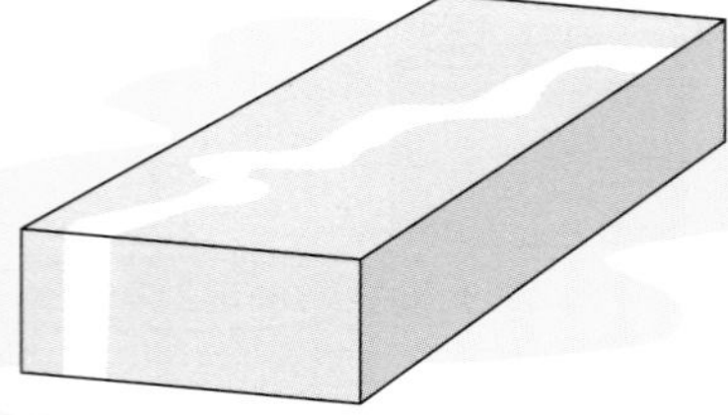

8 I clean my teeth twice a day. Each time I brush my teeth I squeeze out a 'cylinder' of toothpaste 0.8 cm in diameter and 2 cm long. What is the volume of toothpaste I use each time I brush my teeth? If I have a 50 ml tube of toothpaste, how long will this last me? (1 ml of substance occupies 1 cm^3 of space.)

9 a) Find the area of the base of this cylindrical container.

b) 7 litres of water are poured into the container. How many cm^3 is this?

c) How deep is the water when it is poured into the container?

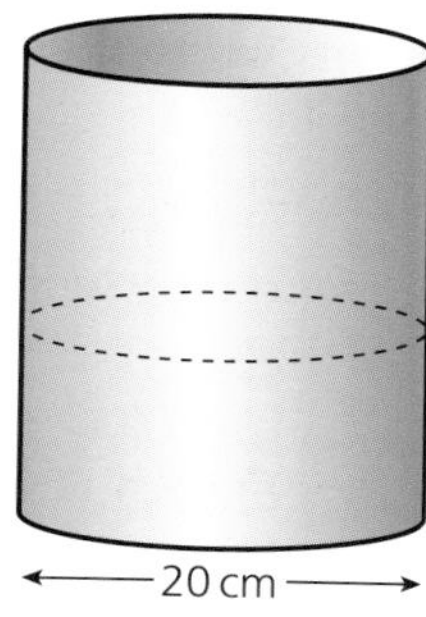

REVIEW 3

Unit 17 Numbers and equations

1 For each of the following, state whether $n > 1$ or $n < 1$:

a) $n \times 3.68 = 6.8816$ b) $41.68 \times n = 43.01376$
c) $0.0467 \times n = 0.0536116$ d) $n \times 7.134 = 6.17091$
e) $n \times 0.0354 = 0.029205$ f) $16700 \times n = 15865$

2 State whether $t > 1$ or $t < 1$ for each of these:

a) $5.1917 \div t = 5.38$ b) $30.9738 \div t = 29.64$
c) $18.6186 \div t = 21.45$ d) $44.992 \div 47.36 = t$

3 Find the false statements without using a calculator:

a) $16.81 \times 1.27 = 21.3487$ b) $0.0863 \times 1.12 = 0.076656$
c) $19.33536 \div 1.056 = 20.31$ d) $41.6245 \div 0.85 = 48.97$

4 Find the value of the following without using a calculator. Look for quick methods.

a) $8765 + 999$ b) $47635 + 9999$ c) $743 + 98$
d) $7426 - 999$ e) $18.437 + 0.999$ f) $6.874 - 0.999$
g) 3210×40 h) $30 \times 200 \times 4000$ i) 0.473×10
j) $2.465 \times 5 \times 2$ k) $5 \times 37.89 \times 2$ l) $30 \times 8.379 \div 3$
m) $27.61 \div 10$ n) $27.61 \div 5$ o) $27.61 \div 50$
p) $184 \div 400$ q) 567×99 r) 470×9.9

5 Copy and complete the solutions to these equations:

a) $5x - 3 = 22$
$5x =$
$x =$

b) $4(x + 7) = 44$
$x + 7 =$
$x =$

c) $\frac{x}{6} - 38 = 2.2$
$\frac{x}{6} =$

d) $\frac{4x - 3}{5} = 7$
$4x - 3 =$

6 Solve the following equations:

a) $8x - 17.6 = 6.4$ b) $7x - 9 = 4x + 18$
c) $17 - (8 - 3x) = x + 5$ d) $\sqrt{x + 7} = 5$

7 Use a calculator to find the exact values of n in question **1** by reversing the process in each case.

8 Use a calculator to find the exact values of t in question **2**.

Unit 18 Hypotheses

9 Lionel is interested in testing a new design of running shoe. He sets up an experiment to see whether the shoes will improve an athlete's running speed.
He selects 10 students from his year group and asks each one to run 200 m wearing their normal trainers, then to run 200 m using the new type of shoe. Can you think of two problems with Lionel's experimental design?

10 Lorraine wishes to compare the results obtained with a reaction-time ruler with those from a computer program designed to test reaction times. (The

computer program asks people to press a particular key when they see a symbol appearing on the screen.)
How should she set up this experiment?

11 The numbers 3, 5, 7, 8 and X are arranged in numerical order.
a) What is the median of these numbers?
b) If the mean equals the median, what is the value of X?

12 The mean height of 8 men is 1.75 m and the mean height of 12 women is 1.65 m. Use this information to find:
a) the total height of the 8 men
b) the total height of the 12 women
c) the mean height of the 20 people taken together as one group.

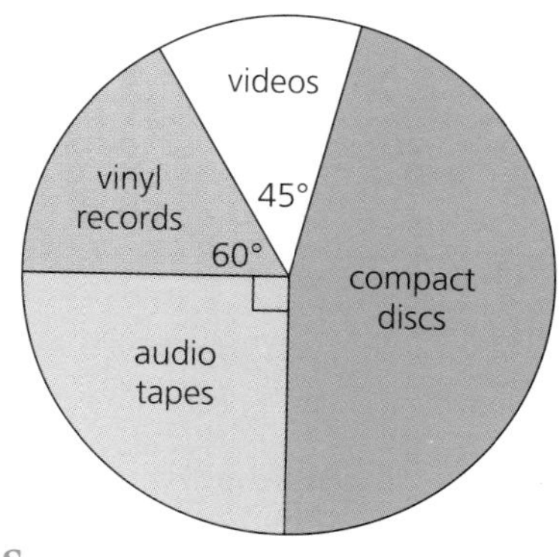

13 The pie chart illustrates the values of various items sold by our local record shop. The total value of the sales was £54 000, so what was the value of:
a) videos b) vinyl records
c) audio tapes d) compact discs?

Unit 19 Factors and inequalities

14 What scale factors may be used in the following situations:
a) to increase an amount by 17.5% b) to reduce an amount by 15%
c) to reduce an amount by 6.8% d) to increase an amount by 0.8%

15 Increase each of the following amounts by 23% using the constant multiplier facility of your calculator. Round the answers to the nearest penny.
a) £45.99 b) £81.45 c) £682.37
d) £7.09 e) £276.50 f) £1 784.80

16 Work efficiently to reduce each of these amounts by 35%. Give your answers to the nearest penny.
a) £11.99 b) £27.99 c) £186.49
d) £3.50 e) £4 762.50 f) £599.99

17 Copy and complete the diagrams below to find the unknown amounts £x.

a) × …
£x → increase by 25% → £47.84

b) × …
£x → reduce by 12.5% → £399

18 The total bill for servicing a vehicle at a garage is £289.05 and includes VAT at 17.5%.
a) What was the cost of servicing the vehicle before VAT was added?
b) Calculate the amount of VAT included in the bill.

19 A portable television is advertised at £219.80 in a sale. What was the original price if it has been reduced by 30%?

20 Solve these inequalities:

a) $x - 3 > 11$ b) $2x < 18$ c) $3x - 1 \le 14$
d) $4x + 3 \ge -5$ e) $4(x + 7) < 12$ f) $2(x - 9) < 3$
g) $\frac{x}{4} \ge 5$ h) $\frac{x+2}{3} > -2$ i) $3 < x + 2 \le 9$
j) $-4 \le 5x + 6 \le 21$

Unit 20 Transformations

21 On a piece of graph paper, draw x and y axes from −12 to +12.
Draw the triangle ABC at A (−3, 1), B (−8, 5), C (−10, −2).
Find the image of ABC under the following rotations:

a) 180°, centre (1, −4). Label this triangle $A_1B_1C_1$.
b) +90°, centre (0, 0). Label this triangle $A_2B_2C_2$.
c) −90°, centre (1, 1). Label this triangle $A_3B_3C_3$.

22 Triangle AOB is mapped onto triangle COD by an enlargement.

a) Where is the centre of enlargement?
b) What is the scale factor?
c) What is the length of AC?

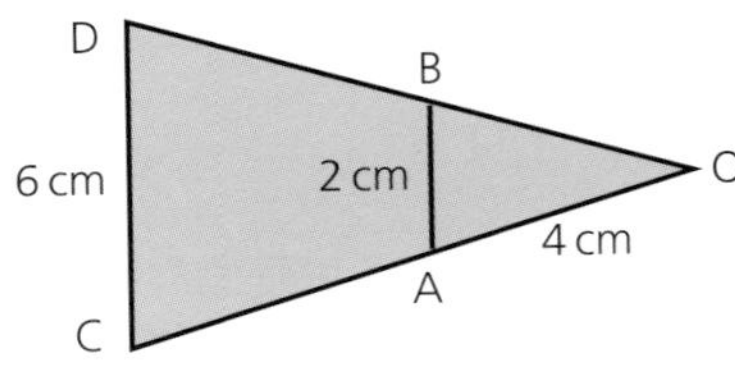

23 On graph paper draw x and y axes extending from −4 to +12.
Draw the triangle XYZ where X is at (6, 3), Y is at (9, 6) and Z is at (12, 6). Triangle XYZ is transformed using an enlargement to form triangle X′Y′Z′ at X′ (4, −1), Y′ (5, 0) and Z′ (6, 0).
Where is the centre of enlargement and what is the scale factor?

24 On a piece of graph paper, draw x and y axes extending from −10 to +10.
Draw the triangle ABC where A is (2, 2), B is (10, 2) and C is (7, 8).
This triangle is then reflected about a mirror line to its new position A′ (0, 0), B′ (0, −8) and C′ (−6, −5). Find the equation of the mirror line.

25 a) Draw triangle ABC with coordinates A (−2, 4), B (−2, 1) and C (−4, 1).
b) Rotate triangle ABC through 180° taking the point (1, 1) as the centre of rotation. Call your new triangle $A_1B_1C_1$.
c) Now translate $A_1B_1C_1$ by moving −6 units in the x direction and +2 units in the y direction. (Call this $A_2B_2C_2$.)
d) Which single transformation will map ABC directly on to $A_2B_2C_2$?

26 a) Draw triangle PQR with coordinates P (0, 0), Q (0, 2) and R (3, 2).
b) First reflect the triangle in the line $y = 0$. (Is this line the x-axis or the y-axis?) Call your triangle $P_1Q_1R_1$.
c) Now reflect $P_1Q_1R_1$ in the line $y = x$ to give $P_2Q_2R_2$.
d) Which single transformation will map PQR directly on to $P_2Q_2R_2$?

Unit 21 Simultaneous equations

27 Use the diagram to find the simultaneous solutions of these equations:

a) $y = x + 2$
   $x + y = 4$

b) $y = 2x - 5$
   $3y = 1 - 2x$

c) $3y = 1 - 2x$
   $y = x + 2$

d) $y = 2x - 5$
   $x + y = 4$

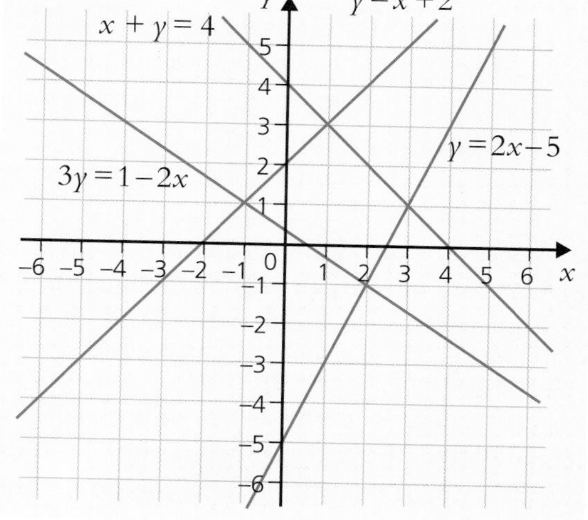

28 Solve these simultaneous equations:

a) $x + 3y = 21$
   $x + y = 9$

b) $5x + 2y = 38$
   $3x + 2y = 30$

c) $4x - 3y = 18$
   $x + 3y = 42$

d) $8x - 5y = 1$
   $7x - 5y = -1$

e) $2x + 5y = 37$
   $x + 2y = 17$

f) $7x + 3y = 34$
   $3x + y = 14$

g) $5x - 2y = 30$
   $x - y = 5$

h) $3x + 5y = 1$
   $2x - y = 5$

29 The cost of a table and four chairs is £247. The table costs £107 more than the cost of each chair.

a) Using £c for the cost of a chair and £t for the cost of the table, form two simultaneous equations in terms of c and t.

b) Solve the equations to find the cost of each chair and the cost of the table.

Unit 22 Frequency tables

30 The vitamin C content of 100 limes was measured in a laboratory and the results recorded correct to the nearest milligram.
Find the mean vitamin C content of these limes.

Vitamin C (correct to nearest milligram)	Frequency
29	11
30	18
31	23
32	19
33	17
34	12

31 A survey was carried out in a library in which the number of books being borrowed by library users was counted. Here are the results:

Number of books	1	2	3	4
Frequency	7	11	7	x

a) If you are told that the mode is 2 books, what is the largest number that x can be?

b) If, on the other hand, you are told that the median is 2, what then is the largest possible value of x?

c) Write an expression for the total number of people involved in the survey (total frequency).

d) Write an expression for the total number of books they borrowed.

e) Use your answers to write an expression for the mean number of books.

f) Find x if the mean number of books is 3.

32 An experiment was set up to test a new brand of super unleaded petrol. It was decided to test its performance in both small cars with 1-litre engines and larger saloon cars with 2-litre engines. Each car was driven on a special test circuit with 10 litres of the new fuel in its tank. The distance travelled was recorded correct to the nearest km. Here are the results of the experiment.

Distance in km	Frequency	
	Small cars (1-litre engine)	Larger cars (2-litre engine)
$60 \le x < 70$	0	5
$70 \le x < 80$	0	3
$80 \le x < 90$	1	4
$90 \le x < 100$	2	12
$100 \le x < 110$	5	8
$110 \le x < 120$	7	3
$120 \le x < 130$	12	0
$130 \le x < 140$	6	0
$140 \le x < 150$	2	0

Draw frequency polygons for both types of car on the same graph. Comment on the differences between the two sets of results.

33 Two dice were thrown together 200 times. Each time the total score was recorded.

a) Find the mean of these scores. (You may use a scientific calculator if you wish.)

Score	2	3	4	5	6	7	8	9	10	11	12
Frequency	6	11	14	21	27	34	30	20	20	10	7

b) Explain why we would expect the mean to be about 7, if the dice are fair.

34 Laura has a Saturday job working as a sales assistant in a shoe shop. Last Saturday she sold 20 pairs of shoes. Make an estimate of the mean price of the shoes she sold. (You may use a scientific calculator if you wish.)

Price of shoes (£)	Frequency
25–34	2
35–44	6
45–54	4
55–64	4
65–74	2
75–84	2
	TOTAL 20

Unit 23 Patterns and primes

35 The first three terms of a sequence are $(4 \times 1) - 3$, $(4 \times 2) - 3$ and $(4 \times 3) - 3$.
a) Write down the next two terms of the sequence.
b) Find the value of the 20th term.
c) Find an expression for the nth term.
d) Which term of the sequence has the value 141?
e) How many terms of the sequence are smaller than 200?

36 A sequence starts with the numbers 7 and 12 and continues in such a way that the differences of consecutive terms are constant.
a) What are the next three terms of the sequence?
b) Find an expression for the nth term.
c) Find the value of the 50th term.
d) The nth term of a second sequence is given by $3n + 50$. List the first five terms of this sequence.
e) Find the value of n for which the nth terms of the two sequences are equal.

37 A Fibonacci sequence starts with two numbers and then each new term is the sum of the two previous terms.
a) Find the next three terms of the Fibonacci sequence 1, 1, 2, 3, 5, ...
b) Find the value of the two missing terms in this Fibonacci sequence:
7, ..., 16, ..., 41
c) If the first three terms of a Fibonacci sequence are x, $2x - 1$ and 11, what is the value of x?

38 a) Continuing in the same way, find the numbers in Patterns 4, 5 and 6.
b) Find the missing values in the patterns below.

2 | 5
7
pattern 1

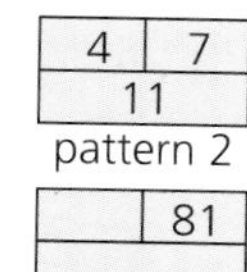

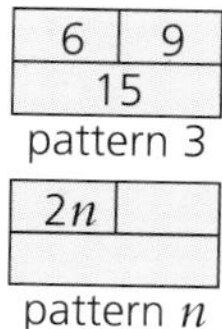

20
pattern 10

39 a) Write 288 as the product of its prime factors.
b) What is the smallest integer value of $n > 0$ such that $288n$ is
(i) a perfect square (ii) a perfect cube?

40 Given that $7875 = 3^2 \times 5^3 \times 7$ and $19845 = 3^4 \times 5 \times 7^2$:

a) find the highest common factor of 7875 and 19 845
b) find the lowest common multiple of 7875 and 19 845.

Unit 24 Areas and volumes

41 The tile shown here is one used for my kitchen floor. These tiles fit together perfectly to make a tessellation. Can you work out how that will be done?
a) Draw a sketch to show how they will fit together.
b) Find the area of one tile.
c) Find the perimeter of a tile.

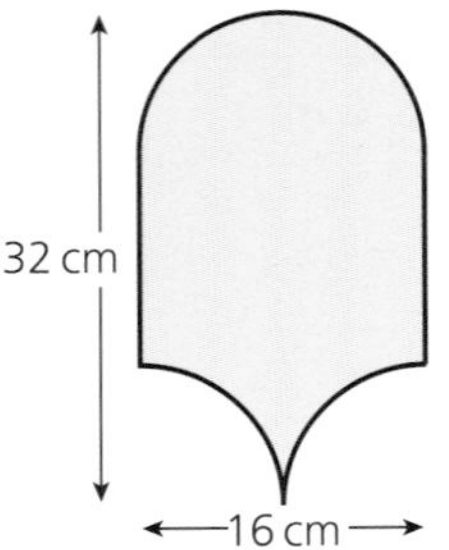

42 Rain which falls onto a flat roof measuring 12 m by 8 m is collected in a container which is a cylinder radius 40 cm. What is the depth of water in the container after a thunderstorm in which 1 cm of rain fell?

43 Find the volume of water in this swimming pool
a) in m^3
b) in litres.

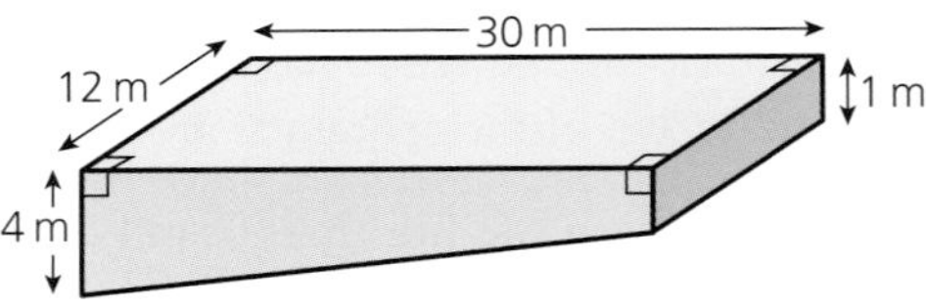

44 A rectangular tank measuring 2 m by 1 m by 1 m high is filled by a pipe with a cross-sectional area of $10\,cm^2$. The pipe delivers $1\,m^3$ of water per minute.
a) Express $1\,m^3$ as cubic centimetres.
b) Give the speed of the water as centimetres per minute.
c) Express this speed as metres per second.
d) How long does it take to fill the tank?

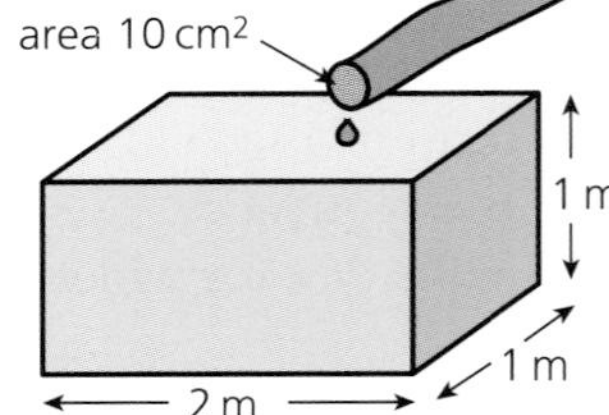

45 a) Taking the radius of the Earth to be 6370 km, find the circumference of the Earth at the equator.
b) Use this to find the velocity of a place on the equator (in km/h) as the Earth rotates.

46 Find the volume of this building and its total surface area (omitting the floor).

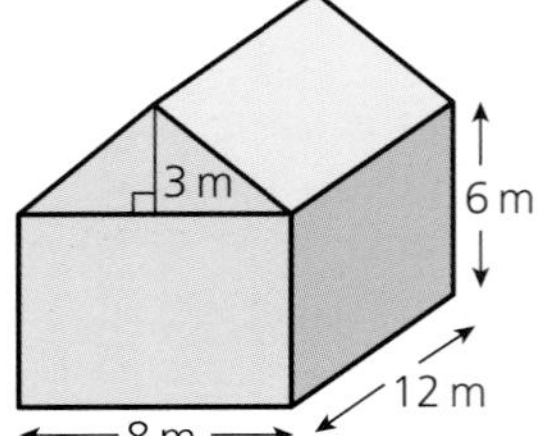

47 A cylindrical can has a radius of 20 cm. It contains water 50 cm deep. A brick is immersed in the water. Calculate the rise in the level of the water if the brick has a volume of 1.5 litres.

ALGEBRA AND GRAPHS (2)

25.1 Further rearrangements

The advice given earlier in the book when solving equations and inequalities involving x was to try to keep the number of xs positive, i.e. to keep the *coefficient* of x positive. However, an awareness of alternative methods not only provides us with a choice but may also contribute to our understanding. Compare the approaches to the problems shown below.

Example

a) Solve the equation $12 - 3x = 7.5$.
b) Solve the inequality $12 - 3x < 7.5$.

Answer

a) The equation $12 - 3x = 7.5$

■ Method (i)

$12 - 3x = 7.5$
$12 = 7.5 + 3x$ — The coefficient of x can be made positive by adding $3x$ to both sides.
$4.5 = 3x$
$1.5 = x$ — x is usually written on the left of the equation so we simply swop sides.
$x = 1.5$

■ Method (ii)

$12 - 3x = 7.5$ — Subtracting 12 from both sides of the equation at the start reduces the number of steps needed in the solution, but we need to be confident in dealing with negative numbers.
$-3x = -4.5$
$x = 1.5$

b) The inequality $12 - 3x < 7.5$

■ Method (i)

$12 - 3x < 7.5$
$12 < 7.5 + 3x$
$4.5 < 3x$
$1.5 < x$ — Note that when we swap sides with an inequality its direction must be reversed.
$x > 1.5$

■ Method (ii)

$12 - 3x < 7.5$
$-3x < -4.5$ — Note that multiplying or dividing an inequality by a negative number reverses its direction.
$x > 1.5$

---

1 Solve the equation $18 - 4x = 11$ by first:
a) adding $4x$ to both sides of the equation
b) subtracting 18 from both sides of the equation.

2 Solve the inequality $\dfrac{11 - 2x}{3} > 15$ by two different methods.
(Hint: the first move is to multiply both sides by 3 in any case.)

3 Solve $15 - 3x < 9 - 4x$ by first:
a) adding $4x$ to both sides of the inequality
b) adding $3x$ to both sides of the inequality.

4 Solve these equations by the method of your choice:
a) $17 - 3x = 9.5$ b) $16 - 5p = 28 - 8p$ c) $19 + 4r = 11r - 16$
d) $4 - 5(n - 3) = 12$ ✓ e) $7 + 4(1 - t) = 17$ f) $3(2v - 1) = 4(7 - v)$

5 Choose your own method to solve these inequalities:
a) $9 - 5u < 19$ b) $4m - 11 > 23 - 13m$ ✓
c) $\frac{31 - 7x}{5} - 6 \geq -4$ d) $\frac{5w + 1}{3} - 9 \leq 2 - w$

6 Make x the subject of these equations:
a) $a - x = b$ b) $p - qx = r$ c) $p(q - x) = r$

A form of equation not considered so far is one in which the unknown value appears in the denominator of a fraction. This situation can occur, for example, when solving problems involving trigonometry which we will meet later in the book. One technique for solving such equations involves multiplying both sides of the equation by the denominator.

Example

Solve: a) $\frac{8}{x} = 0.731$ b) $\frac{3.72}{x - 4} = 0.8713$ c) $\frac{x + 3}{x - 1} = 4$

Answer

a) $\frac{8}{x} = 0.731$ Multiply both sides of the equation by x.

$8 = 0.731x$ Now divide both sides by 0.731 and write x on the left-hand side.

$x = \frac{8}{0.731}$

$x = 10.9$ (to 3 S.F.) In the absence of any guidance about accuracy, the answer may be rounded to 3 S.F.

b) $\frac{3.72}{x - 4} = 0.8713$ Multiply both sides by $(x - 4)$. Note the need for brackets.

$3.72 = 0.8713(x - 4)$

$x - 4 = \frac{3.72}{0.8713}$ Rather than multiply out the brackets it is simpler to divide by 0.8713. Note that $x - 4$ has been written on the left.

$x = \frac{3.72}{0.8713} + 4$ The calculation may be carried out in one key sequence as 3.72 [÷] 0.8713 [+] 4 [=]

$x = 8.27$ (to 3 S.F.)

c) $\frac{x + 3}{x - 1} = 4$ Multiply both sides by $(x - 1)$.

$x + 3 = 4(x - 1)$ Since x appears more than once we need to multiply the brackets out.

$x + 3 = 4x - 4$

$7 = 3x$ Subtracting x from both sides.

$x = \frac{7}{3}$ The answer may be left as a fraction.

7 Solve these equations giving x to 3 S.F. in each case:

a) $\frac{11}{x} = 0.2379$ ✓ b) $\frac{17}{x} = 2.367$ c) $\frac{5.72}{x} = 1.378$

d) $\frac{1}{x} = 12.62$ e) $\frac{10}{x} = 12.62$ f) $\frac{100}{x} = 12.62$

g) $\frac{4.71}{x-3} = 0.2853$ h) $\frac{15.3}{x+2} = 2.718$ i) $\frac{0.876}{x-5} = 0.3274$

j) $\frac{7.31}{x} + 11 = 17.6$ k) $\frac{34.7}{x} - 5.1 = 2.93$ l) $\frac{16.8}{x} - 10 = -4.9$

8 Solve these equations, leaving each answer as a fraction in its lowest terms. In each case, predict in advance whether $x > 1$ or $0 < x < 1$.

a) $\frac{14}{x} = 21$ ✓ b) $\frac{33}{x} = 44$ c) $\frac{45}{x} = 35$

d) $\frac{27}{x} = 54$ e) $\frac{45}{x} = 36$ f) $\frac{8.1}{x} = 24.3$

9 Solve these equations. In each case the unknown value is a positive whole number.

a) $\frac{x}{x-3} = 4$ b) $\frac{6x}{x+1} = 3$ c) $\frac{3x}{2x+5} = 1$

d) $\frac{5x}{x+2} = 4$ e) $\frac{7x}{x+6} = 5$ f) $\frac{4x+9}{2x-3} = 7$

10 Solve these equations. As a check, each unknown value is a whole number.

a) $\frac{15}{10-x} = 5$ b) $\frac{21}{11-x} = 3$ c) $\frac{35}{3-x} = 7$

d) $\frac{12}{1-x} = -4$ e) $\frac{36}{7-x} = 4$ f) $\frac{24}{x-9} = -8$

11 a) By considering the gradient of the line AB form an equation involving d.

b) Solve the equation and use the result to find the distance AC.

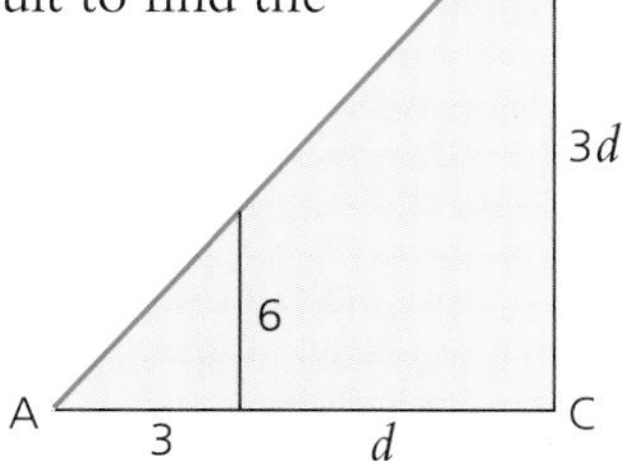

12 The points P and Q lie on the line with equation $y = 5x + c$.

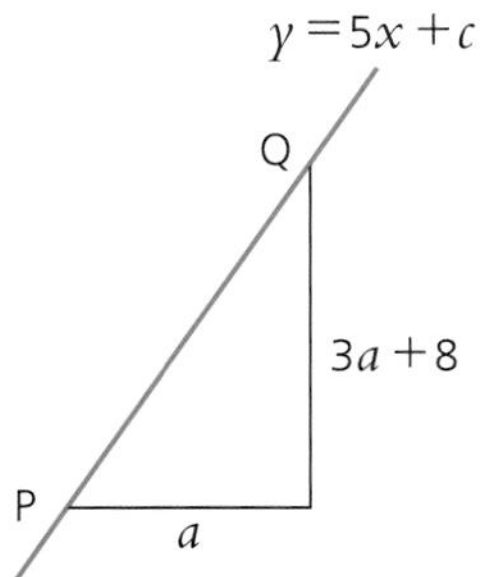

a) Find an expression for the gradient of the line in terms of a.

b) Solve an equation involving the gradient to find the value of a.

c) Given that the coordinates of P are (1, 8) find the coordinates of Q.

d) Find the value of c.

13 In physics, the pressure of a force is given by the force divided by the area on which it acts.

a) Using P to represent the pressure in newtons per square metre, F to stand for the force in newtons and A for the area in square metres, write a formula for P in terms of F and A.

b) Solve an equation to find the value of A when $F = 87.75$ and $P = 22.5$.

This is much simpler than it sounds! Don't worry about the units.

25.2 The reciprocal

The reciprocal of a number x is given by $\frac{1}{x}$, i.e. $1 \div x$. The reciprocal is so important in mathematics that all scientific calculators have a special key for finding the reciprocal of an input value. Depending on the model of calculator the key may be labelled as $\frac{1}{x}$ or x^{-1}.

1 Copy and complete the diagram below to show that $\frac{1}{x}$ is the same as x^{-1}.

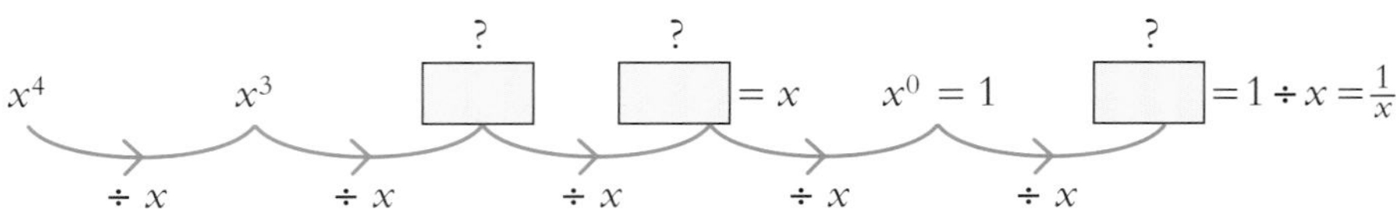

2 a) Copy the table below and use a calculator to find the missing values of y (correct to 2 significant figures) where $y = x^{-1}$.

x	0.2	0.25	0.5	1	2	4	5
y	5				0.5		

b) Plot the (x, y) values using axes labelled from 0 to 5. Join the points with a smooth curve.

c) Draw a line of symmetry on the graph and state its equation.

3 Describe how the reciprocal of x changes as:

a) x takes larger and larger values b) x *reduces* towards zero.

4 a) Given that the points with coordinates (0.1, 10), (0.02, 50) and (25, 0.04) lie on the graph of $y = \frac{1}{x}$, find without calculation the values of u, v and w such that $(50, u)$, $(10, v)$ and $(0.04, w)$ lie on the graph.

b) If the point with coordinates (p, q) lies on the graph of the reciprocal function, what other point must lie on the graph?

c) If the reciprocal of m is n, what is the reciprocal of n?

d) What is the reciprocal of the reciprocal of (i) 2 (ii) 25 (iii) r?

5 a) Draw the graph of $y = \frac{1}{x}$ for values of x from -5 to 5 (not including 0).

b) Give the equations of any lines of symmetry for the curve.

c) Describe any rotational symmetry.

d) What happens to the reciprocal of x, as x *increases* towards zero?

e) Explain why it is not possible to find the reciprocal of zero.

6 a) Sketch what you think the graph of $y = -\frac{1}{x}$ should look like.
b) Plot some points to check the accuracy of your sketch.
c) Describe the relationship between the graphs of $y = \frac{1}{x}$ and $y = -\frac{1}{x}$.

Written as a fraction, the reciprocal of 2 is $\frac{1}{2}$. The reciprocal of $\frac{1}{2}$ may now be written as $\frac{1}{\frac{1}{2}}$. Using the idea of equivalent fractions, $\frac{1}{\frac{1}{2}} = \frac{1 \times 2}{\frac{1}{2} \times 2} = \frac{2}{1} = 2$.

---

7 Use the method shown above to find the reciprocal of a) $\frac{1}{3}$ b) $\frac{1}{x}$.

8 Write down the reciprocal of each of these:
a) 5 ✔ b) $\frac{1}{5}$ c) 29 d) $\frac{1}{29}$

9 Simplify:
a) $\left(\frac{1}{8}\right)^{-1}$ ✔ b) $\left(\frac{1}{36}\right)^{-1}$ c) $\left(\frac{1}{x}\right)^{-1}$ d) $\left((a)^{-1}\right)^{-1}$

10 a) Describe the process that undoes finding the reciprocal of a number.
b) Solve the equation $\frac{1}{x} = 8$ by first multiplying both sides by x. Give your answer as a fraction.
c) Solve the equation $\frac{1}{x} = 8$ by finding the reciprocal of both sides.

11 a) Copy and complete the steps in this process:
$$\left(\frac{2}{3}\right)^{-1} = \frac{1}{?} = \frac{1 \times 3}{? \times 3} = ?$$
b) Use the same method to find $\left(\frac{a}{b}\right)^{-1}$.

12 Write the reciprocal of each of these as a fraction:
a) $\frac{5}{4}$ ✔ b) $\frac{7}{2}$ c) $\frac{5}{9}$ d) $\frac{11}{12}$
e) $\frac{p}{q}$ f) $\frac{p+3}{q}$ g) $\frac{t}{u+v}$ h) $\frac{x+y}{x-y}$

A whole number may be written as a fraction with any denominator that we care to choose, e.g. $3 = \frac{3}{1} = \frac{12}{4}$. It follows that a mixed number such as $3\frac{1}{4}$ may be written as an improper fraction as $\frac{12+1}{4} = \frac{13}{4}$.

In the same way, $5\frac{2}{3} = \frac{15+2}{3} = \frac{17}{3}$ and $11\frac{3}{5} = \frac{55+3}{5} = \frac{58}{5}$.

---

13 Write these mixed numbers as improper fractions:
a) $2\frac{1}{4}$ b) $5\frac{1}{2}$ c) $4\frac{2}{3}$ d) $1\frac{5}{8}$

14 Find the reciprocal of each of these by first writing them as improper fractions:
a) $6\frac{1}{4}$ b) $9\frac{1}{2}$ c) $3\frac{4}{5}$ d) $1\frac{11}{19}$

15 Solve these equations by finding the reciprocal of both sides:

a) $\frac{1}{x} = 11$ b) $\frac{1}{x} = \frac{7}{2}$ c) $\frac{1}{x} = \frac{1}{9}$ d) $\frac{1}{x} = 4\frac{1}{4}$

e) $\frac{3}{x} = 7$ f) $\frac{5}{x} = \frac{7}{2}$ g) $\frac{4}{x} = 6\frac{1}{2}$ h) $\frac{1}{x-1} = 3\frac{1}{2}$

In electricity theory, if two resistances of R_1 ohms and R_2 ohms are connected in parallel then the combined resistance is R ohms, where the value of R is given by $\frac{1}{R} = \frac{1}{R_1} + \frac{1}{R_2}$.

Example

Find the combined resistance when two resistances of 7 ohms and 12 ohms are connected in parallel.

Answer

$\frac{1}{R} = \frac{1}{7} + \frac{1}{12}$ Try the key sequence 7  12 

$\frac{1}{R} = 0.226\,190\,476$ To find R take the reciprocal of both sides

$R = 4.421\,052\,632$

The combined resistance is 4.42 ohms (to 3 S.F.)

---

16 Find the combined resistance when these are connected in parallel:

a) 9 ohms and 7 ohms b) 15 ohms and 16 ohms

c) 3.8 ohms and 7.1 ohms d) 0.8 ohms and 6.9 ohms

17 The formula for two resistances in parallel is easily extended for any number of resistances, e.g. $\frac{1}{R} = \frac{1}{R_1} + \frac{1}{R_2} + \frac{1}{R_3}$.

Find the total resistance when the following are connected in parallel:

a) 6 ohms, 8 ohms and 11 ohms

b) 4.2 ohms, 3.7 ohms and 9 ohms

c) 12.8 ohms, 16.5 ohms, 22.3 ohms, 14.9 ohms and 17.6 ohms.

18 In optical theory, the object distance u, image distance v and focal length f of a lens are related by the formula $\frac{1}{u} + \frac{1}{v} = \frac{1}{f}$.

Hayley and Alistair find that, for a particular lens, when the object distance is 35 cm, the image distance is 62 cm. What is the focal length of the lens?

19 Andrew is using a lens with a focal length of 40 cm in an experiment.

He needs to calculate the value of the object distance for an image distance of 90 cm. The lens formula given in the previous question may be rearranged as

$$\frac{1}{u} = \frac{1}{f} - \frac{1}{v}$$

Use this formula to find the object distance in Andrew's experiment.

If one person can complete a particular task in time t_1 and a second person can complete the same task in time t_2, we would expect that the time taken to complete the task, working together, is less than either of t_1 or t_2. Intuition suggests that addition should be involved but the answer is clearly not $t_1 + t_2$. The solution actually involves the *addition of reciprocals*. If the required time is given by t, then $\frac{1}{t} = \frac{1}{t_1} + \frac{1}{t_2}$

This principle can be adapted to different situations.

---

20 a) If the hot tap alone can fill a bath in 6 minutes, and the cold tap alone can fill the bath in 3 minutes, how long does it take to fill the bath using both taps?

b) Tom can complete a course of bricks in 20 minutes but his apprentice takes 30 minutes. How long should it take them if they work together?

c) Evan and Julie often travel between Bridlington and York. Julie can complete the journey by car in 40 minutes whereas Evan usually takes an hour in his truck. If they set off in opposite directions at the same time, how long should it be before they meet?

26 PYTHAGORAS AND LOCI

26.1 Right-angled triangles

This diagram shows a right-angled triangle (shaded). Its two shortest sides are 5 cm and 3 cm long. An exact square has been drawn on each of the three sides.

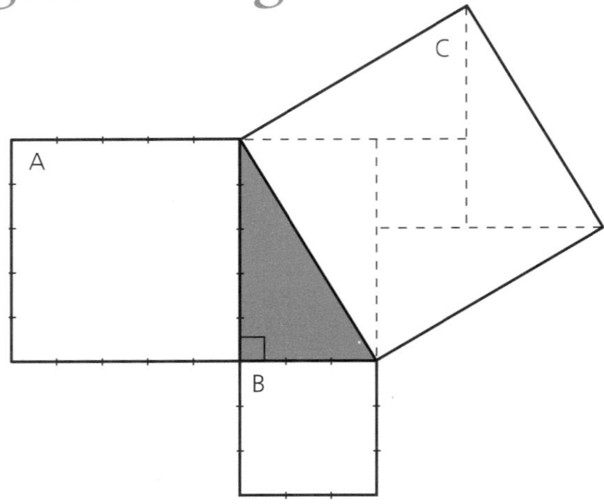

1 a) What is the area of square A?
b) What is the area of square B?
c) What is the area of square C? ✔
d) The next diagram shows how the pieces in square C can be rearranged to make two squares exactly equal to square A and square B. Can you work out how this was done?

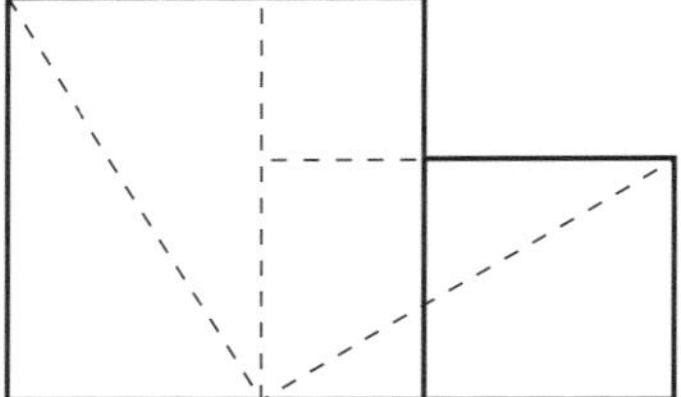

2 Investigate some more right-angled triangles. Draw each one on 1 cm squared paper. Carefully draw a square on each side of the triangle.
Make a table of your results like this:

Area of square A	Area of square B	Area of square C
25	9	

Square C is always the largest square. It is drawn on the longest side of the right-angled triangle. This side is called the **hypotenuse**.
What do you notice about the areas of the squares? Is there a connection between the area of square C and the other two? ✔

3 ✔ This is a right-angled triangle.
a) What is the area of the square drawn on the hypotenuse?
b) How long are the sides of that square? (Use the √ key on your calculator.) Write your answer to one decimal place.

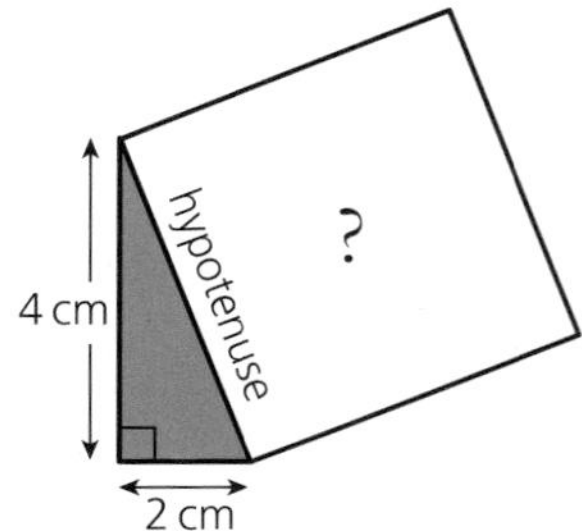

26.2 Pythagoras' theorem

Pythagoras' theorem gives the relationship between the lengths of the sides in a right-angled triangle. The theorem states:

The square on the hypotenuse equals the sum of the squares on the other two sides.

$c^2 = a^2 + b^2$

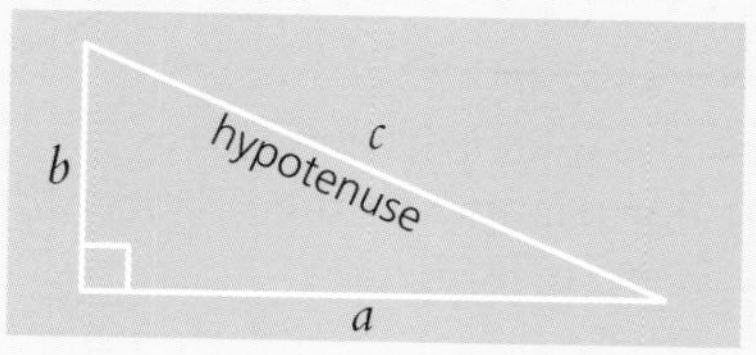

The hypotenuse is always the longest side in the triangle and is opposite the right angle.

Pythagoras was a Greek mathematician who lived from about 580 BC to 500 BC. He learned about this property of right-angled triangles while travelling in Babylonia. The ancient Egyptians also knew about this property although they did not formally write it down as a mathematical theorem.

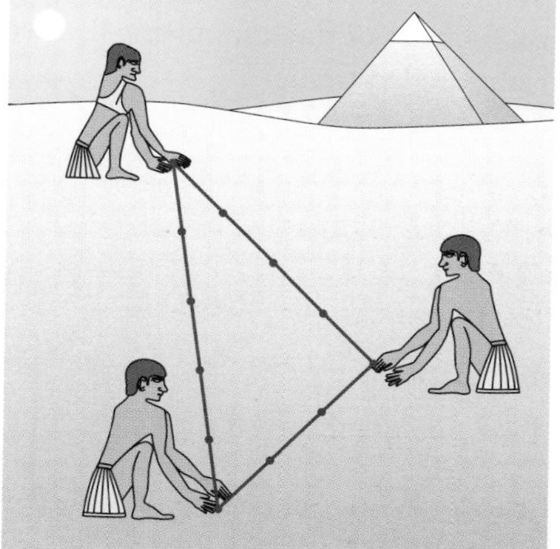

The ancient Egyptian surveyors needed a simple way of ensuring that the corners at the base of each pyramid would all be right angles.

They used a rope 12 units long. Each unit was marked with a knot. Three slaves were needed. One held both ends of the rope. The second slave held a knot 3 units from the end, while the third slave held a knot 5 units from the other end.

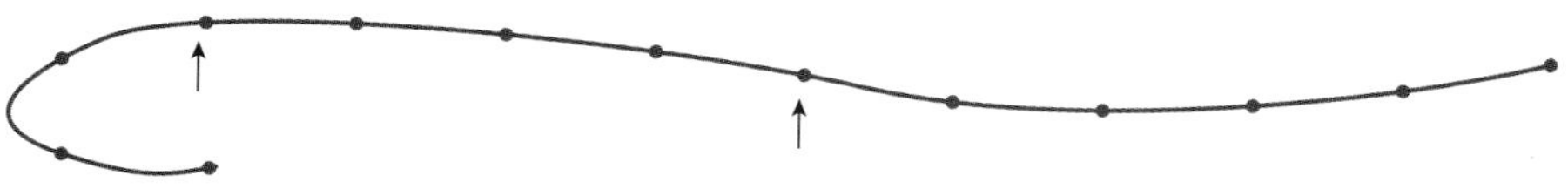

1 Make a drawing of the rope triangle.
  a) Where will the right angle be?
  b) Will this always work? Why?
  c) How many units long is the hypotenuse?

2 Builders today still use a similar idea, but they usually use a larger triangle to check that a corner is a true right angle.
How long should the hypotenuse be on this right-angled triangle?

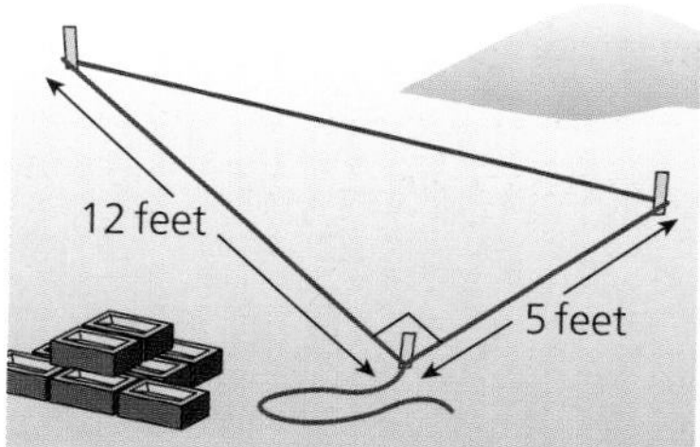

3 a) Name the hypotenuse in each of these triangles:

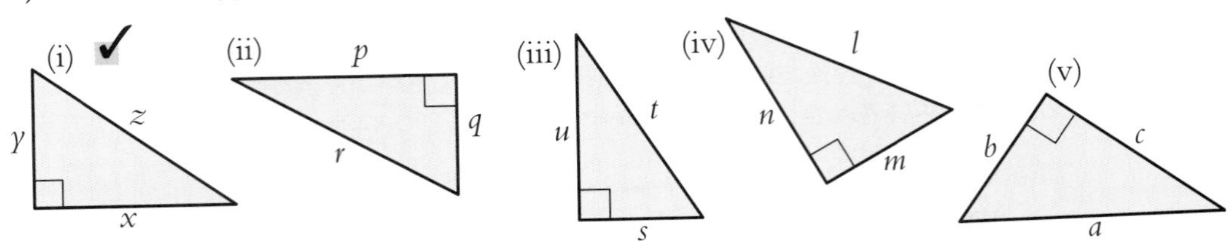

b) For triangle (i) the relationship between the lengths of the sides is $z^2 = x^2 + y^2$.
Write down the relationship between the lengths of the sides for the other triangles.

4 Which of these triangles have a right angle? Try out Pythagoras' theorem on each set of three numbers. If it works, you know you have a right-angled triangle.

a) sides: 6 cm, 8 cm and 10 cm ✓
b) sides: 1 cm, 2 cm and 3 cm ✓
c) sides: 10 cm, 24 cm and 26 cm
d) sides: 12 cm, 14 cm and 20 cm

26.3 Using Pythagoras' theorem

Example

Find the length of PR.

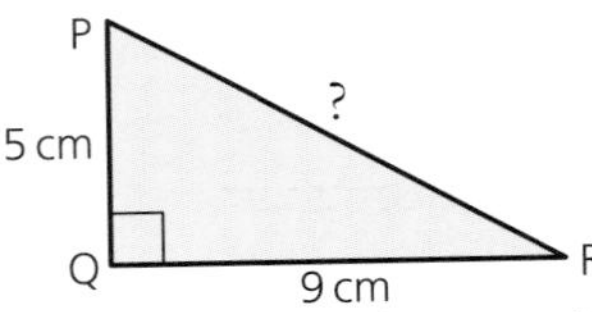

Answer

From the diagram, PR is the hypotenuse (the longest side and opposite the right angle). From Pythagoras' theorem:

$PR^2 = PQ^2 + QR^2$

$PR^2 = 5^2 + 9^2 = 25 + 81 = 106$

$PR = \sqrt{106} = 10.3$ cm (correct to 1 decimal place)

Example

Find the length of XY.

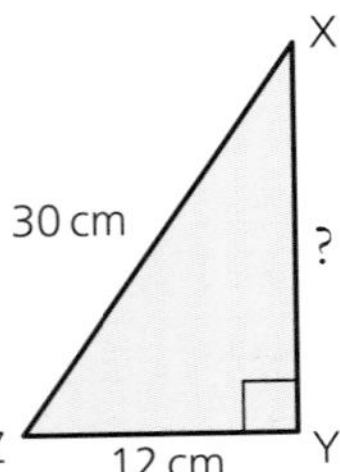

Answer

In this triangle XY is *not* the hypotenuse. Using Pythagoras' theorem:

$XZ^2 = XY^2 + YZ^2$

$30^2 = XY^2 + 12^2$

$900 = XY^2 + 144$

$900 - 144 = XY^2$

So $XY^2 = 756$

$XY = \sqrt{756} = 27.5$ cm (correct to 1 decimal place)

1 Find the length of the unknown side in each of these triangles. Give your answers correct to 1 decimal place.

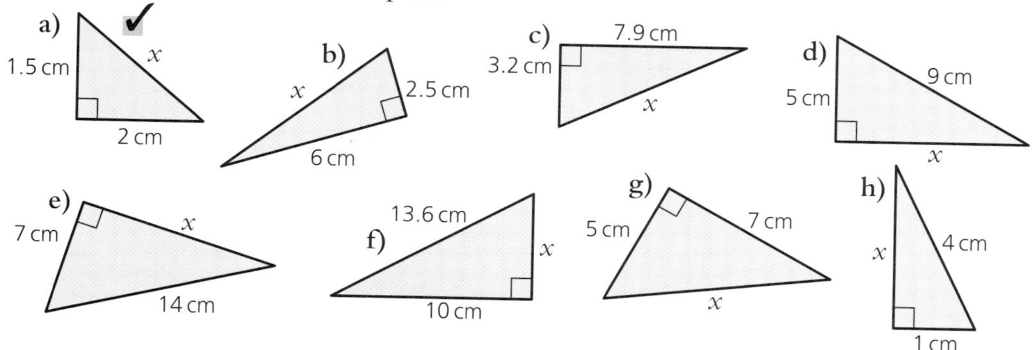

2 A football pitch has been marked out in a field. To check whether the corners are true right angles the two diagonals are measured. If the sides of the pitch are 110 m and 70 m, what should be the length of each diagonal?

26.4 Pythagorean triples

1 a) Find the lengths of the unknown sides in these right-angled triangles.

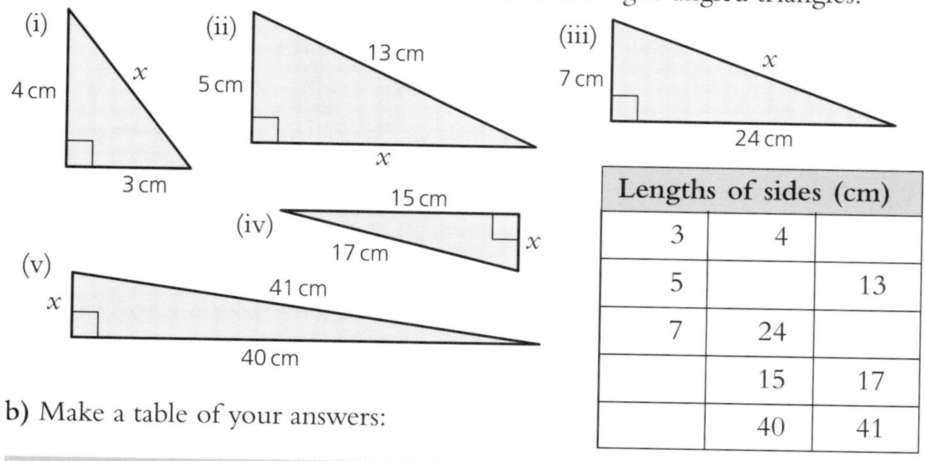

b) Make a table of your answers:

Lengths of sides (cm)		
3	4	
5		13
7	24	
	15	17
	40	41

These are all right-angled triangles whose sides are a whole number of units long. They are called **Pythagorean triples**. They are often very useful when solving problems, especially the first two: 3, 4, 5 and 5, 12, 13.

1 Here are three examples of '3, 4, 5' triangles. Find the length of the hypotenuse in each triangle. Explain why each one is a '3, 4, 5' triangle.

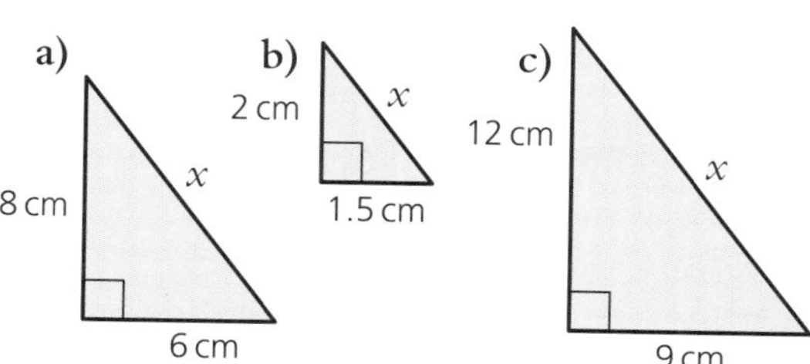

2 The following problems can all be solved using Pythagorean triples. Start by identifying which triple has been used, so that your working out becomes simpler. Find the lengths of the unknown sides.

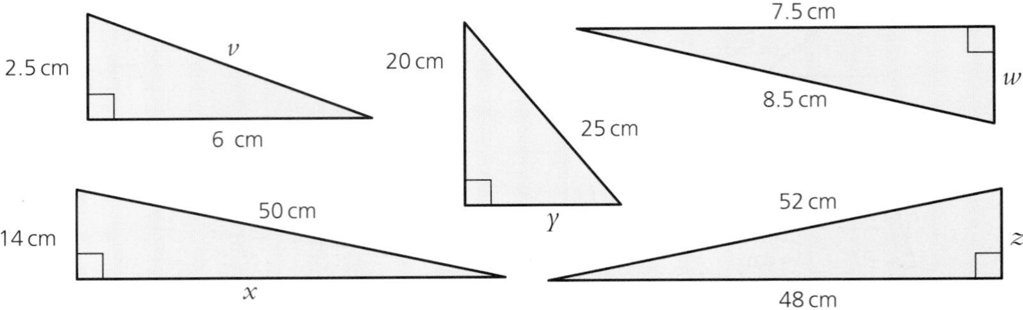

3 The longer side of a rectangular field is 240 m long. There is a footpath going diagonally across the field. This footpath is 250 m long.

a) Draw a sketch of the field.

b) Find the length of the shorter side of the field.

c) Find the perimeter of the field.

4 ✓ A pair of stepladders is 2 m tall when the steps are folded closed. When the steps are open, the feet are 1.4 m apart. How high above the ground is the top of the ladder, when the steps are open?

5 Ronnie's little sister has a kite like this:

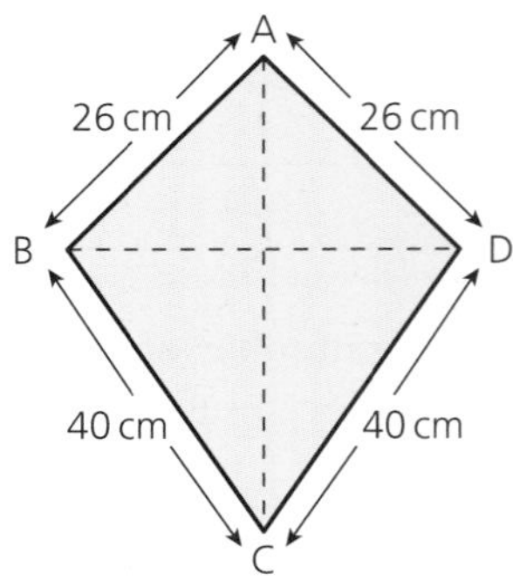

The cane support which stretches across from B to D measures 48 cm. The support from A to C has broken. How long is the cane which Ronnie needs to buy to mend the kite?

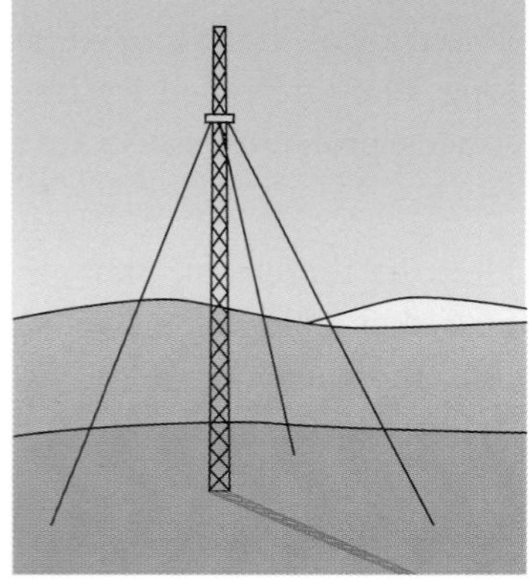

6 A radio mast is supported by three cables. The cables are attached to the mast 25 m above the ground and they extend out 10 m away from the foot of the mast at ground level.

a) What is the length of one cable?

b) What is the total length of all three?

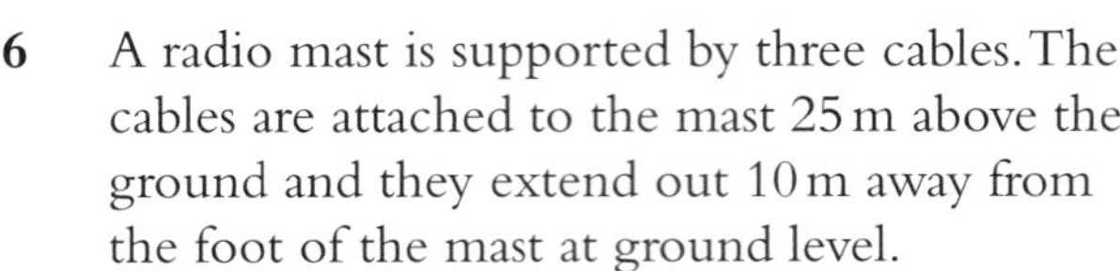

7 ✓ A is the point (–8, –2). B is the point (4, 3).

a) What is the length AC?

b) What is the length BC?

c) What is the length AB?

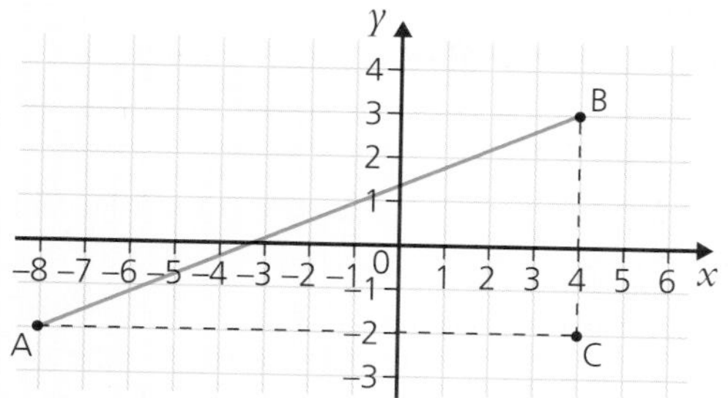

8 A spiral is made by drawing a series of right-angled triangles.

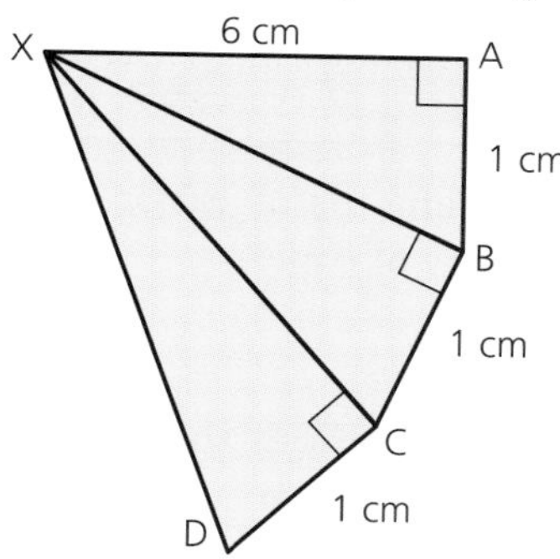

a) Find the length of XB keeping the √ sign.

b) Find the length of XC again keeping the √ sign.

c) What will be the length of the tenth hypotenuse? and the fiftieth?

9 This is a sketch of a garden shed. Find:

a) the area of the end wall (shaded)

b) the volume of the shed in m^3

c) the total area of all four walls

d) the area of the sloping roof.

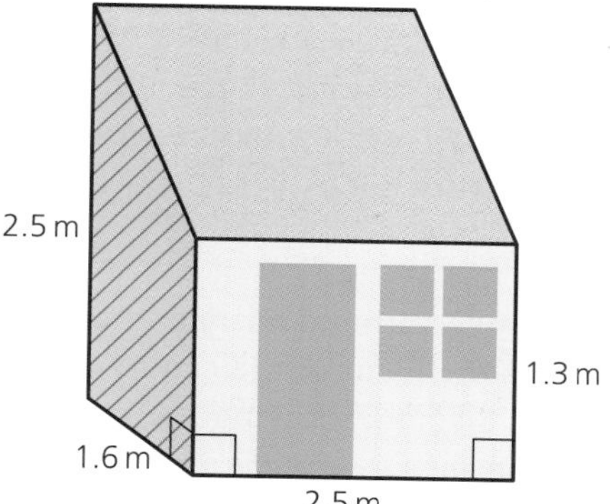

10 For each of the following shapes find x, then find the area:

a)

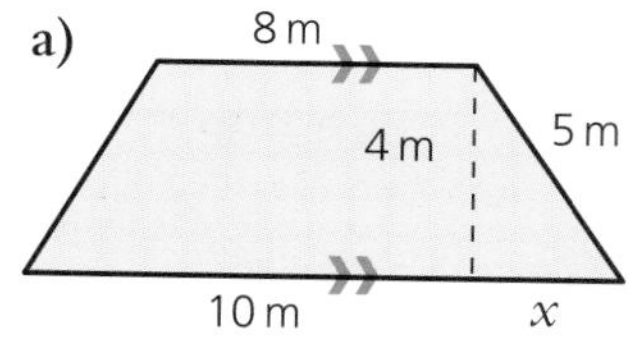

b)

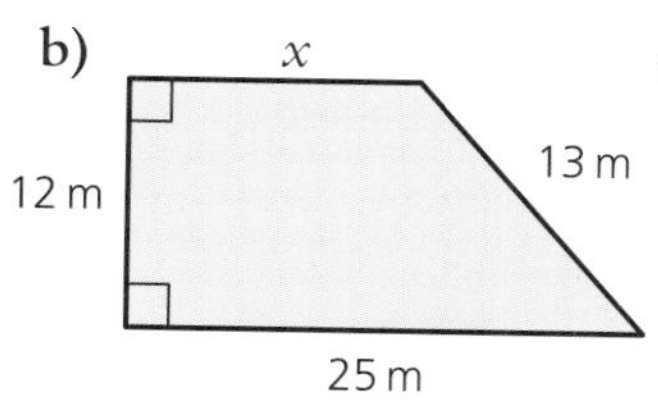

c)

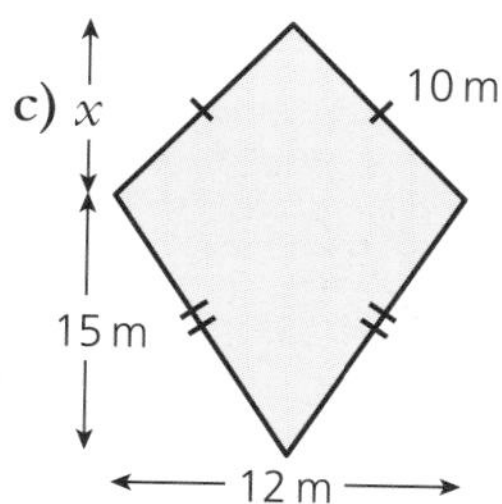

11 A rectangular box measures 60 cm by 20 cm by 30 cm. Calculate the length of the longest stick which will fit into the box.

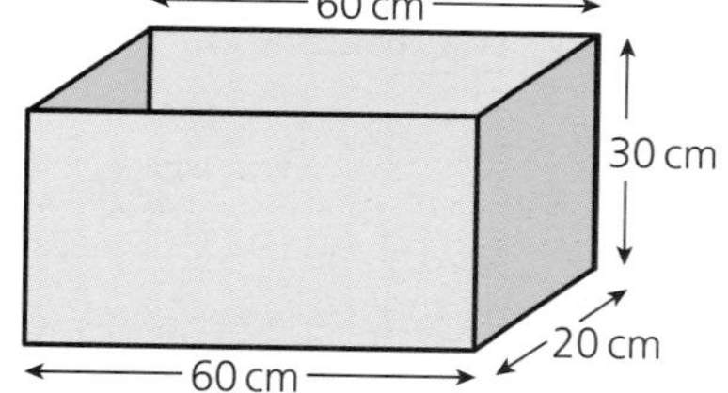

26.5 Loci

Investigation

For this investigation you need a circular object which can be rolled along. A plastic cup is ideal, alternatively use a coin or a circular disc.

- Imagine the object rolling along the desk. Can you predict the path of the centre of the circle? Roll the object along the desk to see if you were right.
- Now try to imagine the path of a point on the circumference of the circle. This is more difficult.

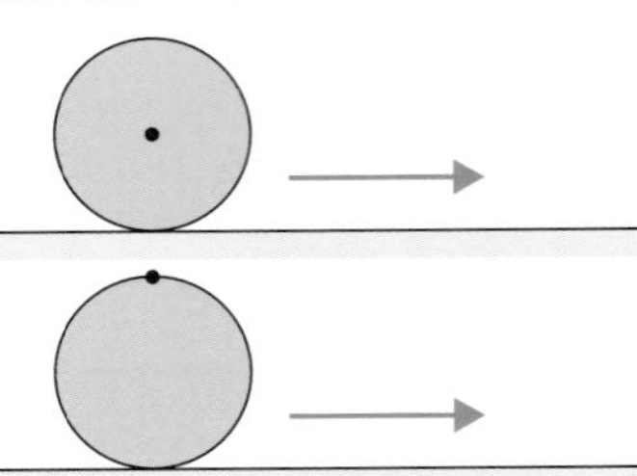

You may find it easier to check your prediction by rolling the object or coin flat against the desk, along a line drawn on a large piece of paper.

Draw a diagram to show the path of this point.

The locus of a point is the set of all the possible positions that it can occupy while obeying some given rule or condition. (The plural of locus is loci.)

1 ✓ A coin is rolled around a larger circular object such as a plate.
a) What is the locus of the centre of the coin?
b) Draw a diagram showing the locus of a point on the circumference of the coin.

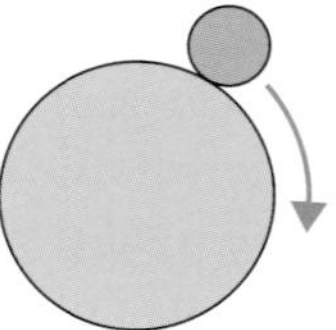

2 A bull is tethered by a rope to a stake in a field. The rope is 10 m long. What is the locus of the bull's head if it walks keeping the rope taut?

3 A moth flies so that its distance from a small light bulb is always 50 cm. What is the locus of the moth as it flies?

4 ✓ In a field, two bulls are tethered by short ropes. There is a distance of 30 m between the stakes (A and B) that they are tied to.
I have to walk across the field and decide to keep an equal distance from both of them at all times.
Draw a sketch showing A and B and the path I must take (the locus of my walk).

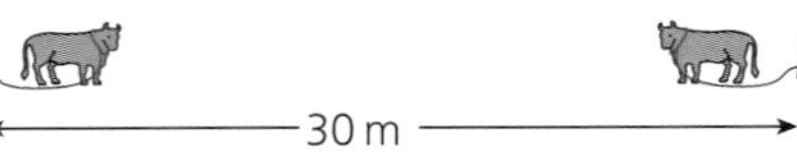

5 This diagram shows two walls in the corner of a playground. A child decides to walk away from the corner at B, keeping an equal distance away from both walls. Sketch his locus. Can you describe it in words?

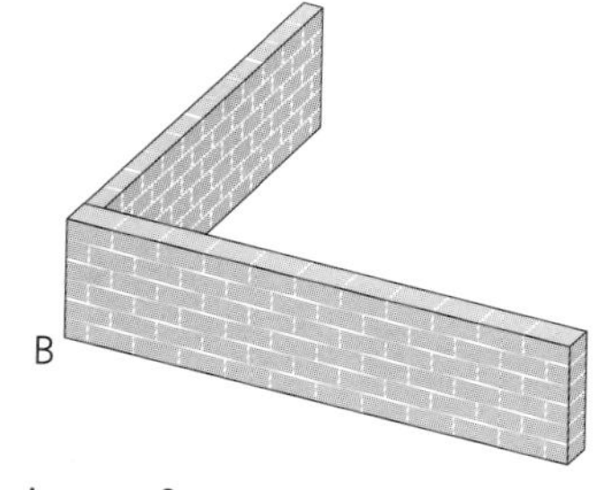

6 You need a set-square or a right-angled triangle cut out of cardboard for this investigation.
Mark two points A and B about 4 cm apart, on a piece of paper.

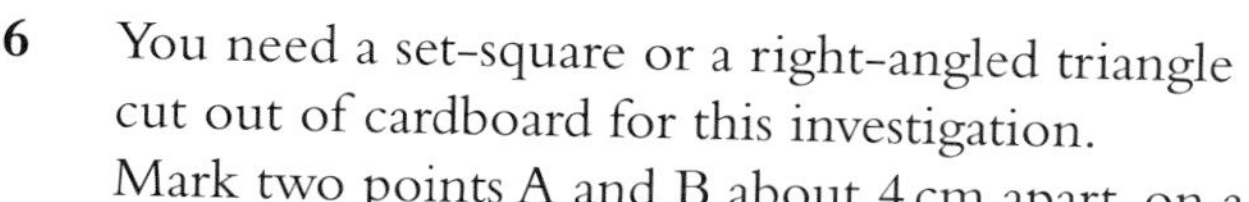

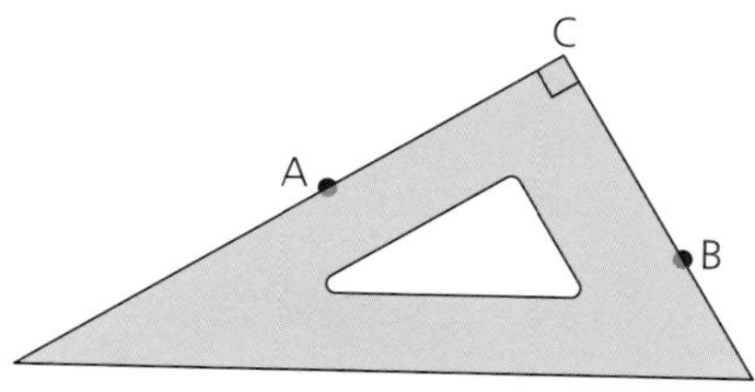

Mark one corner of your set-square or triangle. Call this point C.
Move the set-square round making sure that it is always touching the points A and B. (Do not lift the set square up off the page.)
Mark the path of point C as it moves round.

7 A ladder is leant against a wall so that it is standing up almost vertically. Unfortunately, the ground is slippery and the ladder slides down the wall. The top of the ladder stays in contact with the wall and the foot of the ladder stays in contact with the ground. You can demonstrate this using a ruler resting against a wall. Draw a series of sketches to show the ladder as it slides down to the ground. What is the locus of point H halfway up the ladder?

26.6 Useful constructions

To find the perpendicular bisector of a line

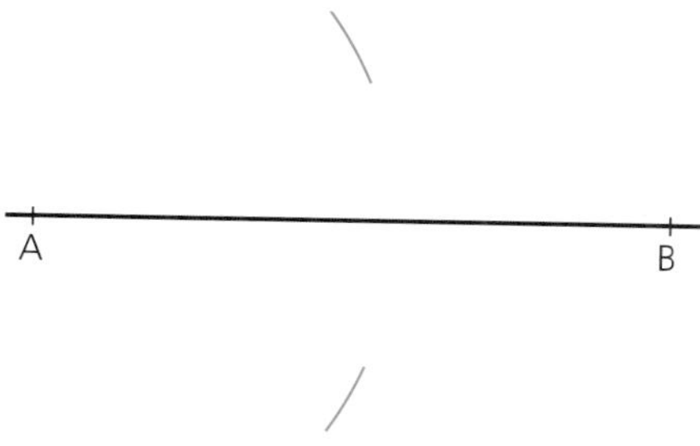

Mark two points A and B and join them with a straight line. Use compasses to draw two arcs using A as the centre and a radius greater than half the distance of AB.

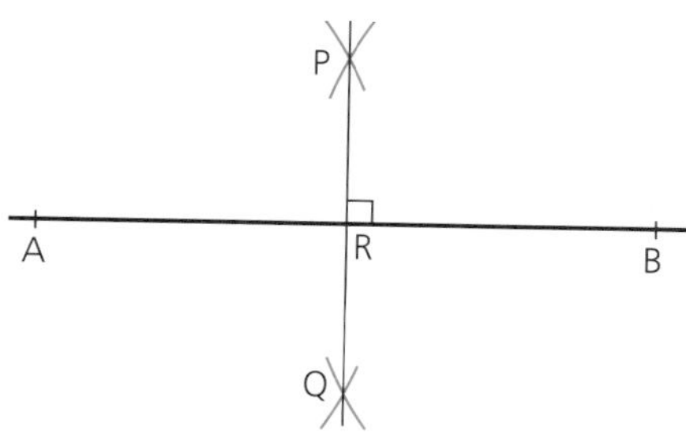

Next draw two more arcs with B as the centre (keeping the compasses the same distance apart).
Join the two points where the arcs cross.
PQ is the **perpendicular bisector** of AB.
R is the midpoint of AB.

■ To bisect an angle

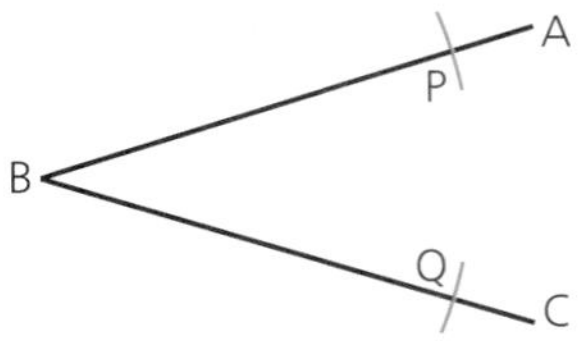

Draw two lines AB and AC to form angle ABC. With compasses draw two arcs from B to cut the lines BA and BC, at P and Q.

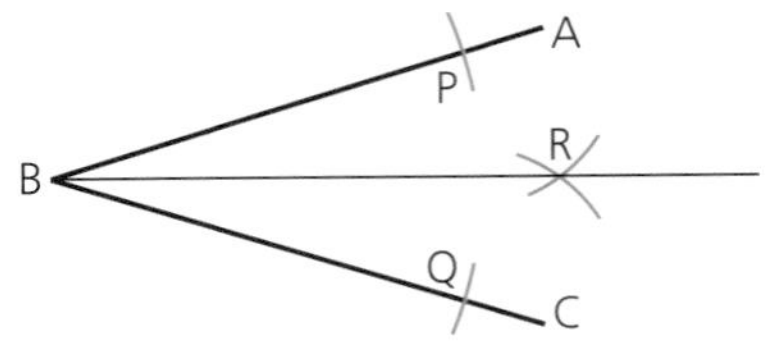

Now use P and Q as centres and draw arcs to cross at R, so that PR = QR. Join BR which is the bisector of angle ABC.

■ To draw parallel lines

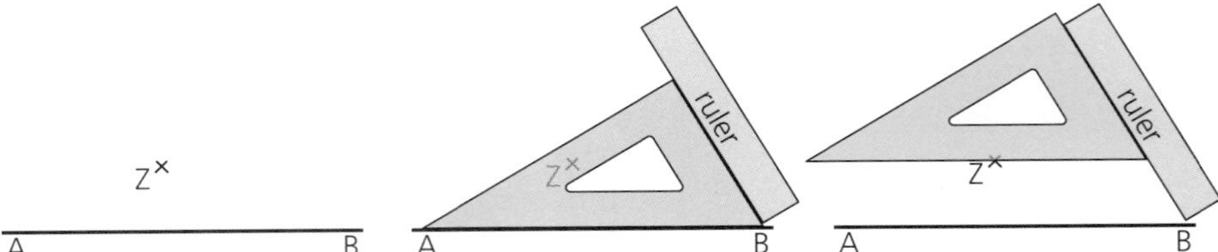

Draw a line AB. To draw a line through Z *parallel* to AB first place your set-square with the longest side on AB. Place a ruler along one of the other sides of the set-square.

Keep the ruler firmly fixed, then slide the set-square up until the longest side passes through Z. Now you can draw in the line parallel to AB.

Draw these loci accurately.

1 A straight line AB is 6 cm long. Draw the locus of points which are 4 cm from AB. (*Hint*: what will happen at each end of the line?) Use a dotted line to show the locus.

2 Sketch the locus of point P in each case. Use a dotted line for the locus and describe it in words.
  a) P is 1 cm from a fixed straight line of indefinite length.
  b) P is 3 cm from a fixed point A.
  c) P is an equal distance from two fixed points B and C (BC is 4 cm).
  d) P is an equal distance from two fixed straight lines DE and DF. The angle EDF is 45°.

3 Two villages X and Y are 30 km apart; X is due east of Y. The doctor's surgery at X will take patients who live within a radius of 20 km of X. The doctor at Y will only accept patients who live within 15 km of Y.
Make a drawing using a scale of 1 cm to represent 5 km. Shade in the area in which people can register with either doctor.

4 The area of the triangle ABC is 32 cm^2. Its base AB is 8 cm long. Draw the locus of point C.

5 A circle has a radius of 7 cm. What is the locus of point P which moves so that it is always 1 cm away from the circumference of the circle?

TRIAL AND IMPROVEMENT

27.1 Solving equations

Some equations may be difficult, if not impossible, to solve simply by rearranging. An alternative approach is to use **trial and improvement**, which involves substituting particular values into one side of the equation to try and reach some target figure on the other side. Using a systematic approach, solutions may be found to a high level of accuracy.

Example

Show that the equation $x^2 + x = 5$ has a solution between 1 and 2 and find the value of this solution correct to two decimal places.

Answer

In this case the 'target figure' on the right-hand side of the equation is 5.

Trying $x = 1$ gives $1^2 + 1 = 2$ which is *too small.*

Trying $x = 2$ gives $2^2 + 2 = 6$ which is *too big.*

It follows that the solution must lie *between* 1 and 2.

The important thing at this stage is that we try to improve our estimate of the solution by *one figure at a time* in a systematic search. It's a good idea to write the results in a table.

x	$x^2 + x$	
1	2	*too small*
2	6	*too big*
1.5	3.75	*too small*
1.7	4.59	*too small*
1.8	5.04	*too big*

If you have a graphics calculator, then keying in an instruction such as:

$? \rightarrow X : X^2 + X$

at the start allows new values to be tried with the minimum of effort

At this stage, the solution is trapped between 1.7 and 1.8 and so the next estimate will include *two* decimal places.

Continuing the process gives:

1.75	4.8125	*too small*
1.78	4.9484	*too small*
1.79	4.9941	*too small*

The solution is now trapped between 1.79 and 1.8 but it isn't yet clear whether the best answer to 2 D.P. is 1.79 or 1.80. To decide, we try the middle value giving $1.795^2 + 1.795 = 5.017025$ which is too big.

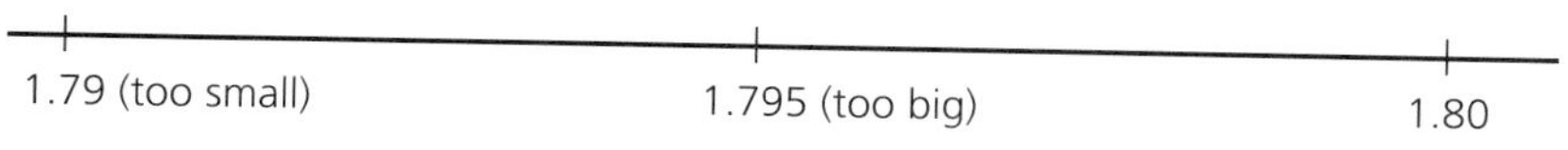

The number line shows that the solution is 1.79 to 2 D.P.

1 The equation $x^2 - 19 = 0$ has a solution between 4 and 5. Copy and complete the process started below to find this solution correct to 1 D.P.

x	$x^2 - 19$	
4	-3	*too small*
5	6	*too big*
4.5	1.25	*too big*
4.3	-0.51	*too small*
4.4		
4.35		

4.35

2 Show that the equation $x^2 - 11 = 0$ has a solution between 3 and 4. Find this solution correct to 1 D.P.

3 Copy and complete the process started here to solve the equation $x^3 = 10$ correct to 2 D.P.

x	x^3	
2	8	*too small*
3	27	*too big*
2.5	15.625	

4 Solve these equations correct to 2 D.P. by trial and improvement:
a) $x^3 = 200$ ✓ b) $x^3 = 30$ c) $x^3 = -500$

5 Find the positive solutions of these equations correct to 2 D.P.:
a) $x^2 - x = 17$ b) $x^2 + x = 9$ c) $x^2 + x = 35$
d) $x^2 - 5x = 11$ e) $x - \frac{1}{x} = 6$ ✓ f) $x - \frac{3}{x} = 8$

6 a) Copy and complete the table below to find the negative solution of the equation $x^2 - 2x = 7$ correct to 1 D.P.

x	$x^2 - 2x$
−2	8
−1	3
−1.5	5.25
−1.7	6.29
−1.8	6.84

Check these results using a calculator

b) There is a second solution near to 4. Find its value correct to 2 D.P.

27.2 Using spreadsheets

Once a spreadsheet is set up to solve a problem it gives the user the power to explore the effect of making changes without having to do the calculations. All of the values shown on the spreadsheet are automatically updated leaving the user free to consider the impact of the changes made.

Spreadsheets are particularly well suited to solving problems by trial and improvement, and the basic model outlined below can be easily adapted to solve a variety of problems.

Note: the detailed instructions relate to the use of Excel but, with some modification, the principles apply to any spreadsheet.

It's helpful to use **labels** to describe what the values in the columns represent

Spreadsheet

	A	B	C	D
1	START	STEP	x	RESULT
2				
3				

Change the **name** of this cell to x

Change the name of this cell to s

Enter the **formula**: $= x$

Enter the formula: $= \text{C2} + s$

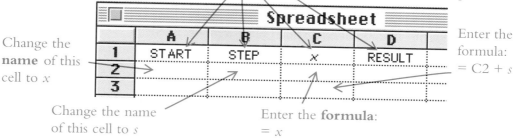

This basic model may now be used to find the positive solution of the equation $x^2 - x = 3$ to 1 D.P. from a starting value of 2 by proceeding as follows:

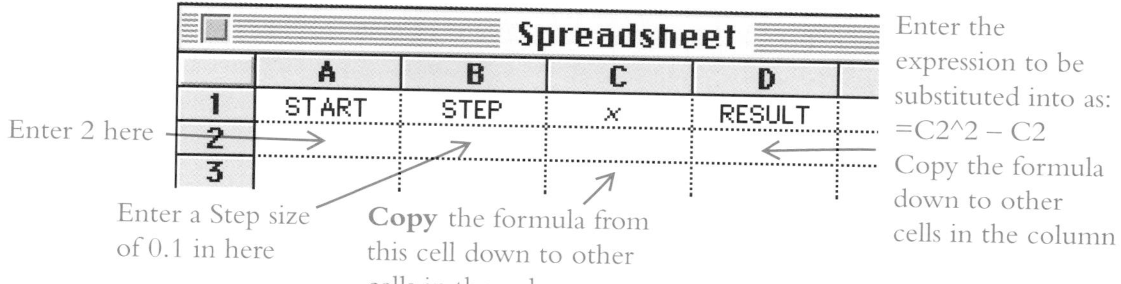
Spreadsheet
A
B
C
D
1
2
3
START
STEP
x
RESULT
Enter 2 here
Enter a Step size of 0.1 in here
Copy the formula from this cell down to other cells in the column
Enter the expression to be substituted into as: =C2^2 – C2
Copy the formula down to other cells in the column

If all goes well, your spreadsheet should now look something like the one here – depending on how far down the columns you copied the formulae.

Spreadsheet

	A	B	C	D
1	START	STEP	x	RESULT
2	2	0.1	2	2
3			2.1	2.31
4			2.2	2.64
5			2.3	2.99
6			2.4	3.36
7			2.5	3.75
8			2.6	4.16
9			2.7	4.59

The solution required is seen to be between 2.3 and 2.4

Improving the accuracy is now simply a matter of changing the Start value to 2.3 and the Step size to 0.01. Entering these figures gives:

Spreadsheet

	A	B	C	D
1	START	STEP	x	RESULT
2	2.3	0.01	2.3	2.99
3			2.31	3.0261
4			2.32	3.0624
5			2.33	3.0989
6			2.34	3.1356
7			2.35	3.1725

The solution must lie between 2.3 and 2.31

The spreadsheet shows that the required solution is 2.3 to 1 D.P.

1 If greater accuracy were required, what should be the next values to be entered as Start and Step?

2 Continuing the process, the following results were obtained:

a) State the value of the solution to 2 D.P.

b) What values should now be used for Start and Step to find the solution to 3 D.P.?

2.302	2.997204
2.303	3.000809
2.304	3.004416

3 The spreadsheet given in the example may also be used to solve any equation of the form $x^2 - x = n$ simply by using new Start and Step values. Use the spreadsheet to find the positive solution of $x^2 - x = 9$ correct to 2 D.P.

If anything more than the target value on the right-hand side of the equation is changed, then a corresponding change must be made to the spreadsheet.

Example

What changes must be made to the spreadsheet in order to solve the equation $x^2 - 11x = 4$?

Answer

This equation requires that the formula at the top of the Results column (i.e. in cell D2) be entered as C2^2 – 11*C2. The formula must then be copied downwards as before.

---

4 Find the positive solution to each of these equations corect to 2 D.P.:

a) $x^2 - 11x = 4$ ✓ b) $x^2 - 11x = 2$ c) $x^2 - 11x = 5.8$

d) $x^2 - 11x = 10.6$ e) $x^2 - 11x = 16.9$ f) $x^2 - 9 = 11x$

5 The diagram shows the graph of the equation $y = x^2 - 11x$.
By referring to the graph, explain why each of the equations in question 4 has one positive solution and one negative solution.

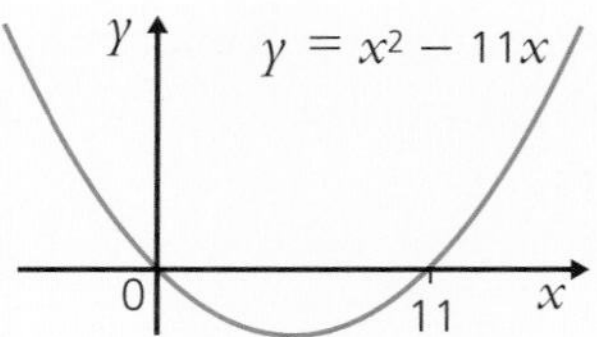

6 The spreadsheet shows values of $x^2 - 11x$ for whole number values of x from 0 to 10.

START	STEP	x	RESULT
0	1	0	0
		1	-10
		2	-18
		3	-24
		4	-28
		5	-30
		6	-30
		7	-28
		8	-24
		9	-18
		10	-10

a) Between which two pairs of consecutive whole numbers is the solution to the equation $x^2 - 11x = -25$ contained?

b) Find both solutions correct to 1 D.P.

7 a) How is the symmetry of the graph of $y = x^2 - 11x$ shown in the figures on the spreadsheet?
b) For what value of x will $x^2 - 11x$ take its lowest value?
c) Find the coordinates of the lowest point on the graph of $y = x^2 - 11x$.

The process for locating negative solutions of equations is the same as for positive solutions though it may be simpler to use a *negative step value.*

Example

Find the negative solution of the equation $x^2 + 2x = 5$ correct to 1 D.P.
Answer

The formula is entered as: =C2^2 + 2*C2

The negative solution lies between −3 and −4

	A	B	C	D
1	START	STEP	x	RESULT
2	0	-1	0	0
3			-1	-1
4			-2	0
5			-3	3
6			-4	8

We have the choice of using −4 as the next start value and 0.1 as the step size, or of taking −3 as the new start value and −0.1 as the step size. The second situation is shown below.

The solution lies between −3.4 and −3.5

	A	B	C	D
1	START	STEP	x	RESULT
2	-3	-0.1	-3	3
3			-3.1	3.41
4			-3.2	3.84
5			-3.3	4.29
6			-3.4	4.76
7			-3.5	5.25

Taking −3.4 as the new start value and −0.01 as the new step size gives:

	A	B	C	D
1	START	STEP	x	RESULT
2	-3.4	-0.01	-3.4	4.76
3			-3.41	4.8081
4			-3.42	4.8564
5			-3.43	4.9049
6			-3.44	4.9536
7			-3.45	5.0025

The spreadsheet shows that the solution is −3.4 correct to 1 D.P.

8 Find the negative solutions to these equations (there may be more than one). Give your answers correct to 1 D.P.

a) $x^2 + 4x = 11$ ✓ b) $x^2 + 4x = 24$ c) $x^2 + 4x = 2$
d) $x^2 + 8x = 31$ e) $x^2 + 10x = -5$ f) $x^2 - 8.9x = 3$
g) $\frac{1}{x} - x = 8$ h) $\frac{1}{x+3} - x = 2$ ✓ i) $\frac{1}{x+4} = x + 3$

The procedures for using spreadsheets to solve equations are easily adapted to solve a whole range of problems concerned with the location of maximum or minimum values.

Example

Find the maximum value of the product of two numbers whose sum is 15.

Some new labels are useful for this problem. Note how the language of algebra may be used to convey the information about the content of the cells.

Answer

Spreadsheet

	A	B	C	D	E
1	START	STEP	x	15 − x	x(15 − x)
2	1	1	1	14	14
3			2	13	26
			3	12	36
			4	11	44
			5	10	50
7			6	9	54
8			7	8	56
9			8	7	56
			9	6	54
			10	5	50
12			11	4	44
13			12	3	36
14			13	2	26
15			14	1	14

The formula for this cell is entered as: = 15 – C2

The formula for this cell is entered as: = C2 * D2

In this example, the symmetry of the figures in the end column shows that the maximum value of the product occurs when x takes the mid-value of 7 and 8, i.e. when $x = 7.5$.

Setting the start value to 7 and the step size to 0.1 gives:

		7.4	7.6	56.24
		7.5	7.5	56.25
		7.6	7.4	56.24

The maximum value of the product under the given conditions is 56.25.

ICT Extra!

Solve this problem using a spreadsheet: What is the maximum area for a rectangular paddock which can be enclosed by a perimeter fence that measures 500 m in total?

9 Find the maximum value of the product of two numbers given that their sum is :
a) 11 b) 25 c) 9.7 d) 41.3 e) 100

10 Use the results of question 9 to suggest a formula for the maximum value of the product of two numbers whose sum is n.

11 A farmer has 106 m of of wire fencing and wants to make a rectangular enclosure with the largest possible area.
a) Find the value of the maximum area.
b) Describe the shape of the enclosure.
c) What if the farmer had a different amount of wire such as 98 m, or 732 m? Try to find a general rule and express it using algebra. Test your rule for further values.

12 A Fibonacci sequence is one in which each new term is the sum of the two previous terms. The first 6 terms of the Fibonacci sequence that starts with the values 1, 1 are shown on the spreadsheet below.

Enter the formula: = A1 + A2 and copy downwards

	A
1	1
2	1
3	2
4	3
5	5
6	8

a) Use a spreadsheet to experiment with different starting values.
b) Find a pair of starting values to give 21 in cell A6.
c) If the number in cell A1 is increased by 1, how does this affect the value in cell A6?
d) If the number in cell A2 is increased by 1, how does this affect the value in cell A6?
e) Using a and b to represent the first two numbers of a Fibonacci sequence find an expression for the sixth term.
f) Check your formula for different starting values.

13 With the spreadsheet set up as for question 12, insert the formula = A2/A1 into cell B2 and copy it downwards.
a) Describe what happens to the numbers in column B as the formulae in columns A and B are copied further downwards.
b) Describe what happens to the numbers in column B for different starting numbers in column A, i.e. for different Fibonacci sequences.

14 The division of a line in such a way that the ratio of the shorter part to the longer part is equal to the ratio of the longer part to the whole, is known as the **Golden Section** and is used extensively in art and architectural design.

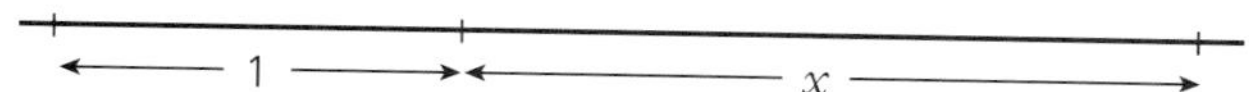

Expressed algebraically, the ratio may be given by $\frac{x}{1} = \frac{x+1}{x}$, i.e. $x = \frac{x+1}{x}$.
a) Use a spreadsheet to find the positive solution to this equation.
b) Comment on where you have seen this value before.

28 PREDICTIONS & COMPARISONS

28.1 Making predictions

You may want to make predictions in all kinds of situations.

- How much should I weigh, given that I am 5'6" tall?
- What should my father's blood pressure be, given that he is 45 years old?
- My cousin is 6 years old next week. What size T-shirt should I buy for her birthday present?
- I have to write a 1500 word essay for English. How many pages will that be?

In all of these situations a useful prediction can be made. This relies on the existence of a strong relationship between the measurement to be predicted and a useful 'predictor' measurement. So height is a good predictor of weight, and you will find a graph linking weight and height in most doctors' surgeries. There will be a chart for age and blood pressure as well.

Joe is doing a project in Biology on child development. He has measured the heights of nine children (all girls) to study growth patterns.

Age (years)	2	4	4	6	7	10	12	13	14
Height (cm)	86	98	108	109	118	136	146	143	145

Can he use his results to predict the height of a 3-year-old girl or a 9-year-old?

The first thing he must do is to draw a scatter diagram to show the relationship between age and height.

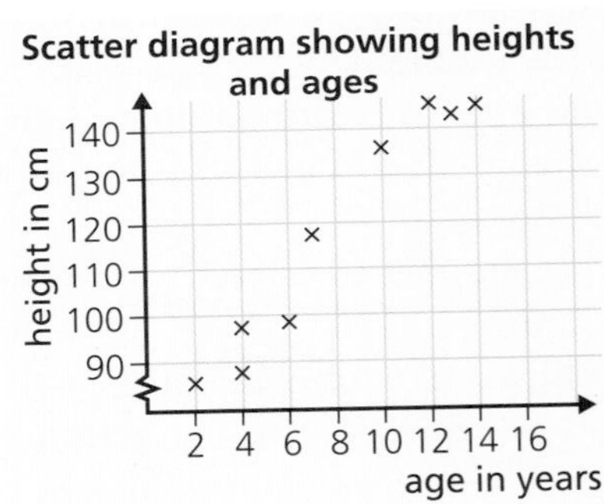

1 a) Do the points seem close to a straight line?
b) Does this graph show a good relationship between age and height?
c) Is it a positive or a negative relationship?
d) Is it sensible to try to make a prediction for the height of a girl aged 3 years?

The 'best fit' trend line is drawn by balancing the number of points above the line by the number of points below it.

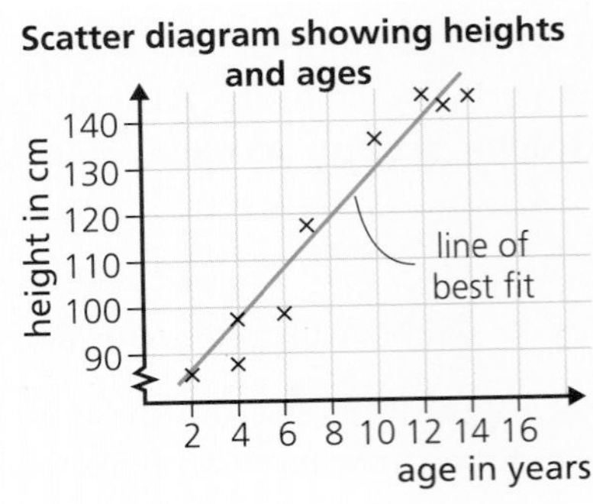

2 a) Use the graph to predict the height of a 3-year-old girl. ✓
b) Predict the height of a 9-year-old girl.
c) How much will a child grow between age 8 and age 9 according to this graph?
d) Explain why your answer to **c)** also tells you the gradient of the line. ✓

3 A group of pupils have been asked to measure the dimensions of various circular objects. Here are their results (in cm):

Object	Diameter	Circumference
table mat	18	57
cotton reel	3.2	10.5
plate	25.6	82.0
saucer	14.2	45
top of wastepaper basket	27.5	85
compact disc	12	38.1
bottle	8	25.4

a) Draw a scatter diagram showing diameter on the x-axis and the circumference on the y-axis.
b) Draw in the line of best fit.
c) Predict the circumference of a circular object which is 10 cm in diameter. ✓
d) Can you think of another way of calculating the answer to **c)**? ✓
e) Find the gradient of the line from your graph.
f) Explain why the gradient of the line should be close in value to 3. ✓

4 Sarah's friend Ben is on a sponsored cycle ride round Britain. Each time he sends her a post card she puts a little flag on her map of Britain and tries to work out how far away from Leeds he is. She does this by measuring the distance between Leeds and his last known position on the map using a ruler. Then she uses the scale on the map to convert this to miles.
Later her uncle shows her a distance chart in a road atlas. She is surprised to find that her distances are all less than those given on the chart. All distances are given in miles.

How far is Ben from Leeds?		
Place	**Sarah's estimate**	**Actual distance by road**
Manchester	38	43
Nottingham	60	73
Birmingham	91	115
London	164	196
Cardiff	169	236
Liverpool	68	72
Blackpool	62	86
Carlisle	88	120
Glasgow	169	215
Edinburgh	152	205
Hull	45	59
York	22	24

a) Draw a scatter diagram showing Sarah's estimate on the x-axis and the actual distance by road on the y-axis.
b) Draw in a 'best fit' line.
c) If Sarah estimates Ben to be 100 miles from Leeds, what is his actual distance likely to be?
d) On the same graph draw the line $y = x$.
e) Explain why this line helps to show that Sarah's estimates are all too low. ✓
f) Can you think of a reason why Sarah's estimates are all too low?

28.2 Errors in prediction

Example

A doctor has been testing her patients for blood cholesterol levels and thinks she has found a relationship between age and the amount of cholesterol in the blood.

a) Which of these four scatter diagrams shows the most suitable line of best fit?
b) Explain the reasons for your choice.

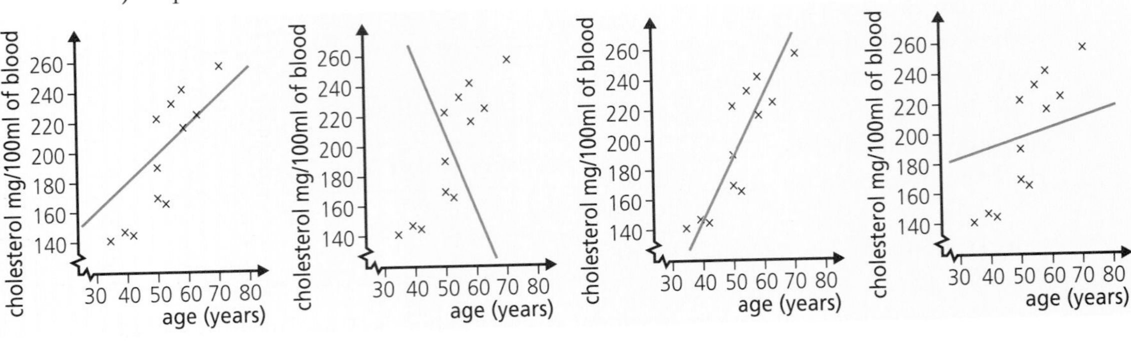

Answer

A line of best fit should be drawn as close as possible to the points on the scatter diagram. Line 3 is a better fit than line 1 because the points are closer to it. This will also help to give more accurate predictions.

---

1 A group of pupils conduct an experiment to see how high a tennis ball will bounce according to the distance it has been dropped. Here are their results:

a) Plot their results on a scatter diagram. (Show the distance fallen on the x-axis.)
b) Predict the height of the bounce for a ball which has been dropped 12 m.
c) Do you think this is an accurate prediction? ✔
d) Do you think the pupils were able to obtain accurate measurements?
e) Does this influence your conclusions?

Distance fallen by ball	Height of bounce
16 m	6 m
15 m	7 m
10 m	$5\frac{1}{2}$ m
8 m	5 m
5 m	3 m
6 m	$3\frac{1}{2}$ m

2 Ramesh is learning to play golf. He has been collecting data at his local golf club. For each hole on the course he found out how far it is from the tee to the hole (in yards) and the average number of strokes needed by members.

Distance in yards	135	160	165	180	260	340	350	350	350
Average score	3.6	3.5	3.7	3.6	4.4	4.6	4.7	4.8	4.9

Distance in yards	350	360	400	400	440	450	480	500	550
Average score	5.0	5.0	5.1	5.2	5.3	5.3	6.0	5.8	5.9

a) Plot a scatter diagram showing distance on the x-axis and average score on the y-axis.
b) Draw in a line of best fit.
c) Predict the average score for a hole which is 200 yards.
d) Do you think this prediction is accurate? ✓

3 Laura measured the heights of various students in her class and then did the same for each person's best friend. Here are her results.

a) Plot these heights on a scatter diagram showing students' heights on the x-axis.
b) Is it easy to draw in a line of best fit?
c) Explain your answer.
d) Can you predict the height of a best friend of a student who is 168 cm tall?
e) Explain your answer.

Student's height		Best friend's height	
Natalie	1.65 m	Jackie	1.73 m
Joe	1.77 m	William	1.70 m
Ramesh	1.82 m	Nina	1.58 m
Liam	1.67 m	Paul	1.64 m
Jessica	1.73 m	Sarah	1.68 m
Sam	1.71 m	Nirmal	1.60 m
Pam	1.64 m	Nessie	1.70 m
Joel	1.62 m	Ross	1.60 m

ICT Extra!

Enter the data for question 2 in this section into a spreadsheet. Try to draw a scatter graph and see if the Chart Wizard will draw in a 'line of best fit' for you.

28.3 Frequency polygons

We often want to compare two frequency distributions. They can be compared by looking at their respective means, medians or modes and their ranges.

Another method is to make a visual comparison by drawing super-imposed frequency polygons.

As part of a project, Barbara is investigating the incidence of road accidents among different categories of road users. The table shows some of the information sent to her by the County Police.

Road accidents: pedestrian injuries by age	
Age	**Frequency**
$0 \le x < 10$	19
$10 \le x < 20$	15
$20 \le x < 30$	4
$30 \le x < 40$	3
$40 \le x < 50$	4
$50 \le x < 60$	2
$60 \le x < 70$	8
$70 \le x < 80$	5

Here is a histogram to illustrate these results.

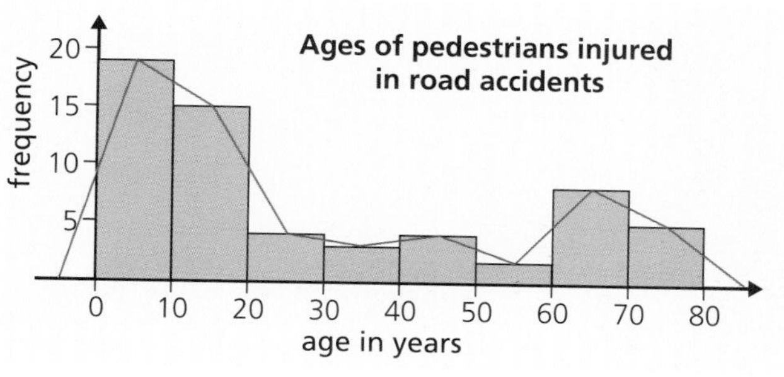

An alternative **frequency diagram** for grouped or continuous data is a **frequency polygon**. The easiest method of drawing a frequency polygon is to mark the centre of the top of each block on the histogram and then to join these points with straight lines (see diagram).

The frequency polygon extends down to the x-axis at either end of the distribution (halfway through the next class interval).

Frequency polygons are very useful for comparing two groups of results as they can be shown together on the same diagram.

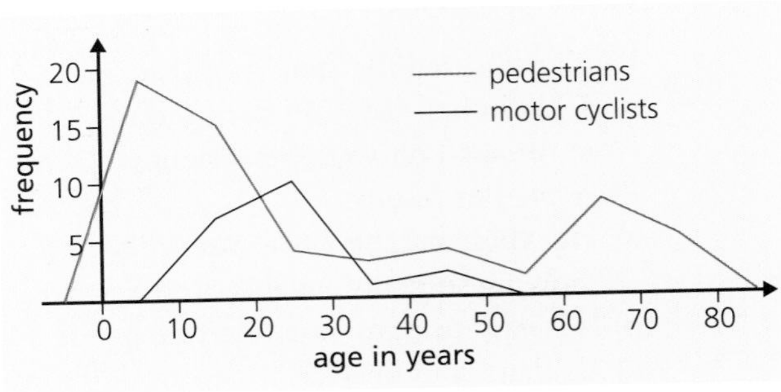

Here is the same frequency polygon showing ages for pedestrian injuries together with ages for motor cyclists' accidents.

The distribution of ages for pedestrians is called a **bimodal** distribution as it has two modes (or two peaks).

---

1 **a)** For pedestrians, which age groups seem to be the most vulnerable?
b) What is the modal age group for motor cyclists injured in road accidents?
c) Describe the differences between the two age distributions.
d) Can you think of any reasons for these differences?

2 The heights of 100 men and 100 women were measured and recorded. The table gives the frequency distributions of both samples.
a) Draw frequency polygons showing heights of both the women and men on the same diagram.
b) What are the modal height intervals for men and for women?
c) Describe the differences in the heights of the two groups.

	Frequency	
Heights in cm	Women	Men
$150 \le x < 155$	4	0
$155 \le x < 160$	13	0
$160 \le x < 165$	29	2
$165 \le x < 170$	30	13
$170 \le x < 175$	17	20
$175 \le x < 180$	4	27
$180 \le x < 185$	3	26
$185 \le x < 190$	0	12
$190 \le x < 195$	0	2

3 ✓ A group of 8-year-olds and a group of 12-year-olds were asked how long they spent playing computer games on a week day. Here are their replies summarised in a frequency table.

Draw frequency polygons on the same axes and comment on the difference between the two age groups.

Time spent playing computer games		
Time in minutes	Frequency	
	8-year-olds	12-year-olds
$20 \le x < 30$	2	0
$30 \le x < 40$	5	0
$40 \le x < 50$	6	0
$50 \le x < 60$	2	2
$60 \le x < 70$	3	1
$70 \le x < 80$	4	0
$80 \le x < 90$	1	4
$90 \le x < 100$	3	6
$100 \le x < 110$	1	3
$110 \le x < 120$	0	5
$120 \le x < 130$	0	6
$130 \le x < 140$	2	7
$140 \le x < 150$	0	2
$150 \le x < 160$	0	0

4 A nurse at a local hospital has collected data on the weights of new-born babies according to whether their mothers smoked or not during pregnancy. In order that the data should be comparable she has not included any premature babies.

Weight in kg of baby at birth	Frequency	
	Mother smoked	Mother did not smoke
$2.0 \le x < 2.5$	1	0
$2.5 \le x < 3.0$	3	1
$3.0 \le x < 3.5$	10	2
$3.5 \le x < 4.0$	6	3
$4.0 \le x < 4.5$	1	9
$4.5 \le x < 5.0$	0	4
$5.0 \le x < 5.5$	0	1

a) Draw frequency polygons for both groups on the same axes.
b) Find the mean weight for both groups.
c) Can you think of other factors which might influence a baby's birth weight?
d) What are your conclusions?

29 FRACTIONS

29.1 Further fractions

The principle of being able to add and subtract *like terms* has already been established where the terms are algebraic, e.g. $3x + 5x = 8x$ and $7ab - ab = 6ab$. However, expressions such as $3x + 5y$ and $7ab - ac$ involve *unlike* terms and cannot be simplified.

This principle applies equally well when dealing with fractions, e.g.

$\frac{2}{7} + \frac{3}{7}$ may be regarded as $2\left(\frac{1}{7}\right) + 3\left(\frac{1}{7}\right) = 5\left(\frac{1}{7}\right)$

i.e. $\frac{2}{7} + \frac{3}{7} = \frac{5}{7}$

In the same way, $\frac{2}{x} + \frac{3}{x} = \frac{5}{x}$

$\frac{11}{15} - \frac{4}{15} = \frac{7}{15}$

and $\frac{11}{x+3} - \frac{4}{x+3} = \frac{7}{x+3}$

---

1 Simplify these expressions:

a) $\frac{8}{19} + \frac{4}{19}$ ✓ b) $\frac{2}{11} + \frac{3}{11}$ c) $\frac{12}{13} - \frac{7}{13}$

d) $\frac{3}{8} + \frac{2}{8} - \frac{4}{8}$ e) $\frac{5}{21} + \frac{7}{21} + \frac{4}{21}$ f) $\frac{7}{20} - \left(\frac{5}{20} - \frac{1}{20}\right)$

g) $\frac{9}{25} - \left(\frac{17}{25} - \frac{12}{25}\right)$ h) $\frac{3}{29} + 2\left(\frac{4}{29} + \frac{3}{29}\right)$ ✓ i) $\frac{99}{100} - 4\left(\frac{77}{100} - \frac{53}{100}\right)$

j) $\frac{9}{x} - \frac{3}{x}$ ✓ k) $\frac{24}{y} + \frac{10}{y}$ l) $\frac{7}{pq} - \frac{2}{pq}$

m) $\frac{15}{t} - \left(\frac{10}{t} - \frac{4}{t}\right)$ n) $\frac{x+3}{y} - \frac{3}{y}$ o) $\frac{x+2}{y} - \frac{7}{y}$

We are able to add and subtract fractions that are not expressed in the same terms, i.e. that have different denominators, by using equivalent fractions.

Example

Calculate and leave your answers in their simplest terms:

a) $\frac{4}{5} + \frac{7}{10}$ b) $\frac{5}{8} + \frac{7}{12}$.

Answer

a) $\frac{4}{5} + \frac{7}{10}$ — $\frac{4}{5}$ is equivalent to $\frac{8}{10}$.

$= \frac{8}{10} + \frac{7}{10}$ — The fractions are now expressed in like terms.

$= \frac{15}{10} = \frac{3}{2}$ — 15 and 10 have a common factor of 5 and so the fraction cancels.

$= 1\frac{1}{2}$ — $\frac{3}{2}$ may be written as a mixed number.

b) $\frac{5}{8} + \frac{7}{12}$

$= \frac{15}{24} + \frac{14}{24}$

$= \frac{29}{24} = 1\frac{5}{24}$

24 is a common multiple of 8 and 12. It follows that both fractions may be written with a denominator of 24.

2 Calculate and leave your answers in their simplest terms:

a) $\frac{4}{5} + \frac{11}{15}$ ✓ b) $\frac{4}{5} + \frac{8}{15}$ c) $\frac{1}{2} + \frac{1}{4}$

d) $\frac{3}{4} + \frac{5}{8}$ e) $\frac{3}{4} + \frac{3}{20}$ f) $\frac{9}{10} - \frac{2}{3}$

g) $\frac{49}{50} - \frac{7}{25}$ h) $\frac{11}{12} + \frac{5}{6} - 1$ ✓ i) $\frac{1}{3} + \frac{3}{5} - \frac{11}{60}$

j) $\frac{11}{12} + \frac{14}{15} + \frac{3}{20}$ k) $\frac{2}{3} + \frac{5}{8} - \frac{7}{24}$ l) $\frac{16}{25} + \frac{7}{10} - \frac{27}{50}$

Fractions that are expressed in algebraic terms may be added and subtracted in the same way, i.e. by finding equivalent forms that have the same denominator.

Example

Simplify using equivalent fractions:

a) $\frac{3}{x} + \frac{5}{2x}$ b) $\frac{2}{3} + \frac{1}{x}$

Answer

a) $\frac{3}{x} + \frac{5}{2x}$

$\frac{3}{x}$ is equivalent to $\frac{6}{2x}$.

$= \frac{6}{2x} + \frac{5}{2x}$

$= \frac{11}{2x}$

Both fractions now have a common denominator of $2x$.

b) $\frac{2}{3} + \frac{1}{x}$

We can use a common denominator of $3x$ giving $\frac{2}{3} = \frac{2x}{3x}$ and $\frac{1}{x} = \frac{3}{3x}$.

$= \frac{2x}{3x} + \frac{3}{3x}$

$= \frac{2x+3}{3x}$

Note: this will not simplify further as the numerator and denominator have no common factors.

3 Copy and complete the following pairs of equivalent fractions:

a) $\frac{4}{x} = \frac{?}{3x}$ ✓ b) $\frac{2}{y} = \frac{?}{5y}$ c) $\frac{3}{q} = \frac{?}{6q}$

d) $\frac{5}{3} = \frac{?}{3x}$ e) $\frac{7}{2} = \frac{?}{2n}$ f) $\frac{8}{3} = \frac{?}{6n}$

g) $\frac{4}{7} = \frac{?}{21y}$ h) $\frac{2}{3x} = \frac{?}{3xy}$ i) $\frac{5}{6u} = \frac{?}{12uv}$

4 Simplify using equivalent fractions:

a) $\frac{2}{x} + \frac{1}{3x}$ ✓ b) $\frac{5}{y} + \frac{1}{2y}$ c) $\frac{10}{3x} + \frac{5}{6x}$

d) $\frac{12}{x} - \frac{7}{2x}$ e) $\frac{1}{R} - \frac{2}{5R}$ f) $\frac{4}{3f} - \frac{1}{15f}$

g) $\frac{3}{4} + \frac{1}{x}$ h) $\frac{2}{3} - \frac{3}{g}$ i) $\frac{9}{n} - \frac{2}{np}$

Whole numbers may also be written as fractions, e.g. $1 = \frac{2}{2} = \frac{7}{7} = \frac{x}{x} = \frac{5y}{5y}$.
This allows us to simplify expressions involving fractions and whole numbers,

e.g. $1 - \frac{3}{20} = \frac{20}{20} - \frac{3}{20} = \frac{17}{20}$

and $\frac{3}{x} - 2 = \frac{3}{x} - \frac{2}{1} = \frac{3}{x} - \frac{2x}{x} = \frac{3-2x}{x}$.

5 Simplify the following:

a) $1-\frac{5}{12}$ ✓ b) $1-\frac{9}{16}$ c) $2-\frac{5}{8}$ d) $\frac{6}{x}+1$ e) $\frac{5}{y}+1$

f) $\frac{2}{a}-1$ g) $\frac{3}{2y}+1$ h) $\frac{4}{5x}-1$ i) $\frac{7}{4d}-1$ j) $\frac{1}{x+3}+1$

k) $\frac{2}{y-3}+1$ l) $\frac{5}{h+7}-1$ m) $\frac{1}{x}+2$ n) $3-\frac{1}{x+2}$ o) $5-\frac{3}{x-2}$

6 Find the next two terms of each of the following sequences:

a) $\frac{1}{10}, \frac{3}{10}, \frac{5}{10}, \frac{7}{10}$ b) $\frac{1}{4}, \frac{3}{8}, \frac{1}{2}, \frac{5}{8}$ c) $\frac{1}{2}, \frac{11}{10}, \frac{17}{10}, \frac{23}{10}$

d) $\frac{5}{16}, \frac{31}{48}, \frac{47}{48}, \frac{21}{16}$ e) $\frac{2}{5}, \frac{13}{20}, \frac{9}{10}, \frac{23}{20}$ f) $\frac{13}{12}, \frac{11}{6}, \frac{31}{12}, \frac{10}{3}$

g) $\frac{3}{x}, \frac{7}{x}, \frac{11}{x}, \frac{15}{x}$ ✓ h) $\frac{x}{y}, \frac{x+3}{y}, \frac{x+6}{y}, \frac{x+9}{y}$ i) $\frac{x}{y+1}, \frac{3x}{y+1}, \frac{5x}{y+1}, \frac{7x}{y+1}$

7 The first four terms of a sequence are $\frac{1}{2}, \frac{1}{2}+\frac{1}{4}, \frac{1}{2}+\frac{1}{4}+\frac{1}{8}, \frac{1}{2}+\frac{1}{4}+\frac{1}{8}+\frac{1}{16}$.

a) Find an expression for the 5th and 6th terms in the same form.

b) Write each of the first six terms as a single fraction.

c) Copy the diagrams below and show the next two diagrams in the sequence.

d) Use the diagrams to explain what happens to the terms of the sequence given in part a) as the sequence progresses.

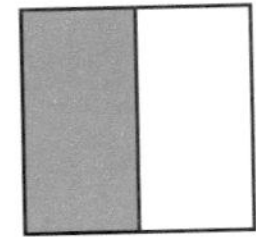
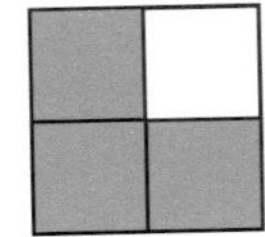
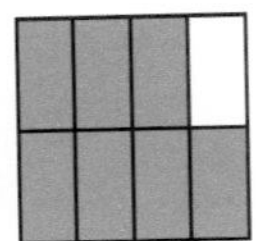

Addition and subtraction involving mixed numbers may be carried out by dealing with the whole numbers and fractions separately.

Example

Calculate the value of the following:

a) $2\frac{1}{3}+5\frac{1}{2}$ b) $11\frac{4}{5}-2\frac{1}{2}$ c) $4\frac{5}{8}+2\frac{3}{4}$ d) $10\frac{1}{4}-4\frac{2}{3}$

Answer

a) $2\frac{1}{3}+5\frac{1}{2}=7+\frac{2}{6}+\frac{3}{6}=7\frac{5}{6}$

b) $11\frac{4}{5}-2\frac{1}{2}=9+\frac{8}{10}-\frac{5}{10}=9\frac{3}{10}$

c) $4\frac{5}{8}+2\frac{3}{4}=6+\frac{5}{8}+\frac{6}{8}=6+\frac{11}{8}=6+1\frac{3}{8}=7\frac{3}{8}$

d) $10\frac{1}{4}-4\frac{2}{3}=6+\frac{3}{12}-\frac{8}{12}=6-\frac{5}{12}=5\frac{7}{12}$

8 Calculate the value of the following:

a) $7\frac{1}{4}+4\frac{2}{3}$ ✓ b) $5\frac{3}{8}+2\frac{5}{16}$ c) $8\frac{1}{3}+6\frac{1}{4}$

d) $5\frac{3}{4}+1\frac{3}{8}$ e) $7\frac{4}{5}+3\frac{1}{2}$ f) $12\frac{7}{9}+2\frac{1}{3}$

g) $8\frac{1}{2}-5\frac{3}{8}$ h) $9\frac{2}{3}-4\frac{1}{2}$ ✓ i) $10\frac{2}{3}-6\frac{2}{5}$

j) $11\frac{1}{4}-4\frac{1}{2}$ k) $17\frac{1}{2}-4\frac{3}{4}$ l) $8\frac{3}{5}-7\frac{9}{10}$

9 My journey home is in three stages. The first stage is across country, using a number of minor roads, and takes $\frac{3}{4}$ hour. The second stage is on a motorway and takes about $1\frac{1}{2}$ hours and the final stage is largely on dual carriageway and takes a further $\frac{3}{4}$ hour. How long does it take me to get home?

10 During a marathon, Norman covers $5\frac{1}{2}$ miles during the first $\frac{1}{2}$ hour. How much further does he have to run to complete the distance of $26\frac{7}{32}$ miles? Norman has set himself a target time of 3 hours for the race; use estimation to decide if he is on schedule. Explain your reasoning.

11 During an experiment, there are only three mutually exclusive outcomes A, B and C. The probability that A occurs is $\frac{11}{24}$ and the probability that B occurs is $\frac{3}{8}$.
a) What is the probability that C occurs?
b) Which event is most likely to occur?
c) Which event is least likely to occur?

12 Each of the figures on the diagram represents a distance in inches. Calculate the labelled values.

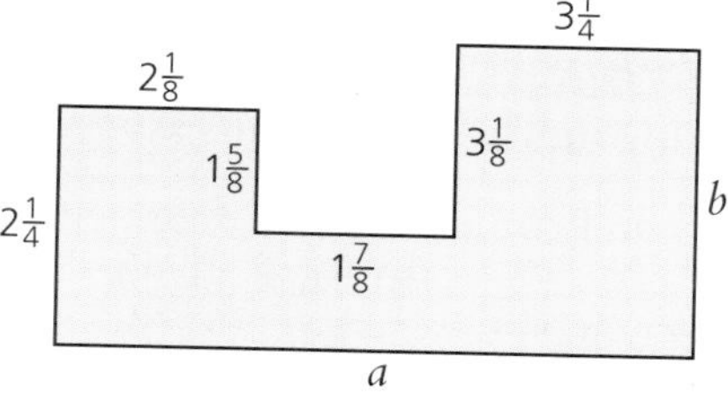

Multiplication involving mixed numbers may be done either by treating the fractions separately or by converting to improper fractions. In any given situation, one approach may prove to be easier than the other.

Note: to divide by a number we multiply by its reciprocal.

Example

Calculate the value of these expressions:
a) $2\frac{1}{3} \times 5$ b) $6\frac{1}{4} \times \frac{3}{5}$ c) $5\frac{1}{4} \div 3\frac{1}{2}$

Answer

a) $2\frac{1}{3} \times 5 = (2 \times 5) + (\frac{1}{3} \times 5) = 10 + \frac{5}{3} = 10 + 1\frac{2}{3} = 11\frac{2}{3}$

b) $6\frac{1}{4} \times \frac{3}{5} = {}^{5}\frac{\cancel{25}}{4} \times \frac{3}{\cancel{5}_1} = \frac{15}{4} = 3\frac{3}{4}$

c) $5\frac{1}{4} \div 3\frac{1}{2} = \frac{21}{4} \div \frac{7}{2} = {}^{3}\frac{\cancel{21}}{\cancel{4}_2} \times \frac{\cancel{2}^1}{\cancel{7}_1} = \frac{3}{2} = 1\frac{1}{2}$ (Note $\frac{2}{7}$ is the reciprocal of $\frac{7}{2}$.)

13 Calculate the value of these expressions:
a) $3\frac{1}{5} \times 4$ b) $1\frac{2}{3} \times 4$ c) $1\frac{3}{5} \times 5$

14 Work out:
a) $5\frac{1}{2} \times 4$ ✓ b) $7\frac{1}{3} \times \frac{4}{11}$ c) $2\frac{1}{4} \times 1\frac{1}{3}$
d) $6\frac{1}{4} \times 1\frac{1}{15}$ e) $\frac{8}{9} \div \frac{2}{3}$ f) $2\frac{4}{5} \div \frac{21}{25}$ ✓
g) $11\frac{2}{3} \div 4\frac{2}{3}$ h) $5\frac{1}{2} \div 3\frac{2}{3}$ i) $5\frac{5}{8} \div 15$

15 Janette is employed as a lunch-time cashier at a Bank. She normally works for $2\frac{1}{2}$ hours each weekday but occasionally works extra hours.
a) How many hours does she work in a normal week?
b) In one particular week she worked an extra $\frac{3}{4}$ hour on three separate days. How many hours did she work altogether?

16 Overtime at the shoe factory is paid at time-and-a-third, so that each hour of overtime counts the same as $1\frac{1}{3}$ hours at the standard rate of pay. Taking the normal working week to be 40 hours, how many hours at the standard rate would be paid for each of the following?
a) 49 hours b) 52 hours c) 61 hours d) 65 hours.

17 Ben works as a labourer on a building site and earns £30 a day for working $7\frac{1}{2}$ hours.
a) How much does he earn each hour?
b) During one week Ben worked an extra 15 hours at time-and-a-third. How much extra did he earn?

18 Copy and complete these statements using fractions:
a) $4 \div ? = 12$ b) $16 \times ? = 24$ c) $15 \times ? = 10$
d) $25 \times ? = 15$ e) $14 \div ? = 21$ f) $5 \div ? = 20$
g) $24 \times ? = 36$ h) $24 \div ? = 36$ i) $18 \div ? = 12$

19 A lottery prize of £$8\frac{1}{4}$ million is shared equally between 11 people. What fraction of £1 million does each receive?

20 Copy and complete these puzzles:

a)

$\frac{1}{2}$	+		=	$1\frac{1}{4}$
+		×		÷
$2\frac{1}{4}$				
=		=		=
	÷	15	=	

b)

24	×	$\frac{3}{4}$	=	
÷				÷
	×	$1\frac{7}{8}$	=	
=				=
40	÷		=	

29.2 Fractions ... continued

The sequence given by

$$A+\frac{B}{2A+B},\ A+\cfrac{B}{2A+\cfrac{B}{2A+B}},\ A+\cfrac{B}{2A+\cfrac{B}{2A+\cfrac{B}{2A+B}}}$$

may be continued indefinitely and gives rise to the term **continued fraction**.

The prospect of calculating any more than the first few terms of such a sequence, even for simple values of A and B, is more likely to generate a feeling of panic than inspiration. However, by using a spreadsheet or graphics calculator the machine is left to cope with the work, and you are free to consider what happens to the sequence as the values of A and B are changed.

Try setting up a spreadsheet as shown below:

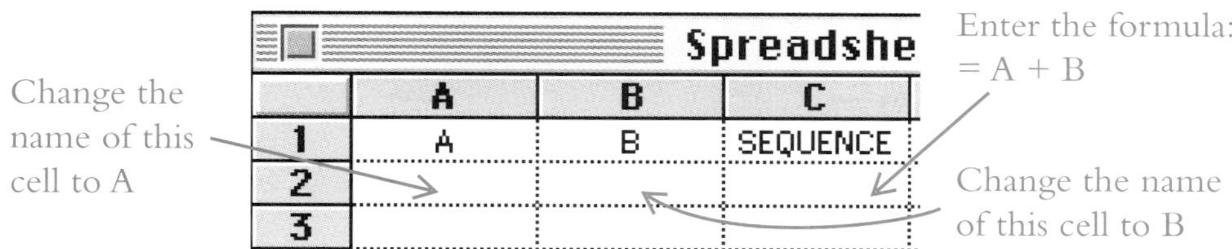
Spreadshe
A
B
C
1
A
B
SEQUENCE
2
3
Change the name of this cell to A
Enter the formula: = A + B
Change the name of this cell to B

As a check, entering the values $A = 1$ and $B = 3$ should produce the value 4 in cell C2.

	A	B	C
1	A	B	SEQUENCE
2	1	3	4
3			
4			

Now enter the formula: = A+B/(A+C2) and copy downwards

This spreadsheet shows some of the results produced in the sequence column when the formula is copied downwards.

Strictly speaking, the sequence starts in cell C3 with the value 1.6.

	A	B	C
1	A	B	SEQUENCE
2	1	3	4
3			1.6
4			2.153846
5			1.95122
6			2.016529

Note: when $A = 1$ and $B = 3$, $A + \dfrac{B}{2A + B} = 1 + \dfrac{3}{2 + 3} = 1\frac{3}{5} = 1.6$

1 Find out what happens as the sequence progresses by copying the formula further down the sequence column.

2 Experiment with different values of A and B and keep a record of your results. Find a formula to describe what happens and check it for further values of A and B.

An alternative to using a spreadsheet is to program a graphics calculator to carry out the same process.

The program given below is written for a Casio calculator but may easily be adapted to work on other makes.

```
? → A
? → B
A + B → C
Lbl 1
A + B ÷ (A + C) → C ◢
Goto 1
```

ICT Extra!

Follow the instructions given here to investigate this sequence involving fractions. Alternatively you may try to use a Casio graphical calculator.

The program requires two input values A and B, which are entered in response to the ? prompt. Pressing the EXE key repeatedly will then produce the figures given in the 'Sequence' column on the spreadsheet.

3 Using a spreadsheet or a graphics calculator, find out what happens if B is replaced by B^2 in the formulae used to calculate new terms of the sequence.

The sequence given by $\dfrac{N}{A} + B,\ \dfrac{\dfrac{N}{A} + B}{A} + B,\ \dfrac{\dfrac{\dfrac{N}{A} + B}{A} + B}{A} + B,\ \ldots$

is different to the one given above, but once again is easily explored with the aid of a graphics calculator or spreadsheet.

The spreadsheet may be set up as shown here.

Spreadsheet

	A	B	C	D
1	N	A	B	SEQUENCE
2	100	2	5	55
3				32.5
4				21.25
5				15.625
6				12.8125
7				11.40625
8				10.70313
9				10.35156
10				

What is going to happen as this sequence is continued?

Re-name the appropriate cells as N, A and B in the usual way.

You will also need to use the formulae =N/A+B and =D2/A+B.

The corresponding graphics calculator program is shown below.
The program requires three input values N, A and B which are entered in response to the ? prompt.

```
? → N
? → A
? → B
Lbl 1
N ÷ A + B → N ◢
Goto 1
```

---

4 Find out what happens to the sequence for different values of N, A and B.

USING PROBABILITY

30.1 Finding relative frequencies

The relative frequency of an event tells us what proportion of the time we can expect that event to happen. It is calculated from:

$$\text{Relative frequency of an event} = \frac{\text{number of times that event occurred}}{\text{total number of trials}}$$

1 Daniel has conducted a survey among year 11 students. He asked them, 'On what day of the week were you born?'
Here is a frequency table of their answers.

'On what day of the week were you born?'		
Day	**Tally**	**Frequency**
Monday	𝍸 𝍸 𝍸 𝍸 𝍸	25
Tuesday	𝍸 𝍸 𝍸 𝍸 |||	
Wednesday	𝍸 𝍸 𝍸 𝍸 ||	
Thursday	𝍸 𝍸 𝍸 𝍸 ||	
Friday	𝍸 𝍸 𝍸 𝍸 𝍸 |||	
Saturday	𝍸 𝍸 𝍸 ||	
Sunday	𝍸 𝍸 𝍸	

a) Write down the frequency for each day.
b) How many students took part in Daniel's survey altogether?
c) The relative frequency for year 11 students being born on a Monday is $\frac{25}{152} = 0.164$

Write down the relative frequencies for the other days of the week.

Day	Relative frequency
Monday	$\frac{25}{152} = 0.164$
Tuesday	
Wednesday	
Thursday	
Friday	
Saturday	$\frac{17}{152} = 0.112$
Sunday	

d) What is the total for the relative frequencies?
Can you explain why you got that answer?
e) Which day of the week had the lowest relative frequency?
f) Which day had the highest relative frequency?
g) What is the relative frequency for being born at the weekend?

2 Nirmal has asked year 11 students: 'How many children are there in your family?'
Here are their replies, recorded as a frequency table:

Number of children in family	Frequency
1	16
2	64
3	43
4	18
5	3
6	5
7	0
8	1

a) How many students took part in Nirmal's survey? ✓
b) What is the relative frequency for a student being an 'only child'? ✓
c) What is the relative frequency for a student being in a three child family?
d) How many students come from families with four or more children?
e) What is the relative frequency for a year 11 student coming from a family with 4 or more children?
f) If I picked out a student at random from this year group and asked them, 'How many children are there in your family?' what is the *most likely* reply?

3 Natalie has done a survey of left-handed people. She only included left-handed people in her survey and she asked each person four questions. Here is a summary of their replies:

	Left	Right
(i) Which hand do you use to hold a cup when you drink?	24	1
(ii) Which hand do you use when you cut paper using scissors?	16	9
(iii) Which hand do you use to hold a comb when you comb your hair?	21	4
(iv) In which hand do you hold a knife when you are eating?	23	2

a) How many people did Natalie include in her survey? ✓
b) What is the relative frequency for a left-handed person holding a pair of scissors in their right hand? ✓
c) What is the relative frequency for a left-handed person holding a cup in their left hand?
d) What is the relative frequency for a left-handed person holding their knife in their left hand?
e) What is the relative frequency for a left-handed person holding a knife in their right hand?
f) What is the total for your answers to **d)** and **e)**? Why is this?

30.2 Cracking a code

The following passage has been written in code:

JQAB QEBLELB H BEOAX.
WL BEHAX OP WHZR BQIA.
WL RLZP IQABLERGZ.
NGBBLAZU PWL ZHNP RQGE BHUN HAB
CHEPOMGZHEZU ZHNP AOFWP ILEL
IHNWLB QRR PWL MHZLABHE. AQI WL
IHN QA WON QIA, WHKOAF WON
QIA CEOKHPL HBKLAPGEL. HZZ WON
BGPOLN WHB JLLA PHXLA MHEL QR.

How can you crack the code and decipher the passage?
Think of some strategies which might help you.

One method of cracking a code is to see which letters are used most often in the code and then to compare these to the relative frequencies of letters used in normal English.

To find the relative frequencies of letters used in English, choose a book written in English, preferably a novel (not a maths text book, please!). Open the book at any page. Make sure that it is a full page of writing.

Make a table showing all the letters of the alphabet. Record each letter, word by word, using tally marks.

---

1 a) Make a list of the 10 letters you find most frequently.
b) If other groups have used different books or pages, put your results together to find your 'top ten letters'.
c) Go back to the coded passage.
Make a frequency table of the letters used in that message.
d) Find the top 10 letters used in the code. These may not be exactly in the same order as those in the books you have used. Try to match up some of the letters with their codes.
e) Which other clues can help you?
f) What do you think the passage says?

2 Do you think the relative frequencies of letters will be the same in another language – say, Welsh, French or Spanish? Choose a language and make a 'top ten' table for the most popular letters.

There is another coded message in the homework book. A different code has been used. Can you decipher that message?

30.3 The 'birds' simulation

This section contains a simulation which describes a year in the life of a native British bird. At each crucial stage of a baby bird's life it has a probability of surviving (or of not surviving). These probabilities have been estimated using relative frequencies. The relative frequencies are based on data painstakingly collected by ornithologists.

The simulation starts in springtime with two birds nesting in your back garden. It then goes through a year in their life cycle. They build a nest and rear their young. The simulation is designed to show how many birds there will be one year later.

You will need:

either two ordinary six-sided dice
or two six-sided spinners
or two hexagonal pencils which have their sides numbered 1 to 6
perhaps a calculator which generates random numbers (optional)

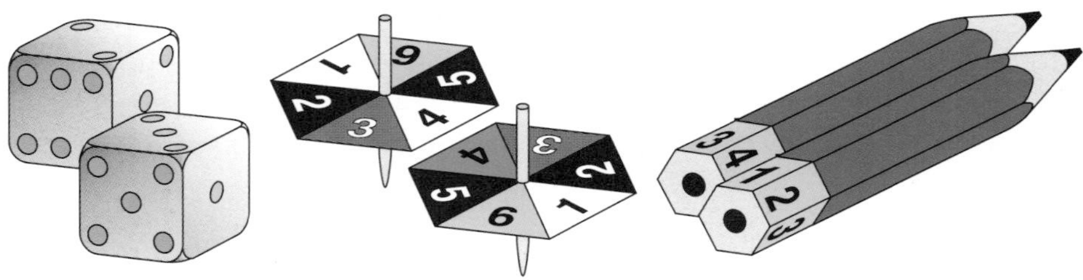

If you decide to use your calculator for parts of this simulation, the instructions are as follows.
To generate random numbers your calculator will have a button labelled RAN#. (If your calculator does not have this button, refer to its instructions.)

If you press RAN# you will see something like this on your display:

0.371

Strictly speaking the RAN# key produces a random number, usually to 3 D.P., and lying between 0 and 1. However for *this* simulation, ignore the 0 and decimal point at the front, and take 3, 7, and 1 as three random numbers. Each time you press RAN# you will get three new random numbers. (Note that the calculator will produce different results to the other methods and so alternative instructions are provided where necessary.)

In the spring, your pair of birds build a nest. The female lays eggs.

Stage 1 *Springtime.*

How many eggs does the female lay?
Throw two dice. Add the scores together, *then add three* to this total.
Record the number of eggs laid.

Stage 2 Will all the eggs hatch?

Each egg has a separate chance of hatching.
Throw a dice once for *each* egg. Make a table for your results.
(Alternatively generate one random number for each chick using a calculator.)
If the score on the dice is 1, 2, 3, 4 or 5, then the egg has hatched. If the score is 6, the egg did not hatch. How many eggs hatched? This is the number of baby chicks progressing on to the next stage.
(If you used a calculator, scores 1 to 8 mean the egg has hatched, 9 or 0 that it has not.)
Record the number of chicks hatched.

Egg number	Score
1	
2	
3	
4	
...	

Stage 3 *Summertime.*

Will the chicks survive and learn to fly?
Each chick has a separate chance of learning to fly.
Throw a dice once for each chick.
(Alternatively, generate one random number for each chick using a calculator.)
If your dice score is 1, 2, 3 or 4 the chick will survive the summer. If the score is 5 or 6 it does not.
(For the calculator, scores 1 to 7 will survive, 8, 9 or 0 do not.)
How many baby birds are alive at the end of the summer? (Count them.)

Chick no.	Score
1	
2	
3	
4	
5	
...	

Stage 4 *Wintertime.*

Do the baby birds survive over the winter?
Throw a dice once for each baby bird. Make a table (as you did at stage 2 or stage 3).
If the score is 1, the chick survives through the winter. Scores 2 to 6 do not survive. If this seems harsh, don't forget that the weather can be very cold and there is a shortage of food.
(Alternatively, use a calculator to generate a random number for each chick. Scores 1 and 2 mean the chick survives the winter, 3, 4, 5, 6, 7, 8, 9 and 0 mean that it does not.)
How many baby birds survive the winter? (Count them.)

Stage 5 Do the parent birds survive the winter?
Throw one dice for each parent. (Or generate one random number.) If the score is 1, 2 or 3 the bird survives, if the score is 4, 5 or 6, it does not. (With the calculator, 1, 2, 3, 4, 5 mean the bird survives, 6, 7, 8, 9 and 0, mean that it does not.)
Record what happens to the parents.

Stage 6 How many birds survive altogether?
Add together the numbers of birds left at stages 4 and 5.

---

1 Collect together all the results from groups in your class for the number of birds (parents and chicks) surviving after one year.

Number of birds surviving	Frequency
0	
1	
2	
3	
4	
5	

2 a) Find the mean number of birds surviving for your class.
b) What would happen to the population if the average number of birds surviving was only one?
c) What would happen if the average number of survivors was 4 or 5?
d) How many should survive from year to year if the population is to remain stable?

3 Now look back at Stage 1 of the simulation. The number of eggs laid by your pair of birds was found by adding 3 to the total score for two dice.
a) What was the smallest number of eggs possible in this simulation?
b) What was the largest?
c) What are all the possible results? To help you answer this question, copy this table. Fill in all the possible outcomes. (Don't forget that you must add 3 to the total for the dice scores.)

Score on dice 1 (columns); **Score on dice 2** (rows)

	1	2	3	4	5	6
1	5			8		
2						
3						
4		9			12	
5						
6		11				

d) What is the probability of the result in each square on the table?

4 Which number of eggs has the highest probability? To help you answer this question, make a list of all the possible outcomes, count the number of ways of obtaining each outcome, and use your answers to help you calculate the probabilities.

Number of eggs	Number of ways of obtaining that result	Probability
5	1	$\frac{1}{36}$
6		
7	3	$\frac{3}{36}$
8		
⋮	⋮	⋮

5 ✓ Which number of eggs is the most likely?

6 Look back at stage 2 of the simulation. What is the probability based on the dice simulation that an egg does *not* hatch?
This probability is closer to the relative frequency calculated by ornithologists observing and counting the number of eggs actually hatching in a large number of nests

7 ✓ Look back at stage 3 of the simulation. What is the probability that a chick does *not* successfully fly the nest if the dice simulation is used?
What is the probability if a calculator is used?
Which of these two probabilities is greater in value?
(In fact, the calculator probability is closer to the relative frequency obtained by ornithologists observing nests and collecting data.)

8 What is the probability that a chick survives the winter (Stage 4)?

9 What is the probability that a parent bird survives the winter (Stage 5)?

10 Why do you think a parent bird is more likely to survive the winter than a chick?

30.4 Graphics calculator

This section gives two programs for a Casio graphics calculator. They can be modified to run with other graphics calculators.

The first program simulates the situation for a single nest and is designed to produce results corresponding to the calculator simulation.

Graphics calculator program 1

Instructions for use

Each time that the program is run the calculator will display:

(i) the number of eggs produced (press EXE to move on)
(ii) the number of eggs that hatch (press EXE).
(iii) the number of chicks that fly the nest (press EXE)
(iv) the number of chicks that survive the winter (press EXE to re-run the program from the start)

Note that if at any stage the number of survivors is zero, EXE will re-run the program from the start.

```
5 + Int(Ran# × 6) + Int(Ran# × 6) → A   generates number of eggs
                                        in nest
A → M ◢                                 displays number of eggs
                                        (press EXE to continue)

Lbl 1
Ran# > 0.7 ⇒ A – 1 → A    determines number of eggs that hatch
Dsz M
Goto 1
A = 0 ⇒ Goto 4
A → M ◢                   displays number of eggs that hatch (press EXE)
Lbl 2
Ran# > 0.7 ⇒ A – 1 → A    determines number of chicks that fly the nest
Dsz M
Goto 2
A = 0 ⇒ Goto 4
A → M ◢                   displays number of chicks that fly the nest
                          (press EXE)

Lbl 3
Ran# > 0.167 ⇒ A – 1 → A  determines number of chicks that
                          survive winter

Dsz M
Goto 3
Lbl 4
A                         displays number of chicks that survive
                          winter. If EXE is pressed now the program
                          will re-run from the start.
```

To appreciate how the simulation can be used to represent the bird population as a whole, we need a new program that will produce results for a large number of nests.

Graphics calculator program 2

To simulate the number of birds surviving to maturity, during their first winter, from a given number of nests.

Instructions for use
In response to the '?' prompt, enter the number of nests to be used for the simulation. The calculator will then display the results in the same way as the first program except that the figures now represent *totals for all of the nests.*

```
? → N        input the number of nests
0 → S  }
0 → T  }
0 → H  }     sets initial totals to zero
0 → F  }
Lbl 0
```

Program	Comment
5 + Int (Ran# × 6) + Int(Ran# × 6) → A	generates number of eggs in a particular nest
A → M	
A + T → T	keeps a running total of all eggs
Lbl 1	
Ran# > 0.7 ⇒ A – 1 → A	determines number of eggs that hatch in a particular nest
Dsz M	
Goto 1	
A = 0 ⇒ Goto 4	
A → M	
A + H → H	keeps a running total of eggs that hatch
Lbl 2	
Ran# > 0.7 ⇒ A – 1 → A	determines number of chicks that fly a particular nest
Dsz M	
Goto 2	
A = 0 ⇒ Goto 4	
A → M	
A + F → F	keeps running total of birds that fly the nests
Lbl 3	
Ran# > 0.167 ⇒ A – 1 → A	determines number of chicks that survive the winter from a particular nest
Dsz M	
Goto 3	
Lbl 4	
A + S → S	
Dsz N	
Goto 0	
T ◢	displays the total number of eggs from all of the nests (press EXE)
H ◢	displays the total number of eggs that hatch (EXE)
F ◢	displays the total number of chicks that fly the nest (EXE)
S	displays the total number of chicks that survive the winter

ICT Extra!

Follow the instructions given here for producing the 'Birds' simulation using a graphics calculator. Can you work out how to do this on a spreadsheet?

31 A CHANGE OF FORM

31.1 Change as a percentage

In Unit 19 the scale factor method was introduced as an alternative way of calculating the final amount after a percentage change, and had the advantage that it could easily be reversed. The method relied on the relationship given below.

original amount × scale factor = final amount (1)

This approach is now adapted to express the change in a value as a percentage increase or decrease, by rearranging the formula so that the scale factor becomes the subject.

Dividing both sides of (1) by the original amount gives:

$$\text{scale factor} = \frac{\text{final amount}}{\text{original amount}}$$

Once the scale factor is known, the corresponding percentage change is easily found.

For example, a scale factor of 1.23 would correspond to 123%, i.e. to a 23% increase. In the same way, a scale factor of 0.86 would correspond to 86% which represents a 14% reduction.

1 Interpret each of the following scale factors as a percentage change and state whether it represents an increase or a reduction.

a) 1.17 ✓	b) 1.29	c) 1.06	d) 0.93 ✓
e) 0.75	f) 0.64	g) 1.025	h) 1.007
i) 0.561	j) 2.3	k) 3.14	l) 5

We are now in a position to compare the scale factor method, for expressing a change in value as a percentage, with the method given in Unit 15.

Example

Before her pay increase, Emma earned £712.51 per month. She now earns £743.67 per month. Express her salary increase in percentage terms.

Answer

■ Method (i) (using the approach of Unit 15)

Actual increase = £743.67 − £712.51 = £31.16

$$\text{Percentage increase} = \frac{\text{actual increase}}{\text{original salary}} \times 100\% = \frac{31.16}{712.51} \times 100\% = 4.373\%$$

giving the percentage increase as 4.37% (to 3 S.F.)

■ Method (ii) (using scale factors)

$$\text{scale factor} = \frac{\text{new salary}}{\text{original salary}} = \frac{743.67}{712.51} = 1.0437\ldots$$

giving the percentage increase as 4.37% (to 3 S.F.)

2 For each of the following pairs of figures, express the increase from the first to the second as a percentage (correct to 3 S.F.)

a) 16.1, 23.5 ✓ b) 87.9, 96.4 c) 36.7, 62.3

d) 72.8, 86.9 e) 416, 480 f) 1642, 1765

g) 12.4, 25.3 h) 67, 186 i) 52.1, 216

3 A newsagent found that monthly sales figures for computer magazines rose from 417 last month to 533 this month, which coincided with the release of some new software. Find the percentage increase in sales.

4 The number of pupils due to start at the school in year 7 next September is 182 compared with 168 in the present year 7.

a) Express the increase in the number of pupils as a percentage.

b) The cost of consumable items for the present year 7 is approximately £1750. How much should be allowed for consumables for the incoming year 7 assuming that prices remain the same?

5 The managing director of a small company is considering how to give a pay rise to all employees as fairly as possible. At the present time, the lowest paid workers earn £550 each month and the highest paid workers earn £3750 per month.

a) Which group of employees would be happiest if everyone is given the same percentage increase in pay? Explain your answer.

b) If the highest paid workers earn £3900 after the pay rise, what is their percentage increase?

c) If the lowest paid people are given the same *actual* increase in pay, what is their corresponding percentage increase?

d) If the managing director decided, instead, to award all employees the same actual increase each year so that after 10 years the lowest paid workers earned £1550 per month:

(i) how much would the highest paid workers earn after 10 years?

(ii) express the new lowest wage as a percentage of the new highest wage.

(iii) Express the £550 as a percentage of £3750.

(iv) Comment on the differences between your answers to (ii) and (iii).

e) Describe, with reasons, what *you* think would be a fair way to award a pay increase.

f) What if the company was going through difficult times and had to reduce everyone's pay?

6 An advertising agency submits plans to a company that involve inceasing the amount spent on advertising by 80% in order to increase profits by an estimated figure of 5%.
Give an example to show that this may not be as foolish as it sounds.

When dealing with an *increase* in value, the scale factor is greater than 1 and the percentage increase is easily recognised from the figures to the right of the decimal point. A percentage *reduction* corresponds to a scale factor less than 1 but its value is not instantly recognisable from the scale factor in the same way.

Example

Average house prices in the UK fell from a peak of £70 602 in July 1989 to £61 583 in July 1995. Calculate the percentage fall in house prices over this time correct to 1 D.P.

Answer

$$\text{Scale factor} = \frac{61\,583}{70\,602} = 0.872\,255\,7...$$

That is, the 1995 figure is 87.2% (to 1 D.P.) of the 1989 figure and so the percentage fall is given by (100 – 87.2)% = 12.8% correct to 1 D.P.

Alternatively, subtracting 1 from the scale factor gives –0.127 744... which again may be interpreted as a 12.8% fall correct to 1 D.P.

---

7 Trends in the value of property are very important to many people and may vary from one area of the country to another. Figures produced by the Halifax Building Society showed the following regional variation in house prices from 1994 to 1995.

Area	1994	1995	% change
E. Anglia	55 360	53 870	
E. Midlands	58 450	58 277	
G. London	77 964	78 402	
N. West	55 351	53 688	
North	52 028	49 884	
S. East	77365	77 730	+ 0.5
S. West	62 193	61 433	
Yorkshire	52 899	51 075	– 3.4

a) Copy the table and complete the final column to an accuracy of 1 D.P.

b) In which area did house prices suffer the greatest percentage fall?

c) Which area showed the greatest percentage increase?

d) The rows of the table are given in alphabetical order based on the area. Produce a new table showing only the Area and % change columns ordered so that the areas with the greatest percentage fall in value are written first.
Comment on what you feel the results show.

8 The effectiveness of the vaccine developed to protect people against diptheria is seen in the statistics for New York City where the mortality rate fell from 785 per 100 000 in 1894 to 1.1 per 100 000 in 1940.
Describe the effectiveness of the vaccine in terms of the percentage reduction in the mortality rate over this time correct to 2 D.P.

The diagram shown below was used in Unit 19 to illustrate how the scale factor approach may be used to *undo* the effect of a percentage change.

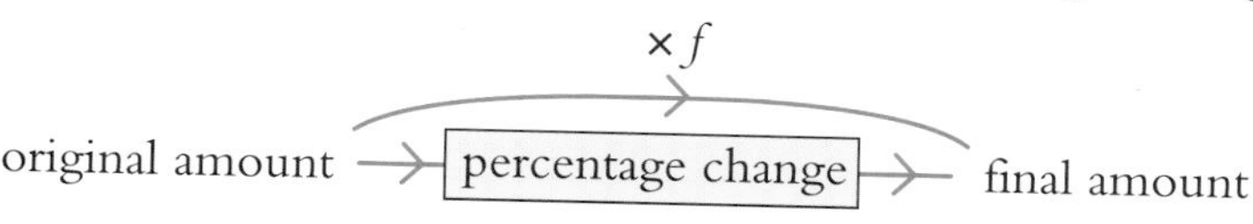

The idea was that the original amount could be found by reversing the process, i.e. by *dividing* the final amount by *f*.

We have since learned that dividing by *f* is the same as multiplying by its reciprocal and so the scale factor that will undo the percentage change is f^{-1}, i.e. $\frac{1}{f}$. This may now be used to express the reverse process as a percentage change.

Example

Crime figures in one area show an increase of 14% on the previous year. By what percentage must the figures now be reduced to return to the previous level?

Answer

The given increase is represented by a scale factor of 1.14 and so the scale factor needed to undo this effect is $1.14^{-1} = 0.877\,19...$ which corresponds to a reduction of 12.3% to 3 S.F.

Note: the percentage reduction was calculated without needing to know the actual crime figures.

---

9 a) Explain why an increase of 14% cannot simply be undone by a 14% reduction.

b) Why is the percentage reduction required *less* than the original percentage increase?

10 Calculate the percentage changes that will undo each of the following:

a) An increase of 20% ✓ b) An increase of 17.5%
c) An increase of 8.6% d) An increase of 45%
e) An increase of 120% f) An increase of 275%
g) A reduction of 30% ✓ h) A reduction of 11.6%
i) A reduction of 68% j) A reduction of 92%.

11 A farmer plans to sell some of his land to a property developer in order to raise a sum of money for investment. During the course of negotiations, a second property developer offers 15% more per acre.
If the farmer accepts the higher offer, how will this affect the amount of land that he has to sell in order to raise the same amount of money for investment?

31.2 Powers and roots

You have already met powers and roots of numbers at different points within the book. In order to deal confidently with more complex situations it is useful to know some rules about them.

An alternative name for the power of a number is its **index** and so the rules for working with powers are sometimes called the **rules of indices**. The most important of these are given below.

Rules	Examples
$a^n = \underbrace{a \times a \times a \times \dots}_{n \text{ terms}}$	$3^4 = 3 \times 3 \times 3 \times 3$ (*Note*: $3^4 = 81 \neq 3 \times 4$)
$a^m \times a^n = a^{m+n}$	$x^3 \times x^5 = x^8$ and $x^{-1} \times x^7 = x^6$
$a^m \div a^n = a^{m-n}$	$x^{12} \div x^3 = x^9$ and $\dfrac{x^4}{x^5} = x^{-1} = \dfrac{1}{x}$
$(a^m)^n = a^{mn}$	$(x^2)^3 = x^6$ and $(x^{-1})^{-1} = x^1 = x$
$a^{-n} = \dfrac{1}{a^n}$	$x^{-2} = \dfrac{1}{x^2}$ and $2^{-3} = \dfrac{1}{2^3} = \dfrac{1}{8}$

Some special results are:

$a^1 = a$ for any value of a
$a^0 = 1$ provided $a \neq 0$.

---

1 Simplify the following expressions:

a) $b \times b \times b \times b \times b$ b) $n^2 \times n^2 \times n^2 \times n^2$ c) $x^3 \times x^4 \times x^2$
d) $g^5 \times g^{-1}$ e) $y^{-1} \times y^4$ f) $s^{-1} \times s$
g) $(x^4)^5$ h) $(c^2)^3 \times c$ i) $(v^3)^3 \div v^2$
j) $\dfrac{w^7}{w^5}$ k) $\dfrac{t^{11}}{t^3 \times t^4}$ l) $\dfrac{q^2 \times q^6 \times q}{q \times q \times q}$
m) $\dfrac{k^6}{k^3}$ n) $k^6 \times k^{-3}$ o) $k^6 \times \dfrac{1}{k^3}$

2 Copy and complete these statements:

a) $a^{\frac{1}{2}} \times a^{?} = a^1 = a$ b) $9^{\frac{1}{2}} \times 9^{?} = 9$ c) $9^{\frac{1}{2}} = ?$

3 Explain why $a^{\frac{1}{2}} = \sqrt{a}$ and find a corresponding result for $a^{\frac{1}{3}}$.

4 Find the value of these without using a calculator:

a) $16^{\frac{1}{2}}$ b) $49^{\frac{1}{2}}$ c) $25^{\frac{1}{2}} \times 16^{\frac{1}{2}}$
d) $8^{\frac{1}{3}}$ e) $125^{\frac{1}{3}}$ f) $64^{\frac{1}{2}} \times 64^{\frac{1}{3}}$
g) $1.78^{\frac{1}{2}} \times 1.78^{\frac{1}{2}}$ h) $(16.72^{\frac{1}{3}})^3$ i) $(871.982)^0$
j) $8.53^{11} \div 8.53^{10}$ k) $\sqrt{7} \times \sqrt{7}$ l) $(\sqrt{3})^4$

m) $\left(\frac{4}{5}\right)^2$ n) $\left(\frac{3}{8}\right)^2$ o) $\sqrt{\frac{16}{25}}$ p) 10^{-1} q) 10^{-2} r) 10^{-3}

5 Simplify the following:

a) $(3x^2)^2$ ✓ b) $(3x^3)^2$ c) $(3x^2)^3$
d) $4x \times 6x^2$ e) $5xy \times 2x^3$ f) $7a^2b \times 10ab^3$
g) $6x^3 \div 3x$ ✓ h) $35p^2 \div 7p^2$ i) $12n \div 3n^2$

6 All scientific calculators have keys for calculating squares and square roots. Write the full key sequence needed to find the value of each of these expressions on your machine. Pay particular attention to the order in which the keys are pressed and include the use of any brackets and 2nd function or inverse keys. Note also whether or not the use of an [=] key is required. *Check* in each case that the calculator gives the answer that you would expect given that $x = 5$ and $y = -4$.

a) x^2 b) y^2 c) x^2y d) xy^2
e) $(xy)^2$ f) $x + y^2$ g) $(x + y)^2$ h) $(x - y)^2$
i) $x - y^2$ j) $3x^2$ k) $-2x^2$ l) $-3y^2$
m) $\sqrt{36}$ n) $\sqrt{-y}$ o) $\sqrt{x + y}$ p) $\sqrt{x - y}$
q) $\sqrt{x^2}$ r) $\sqrt{y^2}$

7 Given that $p = -2.74$ and $q = 11.9$ find the value of these expressions correct to 3 S.F. In each case check that the answer is sensible.

a) p^2 b) $\sqrt{q}$ c) $p + \sqrt{q}$
d) p^2q e) pq^2 f) $(pq)^2$
g) $\sqrt{p^2 + q^2}$ h) $\sqrt{q^2 - p^2}$ i) $(p + \sqrt{q})^2$

8 State whether $\sqrt{x} < x$, $\sqrt{x} = x$ or $\sqrt{x} > x$, in each of the following situations:

a) $x = 1$ b) $x > 1$ c) $x = 0$ d) $0 < x < 1$

9 a) Predict what will happen to the terms of the sequence, in which each new term is the square root of the previous term, for the following starting values:
(i) $u_1 = 9$ (ii) $u_1 = 900$ (iii) $u_1 = 0.09$ (iv) $u_1 = 0.0009$
b) Describe how to use a scientific calculator to investigate these sequences using as few key strokes as possible.
c) Describe how the sequences might be produced using a spreadsheet.
d) Use a calculator or spreadsheet to test your predictions.

For the calculation of higher powers and roots most scientific calculators have keys labelled [x^y] (or [y^x]) and [$\sqrt[x]{\ }$].

Investigate the use of these keys on your calculator and keep notes on any important point that you discover. Include some worked examples for future reference.

10 Find the value of each of the following correct to 3 S.F.

a) 2.4^3 b) 1.7^5 c) 3^{10}

d) $\sqrt[3]{16}$ e) $\sqrt[3]{82}$ f) $\sqrt[3]{-124}$

11 Solve these equations by reversing the process, giving your answers to 3 S.F.

a) $x^3 = 12.8$ b) $x^3 = -76.5$ c) $x^5 = 632$

d) $\sqrt[4]{x} = 1.79$ e) $\sqrt[3]{x} - 5 = 0.32$ f) $\sqrt[5]{x + 7} = 2.4$

Find out how to use your calculator memory. There may be a key labelled STO or Min for putting numbers into the memory and a key labelled RCL, MR or RM for displaying the value stored. There may also be M+ and M– keys for changing the contents of the memory by adding or subtracting the value shown on the display. The memory contents may be cleared by storing the number zero.

Once a number is stored in memory it may be recalled at any time to be used within a calculation. Another number available for use is π.

---

12 Find the value of these expressions to 3 S.F. taking $h = 5.4$ and $r = 18.736\,59$. You will find it helpful to store the value of r in the calculator memory.

a) πr^2 ✓ b) $2\pi r$ c) $\pi r^2 h$ d) $2\pi rh$

e) $\pi(r^2 - 6.8^2)$ f) $4\pi r^2 h$ g) $2\pi r(r + h)$ h) $\frac{4}{3}\pi r^3$

31.3 Standard form (1)

When multiplying very large or very small numbers we tend to carry out the calculation in two parts. For example, to find $3\,000\,000 \times 200\,000$ we might start with the fact that $3 \times 2 = 6$ and then multiply the corresponding place values to obtain the answer 600 000 000 000. That is, we can organise the calculation so that we multiply two numbers between 1 and 10 and then consider the combination of place values separately.

The calculation $3\,000\,000 \times 200\,000$ may be set out as

$(3 \times 10^6) \times (2 \times 10^5)$

Between 1 and 10
This is needed to represent the place value of the 3
Between 1 and 10
This shows the place value of the 2

The place value of the product is given by $10^6 \times 10^5 = 10^{11}$ and so the answer may be written as 6×10^{11}.

Writing the answer in this form is less cumbersome than writing 6 followed by 11 zeros. In general, a number written as $A \times 10^n$ where $1 \leq A < 10$ and n is an integer (i.e. a positive or negative whole number) is said to be in **standard form**.

Example

Write these numbers in standard form:

a) 700 000 000 b) 42 000 c) 1 380 000

Answer

a) 700 000 000 is written as 7×10^8.

b) 42 000 is written as 4.2×10^4.

A decimal point is needed to ensure that $1 \leq A < 10$

The value of n may be thought of as the number of places that the decimal point must be moved to the right to restore the place value of the original number

c) In the same way, 1 380 000 is written as 1.38×10^6.

Example

Find the value of these in standard form:

a) 34 000 000 × 2 000 000 b) 7 000 000 000 × 50 000 000

Answer

a) 34 000 000 × 2 000 000
$= (3.4 \times 10^7) \times (2 \times 10^6)$
$= 6.8 \times 10^{13}$

b) 7 000 000 000 × 50 000 000
$= (7 \times 10^9) \times (5 \times 10^7)$
$= 35 \times 10^{16}$
$= 3.5 \times 10^{17}$

This is not yet in standard form because $A > 10$

---

1 Write these numbers in standard form:

a) 9 000 000 ✓ b) 30 000 c) 500 000
d) 23 000 e) 678 000 f) 912 000 000 000
g) 37×10^5 ✓ h) 89×10^6 i) 600×10^{12}
j) 120×10^8 k) 27.3×10^7 l) 345×10^{23}
m) 0.7×10^6 n) 0.247×10^{11} o) 0.0034×10^{18}
p) 0.1×10^{15} q) 0.00098×10^{20} r) 0.0000675×10^{29}

2 The speed at which light travels is 186 000 miles per second. To appreciate just how fast this is, if a car could travel at the speed of light it could go all the way around the Earth approximately 7 times every second. The average distance from the Sun to the Earth is 93 000 000 miles and this distance is so great that light from the Sun takes about 8 minutes to reach Earth. However, some stars called super giants are so huge that they could occupy all of the space contained by the Sun, the Earth and all the space in between, many times over. One such star called Betelgeuse, in the constellation of Orion, has a diameter of 400 million miles. Fortunately, this star is so far away (approximately 1 820 000 000 000 000 miles) that light from it takes 310 years to reach us.

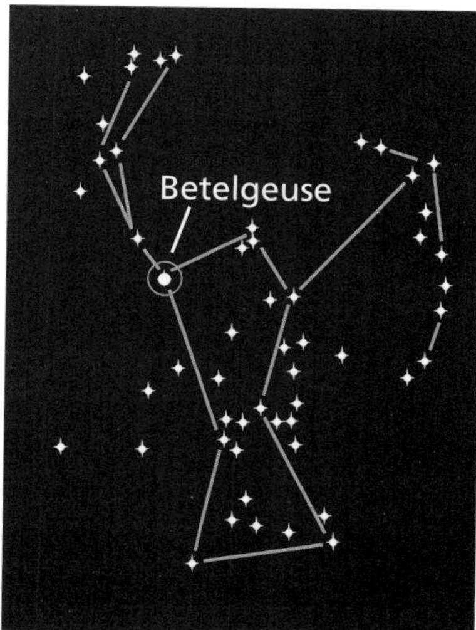

Compared with some stars, though, this is a near neighbour as light from the furthest star takes about 14 000 million years to come this way.

Express the underlined numbers in standard form.

3 Find the value of these in standard form:

a) $(3.6 \times 10^4) \times (2 \times 10^5)$ ✓ b) $(2.4 \times 10^{18}) \times (4 \times 10^7)$
c) $(4.1 \times 10^{11}) \times (2 \times 10^9)$ d) $(6.4 \times 10^{15}) \times (6 \times 10^{14})$
e) 40 000 000 × 200 000 000 f) 160 000 × 3 000 000
g) 513 000 × 4 000 000 h) 8 240 000 × 50 000 000

4 Use the fact that $5.78 \times 4.39 = 25.4$ (to 3 S.F.) to find the value of these in standard form to an accuracy of 3 S.F.

a) $(5.78 \times 10^9) \times (4.39 \times 10^6)$ ✓ b) $(4.39 \times 10^{17}) \times (5.78 \times 10^{11})$
c) 578 000 × 439 000 d) 57 800 × 4 390 000
e) 43 900 000 × 5 780 000 f) $(2.89 \times 10^8) \times 4390 \times 2000$

When writing numbers in order of size the most important consideration is the **place value** of the figures, e.g. $0.4 > 0.09$ because the 4 has the higher place value. The same principle holds when comparing numbers written in standard form, e.g. $9.79 \times 10^7 < 2 \times 10^8$.

---

5 Copy and compare the following pairs of numbers using $<$ or $>$ as appropriate:

a) 3.67×10^5, 8.1×10^3 b) 9.23×10^6, 9.24×10^5
c) 4.61×10^{11}, 3.89×10^{10} d) 4.61×10^{10}, 3.89×10^{11}

6 This table shows the average distance from the Sun of the planets in our solar system, arranged in alphabetical order. Re-order the information according to their distance from the Sun, showing the nearest at the top.

Planet	Distance from Sun (km)
Earth	1.5×10^8
Jupiter	7.78×10^8
Mars	2.28×10^8
Mercury	5.8×10^7
Pluto	5.92×10^9
Saturn	1.43×10^9
Uranus	2.87×10^9
Venus	1.08×10^8

Addition and subtraction of numbers expressed in standard form requires careful consideration of the place value of the numbers involved.

Example

Find the value of these in standard form correct to 2 S.F.

a) $(3.7 \times 10^8) + (6.5 \times 10^8)$ b) $(1.2 \times 10^{15}) - (8.6 \times 10^{14})$

Answer

a) $(3.7 \times 10^8) + (6.5 \times 10^8) = 10.2 \times 10^8 = 1.02 \times 10^9$

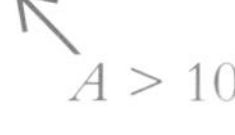

Both numbers have the same value of n, and so the place values correspond, allowing us to add the 3.7 and 6.5 directly

b) $(1.2 \times 10^{15}) - (8.6 \times 10^{14}) = (12 \times 10^{14}) - (8.6 \times 10^{14}) = 3.4 \times 10^{14}$

Writing the first number in this way gives both numbers the same value of n

---

7 Find the value of these in standard form correct to 2 S.F.:
a) $(3.1 \times 10^{15}) + (8.4 \times 10^{15})$
b) $(7.39 \times 10^{8}) - (5.2 \times 10^{8})$
c) $(4.6 \times 10^{17}) + (9.3 \times 10^{16})$
d) $(2.81 \times 10^{12}) - (9.3 \times 10^{11})$

8 Use the information given in the table in question 6 to answer these questions, giving the results to 2 S.F.
a) How much further is Pluto from the Sun than Jupiter?
b) How much closer is Mercury to the Sun than the Earth?
Explain why the information in the table cannot be used to find the distance between the planets in the same way.

9 Find the *minimum* distance between Saturn and Earth to 2 S.F.

Standard form may also be used to represent very small numbers by taking n to be *negative*.

Example

Write these numbers in standard form:
a) 0.000 000 06 b) 0.000 074

Answer

a) 0.000 000 06 is written as 6×10^{-8} in standard form.

Note: $10^{-8} = \frac{1}{10^8}$, i.e. 10^{-8} is the *reciprocal* of 10^8.
It follows that multiplying by 10^{-8} has the same effect as dividing by 10^8 which reduces the place value of the 6 to its value in 0.000 000 06.

b) In the same way, $0.000\,074 = 7.4 \times 10^{-5}$ Interpret this as meaning that the decimal point in 7.4 would be written 5 places further to the *left* in the usual notation

---

10 Write these numbers in standard form:
a) 0.000 007 ✓
b) 0.000 000 058
c) 0.000 000 000 763
d) 0.000 096
e) 0.74×10^{-3} ✓
f) 0.008×10^{-7}
g) 12×10^{-8}
h) 246×10^{-9}

11 Arrange the following numbers in order of size, smallest first:
(2.37×10^{-8}), (6.41×10^{-5}), (7.83×10^{-6}), (9.89×10^{-9}), (5.32×10^{-8})

12 Copy and compare the following pairs of numbers using $<$ or $>$ as appropriate:
a) 4.5×10^{-7}, 6.2×10^{-8}
b) 7.3×10^{-9}, 1.6×10^{-5}
c) 6.3×10^{-4}, 8.1×10^{-3}
d) 9.1×10^{-15}, 8.6×10^{-15}
e) 3.8×10^{-6}, 0.000 076
f) 0.000 000 000 253, 2.53×10^{-9}

13 The *Guinness Book of Records* contains a reference to the slowest machine which is used for testing stress corrosion. It can be controlled at a speed as slow as one million millionth of a millimetre per minute.
Express the speed of this machine using standard form.

Calculations involving very small numbers represented in standard form follow exactly the same rules as for very large numbers. It is worth noting however, that the simple techniques used for checking numerical answers, used earlier in the book, are just as important at this stage and are just as easy to apply.

Example

Calculate and comment on the size of the answer in each case:

a) $(4 \times 10^{-5}) \times (1.7 \times 10^{-4})$
b) $(3.1 \times 10^{8}) \times (5 \times 10^{-6})$
c) $(3.6 \times 10^{-16}) + (7.2 \times 10^{-15})$

Answer

a) $(4 \times 10^{-5}) \times (1.7 \times 10^{-4}) = 6.8 \times 10^{-9}$ ← $-5 + -4 = -9$
In this case both numbers lie between 0 and 1 and so each has a reducing effect on the other, which accounts for the answer being so small.

b) $(3.1 \times 10^{8}) \times (5 \times 10^{-6}) = 15.5 \times 10^{2} = 1550$ ← $8 + -6 = 2$
Multiplication by (5×10^{-6}) has a dramatic reducing effect and the answer, in this case, is small enough to write without using standard form.

c) $(3.6 \times 10^{-16}) + (7.2 \times 10^{-15}) = (0.36 \times 10^{-15}) + (7.2 \times 10^{-15})$
$= 7.56 \times 10^{-15}$

The larger number dominates the size of the final answer, which is best expressed in standard form.

---

14 Find the value of these. In each case check that the answer is reasonable.

a) $(2.4 \times 10^{-7}) \times (3 \times 10^{-5})$ ✓
b) $(1.3 \times 10^{-9}) \times (6 \times 10^{-8})$
c) $(3.21 \times 10^{11}) \times (2 \times 10^{-8})$
d) $(6.5 \times 10^{16}) \times (4 \times 10^{-10})$
e) $(2.6 \times 10^{-5}) + (8.7 \times 10^{-5})$
f) $(3.62 \times 10^{-11}) + (1.93 \times 10^{-11})$
g) $(7.5 \times 10^{-20}) - (4.8 \times 10^{-20})$
h) $(9.3 \times 10^{-16}) - (5.7 \times 10^{-16})$

15 Copy and complete the following calculations:

a) $(8.1 \times 10^{-7}) + (4 \times 10^{-8}) = (8.1 \times 10^{-7}) + (\quad \times 10^{-7}) =$
b) $(1.6 \times 10^{-23}) - (8.7 \times 10^{-24}) = (1.6 \times 10^{-23}) - (\quad \times 10^{-23}) =$

16 Find the value of $(3.27 \times 10^{8}) + (9.89 \times 10^{-5})$ to 3 S.F.
Explain how the answer may be obtained without calculation.

Division of numbers in standard form may also be carried out without a calculator. The use of a calculator for standard form calculations will be considered later.

Example

Calculate and leave your answer in standard form: $(8.4 \times 10^7) \div (4 \times 10^{-5})$.

Answer

$$(8.4 \times 10^7) \div (4 \times 10^{-5}) = \frac{8.4 \times 10^7}{4 \times 10^{-5}}$$

$$= \frac{8.4}{4} \times \frac{10^7}{10^{-5}}$$ Dividing by 4×10^{-5} has an enlarging effect

$$= 2.1 \times 10^{12}$$

17 Calculate and leave your answers in standard form:

a) $(9.6 \times 10^{15}) \div (3.2 \times 10^7)$

b) $(7.6 \times 10^{21}) \div (1.9 \times 10^6)$

c) $(8.5 \times 10^{11}) \div (1.7 \times 10^{-9})$

d) $(6.3 \times 10^{14}) \div (2.1 \times 10^{-8})$

e) $(6 \times 10^7) \div (1.5 \times 10^{16})$

f) $(5.7 \times 10^6) \div (1.9 \times 10^{12})$

MEASUREMENTS

32.1 Accuracy of measurement

We do not always use the same level of accuracy in measurements. The level of accuracy chosen may depend on how the measurements are taken and what they will be used for.

1 Here are some situations in which time is measured, together with the degree of accuracy which is commonly used. Can you match them up?

Situation
a) Downhill skiing race
b) Coursework deadline
c) Time to cook cake (as given in recipe)
d) Train timetable
e) 100 m sprint
f) Marathon
g) Trek across ice to South Pole

Accuracy
nearest minute
nearest $\frac{1}{100}$ second
nearest day
nearest $\frac{1}{100}$ second
nearest 5 minutes
nearest second
nearest day

Write your answers as, for example, **b)** = nearest day

2 Wayne (in the centre of the photograph) has measured his height as 175 cm and claims this is accurate to the nearest cm.

a) What is the shortest height which can be rounded up to 175 cm? ✓

b) What is the shortest height which will be rounded up to 176 cm?

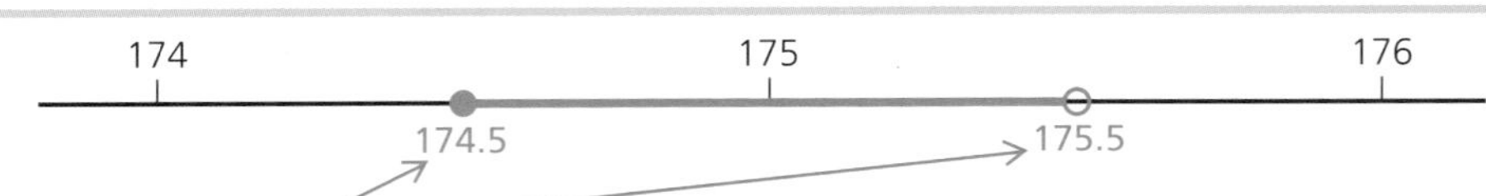

These two measurements are the limits to Wayne's actual height. If h cm stands for his height, we can write this as:

$$174.5 \leq h < 175.5$$

174.5 cm is the **lower limit** (or **lower bound**) for Wayne's height.
175.5 cm is the **upper limit** (or **upper bound**) for Wayne's height.
Any measurement below this is recorded as 175 cm, but if it actually reaches 175.5 it has to be recorded as 176 cm.

3 Wayne decides to measure his height to the nearest mm in order to be more accurate. He claims he is 175.3 cm tall and declares this is 'spot on'.

a) What is the shortest height which can be recorded as 175.3 cm (accurate to the nearest mm)? ✓

b) What is the shortest height which will be recorded as 175.4 cm?

c) Complete this statement about Wayne's height accurate to the nearest mm (remember, he claims to be 175.3 cm tall):

$\ldots \leq h < \ldots$ ✓

4 Decide on the lower and upper limits for the measurements given here. If the stated measure has no decimal places you must assume that the measurement was rounded to the nearest whole unit. If one decimal place is given, then assume that measurements were rounded to one decimal place, and so on. Copy and complete the table.

	Stated measure	Interval
a)	12 km	$11.5 \leq x <$
b) ✓	12.3 km	$\leq x <$
c)	12.0 km	$\leq x < 12.05$
d)	76 m	$\leq x <$
e)	76.5 m	$76.45 \leq x <$
f)	76.0 m	$\leq x <$
g)	125 cm	$\leq x <$
h)	125.7 cm	$\leq x <$
i)	125.76 cm	$\leq x <$

In general, if a measurement is accurate to some given amount, the maximum error is half that amount.

Example

For each of the measurements given in this question, write down the lower and upper limits.

a) A car has an average speed of 55 km/h to the nearest km/h.

b) A crop of apples weighed 8700 metric tonnes correct to the nearest 100 tonnes.

Answer

a) The true average speed x (in km/h) must lie between these limits:

$$54.5 \leq x < 55.5$$

So the lower limit is 54.5 km/h and the upper limit is 55.5 km/h.

b) The weight of apples was 8700 metric tonnes correct to the nearest 100 tonnes. The error in measurement can be 50 tonnes either side in this example, i.e. the maximum error is a half of 100 tonnes.
In this case the lower limit is 8650 tonnes and the upper limit is 8750 tonnes.

5 For each of the measurements given here, write down the lower and upper limits to give the interval in which the measurements must lie in the form:

$\ldots \leq x < \ldots$

a) The length of my ruler is 31 cm correct to the nearest cm.
b) The length of my bedroom is 4200 mm correct to the nearest 100 mm. ✓
c) The length of my garden is 16 m correct to the nearest metre.
d) The weight of a bag of cement is 50 kg correct to the nearest kg.
e) Jackie's speed correct to 3 significant figures was 8.25 m/s.
f) The weight of the sugar in a bag is 2 kg correct to the nearest 10 g.
g) My weight is 55.5 kg correct to the nearest 0.1 kg.
h) The distance from my home to school is 4 miles correct to the nearest $\frac{1}{2}$ mile.

32.2 Combined errors

Example

Joe has measured the sides of a small, square mosaic tile as 20 mm correct to the nearest mm.
What are the upper and lower bounds for:
a) the perimeter
b) the area?

Answer

a) Each side lies in the interval:

$19.5 \leq x < 20.5$

The perimeter = $4x$.

This must lie in the interval: $19.5 \times 4 \leq 4x < 20.5 \times 4$

$78 \leq 4x < 82$

So the upper and lower bounds of the perimeter are 82 mm and 78 mm.

b) The area must lie in the interval: $19.5^2 \leq x^2 < 20.5^2$

$380.25 \leq x^2 < 420.25$

So the upper and lower bounds of the area are 420.25 mm^2 and 380.25 mm^2.

1 A rectangle measures 20 cm by 15 cm both correct to the nearest cm. Find
a) the upper and lower bounds for its length and width
b) the upper and lower bounds for its area.

2 ✓ The dimensions of a rectangular box are 10 cm by 6 cm by 8 cm. Find the upper and lower limits for the volume of the box if each of the original measurements is correct to the nearest cm.

3 A triangle has a base 8.2 cm and height 6.5 cm, both measurements being correct to the nearest mm.
Find the upper and lower limits for the area of the triangle.

4 The radius of a circle has been measured as 3 cm correct to the nearest cm. Taking π as 3.14, find the lower and upper bounds for:
a) the circumference
b) the area.

5 The length of an edge of a cube is known to be 8 cm measured to the nearest cm.
a) What is the least possible volume of the cube?
b) What is the upper limit for its surface area?

6 The base of a triangle is given as 8 cm and the area as 30 cm^2, each correct to the nearest unit.
a) What is the smallest possible area of the triangle?
b) What is the upper limit for the length for the base of the triangle?
c) Use these answers to find the smallest possible perpendicular height for that triangle. (Give your answer correct to 3 decimal places.)
d) Find the largest possible value for the perpendicular height.

7 The average weight of each of the four oarsmen of a coxless four is 89 kg. Between what limits does the total weight of the four lie?

8 A man uses a walking stick to measure the size of an allotment. The walking stick is 0.9 m long accurate to 1 significant figure.
a) The man estimates the length of the allotment to be 36 m. How many lengths of the walking stick must that have been?
b) Find the limits for the length of the walking stick.
c) Find the limits for the length of the allotment.

Weight, along with other measures such as height, temperature, angle and so on, can be rounded up or down to the nearest unit according to the level of accuracy required.

9 How would 58.2 kg be written correct to the nearest kg?

10 What weight would be recorded for 58.6 kg correct to the nearest kg?

11 Give the upper and lower limits for a weight recorded as 47 kg.

32.3 Measuring age

Age differs from all other continuous measurements in that it is always **rounded down**.

Someone giving his age as 16 years could be celebrating his 16th birthday that day or, at the other extreme, be about to celebrate his 17th birthday the following day. So 'age 16' covers a range of ages which can be written as: $16 \le x < 17$.

1 ✓ Give the true range of ages included in the following age groups.

	Age group	True age range
a)	5	$\le x <$
b)	0–1	$\le x <$
c)	10–19	$\le x <$
d)	70–84	$\le x <$

2 This has implications for work in data handling where the variable measured is age.
The following table gives the ages of people coming into a hospital casualty department for treatment on one day in winter:

a) Copy the table, including the true age range for each group.

b) Draw a histogram showing the true age range for each group on the horizontal axis.

c) This distribution can be described as 'bimodal'. Explain what this means and why it may have arisen in this case.

Age	Frequency	True age range
0–9	11	$\le x <$
10–19	13	$\le x <$
20–29	3	$\le x <$
30–39	4	$\le x <$
40–49	2	$\le x <$
50–59	6	$\le x <$
60–69	7	$\le x <$
70–79	2	$\le x <$

d) What is the midpoint of the true age group $0 \le x < 10$?

e) Use the true midpoint of each age group to find an estimate of the mean age of patients that day. ✓

ICT Extra!

Can you remember how to use a calculator to find an estimate of the mean of the ages given in question 2? Look back to Unit 22, *page 216* if you have forgotten.

32.4 Compound measures

Speed is the rate at which a moving object covers a certain distance in one unit of time. The most common units for measuring speed are kilometres per hour (km/h), miles per hour (m.p.h.) and metres per second (m/s). These units are examples of **compound measures**, since they involve a mixture of more basic measures such as metres and seconds.

Fuel consumption is the rate at which fuel is used and is commonly measured as miles per gallon (m.p.g.) or kilometres per litre (km/l).

For methods of transport using vast quantities of fuel, such as flight, the rate of fuel consumption may be expressed as gallons per mile or litres per second.

Coverage of fertiliser, paint, grass seed and so on is expressed in compound measures. These may be litres per square metre (l/m^2) or grams per square metre (g/m^2).

Example

Express a speed of 30 m.p.h. in **a)** km/h, **b)** m/s using the approximation that 8 km ≈ 5 miles.

Answer

a) 30 m.p.h. $= \dfrac{30 \times 8}{5}$ km/h = 48 km/h b) 48 km/h $= \dfrac{48 \times 1000}{60 \times 60}$ m/s $= 13.\dot{3}$ m/s

1 Express 50 km/h in m/s. ✓ **2** Express 100 m/s in km/h.

3 Express 40 km/h in m.p.h. ✓ **4** Express 70 m.p.h. in km/h.

5 Express 25 litres/second as gallons per minute (1 gallon ≈ 4.5 litres).

6 The average petrol consumption for my car driving around town is 35 m.p.g. If I put 25 litres of petrol into the tank, how far will I be able to travel? (1 gallon is approximately 4.5 litres.) ✓

7 A petrol pump can deliver petrol at the rate of 1 litre/second. How long does it take to fill a tank which holds 20 gallons?

8 A bottle of liquid fertiliser contains 500 ml. The instructions on the bottle advise that it should be diluted at the rate of 5 ml of fertiliser to 4 litres of water. The diluted mixture is applied at the rate of 250 ml/m^2. What area will the contents of the bottle cover?

32.5 Average speed

The distance from my home in Manchester to Newcastle is 150 miles. This journey takes me three hours by car. While I cannot drive at the same speed continuously, I can say that my average speed is 50 miles per hour.

$$\text{Average speed} = \frac{\text{TOTAL distance travelled}}{\text{TOTAL time taken}}$$

1 a) Rearrange the formula for average speed to give an expression for calculating time.
b) Find the time taken to travel 180 miles at 50 m.p.h. ✓

2 a) Rearrange the formula for average speed to give a formula for calculating distance.
b) Find the distance between two airports if a plane flying at an average speed of 400 km/h took 1 h 15 min to complete the journey.
c) Find the average speed if the distance is 140 km and the time taken is $3\frac{1}{2}$ hours.

3 ✓ A goods train travels between two towns 270 km apart in 9 hours. On the return journey a great deal of the track is going uphill and the average speed is reduced by 3 km/h.
a) Find the average speed on the the outward journey.
b) Find the average speed on the return journey.
c) How long does the return journey take?

4 In winter a train travels between two towns 264 km apart at an average speed of 72 km/h.
a) Find the time taken for the journey in winter (in hours and minutes).
b) In summer the journey takes 22 minutes less than in winter. Find the average speed in summer.

5 A motorist travelling at a steady speed of 90 km/h covers a section of motorway in 25 minutes. After a speed limit is imposed, he finds that it takes him 5 minutes longer than before to complete the same section, if he sticks to the maximum speed allowed. What is the new speed limit?

6 ✓ A van driver travels 136 miles at an average speed of 32 miles per hour. On the return journey he is able to increase his speed to 40 m.p.h.
a) Find the time taken for the outward journey.
b) Find the time taken for the return journey.
c) Find the average speed for the round trip.

7 For the first $1\frac{1}{2}$ hours of a 91 mile journey, the average speed was 30 m.p.h. The average speed for the second part of that journey was 23 m.p.h.
a) Find the time taken on the second part of the journey.
b) Find the average speed for the entire journey.

8 I cycle 10 km at a speed of 20 km/h, then a further 10 km at a speed of 15 km/h. Find my average speed over the full 20 km.

9 A greyhound runs 400 metres in 50 seconds.
a) Calculate its average speed in m/s.
b) What is this expressed in km/h.?

REVIEW 4

Unit 25 Algebra and graphs (2)

1 Solve these equations:

a) $25 - 3x = 13$ b) $100 - 9x = 37$ c) $8 - 5x = 18$

d) $4 - 6x = -5$ e) $21 = 30 - \frac{x}{4}$ f) $-5 = 11 - \frac{x}{2}$

g) $\frac{7 - x}{3} = 2$ h) $\frac{4 - x}{3} = 2$

2 Solve the following inequalities:

a) $3x - 5 > 7$ b) $4x - 6 < -2$ c) $2x + 9 \leq 14$

d) $5x + 4 > -6$ e) $3(x - 7) > 15$ f) $4(x - 5) \geq -12$

g) $12 - 3x < 4.5$ h) $8 - 5x > 11$ i) $\frac{x + 4}{3} \leq 2$

j) $\frac{9 - x}{4} > -6$

3

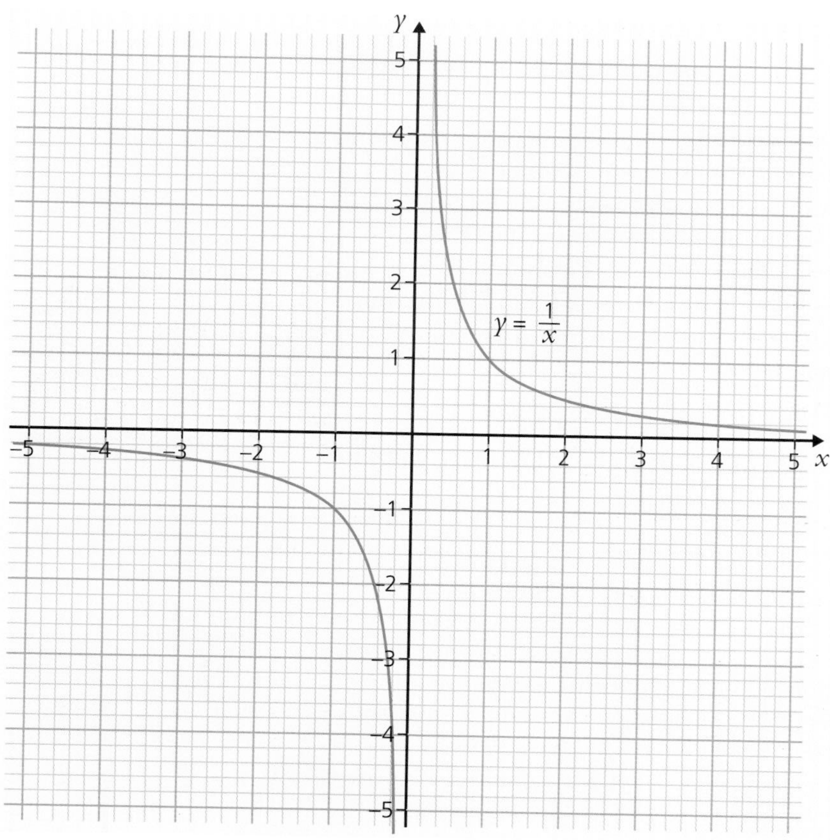

a) Use the graph to find the approximate value of each of these:

(i) $\frac{1}{2.7}$ (ii) $\frac{1}{0.9}$ (iii) $\frac{1}{-1.6}$ (iv) $\frac{1}{-0.3}$

b) Use the graph to solve the following equations correct to 1 D.P.

(i) $\frac{1}{x} = 3.6$ (ii) $\frac{1}{x} = 0.7$ (iii) $\frac{1}{x} = -3.1$ (iv) $\frac{1}{x} = -0.8$

4 If your calculator has an ANS key, follow these instructions:

- enter 4 = (or 4 EXE)
- press ANS followed by x^{-1}
- press = = = ... or EXE EXE EXE ....

a) Describe what happens.
b) Try different starting values and explain the results.

Unit 26 Pythagoras and loci

5 The following table shows the first few Pythagorean triples. The numbers are all examples of length of sides of right-angled triangles. Each one has side c as the hypotenuse, so that $a^2 + b^2 = c^2$.

Triad	a	b	c
1st	3	4	5
2nd	5	12	13
3rd	7	24	25
4th	9	40	x
5th	11	y	61
6th	z	84	85
7th			
8th			
9th			

a) Copy the table and calculate the missing values x, y and z using Pythagoras' theorem.
b) Look at the numbers in column a. Can you work out a pattern? Fill in the next three numbers down to the 9th triad.
c) Look at the numbers in column c. Write down the difference between each number and the one above it. Can you spot the pattern? Fill in the next three numbers.
d) There is also a pattern in column b. Work out the next three numbers using any method you like.

6 Find the area of material needed to make this kite.

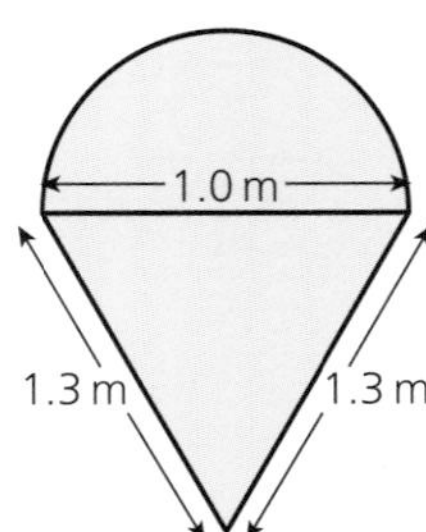

7 This equilateral triangle forms the end of a prism which is 5 cm long.

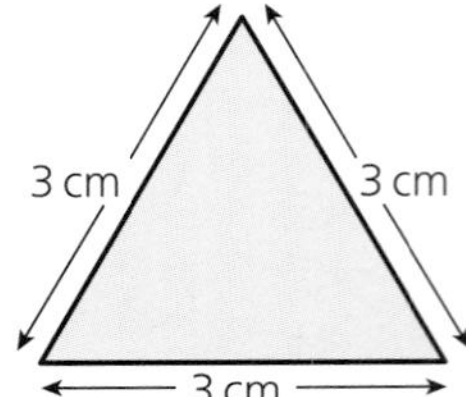

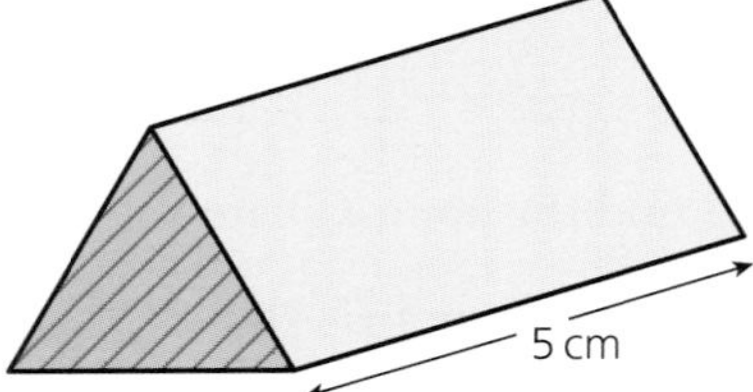

a) Find the volume of the prism.
b) Find the total surface area.

8 Lines AB and CD are parallel. Draw a sketch showing the locus of point P which is allowed to move so that it is an equal distance from AB and CD.

9 Line AB is 4 cm long. I decide to draw a triangle ABC with AB as one of the sides and with an area equal to $6\,cm^2$.
Sketch the locus of all possible positions of the vertex C.

10 ABCD is a parallelogram with an area of $40\,cm^2$. The base of the parallelogram AB is 8 cm long. Find the locus of the point of intersection of the diagonals.

Unit 27 Trial and improvement

11 a) Use the information given here to state the solution of $x^3 + x = 11$ correct to 2 D.P.
b) Explain, with the aid of a number line, how you were able to make your decision in part a).

x	$x^3 + x$
2.07	10.939 743
2.09	11.219 329
2.08	11.078 912
2.075	11.009 171 87

12 Copy and complete the working shown here to find the solution of $x^3 + x = 100$ correct to 2 D.P.

x	$x^3 + x$
4.5	95.625
4.6	101.936

13

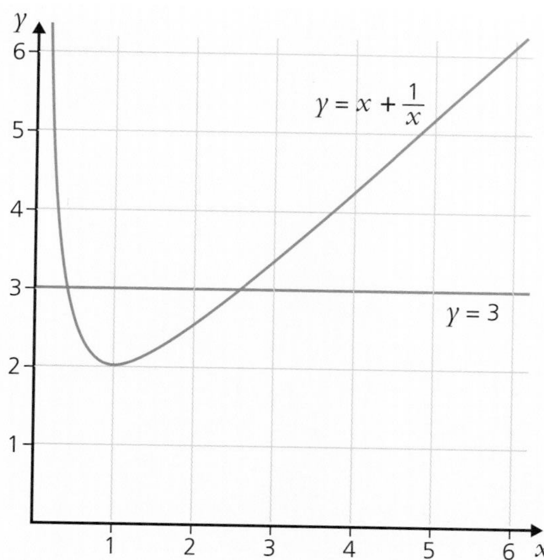

a) Use the diagram to find the approximate solutions of $x + \frac{1}{x} = 3$.
b) Use trial and improvement to find these solutions to 3 D.P.
c) For what value of x does $x + \frac{1}{x}$ take its minimum value?

Unit 28 Predictions and comparisons

14 A coastguard conducts an experiment to determine how far it is possible to see on a clear day from different heights above sea level. The heights were measured in metres and the distances in km.

Height in metres	1.5	3	4.5	6	7.5	9
Distance in km	4.0	5.6	7.0	8.1	9.2	10.2

a) Plot these results on a scatter graph showing height on the x-axis and distance on the y-axis.
b) Draw in a line of best fit.
c) Use your graph to estimate the distance the coastguard would be able to see from a height of 4 metres.

15 It is a well-known fact that air pressure decreases with altitude. (This is why climbers have to use pressure cookers to cook their food at high altitude.) The table below gives the barometer reading (in cm) for various heights measured in metres above sea level on a particular day.

Altitude (m)	0	1500	3000	4500	6000	7500
Barometer reading	76.2	63.5	52.1	43.2	36.8	30.5

a) Draw a scatter graph showing altitude on the x-axis and barometer reading on the y-axis.
b) Draw in a line of best fit.
c) Use the line to estimate the barometer reading at a height of 750 m above sea level.
d) Also estimate the altitude which will have a barometer reading of 50 cm.

Unit 29 Fractions

16 Simplify the following:

a) $\frac{2}{9}+\frac{5}{9}$ b) $\frac{11}{16}+\frac{4}{16}$ c) $\frac{15}{31}-\frac{11}{31}$

d) $\frac{27}{19}-\frac{10}{19}$ e) $\frac{23}{25}+\frac{11}{25}-\frac{9}{25}$ f) $\frac{47}{60}-\frac{21}{60}-\frac{6}{60}$

g) $\frac{9}{10}-\frac{3}{5}$ h) $\frac{19}{24}-\frac{5}{8}$ i) $\frac{13}{15}+\frac{4}{5}$

17 New houses are often decorated throughout in the same colour by the builder. The amounts needed for the rooms in a small two-bedroomed house are shown in the table.

Room	Number of tins
Kitchen	$\frac{3}{4}$
Lounge/dining	$1\frac{3}{4}$
Hall and stairs	$\frac{3}{4}$
Bedroom 1	$1\frac{1}{4}$
Bedroom 2	$1\frac{1}{4}$
Bathroom	$\frac{1}{2}$

a) How much paint is needed altogether?
b) How many tins would you need to buy to do the work yourself?

18 Work out:

a) $\frac{2}{3}$ of 24 b) $\frac{3}{5}$ of 60 c) $\frac{3}{4}$ of 60

d) $4 \times 3\frac{1}{2}$ e) $6 \times 1\frac{1}{4}$ f) $2\frac{1}{2} \times 1\frac{1}{2}$

g) $6 \div 1\frac{1}{2}$ h) $1\frac{1}{2} \div \frac{3}{4}$ i) $6 \div \frac{3}{4}$

19 Use the fact that 1 km is approximately $\frac{5}{8}$ mile to answer these questions.
a) Some college students take part in a sponsored walk of 40 km to raise money for charity. How many miles did they have to walk?
b) The speed limit on the motorways in the UK is 70 m.p.h. What is this speed in km/h ?

Unit 30 Using probability

20 You are allowed to pick three numbers from the list: 3, 4, 5 and 6.
You may use any number as often as you like.
a) Write down all 20 possible selections.
b) Now imagine the numbers represent lines with those lengths measured in cm. If the selection is made at random, what is the probability that you could make:
(i) an equilateral triangle
(ii) an isosceles triangle
(iii) any triangle?

21 Jasmine thinks that the bus to school each day is twice as likely to be full, as it is to have room for her.
If she is correct, what is the probability that the bus will be full?

22 This table gives the marks scored last year by 500 candidates in a maths exam.

Marks	Frequency
1–5	10
6–10	41
11–15	72
16–20	83
21–25	94
26–30	81
31–35	71
36–40	27
41–45	13
46–50	8

a) Find the middle value for each class interval. Use these to calculate an estimate of the mean mark.

b) It is decided to award grades as follows:

Grade A	41 marks and above
Grade B	31 marks and above
Grade C	21 marks and above
Grade D	11 marks and above
Fail	10 marks and below

Find the relative frequency for each of the grades A, B, C and D. Which grade has the highest relative frequency?

c) Ruth's teacher estimates that 1 candidate in 10 will fail the exam each year. Do these figures support that view? Explain your answer.

Unit 31 A change of form

23 For each of the following pairs of values, express the increase from the first to the second as a percentage change correct to 1 D.P.

a) 63, 67 **b)** 29, 33 **c)** 182, 186
d) 100, 105.9 **e)** 100, 175.9 **f)** 200, 249
g) 14, 34 **h)** 246, 750 **i)** 0.98, 2.37
j) £8.25, £11.36 **k)** £49.99, £59.99 **l)** 75p, £1.75
m) 8.7 kg, 10.3 kg **n)** 470 g, 1 kg **o)** 1473 mm, 2 m

24 In the previous question, the actual differences for the first three pairs of values are the same, i.e. 4. Explain why the *percentage change* is not the same in each case.

25 For each of these pairs, express the reduction from the first value to the second as a percentage change correct to 3 S.F.

a) 58, 37 **b)** 128, 46 **c)** 6.83, 0.27
d) £86.43, £62.99 **e)** £15 432, £11 500 **f)** £3.87, 88p
g) 2.86 m, 92 cm **h)** 1.36 l, 850 ml **i)** 1 minute, 47 seconds

26 In a science experiment, some students calculated the speed at which sound travels through the air to be 348 metres per second. Taking the correct value to be 330 metres per second, find the percentage error in the experimental value.

27 **a)** During a sale, the prices of selected items were reduced by 30%. Once the sale ended any remaining items were returned to their normal price. What would each of the following prices become after the sale?
(i) £43.40 (ii) £62.30 (iii) £116.90

b) Express the change from the sale price to the normal price as a percentage increase.

28 Simplify:

a) $x^2 \times x^5$ b) $q^6 \div q^3$ c) $2x \times 3x$

d) $5xy^2 \times 3x^2$ e) $(4x^3)^2$ f) $\frac{12t^7}{3t^2}$

g) $\sqrt{8.7} \times \sqrt{8.7}$ h) $(143.27)^0$ i) $\left(\frac{1}{2}\right)^{-3}$

29 Write the following in standard form:

a) 34 000 000 b) 1 760 000 c) 0.000 38

d) 0.000 002 73 e) 634.8×10^5 f) $0.008\,76 \times 10^{-5}$

30 Find the value of these in standard form (without using a calculator):

a) $(4.3 \times 10^5) \times (3 \times 10^6)$ b) $(2.6 \times 10^8) \times (5 \times 10^{-11})$

Unit 32 Measurements

31 The height of a cylinder is 6 cm correct to the nearest cm, and the radius is 4 cm, measured to the same level of accuracy.

a) Give the lower and upper limits for both the height and the radius.

b) What is the upper limit for the volume of the cylinder?

c) What is the smallest possible area of the label which could be wrapped round the cylinder?

32 Choose the correct answer from A, B, C or D for each question:

a) A journey lasts for 45 minutes and the average speed is 72 km/h. What is the distance travelled?

A 24 km B 48 km C 54 km D 108 km

b) A lorry travels 30 km at 50 km/h. The time taken for the journey in minutes is:

A 100 B 36 C 30 D 60

c) A girl takes 15 minutes to walk to school at a speed of 5 km/h. How long would it take her if she cycled at 15 km/h?

A 45 min B 75 min C 5 min D 10 min

d) A car travels 60 km at 60 km/h and 75 km at 50 km/h. Its average speed is:

A 70 km/h B 65 km/h C 55 km/h D 54 km/h

e) A bus travels for 3 hours at an average speed of 55 km/h and for 2 hours at an average speed of 60 km/h. The distance it has travelled is:

A $57\frac{1}{2}$ km B 285 km C 258 km D 115 km

33 Water flows through a pipe at a speed of 10 cm/s. The pipe has an internal diameter of 3 cm.

a) Find the cross-sectional area of the pipe.

b) Find the volume of water which flows through the pipe in (i) one second (ii) one minute.

c) Convert your last answer into litres.

33 CALCULATOR PROBLEMS

33.1 Standard form (2)

At the start of the previous section on standard form (31.3) we found that

$3\,000\,000 \times 200\,000 = 6 \times 10^{11}$

Enter the calculation in the usual way on your calculator and observe how the result is displayed. The answer is too large for the calculator to display as 600 000 000 000 and so it will automatically switch to *standard form*. It is important that you understand the way that your calculator displays standard form, so that you can recognise when this happens, and equally important that you write such numbers correctly – do *not* simply copy the display.

1 Use your calculator to find the value of each of these to an accuracy of 3 S.F. Present the answers in standard form using the established notation.

a) $3\,610\,000 \times 847\,000$ ✓
b) $29\,000\,000 \times 670\,000$
c) $84\,000 \times 27\,100 \times 9200$
d) $47\,300 \times 39\,000 \times 1\,280\,000$
e) $76\,000\,000 \times 42\,000 \times 8300$
f) $872\,000 \times (7643)^2$

These brackets are only included to highlight the fact that 7643 is raised to a power. They are not needed as part of the key sequence.

$$0.000\,07 \div 20\,000\,000 = \frac{0.000\,07}{20\,000\,000} = \frac{7 \times 10^{-5}}{2 \times 10^{7}} = 3.5 \times 10^{-12}$$

Use your calculator to find the value of $0.000\,07 \div 20\,000\,000$ and compare what the calculator displays with the result shown above. Some calculators will display answers in standard form whenever the value is less than 10^{-3}. Experiment to find the point at which your calculator switches to standard form.

2 Find the value of these to 3 S.F. Write your answers in standard form using the established notation.

a) $0.000\,079 \div 876\,000$ ✓
b) $0.000\,023 \div 649\,000$
c) $(0.043 \div 36\,000) \div 28\,000$
d) $(0.000\,34 \div 87\,000) \div 41\,000$
e) $0.000\,762 \times (58\,000\,000)^{-1}$
f) $(927\,000 \times 430\,000)^{-1}$
g) $0.23 \div (149\,000)^2$
h) $3600 \div (867\,000)^3$

3 The distance that light travels in a year is used as a unit of distance in space known as a **light year**. Given that light travels 186 282 miles each second, find how many miles are equivalent to a light year correct to 4 S.F., taking a year to consist of 365.24 days.

4 Our Sun and all the planets in the Solar System belong to a galaxy called the Milky Way, believed to contain 100 000 million stars and measuring over 60 000 light years across. Find this distance in miles to 3 S.F.
For interest, there are estimated to be be ten billion galaxies in the Universe.

Scientific calculators have a special key that allows numbers to be entered directly in standard form. On most calculators this key is labelled EXP but on some it is labelled EE . The use of this key greatly extends the range of numbers that a calculator is able to work with.

Example

a) Find the value of $(2.397 \times 10^{15}) \times (6.382 \times 10^{11})$ correct to 3 S.F.
b) Calculate $(7.31 \times 10^{-24}) \div (3.49 \times 10^{-16})$ correct to 2 S.F.

Answer

a) Key this in as

2.397 EXP 15 × 6.382 EXP 11

giving $1.529\,765\,4 \times 10^{27} = 1.53 \times 10^{27}$ (to 3 S.F.)

Remember to write the answer using the correct notation

b) Key this in as

7.31 EXP 24 +/− ÷ 3.49 EXP 16 +/− ←

giving $2.094 \ldots \times 10^{-8} = 2.1 \times 10^{-8}$ (to 2 S.F.)

Some calculators have a special (−) key which would be pressed *before* the 16 is entered

---

5 Find the value of these in standard form correct to 3 S.F.

a) $(4.72 \times 10^{9}) \times (6.89 \times 10^{12})$ ✓
b) $(7.59 \times 10^{23}) \div (4.62 \times 10^{8})$
c) $(8.63 \times 10^{14}) \times (9.42 \times 10^{-6})$ ✓
d) $(5.35 \times 10^{7}) \div (8.79 \times 10^{-9})$
e) $(3.47 \times 10^{-19}) \times (6.38 \times 10^{-18})$
f) $(4.37 \times 10^{-5}) \div (9.21 \times 10^{-16})$
g) $(2.67 \times 10^{18}) + (3.72 \times 10^{16})$
h) $(4.23 \times 10^{-19}) + (8.48 \times 10^{-18})$
i) $(1.57 \times 10^{25}) - (8.33 \times 10^{24})$
j) $(7.34 \times 10^{-21}) - (9.92 \times 10^{-22})$

6 Imagine that you have a *large* sheet of paper that you tear in half, placing one half on top of the other, and that you are capable of repeating this process, with the pile obtained, as often as you like.

a) Given that 100 sheets of this paper would make a pile 1 cm high, estimate, without using a calculator, the height of the pile produced if you were to go through the process 50 times.
b) Express the number of pieces obtained in part a) as a power of 2.
c) Use a calculator to find the height of the pile in appropriate units.
d) If the surface area of the Earth is $5.1 \times 10^{8}\,\text{km}^2$ to 2 S.F., express its area in m^2.
e) If the *large* sheet referred to above had an area equal to the surface area of the Earth, calculate the area of each of the pieces obtained if it was torn in half 50 times as in part a). Give your answer in m^2 to 2 S.F.

7 The mass of the Earth is 5.974×10^{21} tonnes and the total mass of water on its surface is 1.41×10^{18} tonnes.
What percentage of the mass of the Earth is made up of water (to 3 S.F.)?

8 Taking the area of the UK to be $2.448 \times 10^{5}\,\text{km}^2$ and the area of the Earth's surface to be $510\,066\,000\,\text{km}^2$, what percentage of the Earth's surface does the UK cover?

33.2 Interest on savings

If you have money to invest, there are many options available which pay interest on the amount that you have in your account. The *rate* of interest paid is given as a percentage and varies between the different banks and building societies. There are also big differences in the rates offered, depending on the type of account and the amount invested. For example, an account which allows you to draw your money out whenever you like is known as an *instant access account* and may pay around 2.5% per year, whereas a long-term investment account, with a high minimum deposit, may offer in the region of 8.5%.

If the interest paid into an account is immediately withdrawn, by the account holder, then the original sum will continue to gather interest at the same rate. This form of interest payment is known as **simple interest**. For example, a monthly income account will pay the account holder a sum of money each month while leaving the original investment untouched.

Example

Calculate the simple interest paid on an investment of £15 000 at 6.08% per year for 7 years.

Answer

The amount of interest paid per year = £15 000 × 0.0608 and so the total simple interest is given by £15 000 × 0.0608 × 7 = £6384.

---

1 ✔ Find the simple interest paid on £12 500 invested for 6 years at 6.23% per year.

2 How much simple interest would be paid on £8400 invested for 10 years at an annual interest rate of 5.98%?

3 How much simple interest would gather on £9600, invested at 6.15% per year, over a period of 6 months?

4 A couple open a monthly income account with a deposit of £35 000, having sold their house for a smaller property. Interest is paid on the account at 0.51% per month.

a) How much do the couple receive as a monthly income?

b) If the interest rate remains the same, how much would the couple be paid over a period of 15 years?

5 Calculate the annual rate of simple interest that would provide an income of £1 190.80 per year on an investment of £18 320.

6 How long would it take an investment of £27 000 to gather £8991 in simple interest at an annual rate of 7.4%?

7 Explain the effect that inflation has on the buying power of a sum of money invested in a monthly income account.

If the interest paid into an account is *not* withdrawn, future interest will be paid on the *total* amount. This form of interest payment is known as **compound interest** and gathers more quickly than simple interest because it is based on amounts that continue to grow. The scale factor approach, used earlier in Unit 19, provides an efficient method of calculating these amounts.

Example

An initial investment of £8000 is put into an account to gather compound interest at a rate of 7.1% per year.

a) What will be the value of the investment after 5 years?

b) How much compound interest will have been paid?

Answer

The total amount after adding each year's interest may be found by multiplying the previous figure by a scale factor of 1.071. This produces a *sequence* as shown below.

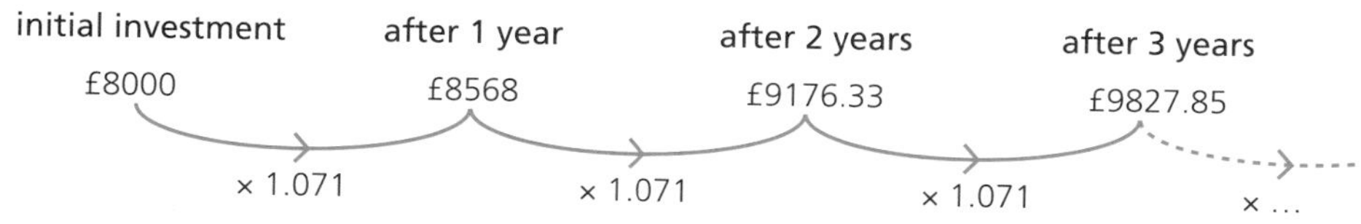

In this way, the value of the investment will have grown, after 5 years, to £8000 × 1.071 × 1.071 × 1.071 × 1.071 × 1.071 = £8000 × $(1.071)^5$

a) The total in the account after 5 years is £11 272.94 to the nearest penny.

b) The total compound interest paid = £11 272.94 – £8000
= £3272.94 to the nearest penny

ICT Extra!

Use a spreadsheet to calculate the compound interest on the investment given in this example. How long will it take for the amount of money to grow to £16 000 and double its size?

8 A sum of £5000 is allowed to gather compound interest at 6.8% per year.
a) Find the scale factor for calculating the new amount from year to year. ✓
b) Find an expression for the value of the investment after four years.
c) Calculate the value of the expression found in part b).
d) Calculate the amount of compound interest accrued after four years.

9 Calculate the total amount when compound interest is added to an initial investment of £10 000 at an annual rate of 7.3% for the following periods of time:
a) 5 years ✓ b) 10 years c) 15 years d) 20 years

10 Calculate the value of the compound interest accrued on £4900 invested for 10 years at the following rates:
a) 5.3% ✓ b) 5.7% c) 6.4% d) 7.2%

11 a) Given that the interest rate is I% per annum, copy and complete the formula for the scale factor R that may be used to calculate the new value of the investment, including compound interest, from year to year.

$R = 1 + \ldots$

b) The initial amount invested is sometimes called the **principal amount**. Using £P to represent the principal amount, find an expression in terms of P and R for the value of the investment, including compound interest, after:
(i) 2 years (ii) 5 years (iii) 10 years
c) Find a formula for the total amount A, including n years of compound interest, in terms of P, R and n.
d) Find the values of R and A given that $I = 8$, $P = 5000$ and $n = 20$.
e) Rearrange the formula to make P the subject.
f) Find the value of P to 2 D.P. given that $A = 8765$, $I = 7.1$ and $n = 25$.

12 The sequences given below show the growth of an initial investment of £450 over a period of five years at 6.7% interest per annum. The top sequence is based on simple interest and the other on compound interest.

Principal amount	Number of years invested				
	1	2	3	4	5
£450	£480.15	£510.30	£540.45	£570.60	£600.75
£450	£480.15	£512.32	£546.65	£583.27	£622.35

a) Continue the simple interest sequence, using the *constant addition* facility of your calculator, to show the pattern of growth for the first 15 years.
b) Continue the compound interest sequence for the same period of time using the *constant multiplier* facility of your calculator.
c) How many years does it take to more than double the principal amount based on
(i) simple interest (ii) compound interest?

33.3 Loan repayment

Loans may be taken out for many purposes and from a variety of sources. In general, the lender will make a profit by adding interest charges to the amount to be repaid. The rate of interest is always given as an **annual percentage rate** (APR) but may vary considerably from one lender to another.

Example

A finance company offers a loan of £2000 at 16% APR, to be repaid in 12 equal monthly payments of £180.45.

a) Find the total amount repaid.

b) Express the interest charges as a percentage of the loan.

Answer

a) Total repaid = £180.45 × 12 = £2 165.40

b) 2 165.4 ÷ 2000 = 1.0827

and so the amount repaid is 8.27% more than was borrowed, i.e. the interest charges amount to 8.27% of the loan.

Note: the percentage calculated in b) is *less* than 16% because, as payments are made, the interest is charged on a *reducing balance*. The 8.27% figure is known as a **flat rate** and refers to the equivalent rate of interest *per year* based on the whole amount.

---

1 A loan of £5000 is repaid at 14% APR in 24 monthly instalments of £238.12.

a) What is the total amount repaid on the loan?

b) Express the charges made as a percentage of the amount borrowed.

c) Find the flat rate of interest and compare this figure with the APR. ✓

2 The monthly repayments on a loan of £10 000 spread over 5 years at 12% APR work out at £219.36.

a) Find the total amount repaid.

b) Calculate the charges as a percentage of the loan.

c) Find the flat rate of interest and compare it with the APR.

3 a) What is the total credit price of the computer?

b) Express the credit charges as a percentage of the cash price.

c) Find the flat rate of interest charged for credit on this offer.

d) Compare the flat rate of interest with the APR.

NO
DEPOSIT
Required
APR 26.8%
Cash Price £1232.57
or
24 monthly payments
of just £65.16

Local newspapers often print advertisements from garages offering finance deals for the purchase of cars and other vehicles. Interest charges are given as an APR and it is useful, when considering a purchase, to be able to work out the cost of the repayments in advance. However, since the APR works on a reducing balance, this is quite a complex task. The flat rate, on the other hand, is much easier to work with and, as the previous questions have shown, the percentage figure for the flat rate is *approximately* half of the APR figure. Using this result we can obtain a good estimate of the size of the repayments.

Example

Mike and Alison are offered £1000 for their old car in part exchange for one priced at £6995 at a garage. They accept the offer and pay an extra £1495 as a deposit.

a) What is the balance to be repaid?
b) If interest is charged at 23.8% APR, and they take three years to complete the payments, approximately how much will they have to pay each month?
c) What is the total credit price for the car?

Answer

a) Part exchange value + deposit = £2495
Balance remaining = £4500

b) Flat rate ≈ $\frac{1}{2}$ × 23.8% = 11.9%
Interest charged at 11.9% × 3 = 35.7%
Total paid in instalments ≈ £4500 × 1.357 = £6 106.50
Monthly payment ≈ £6 106.50 ÷ 36 = £169.625 ≈ £170

c) Total credit price = £2495 + £6 106.50 = £8 601.50 ≈ £8600

Use the approximate flat-rate values to find the answers to the following questions to the nearest £10.

4 Katherine saves £1000 as a deposit on a new car costing £7500 and repays the balance in monthly instalments over four years at 16% APR.
a) How much will she need to pay each month?
b) How much does she pay for the car altogether?

5 Steve's first car is priced at £1995 at a garage. He pays a deposit of £95 and the balance over 24 months at 26.4% APR.
a) How much is each monthly payment?
b) What is the total credit price of the car?

6 A couple need to borrow £4000 to buy a car and consider whether to repay the loan in 1 year or spread their monthly payments over 3 years. Interest is charged at 22.6% APR.
a) What would be the advantage of repaying the loan in 1 year?
b) Why might they need to repay the loan over 3 years?
c) What is the total amount repaid in each case?
d) What is the difference in the monthly instalments?

The *exact* value of a monthly loan repayment may be found using the formula given below.

Using £L = loan

n = number of payments needed to repay loan

$$R = \sqrt[12]{1 + \frac{\text{APR}}{100}}$$

Each payment is given by $\dfrac{LR^n(R-1)}{R^n - 1}$.

Example

Calculate the monthly repayment on a personal loan of £10 000 repaid over 5 years at 16.1% APR. Find the total amount paid.

Answer

$R = \sqrt[12]{1.161} = 1.012517842$ (store this in the calculator memory)

$L = 10\,000$ and $n = 60$

Using the formula, the monthly repayment is £238.01 (to the nearest penny).
Total amount paid = 60 × £238.01 = £14 280.60.

---

7 Find the monthly payment needed to repay a loan of £8500 over 4 years at 18.2% APR. How much is paid in total?

8 What are the monthly payments on a mortgage of £40 000 taken out over 25 years based on an interest rate of 8.2%?
If the interest rate is increased by 1%, what difference does this make to each month's payment?

34 CUMULATIVE FREQUENCY

34.1 Median and range

Sarah has decided to do a project on 'Sport'. Here are some of the data she has collected:

Times in seconds for year 11 pupils running 100 m

16 11 13 14 15 13 15 20 12 14 14

Times in seconds for year 11 pupils swimming 100 m

65 72 93 81 95 130 97 89 93 82

In her report she decides to give the median as a typical time for each event, and the range as a guide to the amount of variability in people's times. To do this, she organises the results for running times in order:

Running times

11 12 13 13 14 (14) 14 15 15 16 20

The **median** is the middle value = 14 seconds.

The **range** is the difference between the highest result and the lowest.

Range = 20 – 11 = 9 seconds

1 ✓ Find the median and range of the swimming times.

2 ✓ How can you give an answer for the median when there is no single result in the middle?

3 ✓ Are there any disadvantages in using the range as a measure of variability?

34.2 The interquartile range

As the largest result and the smallest result may not be typical results (look at the longest times in the running and swimming data!), many people prefer to focus on the middle 50% of a group. The variation within this central (and hopefully typical) 50% is called the **interquartile range**.

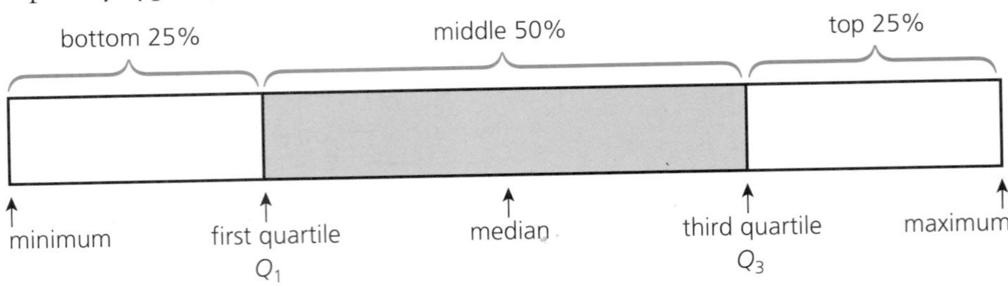

In order to calculate the interquartile range, the values of the **first quartile** (Q_1) and the **third quartile** (Q_3) must be found. These two points occur *one quarter* of the way through the results and *three quarters* of the way through.

An easy way of finding the quartiles is to arrange your results in order and then to write them as a 'W' like this:

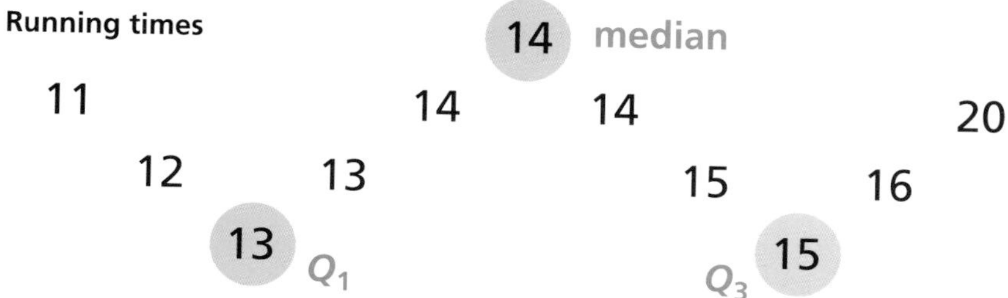

The median is at the top of the W and the quartiles are at the bottom.

The interquartile range is $Q_3 - Q_1$ which is $15 - 13 = 2$ seconds.

So for running times, the middle 50% were all within 2 seconds.

1 ✓ Use this method to check that you have the right answer for the median for swimming times. Find the first and third quartiles. How much variation was there among the middle 50% (the interquartile range)?

2 ✓ Ben asked his friends at Games Workshop their ages. Here are the answers they gave:

11 15 14 17 16 14 15 15 16 19 14 13

Find the interquartile range for these data.

3 He also asked everyone there to count the number of times they had been to the Games Workshop in November. He made their answers into a table:

Number of visits in Nov	1	2	3	4	5	6	7	8
Frequency	4	6	3	5	1	3	1	2

a) How can you find out how many people Ben asked?
b) How can you find the median? ✓
c) How can you find the quartiles?
d) Write down the answer to each question in parts a) to c).

4 Sally did a survey of amounts spent in the canteen. Here are some of her results:

Person	A	B	C	D	E	F	G	H	I	J	K	L
Number of items	4	3	1	6	4	1	2	3	4	4	2	2
Amount spent (p)	98	71	35	143	95	38	70	85	90	98	66	68

a) Find the median and the first and third quartiles for:
(i) the number of items (ii) the amount spent.
b) Find the range and interquartile range for:
(i) the number of items (ii) the amount spent.

5 Sally asked people:
'How many times did you eat school lunch in the canteen last week?'
Here are their answers. Find the median and interquartile range.

No. of times	0	1	2	3	4	5
Frequency	8	3	2	1	3	13

6 Compare the heights of girls and boys in this class.

Girls' heights (in cm)
165 163 159 175 174 162 165 168 170 172 163 160
169 167 166

Boys' heights (in cm)
158 163 179 177 168 164 172 171 164 170 174 173
172 169 170

a) Find the median and the interquartile range for both groups. Comment on the differences.

b) What do these figures tell you?

Investigation

1 Can you make up:

- two data sets which are different but have the same median?
- two different data sets which have the same quartiles?
- two different data sets which have the same medians and quartiles?
- two more different data sets with the same interquartile range?

2 Ask people...

- Ask two groups of people (parents and pupils, say) how many videos or TV films they watched last week.
- Ask two groups of pupils (such as year 7 and year 11) how long they spent doing homework last night.
- Ask two groups of pupils (boys and girls, perhaps) what size shoes they wear.

Give the median and the interquartile range for each group and use these measures to make a direct comparison of the two sets of data.

34.3 Cumulative frequency graphs

Richard is writing a report called 'Who uses public transport?'.

He has carried out a survey of bus passengers' ages at different times of day. Here are his results for Tuesday:

Age of passenger in years	Frequency	
	10 am	4 pm
$0 \le x < 10$	5	4
$10 \le x < 20$	0	11
$20 \le x < 30$	4	2
$30 \le x < 40$	2	2
$40 \le x < 50$	1	4
$50 \le x < 60$	2	0
$60 \le x < 70$	9	1
$70 \le x < 80$	3	0

1 ✔ a) How many people were travelling on the bus at 10 am?
b) What is their median age?

You may have been able to work out that the median age is somewhere between 50 and 60 years.

We can get a more precise answer by drawing a **cumulative frequency graph** and we can also use this to find the quartiles.

Before we draw a graph we need to make a **cumulative frequency column**. This is found by adding up the frequencies as we go down (sometimes called a running total).

Ages of passengers at 10 am				
Age	Frequency		Cumulative frequency	Age
$0 \le x < 10$	5		5	<10
$10 \le x < 20$	0	0 + 5 = 5 →	5	<20
$20 \le x < 30$	4	4 + 5 = 9 →	9	<30
$30 \le x < 40$	2	2 + 9 = 11 →	11	<40
$40 \le x < 50$	1	1 + 11 = 12 →	12	<50
$50 \le x < 60$	2	2 + 12 = 14 →	14	<60
$60 \le x < 70$	9	9 + 14 = 23 →	23	<70
$70 \le x < 80$	3	3 + 23 = 26 →	26	<80

The table shows that 5 passengers were younger than age 10, 9 were younger than age 30 and so on; and that there were 26 passengers in all.

To draw a cumulative frequency graph, plot the points using the last two columns but note that:

- x coordinate = upper age limit for each group
- y coordinate = cumulative frequency

The first point is (10, 5). The next is (20, 5), then (30, 9) and so on.

Since no passengers were less than age 0, the graph starts at (0, 0). The points are joined by straight lines.

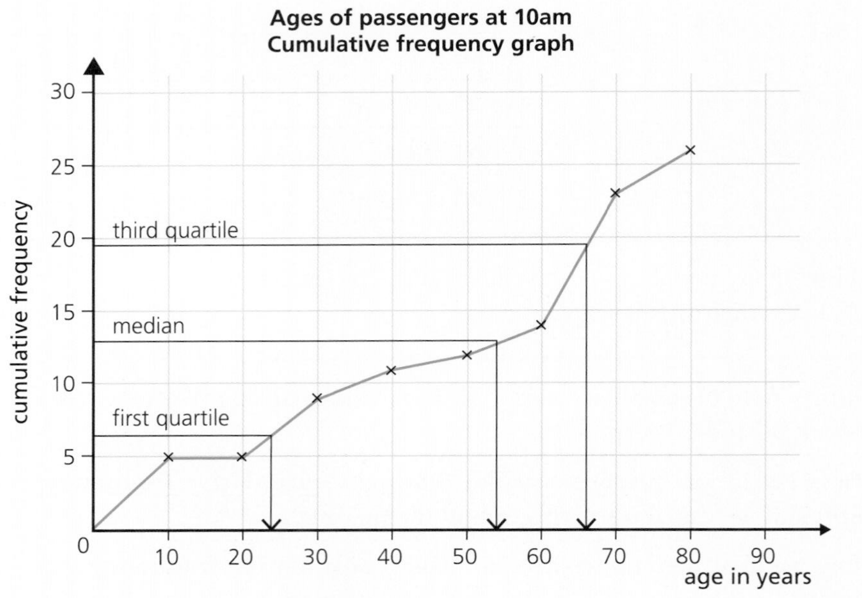

The graph can then be used to find the median, and the first and third quartiles.

To find the median age: half the passengers are younger than the median age. $\frac{1}{2}$ of 26 = 13 passengers. Reading this off the graph, the median age is 54 years.

The first quartile: a quarter of the passengers must be younger than the first quartile. $\frac{1}{4}$ of 26 = 6.5. Reading this off the graph, the first quartile is age 23 years.

The third quartile: three quarters of the passengers must be younger than the third quartile. $\frac{3}{4}$ of 26 is 19.5. Reading this off the graph, the third quartile is age 66 years.

2 This graph shows the cumulative percentages for pedestrians killed in road accidents.

a) What is the median age of pedestrians killed in road accidents? ✓
b) Find the first and third quartiles. ✓
c) What percentage are aged under 20? ✓
d) What percentage are aged under 60?
e) What percentage are aged over 60?
f) Can you tell from the graph which age group had very few pedestrians killed in road accidents?
g) Which two groups are most at risk?
h) Find the interquartile range.

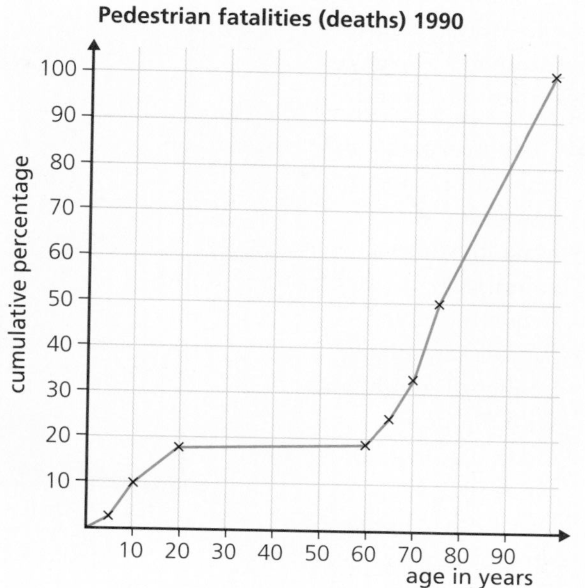

3 These tables give percentages of young females and males aged 16–19 and their heights in centimetres.

Females		Males	
Height (cm)	**%**	**Height (cm)**	**%**
$145 \le x < 150$	2	$155 \le x < 160$	2
$150 \le x < 155$	10	$160 \le x < 165$	6
$155 \le x < 160$	30	$165 \le x < 170$	15
$160 \le x < 165$	31	$170 \le x < 175$	28
$165 \le x < 170$	19	$175 \le x < 180$	31
$170 \le x < 175$	7	$180 \le x < 185$	13
$175 \le x < 180$	1	$185 \le x < 190$	4
		$190 \le x < 195$	1

a) Draw a cumulative percentage table for each group. ✓
b) Draw cumulative percentage graphs for each group. ✓
c) Find the median height for females aged 16–19. ✓
d) Find the median for males' heights.
e) Find the interquartile ranges for each group.
f) Write a statement comparing the heights of males and females aged 16–19.

4 Sanjay has taken the temperatures of 50 people using a clinical thermometer as part of his project on 'Health'.

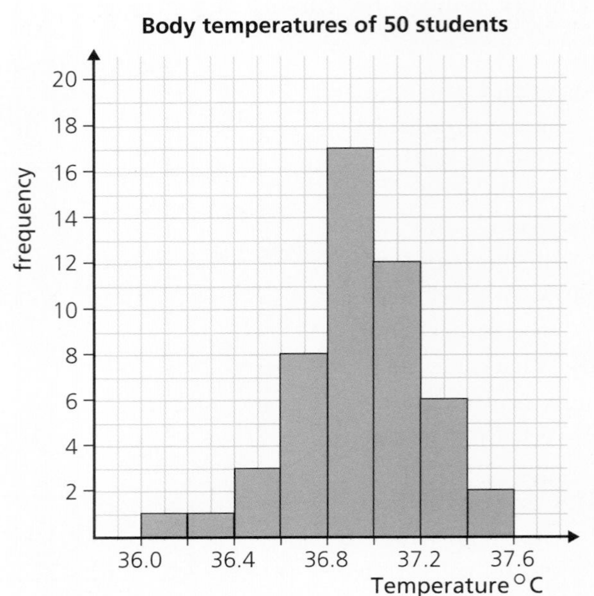

a) Draw up a frequency table from Sanjay's histogram. ✓
b) Make this into a cumulative frequency table.
c) Sanjay's cumulative frequency graph starts with the points (36.0, 0), (36.2, 1), (36.4, 2). What other points should he plot?
d) Draw the cumulative frequency graph.
e) Find the median body temperature.
f) What is the interquartile range?

5 Look back at Richard's survey of bus passengers on page 323.
a) Draw up a cumulative frequency table for the ages of passengers travelling at 4 pm.
b) Draw a frequency graph.
c) What is the median age of passengers at 4 pm?
d) What is the interquartile range?
e) Write two sentences comparing the ages of passengers at 10 am and 4 pm. ✓
f) What kind of passengers were the largest group of passengers at (i) 10 am? (ii) 4 pm?

Investigation

Choose one of the following investigations. Find out:
a) The journey times for pupils in your class from home to school.
b) How much everyone in your class weighed when they were born.
c) How long people estimate as being one minute. (You will have to ask each person in your sample to do this one at a time, otherwise they may help each other.)
d) Ask a sample of adults how much they earned as their first week's wages in their first ever job.

For the data you have collected, write about the median, the range and the interquartile range. (If you are able to ask your question to another group of people, another class, say, you can make a comparison of the two.)

34.4 Grouped discrete data

The cumulative frequency graphs that you have drawn so far have all been for continuous data (obtained by measuring).

It is also possible to draw a cumulative frequency graph for grouped discrete data (results which were originally obtained by counting).

For continuous data, the value of the cumulative frequency tells you how many results are *less than* the upper boundary of each class interval.

For discrete data, the cumulative frequency gives the number of results which are *less than or equal to* the upper boundary of each class interval.

1 Joe has counted the pulse rates of pupils in his class:

Beats per minute	Frequency
60–64	2
65–69	5
70–74	4
75–79	12
80–84	4
85–89	2
90–94	1

a) Find the cumulative frequencies. ✓
b) Draw a cumulative frequency graph. ✓
c) Find the median and the interquartile range.

2 Louise has done a survey among her friends to find out how many posters they have on their bedroom walls. Here are her results:

Posters	Frequency
0–4	4
5–9	3
10–14	5
15–19	6
20–24	2
25–29	3

Draw a cumulative frequency graph to find the median and the interquartile range.

34.5 Using a spreadsheet

A spreadsheet such as Excel can easily be used to calculate cumulative frequencies and display them graphically.

The data on heights of young people aged 16–19 (question 3, page 325) are shown again here as an example.

Spreadsheet

	A	B	C	D	E
1	Heights	Percentage	Cumulative	Percentage	Cumulative
2	in cm	of	percentage	of	percentage
3	below	females	females	males	males
4					
5	150	2	2	0	
6	155	10	12	0	
7	160	30	42	2	
8	165	31	73	6	
9	170	19	92	15	
10	175	7	99	28	
11	180	1	100	31	
12	185	0	100	13	
13	190	0	100	4	
14	195	0	100	1	
15					

Step 1 Enter column titles.
Enter upper limit of each class interval in column A.
Enter the frequencies (or percentages as shown here) in column B.

Step 2 In cell C5 enter the formula
= B5 + C4
Copy this formula down column C.

An equivalent formula can be entered into cell E5 if needed:
= D5 + E4
Again, copy this down column E.

The cumulative frequencies can then be displayed on a graph. Highlight the data in column A, then holding down the Ctrl key highlight the data in column C and/or E. Now select Chart from the Insert menu (or press the Chart Wizard key) and follow the on-screen instructions to create a line graph.

---

1 Complete the spreadsheet and draw the two cumulative frequency graphs.

2 Enter some of your own data and use the spreadsheet to find the cumulative frequencies.

ICT Extra!

Follow the instructions given here to draw up a cumulative frequency table. Then can you find a way to draw a cumulative frequency graph on your spreadsheet?

35.1 Manipulating equations

The balancing approach to solving equations, considered earlier, can also be used to change the form of an equation to suit a particular purpose.

We found in Unit 13 that the graph of an equation of the form $y = mx + c$ would be a straight line with gradient m and y-intercept at c. Such an equation is said to be in **gradient-intercept form** and the ability to rearrange an equation to match this form allows us to make use of these results.

Example

Show that the graph of the equation $2y - 3x = 8$ is a straight line and find its gradient and y-intercept.

Answer

$2y - 3x = 8$ add $3x$ to both sides of the equation
$2y = 3x + 8$ divide both sides by 2
note that $(3x + 8) \div 2 = \frac{1}{2}(3x + 8) = 1.5x + 4$ giving
$y = 1.5x + 4$ which is in the form $y = mx + c$.

It follows that the graph is a straight line with gradient 1.5 and y-intercept at 4.

---

1 Rearrange the following equations to put them into gradient-intercept form. State the value of the gradient and y-intercept in each case.

a) $4y = 8x + 12$
b) $3y - 5 = 6x + 4$
c) $y - 3x = 7$
d) $y - 4x + 2 = 0$
e) $2y - 6x = 12$
f) $7y - 21x - 14 = 0$
g) $2y + 3 = 7x + 9$
h) $5y - 6x = 4x + 15$
i) $3y - (x - 11) = 2x + 14$
j) $4(y - 3x) - 5 = 4x + 3$
k) $y + 4(3 - 2x) = x + 20$
l) $y - 7(x + 2) = 3x + 1$

In some situations the values of the gradient and/or the y-intercept may be negative. They may also be expressed as fractions.

Example

Put these equations in the form $y = mx + c$. Sketch each graph and find the gradient and the y-intercept.

a) $y + 2x = 5$ b) $3y - x + 2 = 0$ c) $\frac{y}{3} + 5 = x$

Answer

a) $y + 2x = 5$ subtract $2x$ from both sides
$y = -2x + 5$

In this case, the gradient is -2 and the y-intercept is at 5.

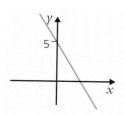

b) $3y - x + 2 = 0$ add x to both sides

$3y + 2 = x$ subtract 2 from both sides

$3y = x - 2$ divide both sides by 3

$y = \frac{1}{3}x - \frac{2}{3}$ note: $(x - 2) \div 3 = \frac{1}{3}(x - 2)$ which may be written as $\frac{1}{3}x - \frac{2}{3}$

It now follows that the gradient is $\frac{1}{3}$ and the y-intercept is at $-\frac{2}{3}$.

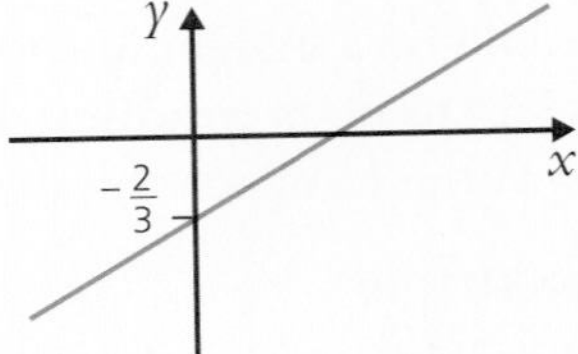

c) $\frac{y}{3} + 5 = x$ subtract 5 from both sides

$\frac{y}{3} = x - 5$ multiply both sides by 3

$y = 3x - 15$ note: $3(x - 5) = 3x - 15$.

We now see that the gradient is 3 and the y-intercept is at -15.

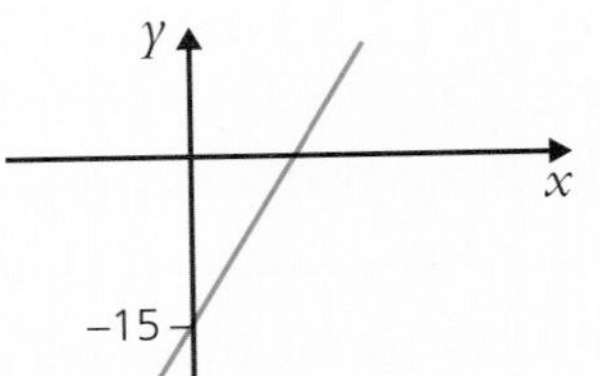

---

2 Put these equations in the form $y = mx + c$. Sketch each graph and state which lines are parallel to the line given by $y = -\frac{2}{3}x + 4$.

a) $y + 3x - 4 = 0$ b) $3y + 2x - 5 = 0$ c) $6y + 4x - 10 = 0$

d) $3y - 2x = -6$ e) $2y - 3x - 8 = 0$ f) $6y - 9x - 24 = 0$

g) $\frac{y}{2} + x - 1 = 0$ h) $\frac{y}{2} + \frac{x}{3} = 4$ i) $\frac{x}{3} = 5 - y$

j) $2x = 1 - 3y$

The ability to manipulate an equation also allows us to rearrange a formula to provide us with new information. This means, for example, that we only need to remember one version of a formula, knowing that it can be adapted to suit a particular problem.

In Unit 7 the formula $v = u + at$ was given as an example of the use of algebra to make a clear statement in order to convey information. One of the advantages of using algebra, given at that time, was that the formula could be rearranged. We are now in a position to do this.

As it stands, v is the **subject** of the equation, i.e. the equation takes the form $v =$ .... This form is most useful when the values of u, a and t are known and we need to calculate the value of v. However, in a particular problem, we may need to know the value of a for some particular values of u, v and t. In this situation we need to make a the subject of the equation.

Example

Rearrange the formula $v = u + at$ to make a the subject.

Answer

$v = u + at$ subtract u from both sides so that the term containing a is isolated.

$v - u = at$ divide both sides by t.

$\frac{v - u}{t} = a$

$a = \frac{v - u}{t}$ the subject is normally written on the left-hand side of the equation.

---

3 a) Rearrange the formula $v = u + at$ to make t the subject.
b) Find the value of t given that $v = 17.7$, $u = 5.7$ and $a = 3$.

4 a) Rearrange the formula $v = u + at$ to make u the subject.
b) Find the value of u given that $v = 12.8$, $a = 0.7$ and $t = 4$.

5 Rearrange each of the equations below to make x the subject:

a) $x + a = b$ b) $x - ab = 0$ c) $x + ab = c$
d) $ax + b = c$ e) $ax - bc = 0$ f) $ax + bc = d$ ✓
g) $\frac{x}{a} = b$ h) $\frac{x - a}{b} = c$ ✓ i) $\frac{x}{a} - b = c$
j) $a(x + b) = c$ k) $x(a + b) = c$ l) $a - (b - x) = c$
m) $\frac{ax}{b} = c$ n) $\frac{ax + b}{c} = d$ ✓ o) $\frac{x + a}{b} - c = d$

6 a) Rearrange the formula $F = ma$ to make a the subject.
b) Find the value of a given that $F = 17.9$ and $m = 5$.
c) Make m the subject of the formula.
d) Find the value of m given that $F = 312$ and $a = 2.5$

7 a) Make g the subject of the formula $F = m(g - a)$.
b) Find the value of g given that $F = 45$, $m = 5$ and $a = 0.81$.

8 a) Make v the subject of the formula $F = \frac{m(v - u)}{t}$.
b) Find the value of v when $F = 10$, $t = 6$, $m = 3$ and $u = 4$.

9 a) Make T the subject of the formula $n = \frac{1}{2l}\sqrt{\frac{T}{m}}$.
b) Find the value of T when $l = 0.5$, $n = 10$ and $m = 4$.

10 There are n students in my class and all but five of them sell t tickets each for a raffle.
a) How many tickets have my class sold so far?
b) If the five remaining students sell $2t + 4$ tickets between them, find a formula for T, the total number of tickets sold.
c) Make t the subject of the formula.

11 The cost, per head, at a wedding reception for n guests is £a for adults and £$(a - 2)$ for children.

a) There are 10 children at the reception, how many adults are there?
b) What is the total cost of the meals for the adults?
c) What is the total cost of the meals for the children?
d) Find a formula for C if the total cost of all the meals is £C.
e) Make a the subject of the formula.

12 The figure below consists of a rectangle of length $3r$ and width $2r$ from which two semicircles of radius r have been removed.

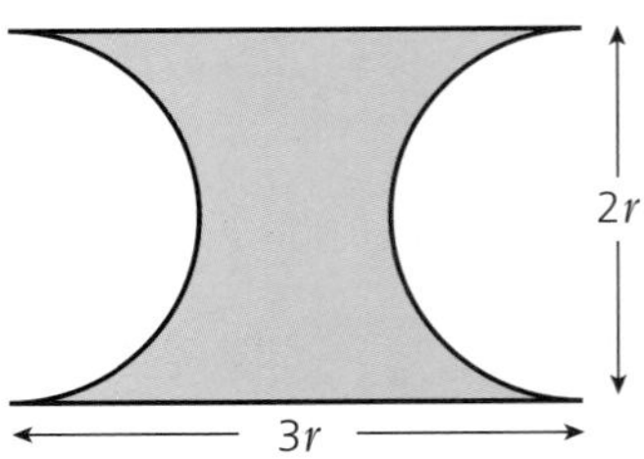

a) Find a formula for the perimeter P of the figure in terms of r.
b) Rearrange the formula to make r the subject.
c) Find a formula for the area A of the figure in terms of r.
d) Make r the subject of the formula found in part c).

35.2 Simultaneous equations

■ The substitution method

Just as with the elimination method (see Unit 21), the idea is to produce a single equation in terms of one of the unknown values. In the substitution method this is done by substituting information from one equation into the other.

Example

Solve the simultaneous equations $x + y = 8$ and $y = x + 2$.

Answer

Labelling the equations makes it easier to show your method.

$$x + y = 8 \qquad (1)$$
$$y = x + 2 \qquad (2)$$

Using equation (2) we can re-write equation (1) by replacing y with $x + 2$, i.e. we can substitute for y in equation (1).

This gives:

$$x + (x + 2) = 8 \qquad \text{remove the brackets and simplify}$$
$$2x + 2 = 8$$
$$2x = 6$$
$$x = 3$$

Substituting for x in equation (2) gives $y = 3 + 2 = 5$.

The required solution is $x = 3$ and $y = 5$.

(*Check*: substituting for x and y in equation (1) gives $x + y = 3 + 5 = 8$.)

Example

Solve simultaneously: $x = y - 5$ (1)

$3y - 2x = 12$ (2)

Answer

Substituting for x in (2) gives

$3y - 2(y - 5) = 12$ brackets are essential here

$3y - 2y + 10 = 12$ care is needed with minus signs

$y + 10 = 12$

$y = 2$

Substituting for y in (1) gives

$x = 2 - 5 = -3$

The required solution is $x = -3$ and $y = 2$.

(*Check*: substituting for x and y in (2) gives $3y - 2x = 6 - (-6) = 12$.)

---

1 Solve these simultaneous equations using the substitution method:

a) $y = x$, $2x + y = 9$ ✓
b) $y = x - 4$, $2x + y = 23$
c) $y = 2x + 1$, $x + 2y = 27$
d) $2y - x = 1$, $x = y + 3$
e) $x + y = 11$, $x = y - 9$
f) $2x - y = 9$, $y = x - 3$
g) $3x - y = 9$, $y = 2x - 4$
h) $2x + y = 5$, $y = x - 7$
i) $x + 3y = 16$, $x = y - 12$

2 Solve these simultaneous equations. Take care to use brackets where necessary.

a) $a = 3b + 1$, $a + b = 9$ ✓
b) $q = 3p - 1$, $p + q = 11$
c) $s = r - 5$, $r + 2s = 17$
d) $m = l - 7$, $3m - l = 3$
e) $3m - 2n = 15$, $n = m - 3$ ✓
f) $4q - t = 1$, $t = 3q + 2$
g) $d = c - 10$, $c + 3d = 2$
h) $2w + x = 13$, $x = w - 17$
i) $2a + e = -1$, $a = e - 16$

In some situations it may be necessary to rearrange an equation to make one of the letters the subject so that the substitution can be made.

Example

Solve the equations $2q - 3p = 2$ and $q - p = 3$.

Answer

$2q - 3p = 2$ (1)

$q - p = 3$ (2) equation (2) is easily rearranged to make q the subject

From (2), $q = p + 3$ (3)

Substituting for q in (1) gives:

$2(p + 3) - 3p = 2$

$2p + 6 - 3p = 2$

$-p + 6 = 2$

$-p = -4$ multiply both sides of the equation by -1

$p = 4$

(continued)

Substituting for p in (3) gives:

$$q = 4 + 3 = 7$$

and so the solution is $p = 4$ and $q = 7$.

(*Check*: substituting for p and q in (1) gives $2q - 3p = 2 \times 7 - 3 \times 4 = 2$.)

3 Solve these simultaneous equations:

a) $3q - 2p = 3$, $p - q = 1$
b) $x - 2y = 2$, $x - 5 = y$
c) $3m - n = 7$, $n - m = 5$
d) $2t + 3u = 11$, $u - t = -8$
e) $h - 2d = 10$, $d - h = -7$
f) $w - 3v - 25 = 0$, $v - 2w = -10$

Depending on the way that the information is presented, sometimes the substitution method provides the most straightforward way to solve simultaneous equations and sometimes the elimination method is easier.

4 Solve the equations given in question 3 by the elimination method.

5 Solve the following equations by either substitution or elimination:

a) $7x + 5y = 76$, $6x + 5y = 73$
b) $4x + y = 41$, $y = x - 4$
c) $x - 3y = 4$, $2x + 3y = 26$

35.3 Multiplying linear expressions

The diagram shows a rectangle $(x + 3)$ units long and $(x + 2)$ units wide.

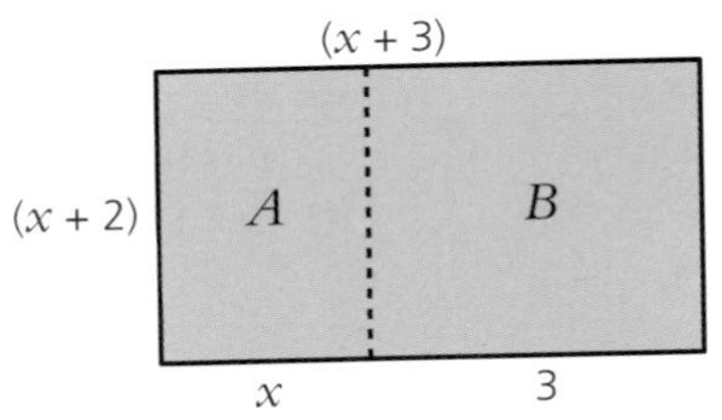

The area of the rectangle is given by $(x + 3)(x + 2)$ square units. However, this area is made up of two parts:

Part	Area (square units)
A	$x(x + 2) = x^2 + 2x$
B	$3(x + 2) = 3x + 6$

It follows that

$$\begin{aligned}(x + 3)(x + 2) &= x(x + 2) + 3(x + 2) \\ &= x^2 + 2x + 3x + 6 \\ &= x^2 + 5x + 6\end{aligned}$$

this may now be simplified by combining the *like terms*

In the same way,

$$\begin{aligned}(x + 4)(x + 1) &= x(x + 1) + 4(x + 1) \\ &= x^2 + x + 4x + 4 \\ &= x^2 + 5x + 4\end{aligned}$$

with practice, this step may be left out

1 Use a diagram to show that $(x + 2)(x + 5) = x^2 + 7x + 10$.

2 Expand the following and simplify the results:

a) $(x + 4)(x + 3)$ ✓ b) $(x + 2)(x + 6)$
c) $(x + 5)(x + 4)$ d) $(x + 10)(x + 1)$
e) $(a + 3)(a + 2)$ f) $(a + 7)(a + 3)$
g) $(p + 6)(p + 4)$ h) $(n + 1)(n + 5)$

Example

Expand and simplify $(x + 3)^2$.

Answer

$(x + 3)^2$ may be regarded as $(x + 3)(x + 3) = x^2 + 3x + 3x + 9 = x^2 + 6x + 9$.

3 Expand and simplify each of the following:

a) $(x + 4)^2$ ✓ b) $(x + 5)^2$ c) $(x + 1)^2$
d) $(a + 2)^2$ e) $(n + 10)^2$ f) $(p + 7)^2$

The approach used for expanding brackets also applies when the brackets include '–' signs.

Example

Expand and simplify:

a) $(x + 2)(x - 3)$ b) $(x - 5)(x + 1)$ c) $(x - 2)(x - 4)$ d) $(x - 5)^2$

Answer

a) $(x + 2)(x - 3) = x(x - 3) + 2(x - 3) = x^2 - 3x + 2x - 6$
$= x^2 - x - 6$ note $-3 + 2 = -1$

b) $(x - 5)(x + 1) = x(x + 1) - 5(x + 1) = x^2 + x - 5x - 5$
$= x^2 - 4x - 5$

c) $(x - 2)(x - 4) = x(x - 4) - 2(x - 4) = x^2 - 4x - 2x + 8$
$= x^2 - 6x + 8$

As before, the middle step may be missed out after some practice.

d) $(x - 5)^2 = (x - 5)(x - 5) = x^2 - 5x - 5x + 25 = x^2 - 10x + 25$

4 Expand and simplify each of these:

a) $(x - 4)(x + 6)$ ✓ b) $(x - 5)(x + 1)$ c) $(x + 3)(x - 4)$
d) $(x + 7)(x - 2)$ e) $(x + 1)(x - 2)$ f) $(x - 4)(x - 3)$ ✓
g) $(x - 4)(x - 1)$ h) $(x - 6)(x - 5)$ i) $(a + 4)(a - 3)$
j) $(m + 1)(m - 9)$ k) $(p - 6)(p + 3)$ l) $(r - 3)(r - 5)$

5 Remove the brackets and simplify:

a) $(x - 4)^2$ ✓ b) $(x - 10)^2$ c) $(p - 6)^2$
d) $(m - 7)^2$ e) $(h - 2)^2$ f) $(k - 3)^2$

More complex expansions may be treated in the same way.

Example

Expand and simplify:

a) $(2x + 3)(3x - 5)$ b) $(5x - 4)^2$ c) $(2a - b)(3a + b)$

Answer

a) $(2x + 3)(3x - 5) = 6x^2 - 10x + 9x - 15 = 6x^2 - x - 15$

b) $(5x - 4)^2 = (5x - 4)(5x - 4) = 25x^2 - 20x - 20x + 16 = 25x^2 - 40x + 16$

c) $(2a - b)(3a + b) = 6a^2 + 2ab - 3ab - b^2 = 6a^2 - ab - b^2$

---

6 Expand and simplify:

a) $(2x + 3)(x + 5)$ ✓ b) $(3x + 2)(2x + 1)$
c) $(4x - 1)(x + 2)$ d) $(6x - 3)(x + 4)$
e) $(5n - 2)(n + 4)$ f) $(2r - 6)(3r + 1)$
g) $(4c - d)(3c - d)$ ✓ h) $(5v - w)(v + 2w)$

7 Remove these brackets and simplify the results:

a) $(2x + 4)^2$ ✓ b) $(3x + 1)^2$ c) $(2x - 5)^2$
d) $(3n + p)^2$ e) $(4q - r)^2$ f) $(3t - 4u)^2$

8 Simplify the following by removing the brackets and collecting like terms:

a) $(x + 2)(x + 3) - x(x + 1)$ ✓ b) $(x - 4)(x + 5) + x(x - 1)$
c) $(n - 5)(n - 2) - n(n - 6)$ d) $(r + 3)^2 - r(r + 2)$
e) $(t + 4)^2 - (t - 4)^2$ f) $(g + 5)^2 + (g - 5)^2$

The process of simplifying an expression may make it easier to solve a problem.

Example

Solve the equation $(x + 4)^2 - (x + 4)(x - 2) = 0$.

Answer

The equation may be written as $(x + 4)(x + 4) - (x + 4)(x - 2) = 0$

Multiplying out gives $x^2 + 4x + 4x + 16 - (x^2 - 2x + 4x - 8) = 0$

↖ note the need to use brackets to show that the whole expression is subtracted

i.e. $x^2 + 8x + 16 - (x^2 + 2x - 8) = 0$

Removing the brackets and simplifying gives $6x + 24 = 0$ and so $x = -4$.

---

9 a) Find an expression for the shaded area of this figure and simplify it as far as possible.

b) If the shaded area = 20 square units, find the value of x.

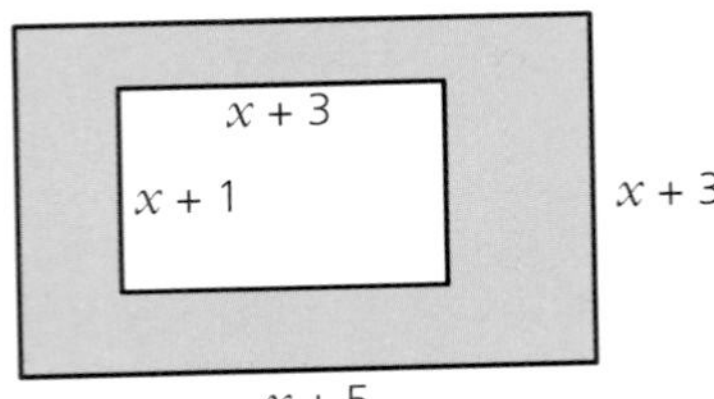

10 Try to solve this puzzle by using n to stand for the unknown number.
'I am thinking of a number.
When I multiply 4 more than this number, by 3 less than it, the result is 8 more than its square.
What is my number?'

11 The two rectangles shown here have the same area. Find the value of x.

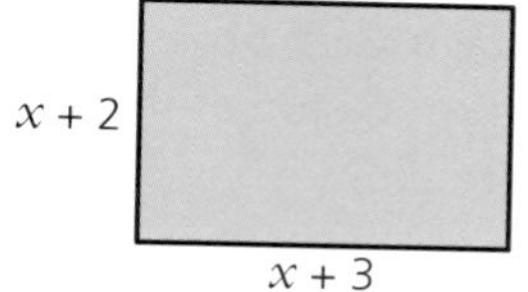

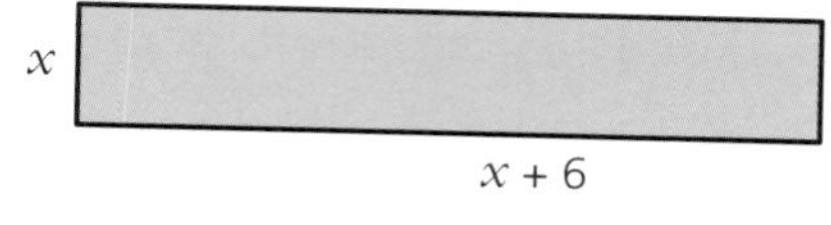

35.4 Highest common factor

The factors of 24 are: 1, 2, 3, 4, 6, 8, 12 and 24.
The factors of 60 are: 1, 2, 3, 4, 5, 6, 10, 12, 15, 20, 30 and 60.

The highest number to appear in both lists is 12. We say that 12 is the **highest common factor** of 24 and 60.

---

1 List all of the factors of 36 and 54 and find the value of the highest common factor.

2 Find the highest common factor of 72 and 120.

3 List all of the factors of 135, 225 and 405. Find the highest common factor of all three numbers.

An alternative method of finding the highest common factor of 24 and 60, for example, is to write them as products of their prime factors.

$24 = 2^3 \times 3$ and $60 = 2^2 \times 3 \times 5$

Both numbers may now be seen to contain a factor of 2^2 and a factor of 3. The highest common factor is therefore $2^2 \times 3 = 12$.

This approach is easily adapted to find the highest common factor of any number of numbers.

Example

Given that $360 = 2^3 \times 3^2 \times 5$, $432 = 2^4 \times 3^3$ and $540 = 2^2 \times 3^3 \times 5$, find the highest common factor of all three numbers.

Answer

All three numbers contain a factor of 2^2 and a factor of 3^2 but only two of the numbers contain a factor of 5.

The highest common factor therefore is $2^2 \times 3^2 = 36$.

4 Find the highest common factor of 1400 and 1500 given that $1400 = 2^3 \times 5^2 \times 7$ and $1500 = 2^2 \times 5^3 \times 3$.

5 Given that $2100 = 2^2 \times 3 \times 5^2 \times 7$, $2700 = 2^2 \times 3^3 \times 5^2$ and $3600 = 2^4 \times 3^2 \times 5^2$, find the highest common factor of the following:

a) 2100 and 2700 b) 2700 and 3600

c) 2100 and 3600 d) 2100, 2700 and 3600

6 a) Write 135, 225 and 405 as products of their prime factors.

b) Use your answer to part a) to find the highest common factor of these three numbers and check that you obtain the same result as in question 3.

The technique of finding the highest common factor of some numbers, by considering their prime factors, may also be used to factorise expressions in algebra.

Example

Factorise $a^2x^3 + a^3x$.

Answer

Treating the letters in the same way as the prime factors, in the questions above, we see that the highest common factor of the two terms is a^2x.

We may now write:

$$a^2x^3 + a^3x = a^2x(x^2 + a)$$

Note: $a^2x \times x^2 = a^2x^3$ and $a^2x \times a = a^3x$.

---

7 a) Find the highest common factor of x^2y^2 and xy^3.

b) Use your answer to part a) to factorise $x^2y^2 + xy^3$.

8 Factorise these expressions by writing the highest common factor outside the brackets:

a) $p^2q + pq^3$ b) $a^2b + abc$ c) $xy^2 + yz$

d) $uv^2 + uv^2w$ e) $m^2n + mn^2$ f) $r^3t^2 + r^2t^2$

The same principle applies to the factorisation of expressions involving sums and differences of any number of terms.

Example

Factorise these expressions:

a) $x^2y^3 - x^2y^2$ b) $a^2b + ab^2 - abc$ c) $4pq^2 + 6pq$ d) $10gt^2 + 15gt - 5g$

Answer

a) $x^2y^3 - x^2y^2 = x^2y^2(y - 1)$

b) $a^2b + ab^2 - abc = ab(a + b - c)$

c) $4pq^2 + 6pq = 2pq(2q + 3)$

d) $10gt^2 + 15gt - 5g = 5g(2t^2 + 3t - 1)$

9 Factorise the following expressions by taking out the highest common factor:

a) $xy^2 + xy + xyz$ ✓ b) $x^2y - xy^2$ c) $xy^3z^2 - x^2yz$

d) $x^2y^2 + x^3z - x^3$ e) $xyz - x^2y - x^2z$ f) $x^2y + x^2y^3 - xy^3$

g) $8x^2y + 12xy$ h) $3xy - 9xz$ i) $6yz + 12xy - 9y$

10 Factorise these expressions:

a) $a^2b^3 + ab^2 - a^3b^2 + a^4b^3$ ✓ b) $u^3v^2w - u^2vw^2 + u^3vw^3 - u^2v^2w$

c) $8pqr - 12pq - 16pr$ d) $35mn^2 + 25m^2n - 20mn$

e) $7abc + 21a^2bc + 14ab^2c$ f) $75h^2x - 50hx + 100hx^2$

36 DIMENSIONS

36.1 Checking with dimensions

1 a) Find the *perimeter* of this rectangle. The unit of measurement used is the centimetre (cm).

b) Find the *area* of the rectangle. The unit of measurement used is the square centimetre (cm^2).

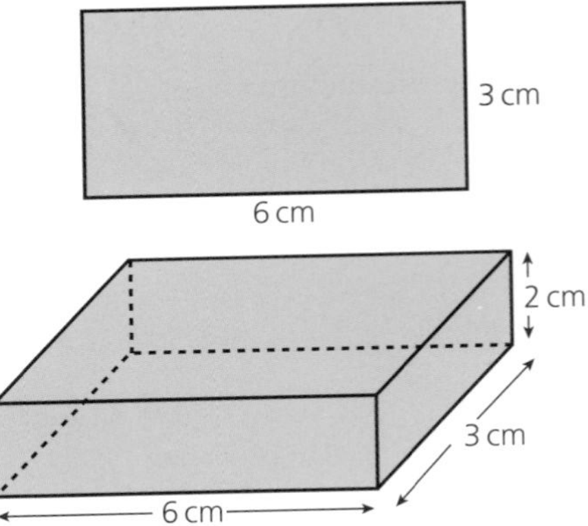

2 Find the volume of this cuboid. The unit of measurement used is the cubic centimetre (cm^3).

In everyday language we say that:

Length is a measurement in *one* dimension.
Area is a measurement in *two* dimensions.
Volume is a measurement in *three* dimensions.

A way of writing this mathematically is to say:

The dimension of perimeter is

length (L).

Note that when lengths are added together we are still working in one dimension.

The dimension of area is

length × length ($L \times L = L^2$).

The dimension of volume is

length × length × length ($L \times L \times L = L^3$).

3 ✔ a) Write down an expression for V, the volume of this cube:

b) What is the unit of measurement used for V if x is measured in centimetres?

c) What is the dimension of V? Is it:

(i) L (ii) L^2 (iii) L^3?

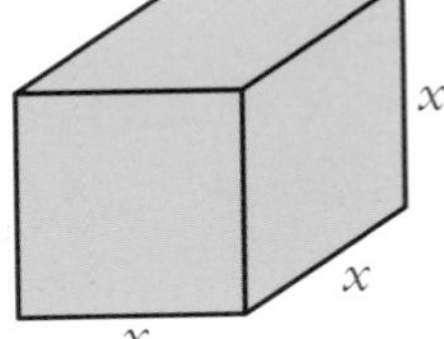

4 a) Write down an expression for A, the surface area of the cube.

b) What is the unit of measurement for A?

c) ✔ What is the dimension of A? Is it:

(i) L (ii) L^2 (iii) L^3?

We can use this simple idea to check a formula.

Example

Jane cannot remember the correct formula for the area of a circle.
Is it $A = \pi d$ or $A = 2\pi r$ or $A = \pi r^2$ or $A = \pi^2 r$?

Answer

She decides to check the dimensions of each formula:

πd	number × length	dimension = L
$2\pi r$	number × number × length	dimension = L
πr^2	number × length × length	dimension = L^2
$\pi^2 r$	number × number × length	dimension = L

Looking at these, Jane decides that the correct formula for area must be $A = \pi r^2$ as it is the only one with the correct dimension for area: L^2.

Note that π does not have a 'dimension'. It has a constant value and does not affect the dimension of a formula. Likewise any number such as 2 or 6 or $\frac{2}{3}$ is dimension-less.

Example

This is a test tube.
Check the dimensions of each of the expressions given here and decide which ones might be a formula for:

a) the surface area
b) the volume.

(i) $2\pi rh$ (ii) $\frac{2}{3}\pi r + \pi r^2 h$ (iii) $2\pi r^2 h^2$
(iv) $\frac{2}{3}\pi r^3 + \pi r^2 h$ (v) $\frac{2}{3}\pi^3 r + \pi r^2 h$ (vi) $2\pi h$

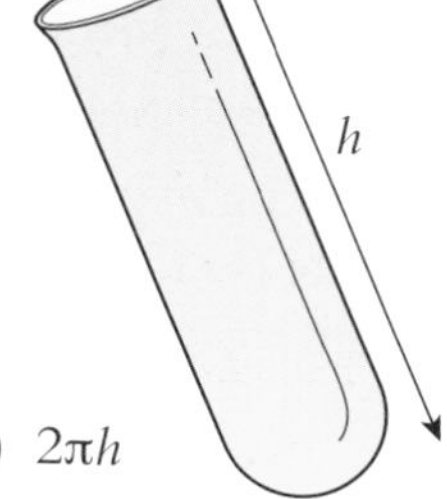

Answer

The dimensions for each expression are:

(i) $2\pi rh$:	number × number × length × length	$= L^2$
(ii) $\frac{2}{3}\pi r + \pi r^2 h$:	number × number × length + number × length² × length	$= L + L^3$ (★)
(iii) $2\pi r^2 h^2$:	number × number × length² × length²	$= L^4$
(iv) $\frac{2}{3}\pi r^3 + \pi r^2 h$:	number × number × length³ + number × length² × length	$= L^3 + L^3 = L^3$
(v) $\frac{2}{3}\pi^3 r + \pi r^2 h$:	number × number × length + number × length² × length	$= L + L^3$ (★)
(vi) $2\pi h$:	number × number × length	$= L$

★ Note that any expressions with mixed dimensions such as number (ii) or number (v) simply do not make sense and are impossible.

a) A formula for surface area must have dimension L^2.
Expression (i) is the only one with these dimensions.
(i) Surface area = $2\pi rh$

b) A formula for volume must have dimension L^3.
Expression (iv) is the only one with these dimensions:
(iv) $V = \frac{2}{3}\pi r^3 + \pi r^2 h$

The dimension method does not tell you if the formula is *correct*, but it could tell you if it is impossible.

1 ✓ Joe has written down the formula for an ellipse as

$A = \pi a^2 b^2$

Explain why he must have copied it down incorrectly, by first finding the dimension of the formula he has written.

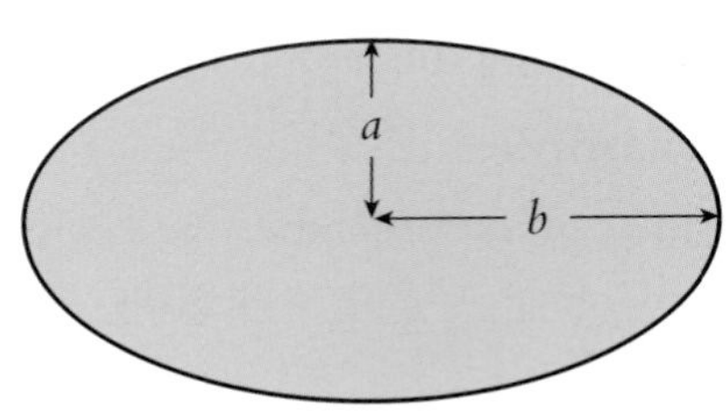

2 ✓ Natalie has found the following formula for the area of a triangle, to be used when the perpendicular height is not known:

$A = \sqrt{s(s-a)(s-b)(s-c)}$

where a, b and c are the lengths of the sides and $s = \frac{1}{2}(a + b + c)$

a) What is the dimension of s?

b) Explain why the dimension of $A = \sqrt{s(s-a)(s-b)(s-c)}$ is correct for area.

For each of questions 3 to 8 give the dimension of each of the alternative formulae and explain your answer.

3 ✓ Which of the following expressions could be a suitable formula for the area of card needed to make this top hat?

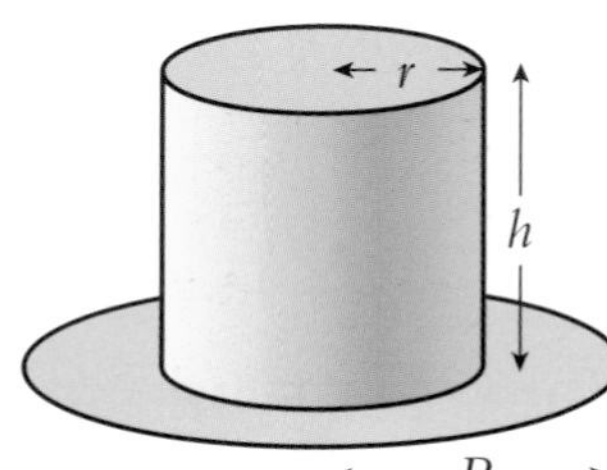

a) $\pi R^2 h - \pi r^2 h$
b) $2\pi R - 2\pi r$
c) $\pi r^2 h$
d) $\pi R^2 + 2\pi rh$
e) $2\pi Rhr$

4 Which of the following expressions could be a formula for **a)** the perimeter **b)** the area of this running track?

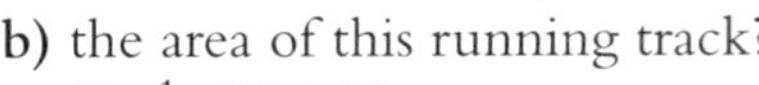

(i) $\frac{1}{4}\pi^2 d + ld$
(ii) $\pi d + 2l$
(iii) $\frac{1}{4}\pi d^2 + ld$
(iv) $\frac{1}{4}\pi^2 d + ld$
(v) $2\pi dl + d^2 l$

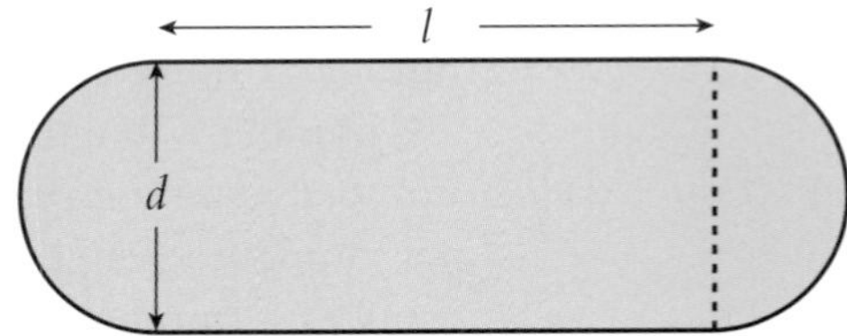

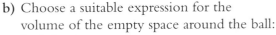

5 A ball just fits inside a box.

a) What must be the size of the box if the ball has a radius r?

b) Choose a suitable expression for the volume of the empty space around the ball:

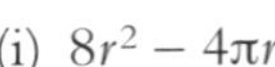

(i) $8r^2 - 4\pi r$
(ii) $6r^2 - 4\pi r^2$
(iii) $6r^2 - \frac{4}{3}\pi r^3$
(iv) $8r^3 - \frac{4}{3}\pi r^3$

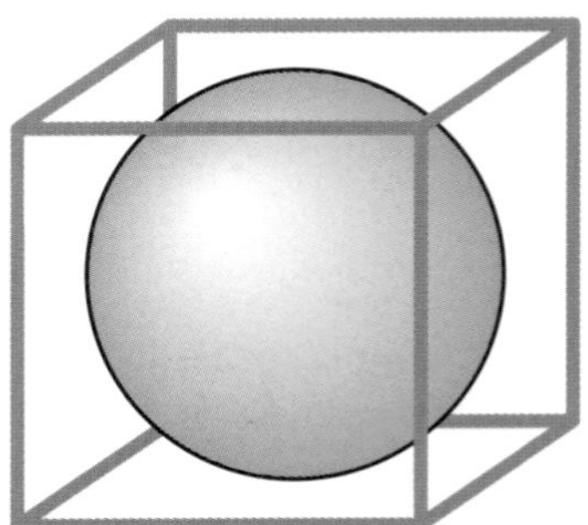

6 Which of the following expressions could be a formula for the volume of this pencil?

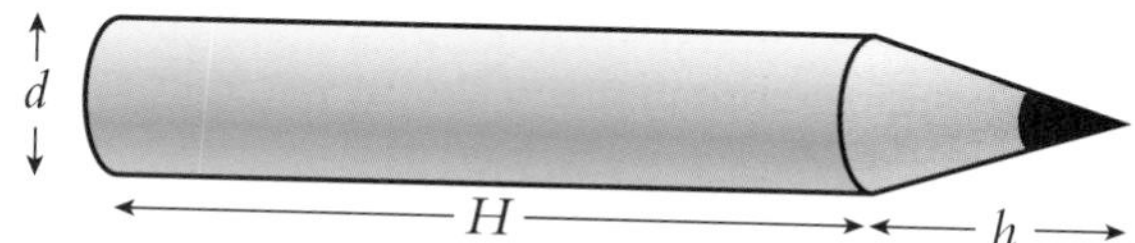

a) $\frac{1}{4}\pi dH + \frac{1}{2}\pi dh$ b) $\pi d(h + H)$ c) $\pi d(\frac{h}{3} + H)$

d) $\frac{1}{4}\pi d^2(\frac{h}{3} + H)$ e) $\frac{1}{12}\pi d^2h + \frac{1}{4}\pi d^2H$

7 The area of metal needed to make this trough is given by:

a) $2a^2 + 2ab + \pi\frac{a^2}{4} + \frac{\pi ab}{2}$ b) $2a^2b + \pi\frac{a^2b}{6}$

c) $4a^2 + 2ab + \frac{\pi a^2b}{8}$ d) $2b + 6a + \pi\frac{a}{2}$

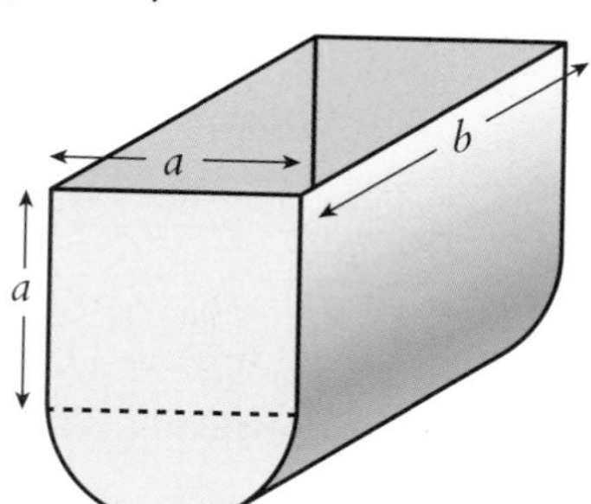

8 The volume of the trough is given by:

a) $6\pi a^2 + 2ab$ b) $a^2b\left(\frac{\pi}{4} + 1\right)$

c) $a^2b + \pi a^2b^2$ d) $a(2b + 6a + \pi)$

36.2 Pictorial representation

INFLATION HITS OUR POCKETS!

1980

1991

The purchasing power of money is falling by the year!
So a £10 note hidden under the bed in 1980 would buy only half the quantity of goods if it was used 11 years later in 1991

1 a) Measure the length and width of the £10 note in 1980.
b) Measure the length and width of the £10 note in 1991.
c) Now calculate the area of each note.
d) Express the area of the 1991 note as a fraction of the area of the 1980 note.
e) Explain why the picture exaggerates the fall in the value of money. ✓

(continued)

f) Which of the following diagrams would be a correct representation of the information contained in the newspaper article?

a)

b)

c)

2

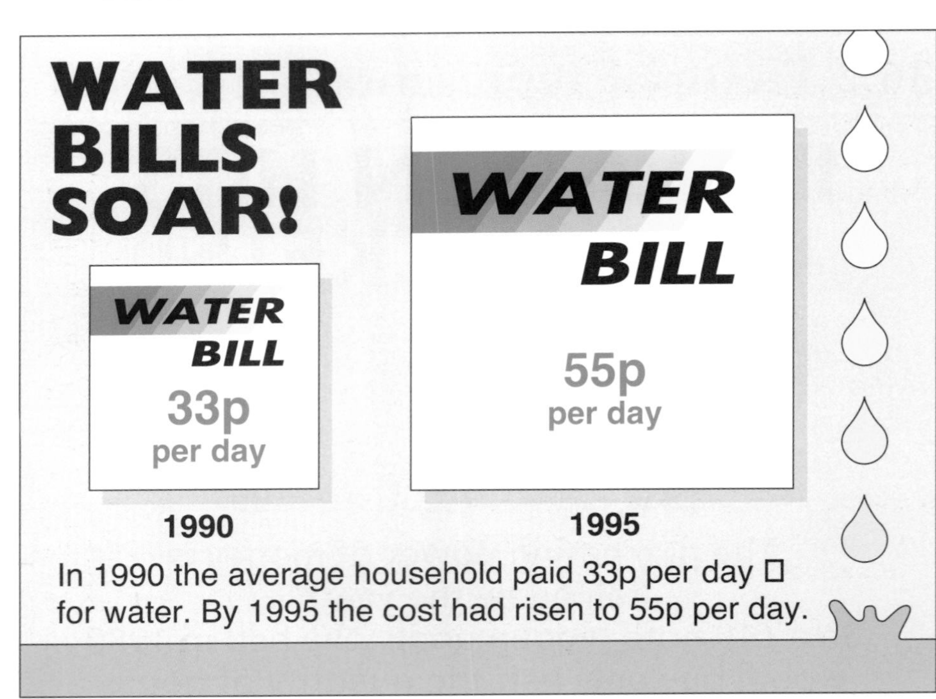

a) Express the costs in 1990 and 1995 as a ratio (in its simplest terms).
b) Measure the length and width of both bills in the picture.
c) What is the area of each bill?
d) Explain why this picture exaggerates the price increase.

36.3 Introducing the tangent

I have recently moved house and there is a very tall conifer tree in my 'new' front garden. It is a fast-growing variety and before it takes over the house I have decided to chop it down. A concerned neighbour asks me if I have checked whether there is room for the tree to fall, without it hitting the house. Neither of us has a tape measure. I don't think that we need a tape measure. I think that if I can measure the angle of elevation to the top of the tree from a position near the house that will be all the information I need.

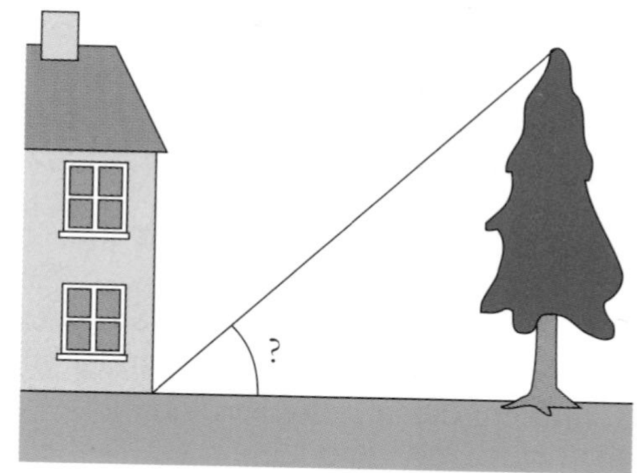

The following investigation shows how I worked that out.

1 On a piece of graph paper, draw a line across the bottom and one up the right-hand side. The horizontal line must show a scale from 0 to 1, marked off in divisions of 0.1. Use the *same scale* to mark off the vertical axis.

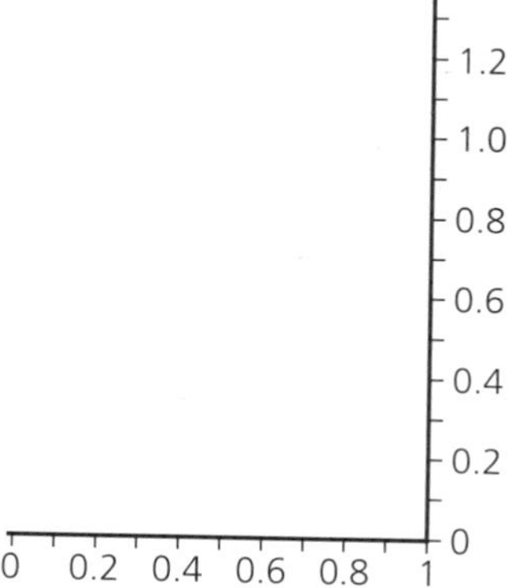

a) Place your protractor on the left-hand side of the paper in such a position that you can measure an angle of 5° at O.

Draw the angle and extend the line across to your vertical axis. Record the height on the vertical axis.

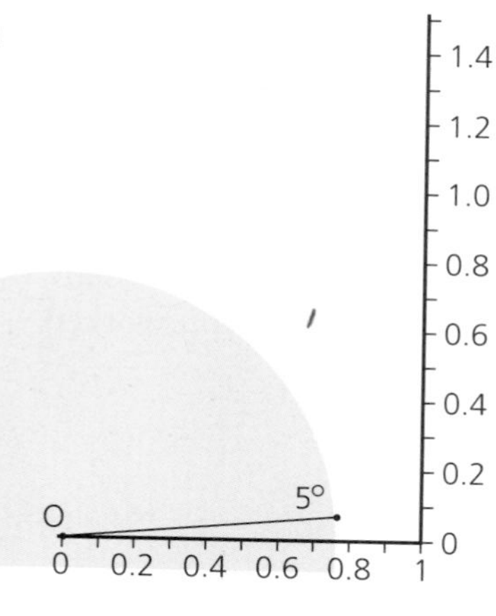

b) Repeat the procedure for 10°, 15°, 20° and so on, recording your results on a table like this:

Angle	Height	
5°	0.09	
10°		
15°		
20°		
25°		
30°		
35°		
40°		
45°		
50°		
55°		

Leave the third column on the table blank. Look at the drawings you have made. Imagine that 'height' on the vertical axis represents the height of the tree, while the distance between the tree and the house is represented by the fixed distance on the horizontal axis. If the tree is taller than the distance away from the house, it could hit the house when it is cut down.

c) ✓ Use your drawings and table of results to try to decide whether the tree will hit the house if the angle of elevation is:
(i) 20° (ii) 35° (iii) 40° (iv) 50°

d) ✓ What is the angle of elevation if the height of the tree exactly equals the distance to the house?

e) For which angles will it be safe to cut the tree down?

This relationship is a very useful one, and the results you have obtained by drawing can be found more accurately by using the **tan** key on your calculator. Exact instructions depend on the calculator model, but you may be able to press **tan** 5 **=** to obtain the first answer.

(Older calculators may require 5 **tan**.)

Use your calculator to obtain the tan (short for tangent) for the other angles in your table of results. Fill these in down the third column on your table. Label this column 'Tangent'.

---

2 a) If θ is 40°, what is the height of triangle A? ✓

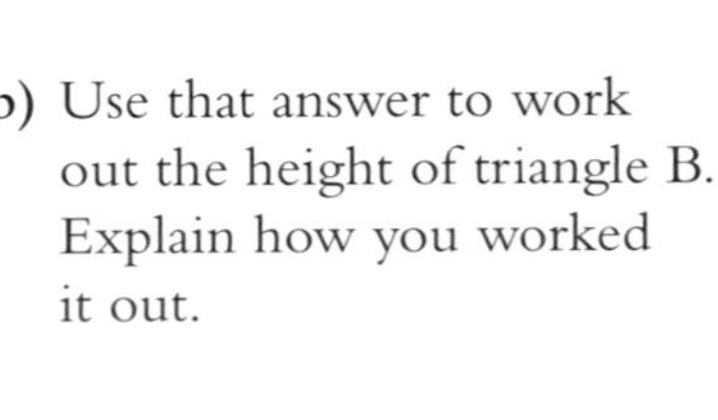

b) Use that answer to work out the height of triangle B. Explain how you worked it out.

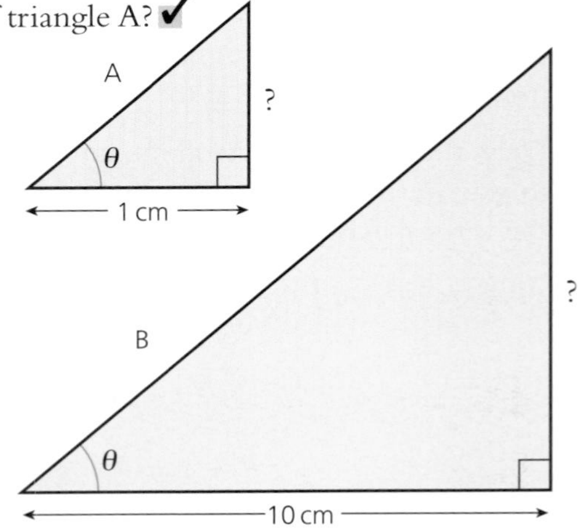

You should have found that triangle B has a height which is 10 times the height of the smaller triangle. This leads to a very useful general result.

The height of a right-angled triangle can be found by $x \times \tan \theta$

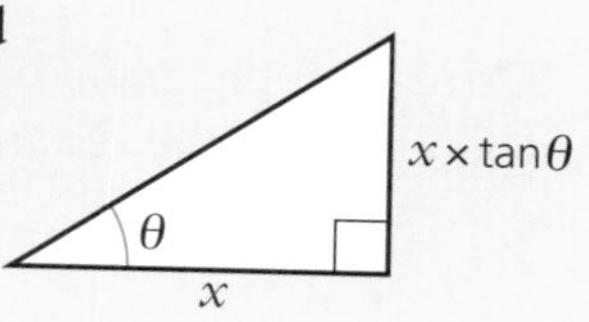

Example

Find y, the height of this triangle (to 1 decimal place).

Answer

$y = 8 \times \tan 33° = 5.1953$

So the height of the triangle is 5.2 cm (to 1 decimal place).

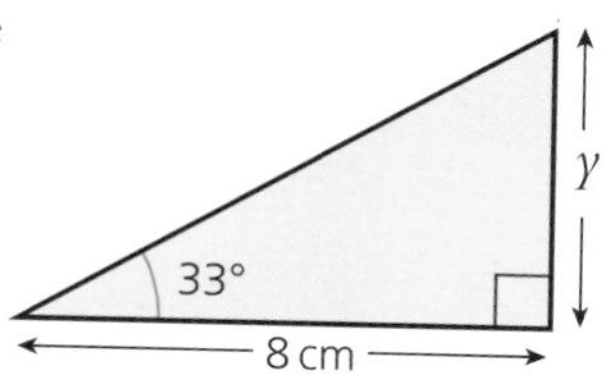

3 ✔ Use the tangent to find the heights (y) of these triangles.

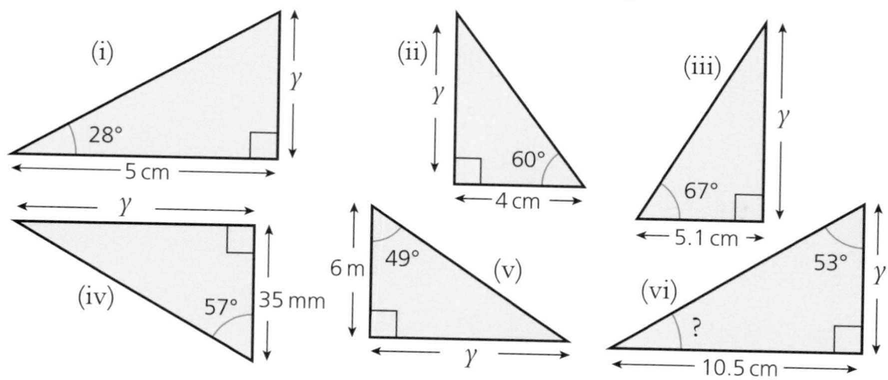

4 I walk 20 m away from my house and measure the angle of elevation of the top of the roof. If this angle is 26°, how tall is my house?

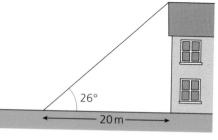

5 The angle of elevation to the top of a flagpole is 35° measured from a point 10 m away from the base of the flagpole. Find the height of the pole.

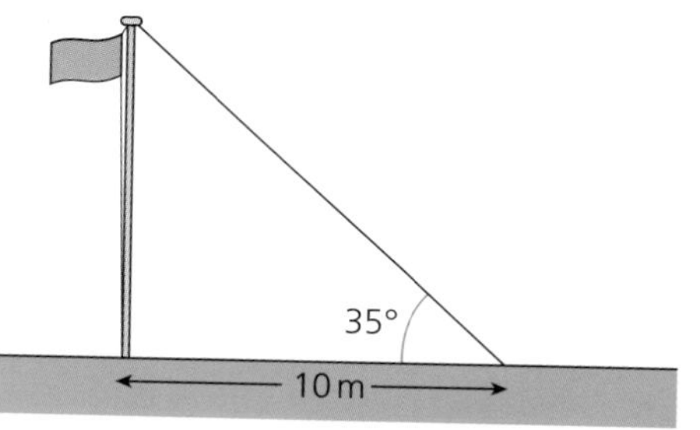

6 A girl 60 m away from a tower measures the angle of elevation to the top as 28°. How tall is the tower?
(Draw your own sketch to help you here.)

7 From the top of a cliff 120 m high the angle of depression of a boat is 33°. Use this sketch to help you calculate the distance of the boat from the cliff.

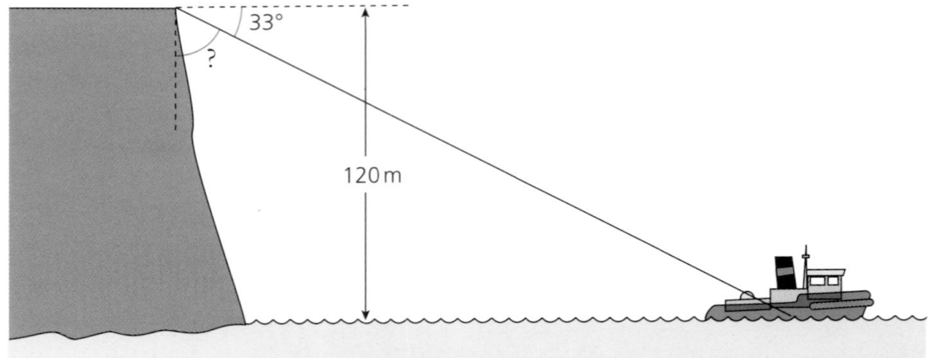

ALGEBRA AND GRAPHS (3)

37.1 Plotting, drawing and solving

By plotting a sufficient number of points, it is possible to draw the graph of an equation with enough accuracy to solve related equations.

Example

Draw the graph of $y = x^2 - 5$ for values of x from -3 to 3 and use it to solve the following equations to 1 D.P.

a) $x^2 - 5 = 0$ **b)** $x^2 - 5 = -2$ **c)** $x^2 - 8 = 0$

Answer

Tabulating values of x in steps of 0.5 provides enough points to draw the curve. Since $y = x^2 - 5$ is a **quadratic** equation, the curve produced is a **parabola** which has one line of symmetry.

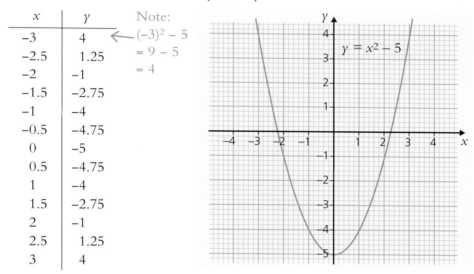

x	y
−3	4
−2.5	1.25
−2	−1
−1.5	−2.75
−1	−4
−0.5	−4.75
0	−5
0.5	−4.75
1	−4
1.5	−2.75
2	−1
2.5	1.25
3	4

Note: $(-3)^2 - 5$
$= 9 - 5$
$= 4$

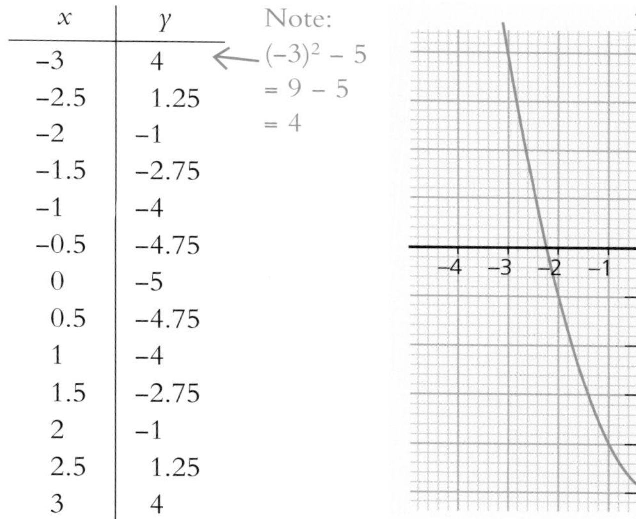

For each equation, the symmetry of the curve shows that there are *two* solutions of opposite sign, i.e. one positive and one negative. The solutions may be found by locating the points of intersection of the curve with the appropriate straight lines.

a) The solutions of $x^2 - 5 = 0$ are found at the points where the curve crosses the line $y = 0$, i.e. the x-axis.
This gives $x = -2.2$ and $x = 2.2$ to 1 D.P.

b) The solutions of $x^2 - 5 = -2$ are found where the curve crosses the line $y = -2$.
This gives $x = -1.7$ and $x = 1.7$ to 1 D.P.

c) Using the graph to solve the equation $x^2 - 8 = 0$ requires re-writing the equation so that $x^2 - 5$ appears on one side.

$x^2 - 8 = 0$ Add 3 to both sides of the equation

$x^2 - 5 = 3$ This shows that the values of x may be found at the intersection of the curve with the line $y = 3$.

This gives $x = -2.8$ and $x = 2.8$ to 1 D.P.

1 Copy and complete the table started below showing $y = x^2 - 2$ for values of x from -3 to 3 in steps of 0.5. Plot the corresponding coordinates and draw a smooth curve through them to give the graph of $y = x^2 - 2$.

x	y
−3	7
−2.5	4.25
−2	2
−1.5	

Use your graph to solve the following equations and state the equation of the straight line needed in each case.

a) $x^2 - 2 = 0$ b) $x^2 - 2 = 3$ c) $x^2 - 2 = 4.5$
d) $x^2 - 2 = -1$ e) $x^2 - 2 = -0.5$ f) $x^2 - 2 = 6$
g) $x^2 - 4 = 3$ h) $x^2 - 6 = 0$ i) $x^2 - 1 = 5$

2 The diagram below shows the graph of the equation $y = x^2 - 7x + 9$.

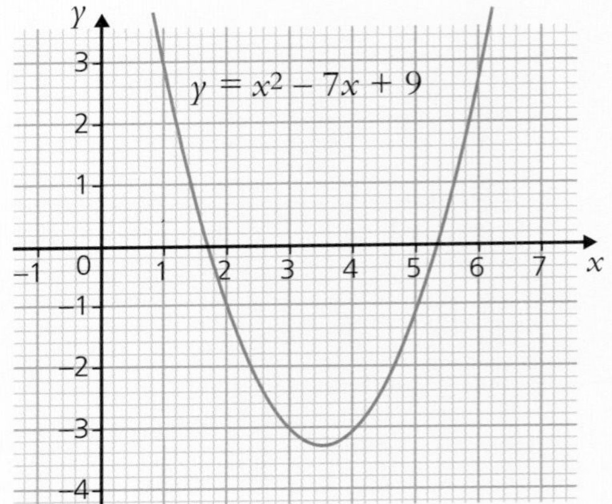

a) Use the graph to solve the equation $x^2 - 7x + 9 = 0$.
b) *Explain* how the graph might be used to solve the equation $x^2 - 7x + 9 = 2$ stating the equation of any extra line needed.

3 State the equations of any extra lines needed to use the graph of $y = x^2 - 7x + 9$ to solve the following equations.

a) $x^2 - 7x + 9 = 3$ b) $x^2 - 7x + 9 = -2$ c) $x^2 - 7x + 9 = 2.5$
d) $x^2 - 7x + 7 = 1$ ✔ e) $x^2 - 7x + 10 = 3$ ✔ f) $x^2 - 7x + 11 = 7$
g) $x^2 - 7x + 8 = -1$ h) $x^2 - 7x + 6 = -2$ i) $x^2 - 7x + 10 = -1$
j) $x^2 - 7x + 6 = 0$ k) $x^2 - 7x + 5 = -3$ l) $x^2 - 7x = -6$

The fact that equations can be rearranged in different ways shows that we have a choice over which graphs to use in order to locate the solutions.

Example

Use the graph of $y = x^2$ together with an appropriate straight line graph to solve the equation $x^2 - 7x + 9 = 0$.

Answer

$x^2 - 7x + 9 = 0$ — add $7x$ to both sides of the equation

$x^2 + 9 = 7x$ — subtract 9 from both sides

$x^2 = 7x - 9$

This shows that the solutions may be found at the points where the graphs of $y = x^2$ and $y = 7x - 9$ intersect.

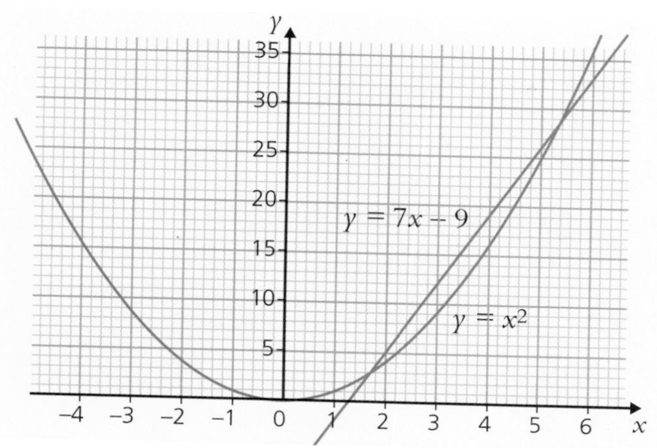

From the graph, the solutions are $x = 1.7$ and $x = 5.3$ to 1 D.P.

Note : the values of x at which graphs of $y = x^2$ and $y = 7x - 9$ intersect are the same as those at which the graph of $y = x^2 - 7x + 9$ cross the x-axis.

---

4 Given that the graph of $y = x^2$ has been drawn, find the equations of the straight lines needed to solve the following equations.

a) $x^2 - 5x + 4 = 0$ ✔ b) $x^2 - 3x + 1 = 0$ c) $x^2 - 8x - 3 = 0$

d) $x^2 - x - 4 = 0$ e) $x^2 + 5x + 4 = 0$ f) $x^2 + 3x - 4 = 0$

5 Given that the graph of $y = x^2 + 5x - 11$ has been drawn, find the equations of the straight lines needed to solve these equations.

a) $x^2 + 3x - 11 = 0$ ✔ b) $x^2 + x - 11 = 0$ c) $x^2 + 5x - 14 = 0$

d) $x^2 + 5x - 20 = 0$ e) $x^2 + 4x - 12 = 0$ f) $x^2 + x - 8 = 0$

g) $x^2 + 2x - 14 = 0$ h) $x^2 + 6x - 15 = 0$ i) $x^2 - 3x + 1 = 0$

6 a) Copy and complete this table for the equation $y = x^2 - 3x - 5$ using values of x from -2 to 5 in steps of 0.5.

x	y
−2	5
−1.5	1.75
−1	−1
−0.5	

Note: $(-2)^2 - 3(-2) - 5 = 4 + 6 - 5 = 5$

If you have a graphics calculator, a short program may be used to produce the y value for any input value of x

b) Draw the graph and find the solutions of the equation $x^2 - 3x - 5 = 0$ correct to 1 D.P. (*The plotted points should lie on a smooth curve.*)

c) Solve the equation $x^2 - 4x - 2 = 0$ by adding an extra line to the diagram. State the equation of the line used.

7 Copy and complete this table of values given that $y = (x - 3)(x - 5)$.

x	y
0	15
1	8
2	
3	
4	
5	
6	

Note: $(0 - 3)(0 - 5) = (-3) \times (-5) = 15$

a) Find the values of x for which $y = 0$.

b) Which of the diagrams below represents the equation $y = (x - 3)(x - 5)$? Explain your reasoning.

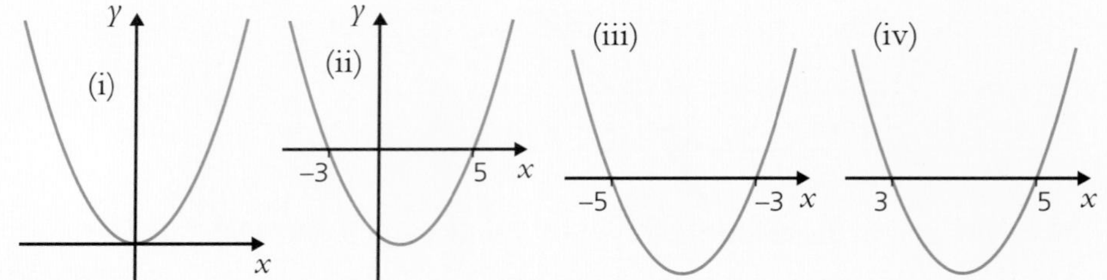

8 Find the values of x for which $y = 0$ in each of the following equations:

a) $y = (x - 2)(x - 7)$ ✓ **b)** $y = (x - 4)(x - 6)$ **c)** $y = (x - 1)(x - 4)$

d) $y = (x + 2)(x - 3)$ **e)** $y = (x + 3)(x - 1)$ **f)** $y = (x + 5)(x - 2)$

9 Find the coordinates of the points at which the graph of $y = (x - 3)(x + 5)$ crosses the x-axis.

The instruction to **draw** the graph of an equation means that an accurate diagram is required. Typically this may then be used to obtain further information by reading off appropriate values. However, the instruction to **sketch** the graph of an equation means that the diagram need only show the graph's main features such as its shape and where it crosses the coordinate axes.

Example

Sketch the graph of the equation $y = (x + 2)(x - 3)$.

Answer

Since the equation would take the form $y = ax^2 + bx + c$ if the brackets were removed, with $a > 0$, the general shape of the curve is:

Such a curve is called a **parabola**.

When $x = 0$, $y = (0 + 2)(0 - 3) = 2 \times (-3) = -6$.

It follows that the curve crosses the y-axis at $(0, -6)$.

$y = 0$ when $x = -2$ and when $x = 3$.

It follows that the curve crosses the x-axis at $(-2, 0)$ and at $(3, 0)$.

Putting all of this information together we obtain the sketch shown here.

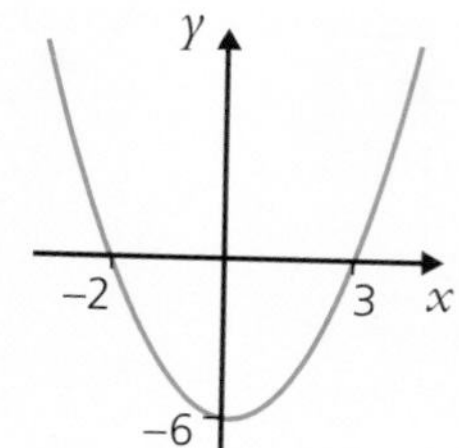

10 Sketch the graph of each of the equations given in question 8.

11 Sketch the graph of the equation $y = (x - 5)(x - 7)$.
Find the minimum value of y. Justify your answer by referring to the symmetry of the graph.

12 Find the equation of each of these parabolas.

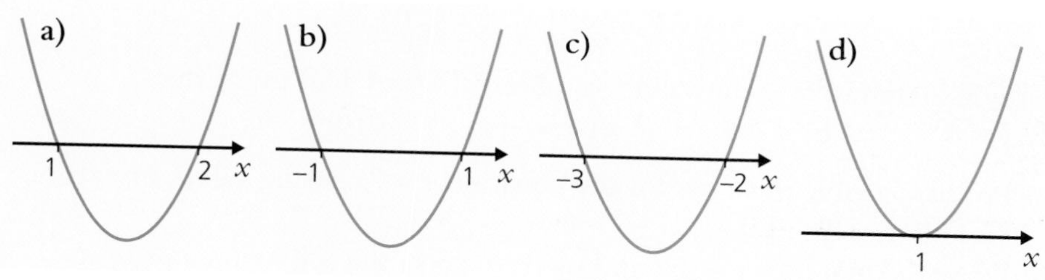

An equation of the form $y = ax^3 + bx^2 + cx + d$ (where $a \neq 0$) is called a **cubic** equation. The highest power of x in such an equation is 3.

Each of these is a cubic equation:

$y = x^3$, $y = 2x^3$, $y = x^3 - 5$, $y = 4x^3 + 2x$, $y = x^3 - 6x^2 + x + 1$

The following are **not** cubic equations:

$y = x^2 + 3x$ (the highest power of x is 2)
$y = x^4 - 2x^3$ (the highest power of x is 4)
$y = x^3 + x^{-1}$ (the equation includes a *negative* power of x)

For $a > 0$ the graph of a cubic equation takes one of these forms:

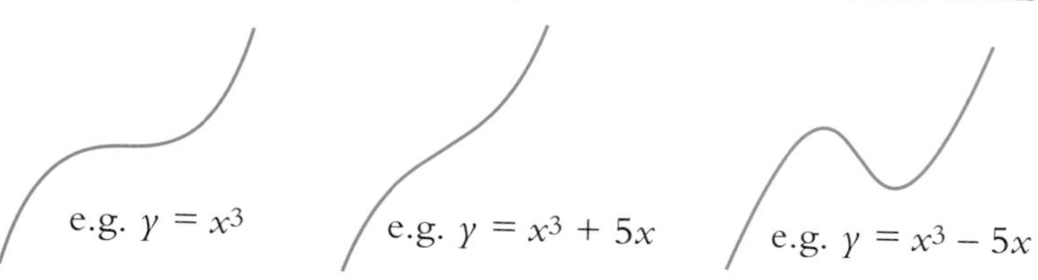

13 Describe each of the following equations as linear, quadratic or cubic:

a) $y = 4x^2 - 3x + 2$ b) $y = 5x + 1$ c) $y = 7x - x^2$

d) $y = x^3 + x^2 - 4$ e) $y = (x + 2)(x - 3)$ f) $y = 1 - x^3$

g) $y = \frac{x + 5}{3}$ h) $y = \frac{x^3}{5} + x^2 + 2$ i) $y = x(x + 4)^2$

14 Find the value of y given that $x = 2.5$ in each of these equations:

a) $y = x^3$ ✔ b) $y = 2x^3$ c) $y = x^3 - 2x^2$

d) $y = (x - 1)^3$ e) $y = x(2x + 3)^2$ f) $y = 20 - 2x^3$

15 This diagram shows the graph of $y = x^3 - 6x$.

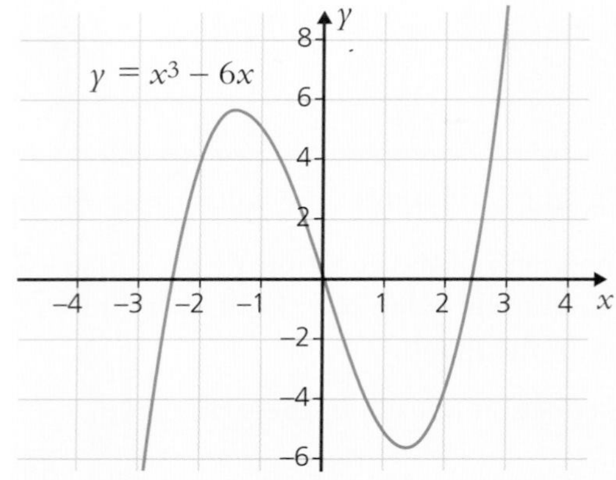

Use the graph to find the value, or values, of x to 1 D.P. given that:

a) $y = 8$ b) $y = 3$ c) $y = -4$ d) $y = -6$

16 a) Produce a table of values for the equation $y = 2x^3$ using values of x from -2 to 2 in steps of 0.4.

b) Draw the graph of $y = 2x^3$ and use it to solve the following equations correct to 1 D.P.

(i) $2x^3 = 12$ (ii) $2x^3 = -15$ (iii) $2x^3 = x + 6$

(iv) $2x^3 = x - 5$ (v) $2x^3 - 4 = x$ (vi) $2x^3 - x = -2$

17 Which of the graphs below represents the equation $y = (x + 3)(x - 1)(x - 2)$? Explain how you made your decision.

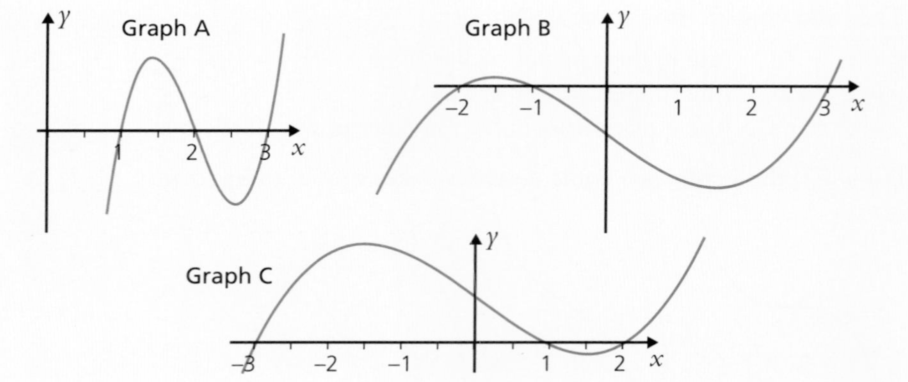

18 The diagram shows the graph of $y = \dfrac{1}{x^2}$.

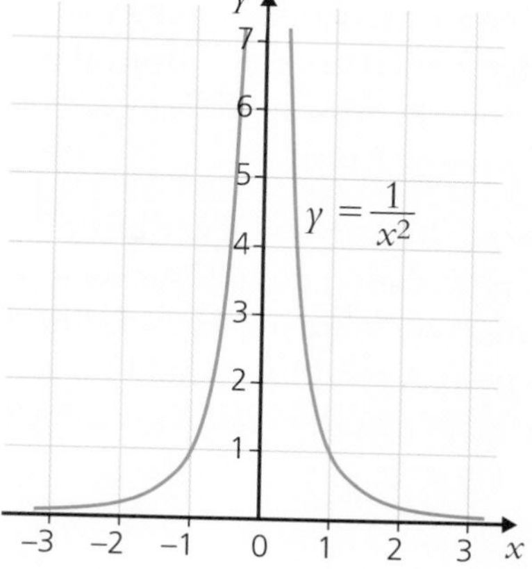

a) Use the graph to find the values of x for the following values of y:
(i) 1 (ii) 4 (iii) 0.25 (iv) 0.5

b) Describe the symmetry of the graph.

c) What happens to the value of y as x gets closer to zero?

d) What happens to y as x becomes very large?

19 a) Copy and complete the table of values for the equation $y = \dfrac{1}{x^2} - 1$.

x	−1.0	−0.6	−0.3	0.3	0.6	1.0	1.4	1.8	2.2	2.6	3
y	0	1.8			1.8				−0.8		

b) Plot the (x, y) values as coordinates and draw the graph of $y = \dfrac{1}{x^2} - 1$.

c) Find the coordinates of two points that satisfy the equation $y = 5 - 2x$.

d) Draw the graph of $y = 5 - 2x$ on the same diagram.

e) Use the diagram to solve the equation $\dfrac{1}{x^2} - 1 = 5 - 2x$.

f) Which of the following equations are also satisfied by the values found in part e)? Explain briefly how you are able to decide.

(i) $\dfrac{1}{x^2} = 6 - 2x$ (ii) $\dfrac{1}{x^2} = 4 - 2x$ (iii) $1 = 4x^2 - 2x^3$

(iv) $1 = 6x^2 - 2x^3$ (v) $2x^3 - 6x^2 + 1 = 0$ (vi) $2x^3 + 4x^2 - 1 = 0$

37.2 Inequalities in two dimensions

As we have already seen, the set of points that satisfy an equation such as $x + y = 4$ may be represented by a line.

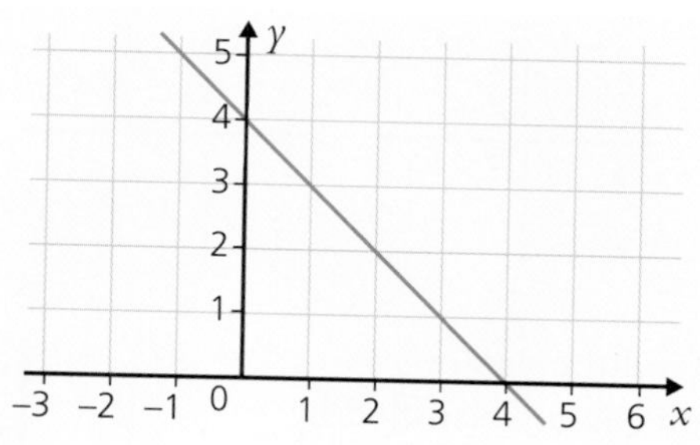

On one side of the line the values of $x + y$ are *always* larger than 4 and on the other side of the line the values of $x + y$ are *always* smaller than 4.

In this way, the line $x + y = 4$ divides the plane into two parts, known as **regions**, defined by the inequalities $x + y < 4$ and $x + y > 4$. The line itself may be described as a **boundary line** for the two regions. In the diagram below, the region given by $x + y > 4$ is shown shaded.

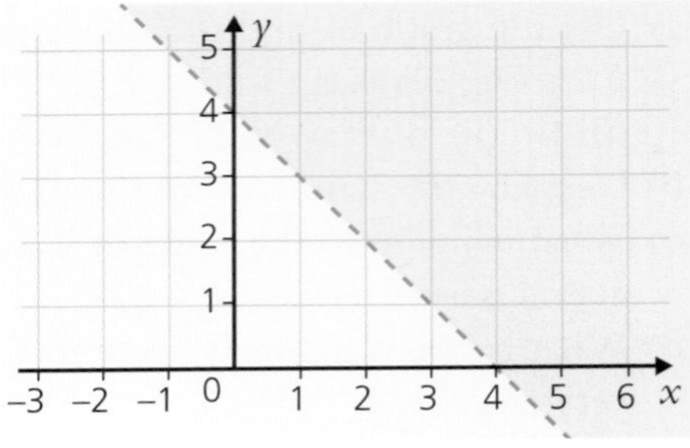

Note that the boundary line $x + y = 4$ is now shown dotted because the points on it are not included in the region. A solid line would be used to represent the region given by $x + y \geq 4$.

1 For each of the points labelled in the diagram state whether $y = 2$, $y < 2$ or $y > 2$.

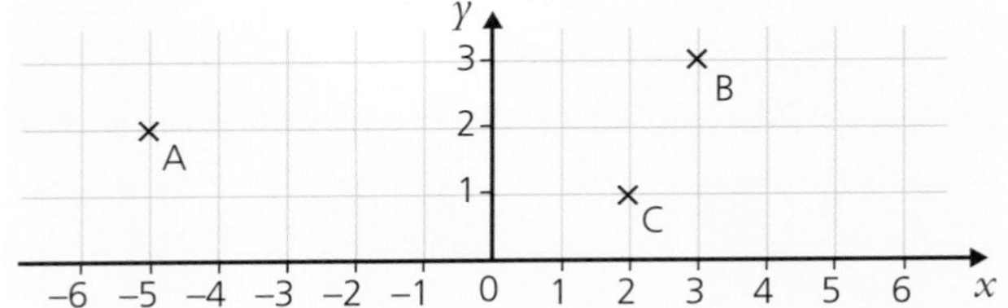

2 Draw diagrams to show the regions given by these inequalities.

a) $y < 2$ ✔ b) $y \geq 2$
c) $x \leq 3$ d) $x > -2$

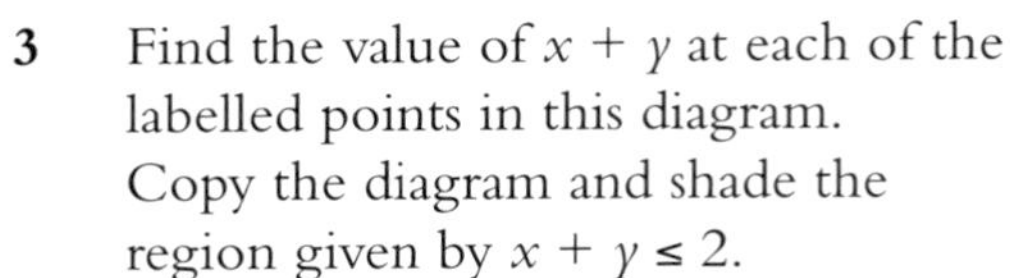

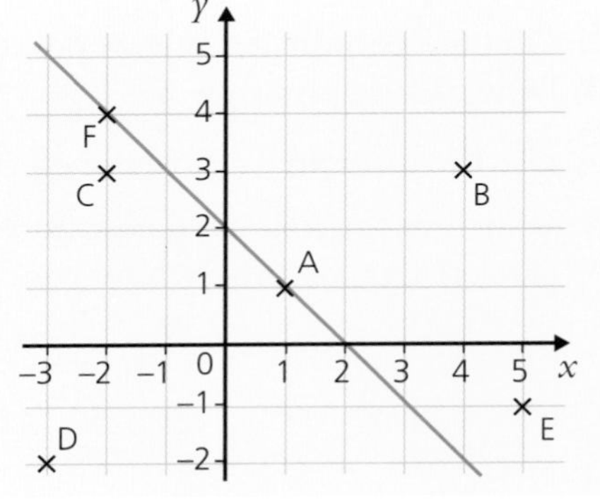

3 Find the value of $x + y$ at each of the labelled points in this diagram. Copy the diagram and shade the region given by $x + y \leq 2$.

4 Use inequalities to describe each of these regions.

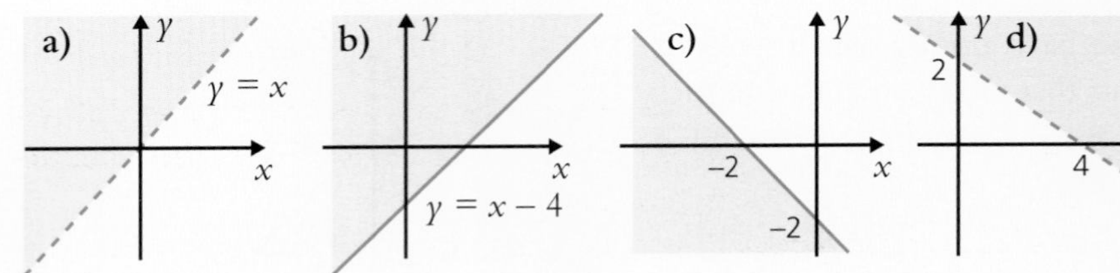

5 Find the *pair* of inequalities satisfied by the shaded regions shown.

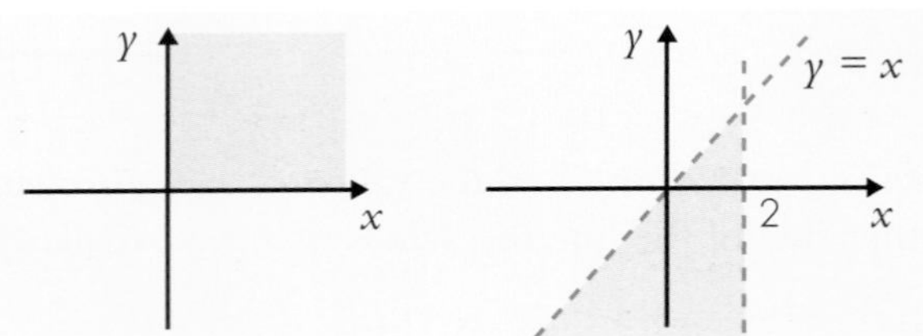

6 Match each of the following sets of conditions to one of the labelled regions.

a) $y \geq 0$, $y \leq x$ and $x + y \leq 5$ ✓
b) $x \geq 0$, $y \geq x$ and $x + y \leq 5$
c) $x + y \geq 5$, $y \leq x$ and $x \leq 5$
d) $x + y \geq 5$, $y \geq x$ and $y \leq 5$

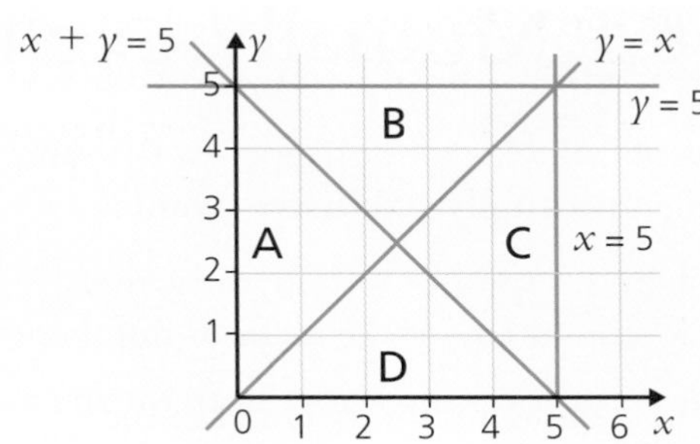

7 a) Using values of x from -3 to 6 and values of y from -6 to 6, draw the graphs of $y = x - 3$, $x = -3$ and $x + y = 3$ on the same diagram.
b) Shade the region given by $x \leq 0$, $y \leq 0$, $x \geq -3$ and $y \geq x - 3$ and label it P.
c) Shade the region given by $x \geq 0$, $y \geq 0$ and $x + y \leq 3$ and label it Q.
d) Use inequalities to define the closed region above P in the diagram.
e) Use inequalities to define the closed region below Q in the diagram.

The technique of using graphs to solve equations may be adapted to find the solution of inequalities.

Example

Use the diagram below to find the values of x for which the following are true:

a) $x^2 - 3x < 2$
b) $x^2 - 3x \geq 2$

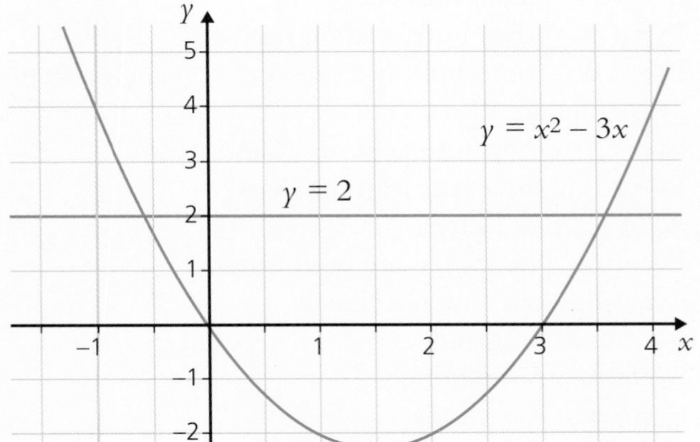

Answer

a) The graph of $y = x^2 - 3x$ intersects the graph of $y = 2$ when $x = -0.6$ and when $x = 3.6$, but lies below it for values in-between. Hence, the solution of $x^2 - 3x < 2$ is $-0.6 < x < 3.6$ (correct to 1 D.P.).
b) The solution of $x^2 - 3x \geq 2$ must be written in two parts as $x \leq -0.6$ or $x \geq 3.6$ (correct to 1 D.P.).

---

8 Use the diagram above to solve these inequalities:
a) $x^2 - 3x < -1$ b) $x^2 - 3x \leq 0$ c) $x^2 - 3x > 1$

9 Draw the graphs of $y = x^2$ and $y = 2x + 1$ on the same axes. Use your diagram to find the values of x for which $x^2 < 2x + 1$.

38 COMBINING PROBABILITIES

38.1 Mutually exclusive events

Events which cannot happen at the same time are called **mutually exclusive events**.

When this spinner is spun, the arrow may stop in any of the sections numbered 1 to 8.

Let event A be 'the arrow stops on an even number.'

Let event B be 'the arrow stops on number 5'.

Events A and B cannot happen at the same time. Events A and B are mutually exclusive.

1 a) If event C is 'the arrow stops at an odd number', are events A and C mutually exclusive? ✓

b) Are events B and C mutually exclusive? ✓

c) Let event D be 'the arrow stops on number 8'. Which events are mutually exclusive with event D?

(i) event A? (ii) event B? (iii) event C?

2 For each example state whether events A and B are mutually exclusive.

✓a) Two coins are thrown.
Event A: they both land on heads.
Event B: one lands on heads and one lands on tails.

b) Two coins are thrown.
Event A: they both land on heads.
Event B: there is at least one head.

c) A cat has two kittens.
Event A: the kittens are both black.
Event B: one kitten is female.

d) It is Sunday morning.
Event A: it is raining.
Event B: it is windy.

e) A card is chosen randomly from a pack of cards.
Event A: it is a King.
Event B: it is a spade.

f) A card is chosen randomly from a pack of cards.
Event A: it is the King of hearts.
Event B: it is a heart.

g) A cat has two kittens.
Event A: the kittens are both black.
Event B: one kitten is black and one is white.

h) I throw a dice.
Event A: I score a six.
Event B: I score a two.

38.2 The addition principle

There is a rule for calculating the probabilities of mutually exclusive events.

When this spinner is spun, each number score is an equally likely outcome.

Event A is 'the arrow stops on an even number'.
Event B is 'the arrow stops on number 5'.

- Find the probability of event A happening.
- Find the probability of event B happening.
- What is the probability that either event A happens or event B? (That is: the probability that I score an even number or a 5.)

If two events A and B are mutually exclusive, the probability of event A or event B happening can be found be adding the probabilities.

P(A or B) = P(A) + P(B)

This is called the **addition principle** (or addition rule).

1 a) What is the probability that the arrow stops on an odd number (event C)?
b) What is P(B or C)?
c) Does P(B or C) = P(B) + P(C)?
d) Explain why the addition principle doesn't apply in this case.

Use the addition principle P(A or B) = P(A) + P(B) to answer these questions, having made sure of course that events A and B are mutually exclusive.

2 Two coins are tossed.
a) Copy and complete this diagram showing all the possible outcomes.

		coin 1	
		heads	tails
coin 2	heads	HH	
	tails		

b) How many possible outcomes are there?
c) Are these outcomes all equally likely?
d) What is the probability of getting two heads or two tails?
e) What is the probability that one coin shows heads and the other shows tails?

3 ✓ A pack of cards is shuffled and one card is drawn out. What is the probability that it is:
a) a King or a Queen?
b) a two, three, four or five?
c) a heart or a diamond?

4 A dice is thrown. What is the probability of scoring a 5 or an even number?

5 Mr Johnson estimates that half of his letters are bills and that half of the rest are 'junk mail' advertising materials. The postman delivers a letter.
What is the probability that it is:
a) what Mr Johnson would classify as 'junk mail'?
b) neither 'junk mail' nor a bill?

6 Two dice are thrown. Find the probability of getting either a total of 11 or the same number on both dice.

7 Every day Mrs Lawton buys a newspaper. She either buys *The Daily Express* with a probability of 0.3 or she buys *The Mirror* with a probability of 0.55. On other days she buys *The Sun*.
What is the probability that she buys either *The Sun* or *The Daily Express* ?

38.3 Independent events

Two events are independent if the outcome of the second event is *not* affected by the outcome of the first.

If there is some influence or changing of probabilities, the events are not independent.

Consider these two events:

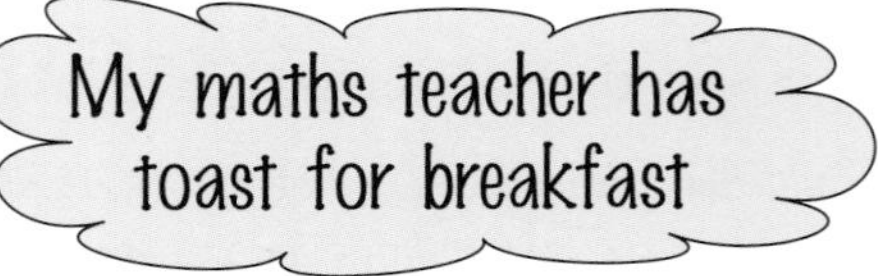

These two events are likely to be **independent** as they are not likely to influence each other.

If, however, my maths teacher happens also to be my mother, then the two events may well not be independent.

---

1 For the events listed below, decide whether event 2 is independent of event 1. Explain your answer each time.

	Event 1	*Event 2*
A ✔	The crowd at a football match cheer and shout.	The striker scores a goal.
B ✔	I cheer when I'm watching a football match on TV.	The striker scores a goal.
C	It rains today.	It rains tomorrow.
D	I catch chicken pox.	My brother catches chicken pox.
E	I miss the bus today.	I arrive late for school today.
F	I miss the bus today.	I miss the bus tomorrow.

G	I throw a dice and score a 2.	I throw the dice again and score another 2.
H	Miss Jones wins a lottery prize this week.	Miss Jones wins a lottery prize next week.

38.4 The multiplication principle

Ramesh and Julie play a game in which two tetrahedral dice are thrown. Here is a net for a tetrahedral dice.

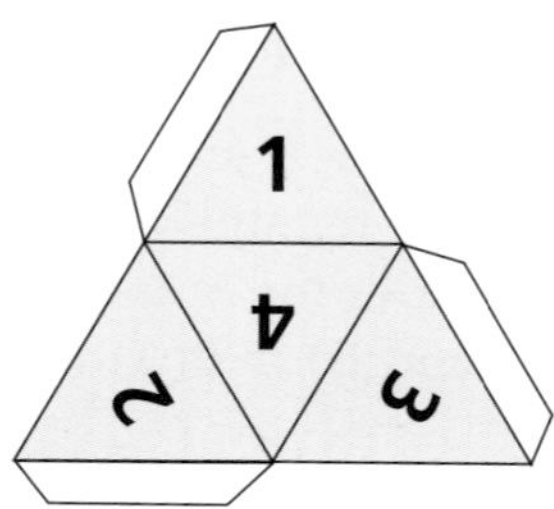

If two of these dice are thrown together, the possible outcomes can be shown on a diagram.

score on dice 2 (columns); score on dice 1 (rows)

	1	2	3	4
1	1, 1	1, 2	1, 3	1, 4
2	2, 1	2, 2	2, 3	2, 4
3	3, 1	3, 2	3, 3	3, 4
4	4, 1	4, 2	4, 3	4, 4

1 a) How many possible outcomes are there?
b) Are they all equally likely?
c) What is the probability of each outcome?

To win the next point, Ramesh must score 3 or higher on dice 1 and a 4 on dice 2.
Let event A be 'scores 3 or higher on dice 1'.
Let event B be 'scores 4 on dice 2'.

score on dice 2 (columns); score on dice 1 (rows)

	1	2	3	4
1	1, 1	1, 2	1, 3	1, 4
2	2, 1	2, 2	2, 3	2, 4
3	3, 1	3, 2	3, 3	3, 4
4	4, 1	4, 2	4, 3	4, 4

event A
event B

The diagram shows 8 outcomes shaded in for event A.

$$P(A) = \frac{8}{16} = \frac{1}{2}$$

There are just 4 favourable outcomes for event B.

$$P(B) = \frac{4}{16} = \frac{1}{4}$$

There are only 2 outcomes where events A and B overlap.

$$P(A \text{ and } B) = \frac{2}{16} = \frac{1}{8}$$

The probability of events A and B happening together is given by the **multiplication principle**.

> **If two events A and B are *independent*, the probability of both A and B happening together can be found by multiplying the separate probabilities for A and B.**
> **P(A and B) = P(A) × P(B).**

---

2 ✓ Check that the multiplication principle works for this example.

Using the multiplication principle eliminates the need to list all the possible outcomes for both events.

3 ✓ a) Use the multiplication principle to find the probability that on her next throw, Julie scores an even number on dice 1 and a 3 or higher on dice 2.
b) Find the probability that Ramesh can finish the game by scoring an even number on both dice.

4 An ordinary six-sided dice is thrown twice.
Find the probability of scoring:
a) a 'five' on the first throw and an even number on the second throw.
b) an even number on both throws.
c) a 'three' on the first throw and a 'two' on the second throw.
d) a 'three' on the first throw and a 'two' on the second throw.
e) a 'three' and a 'two' in either order.

5 A coin is thrown twice. Find the probability of:
a) tails on the first throw.
b) tails both times.
c) heads on the first throw and tails on the second.
d) heads and tails in either order.

6 Jackie travels to school by bus. She estimates that the first bus that comes along is twice as likely to be full as it is to have room for her.
a) What is the probability that the first bus that comes along tomorrow morning will have room for her?
b) What is the probability that she will be lucky two mornings in a row and catch the first bus both times?

(continued)

c) What is the probability that she will have to wait for a later bus two mornings in a row?
d) Do your answers to b) and c) add up to 1? Explain the reason why (or why not).

7 An angler knows from long experience that when he catches a fish the probability that it is too small to take home is 0.7. Find the probability that:
a) if he catches two fish both are too small to take home.
b) if he catches two fish either one will be large enough to take home.

8 The probability that Joanne is late for school is 0.25. The probability that Sally is late is 0.2.
a) What is the probability that both girls are late for school?
b) Why must we assume that these two girls do not know each other?

Probability game

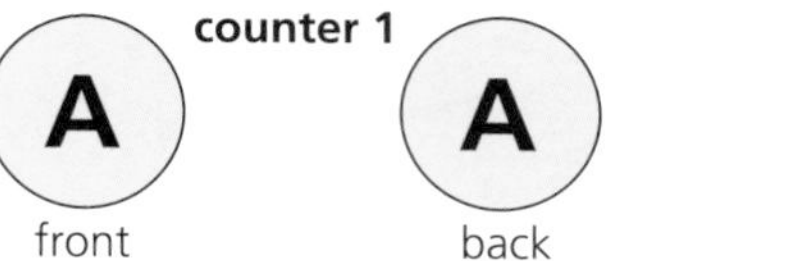

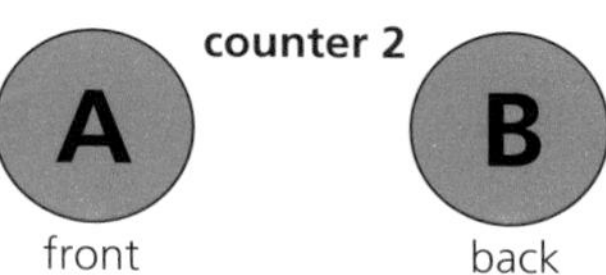

This is a matching game. It uses two counters or plastic discs and a plastic cup.

The first counter has 'A' written on both sides, the second has 'A' on the front and 'B' on the back.

If you do not have counters, pieces of card or even paper can be used.

To play the game:
Shake the counters in the cup and tip them out onto the table. You win if the letters match. You lose if they don't match.

Before you play, which do you think is more likely: that the letters will match or that the letters will not match?

1 Draw up a table like this to record your results:

Result	Tally	Frequency
Match		
Don't match		

Play the game 30 times and enter your results.
a) Are the results as you expected?
b) Use your results to calculate the relative frequency of a 'match'.

Here is a table which we can use to work out the probability of a 'match' theoretically:
Copy the table and decide which outcomes are a 'match' and which ones 'don't match'.

		counter 2	
		front A	back B
counter 1	front A	match	?
	back A	?	?

2 a) Are all four outcomes equally likely?
b) What is the probability of a 'match'?
c) What is the probability of 'don't match'?
d) How close is the probability you have just calculated in part b) to the relative frequency you found in 1 b)?
e) What would you expect to happen to the relative frequency if more games are played?

38.5 Tree diagrams

A tree diagram is a different way of showing all the different outcomes in a complex situation. This is a tree diagram for the counter-matching game you have just done.

It starts with two branches to show the possible outcomes for the first counter.

Counter 1

probability = $\frac{1}{2}$ A (front)

probability = $\frac{1}{2}$ A (back)

Each possible outcome is shown as a branch on the tree diagram. The probability of that outcome is written on the branch.

More branches are needed to show what happens with the second counter:

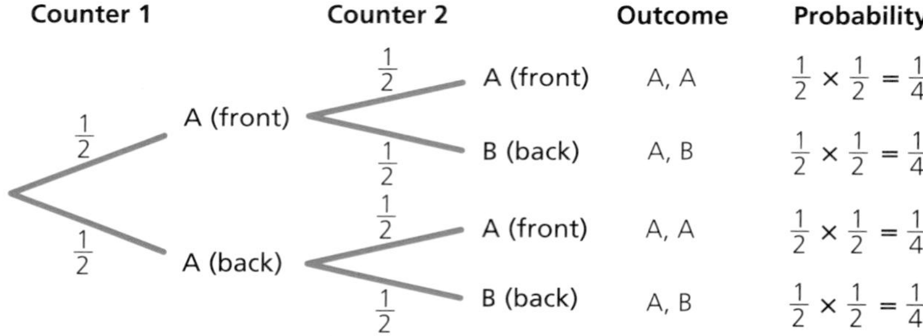

To find the probability of each combined event such as 'A on counter 1 followed by A on counter 2', you multiply the probabilities on the branches of the tree diagram . Notice that there are two ways of obtaining 'A, A' and that these are added together to give a total probability of $\frac{1}{2}$ for a 'match'.

Imagine that you are to play the game 'Do they match?' with two 2-pence coins.

coin 1

heads

tails

coin 2

heads

tails

1 Which do you think is more likely: that the coins will match or that they won't match?

2 Draw up a table like this to show all the possible outcomes:

		coin 2	
		heads	tails
coin 1	heads	match	
	tails		

a) Are all four outcomes equally likely?
b) What is the probability of a 'match'?

3 a) Copy and complete this tree diagram to show all the possible outcomes:

Coin 1		Coin 2		Outcome	Probability
$\frac{1}{2}$	heads	?	heads	H, H	$\frac{1}{2} \times \frac{1}{2} = \frac{1}{4}$
		?	tails	…, …	……
$\frac{1}{2}$	tails	$\frac{1}{2}$		T, H	……
		$\frac{1}{2}$		…, …	$\frac{1}{2} \times \frac{1}{2} = \frac{1}{4}$

b) Explain how you can find the probability of a 'match' from your tree diagram.

4 A multiple choice test has five possible answers for each question. Joanne finds that there are two questions in the test for which she does not know the answers. So she decides to guess.

a) What is the probability that she guesses the correct answer for the first question whose answer she does not know?
b) Copy and complete this tree diagram.

First guessed question		Second guessed question		Outcome	Probability
?	right	$\frac{1}{5}$	right	R, R	
		$\frac{4}{5}$	wrong	R, W	
$\frac{4}{5}$	wrong	?	right	W, R	$\frac{4}{5} \times \frac{1}{5} = \frac{4}{25}$
		?	wrong	W, W	

Use the tree diagram to find the probability that:
c) Joanne guesses both answers correctly
d) Joanne guesses both answers incorrectly
e) she guesses either one of the answers correctly
f) she guesses at least one answer correctly.

5 a) Copy and complete this tree diagram to show the outcomes for two throws of this dice. It has two black faces and four blue faces.

First throw		Second throw		Outcome	Probability
$\frac{1}{3}$	black	?	……	black, black	$\frac{1}{3} \times \frac{1}{3} = \frac{1}{9}$
		?	……	…, …	……
?	blue	?	black	…, …	……
		?	blue	…, …	……

b) You win a point if you throw the same colour twice. What is the probability of winning a point?

6 One call in every four received by the fire brigade is a false alarm. Find the probability of one false alarm among the next three calls.
Draw a tree diagram to help you. (Don't forget that the false alarm could be any one of those three calls.)

First call		Second call	Third call	Outcome	Probability
$\frac{1}{4}$	false alarm	F	F	F, F, F	
			R	F, F, R	$\frac{1}{4} \times \frac{1}{4} \times \frac{3}{4} =$
		R	F		
			R		
$\frac{3}{4}$	real	F	F		
			R		
		R	F		
			R		

7 The probability that it is raining at 8.30 am on any day is $\frac{1}{4}$. Joe leaves home for school at 8.30 in the morning. If it is raining there is a probability of $\frac{2}{3}$ that he will be able to find his coat. If it is not raining there is a probability of $\frac{1}{10}$ that he will put a coat on.
What is the probability that if I meet him on his way to school he is not wearing a coat?
Use this tree diagram to help you.

Is it raining?		Does Joe wear a coat		Outcome	Probability
$\frac{1}{4}$	raining	$\frac{2}{3}$	coat	R, C	……
		?	no coat	R, N	……
?	dry	$\frac{1}{10}$	coat	D, C	……
		$\frac{9}{10}$	no coat	D, N	……

8 The probability that Sarah wakes up late in the morning is 0.6. When she wakes up late the probability that she is late for school is 0.9. If she is not late waking up the probability that Sarah is late for school is only 0.2.

a) Draw a tree diagram to show the two events: 'waking up' followed by 'arriving at school'.
b) What is the probability that Sarah does not wake up late?
c) Fill in all the probabilities needed on your tree diagram.
d) What is the probability that Sarah arrives at school on time?

9 Each evening Mr Gillespie either watches television or reads a book. The probability he watches television is $\frac{4}{5}$. If he does watch television the probability that he falls asleep is $\frac{1}{4}$. If he reads a book the probability that he falls asleep is $\frac{1}{2}$.

a) What is the probability that Mr Gillespie watches television and falls asleep? ✔
b) What is the probability that Mr Gillespie reads a book and falls asleep?
c) What is the probability that he falls asleep during either activity?

39.1 Journey graphs

One of the important features of this GCSE course is the requirement to present and interpret information in graphical form. To understand and describe the features of distance–time and speed–time graphs, in particular, relies on the use of skills developed earlier in the book:

- reading and interpreting scales in appropriate units;
- examining points of intersection and appreciating their significance;
- calculating and interpreting gradients of lines;
- calculating and interpreting areas under graphs.

Example

Jasmine and Caroline have a race over two lengths of a swimming pool. The distance–time graph for the race is shown below.

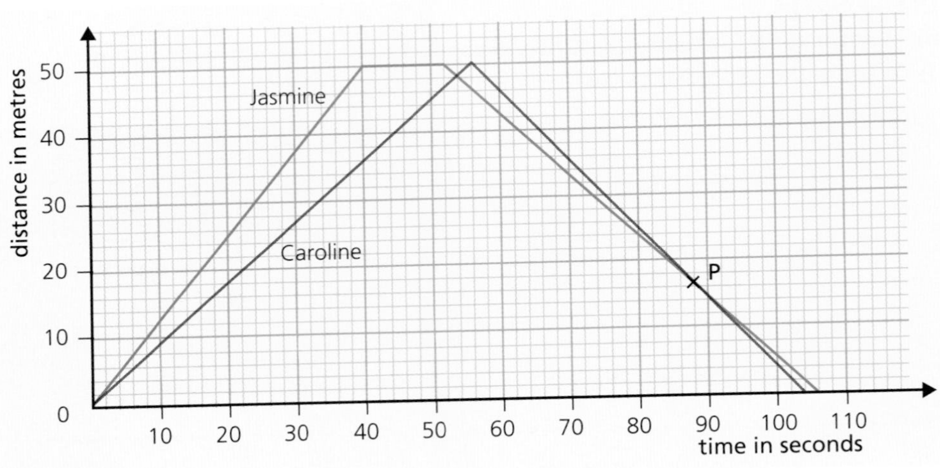

a) What is the length of the swimming pool?
b) Who swam faster at the start? How can you tell?
c) For what length of time are they swimming in opposite directions?
d) The graphs intersect at P. What happened at that time?
e) What was Jasmine's speed during the first length?
f) What was Caroline's average speed for the whole race?
g) Describe Jasmine's tactics. Were they successful?

Answer

a) 50 m
b) Jasmine. Her graph is steeper than Caroline's at the start.
c) 4 seconds, i.e. between 52 and 56 seconds from the start.
d) Caroline overtook Jasmine.
e) 1.25 m/s. (This is given by the gradient of the line.)
f) 0.96 m/s. (Average speed = Total distance ÷ Total time.)
g) Jasmine swam the first length very fast and then rested at the far end. She set off again after 12 seconds, which allowed her to start the return journey ahead of Caroline. But she lost to Caroline in the end.

When interpreting the shape of a graph, care must be taken to consider the labelling of the axes. For example, the speed-time graph shown here appears very similar to Jasmine's distance-time graph but the interpretation is very different.

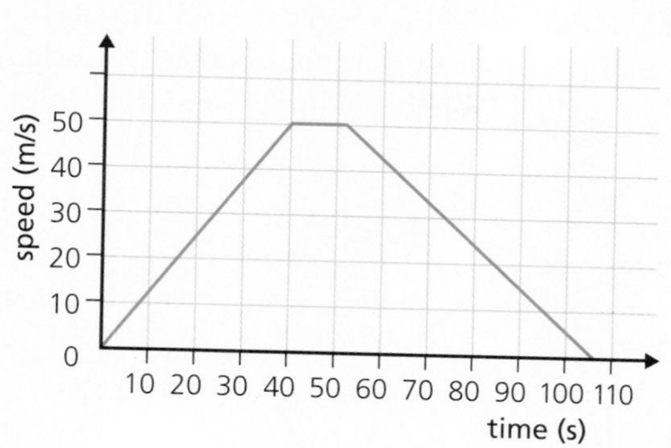

- The first section of the graph represents a steady increase in speed from rest to 50 m/s in a time of 40 seconds.
- The horizontal section of the graph shows that a constant speed of 50 m/s is maintained for the next 12 seconds.
- The final section shows that the speed is reduced from 50 m/s to rest at a steady rate over the next 54 seconds.

The area under a speed-time graph gives the distance travelled.
speed (m/s) × time (s) = distance (m)

Using the formula for the area of a trapezium gives the distance as

$$\frac{50}{2}(106 + 12)\text{m} = 25 \times 118\text{m}$$
$$= 2950\text{m}$$

1 This distance-time graph represents a race over 100 m between Robert and Ben in which Robert gives Ben a head-start.

a) Who won the race?
b) How long did Robert wait at the start?
c) At what distance from the finish line were they level with each other?
d) What was Ben's speed?
e) What was Robert's average speed?

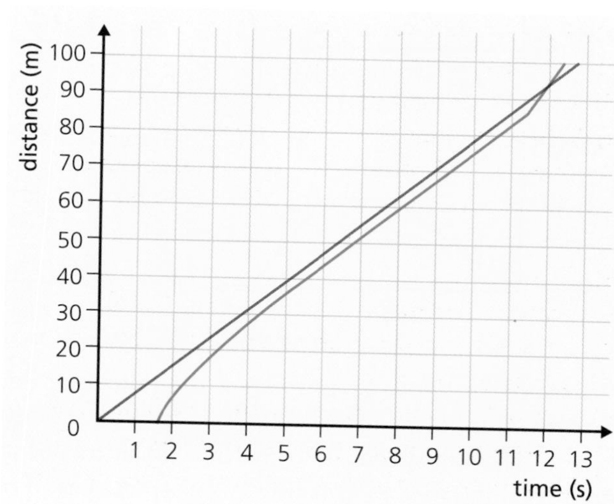

2 Sukjinder travels to school each day on his bicycle. The first part of his journey is down-hill but then the road flattens out and continues, through some traffic lights, past the supermarket at steady speed, to the final stage which is up-hill. Here is Sukjinder's speed-time graph for a particular day.

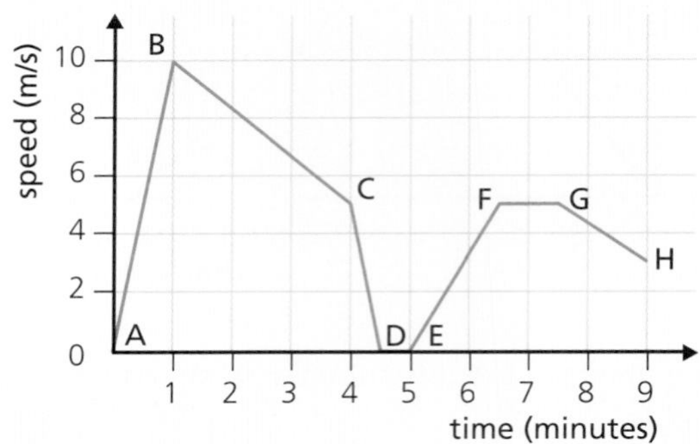

a) How long did Sukjinder take to get to school?
b) What colour do you think the traffic lights were as he approached?
c) What was his maximum speed?
d) Which two of the labelled points mark the section of the graph where he passed the supermarket?
e) Describe what was happening on Sukjinder's journey in each of the following sections.
(i) AB (ii) BC (iii) DE (iv) GH
f) How far in metres does Sukjinder travel to school?
g) What was his average speed in m/s on the day shown by the graph?

3 **Graph A**

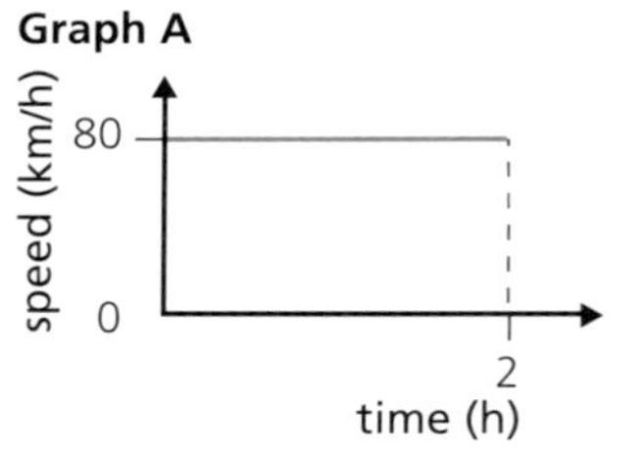

Graph B

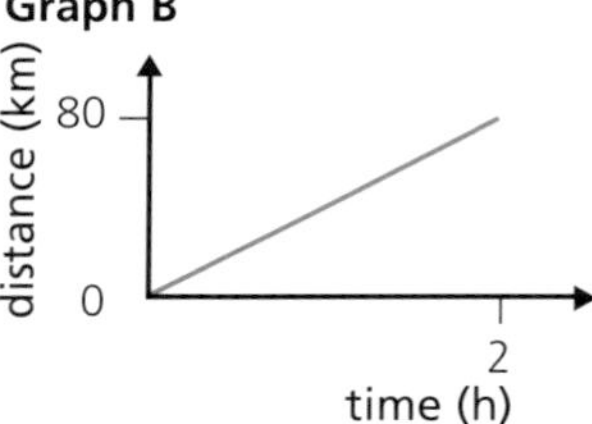

Graph C

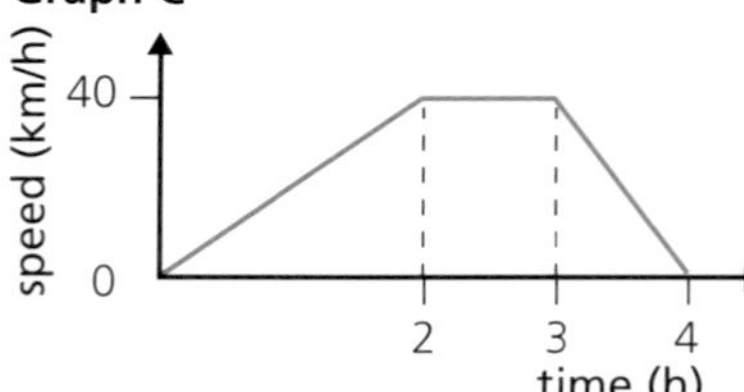

Graph D

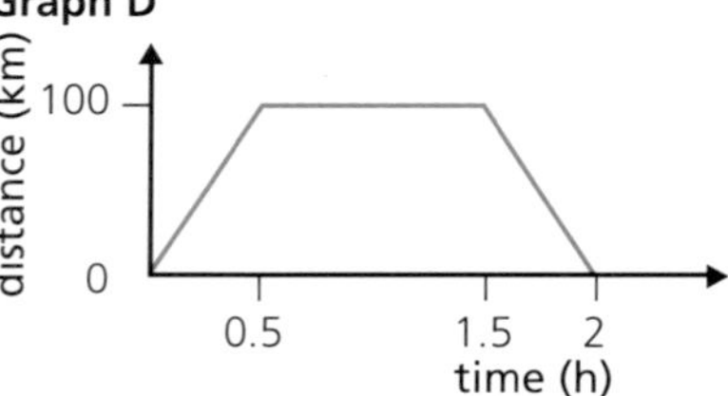

Which of the above graphs *include* the following information as a feature.

a) A maximum speed of 40 km/h
b) A constant speed of 80 km/h
c) A maximum speed of 80 km/h
d) A total distance of 160 km
e) A total distance of 100 km
f) A period of no movement
g) A return journey
h) An average speed of 40 km/h

39.2 Quadratic equations

The use of mathematics to solve problems, as described in Unit 9, depends on the ability to solve equations, and there are many situations in which the type of equation produced is a **quadratic**. An example of such a problem is given later in this unit but first we will consider how factorisation may be used to find the solutions.

Example

Solve the equations:

a) $x^2 - 5x = 0$ b) $3x^2 + 6x = 0$

Answer

a) Factorising the equation gives $x(x - 5) = 0$.
Writing the equation in this form we see that two numbers, namely x and $(x - 5)$, are multiplied together to make zero. This can only happen if either $x = 0$ or $x - 5 = 0$, giving the solutions of the equation as $x = 0$ and $x = 5$.

b) Factorising gives $3x(x + 2) = 0$.
So either $3x = 0$ or $x + 2 = 0$ giving the solutions as $x = 0$ and $x = -2$.

---

1 Solve these equations. Some may need to be rearranged before they can be factorised.

a) $x^2 - 7x = 0$ ✓ b) $x^2 - 11x = 0$ c) $x^2 + 3x = 0$
d) $5x^2 - 10x = 0$ e) $3x^2 + 12x = 0$ f) $8x^2 + 24x = 0$
g) $6x^2 = 12x$ ✓ h) $7x^2 = 21x$ i) $10x^2 = 30x$
j) $6x^2 + 11 = 12x + 11$ k) $8x^2 - 9 = 40x - 9$ l) $5x^2 + 12x = 3x^2$

We know that the graph of a quadratic equation is a **parabola**. If we also know where the graph crosses the axes then we are able to sketch the curve.

Example

Sketch the graph of $y = x^2 + 3x$.

Answer

The graph crosses the **x-axis** when $y = 0$,

i.e. when $x^2 + 3x = 0$

giving $x(x + 3) = 0$

i.e. when $x = 0$ and when $x = -3$.

The graph crosses the **y-axis** when $x = 0$,

i.e. when $y = 0 \times 3 = 0$.

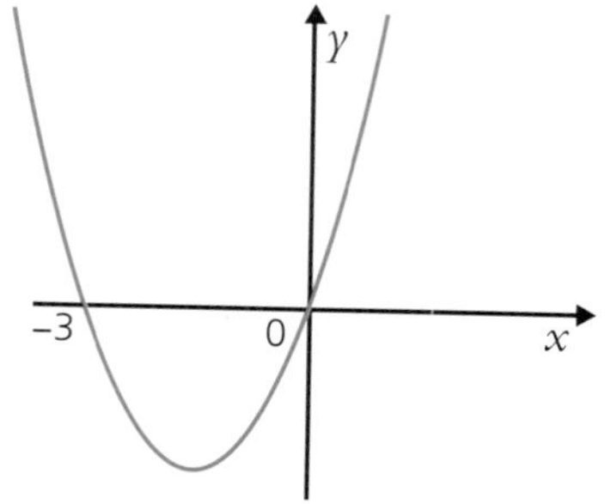

---

2 Sketch the graphs of the following equations:

a) $y = x^2 - 4x$ ✓ b) $y = x^2 + 2x$ c) $y = 3x^2 - 6x$
d) $y = 2x^2 + 8$ e) $y = x^2 + x$ f) $y = 2x^2 - x$

Factorising an expression of the form $ax^2 + bx + c$ will usually require double brackets.

Example

Factorise:

a) $x^2 + 3x + 2$ b) $x^2 - x - 2$

Answer

a) We start by writing $x^2 + 3x + 2 = (x \ldots\ldots)(x \ldots\ldots)$
and then complete the expression in brackets to make the equation balance.

Try $(x + 1)(x + 2)$
Expanding gives $x^2 + 2x + x + 2$
$= x^2 + 3x + 2$
and so $x^2 + 3x + 2 = (x + 1)(x + 2)$.

b) Starting with $x^2 - x - 2 = (x \ldots\ldots)(x \ldots\ldots)$

Try $(x - 1)(x + 2)$
Expanding gives $x^2 + 2x - x - 2$
$= x^2 + x - 2$
Try $(x + 1)(x - 2)$
Expanding gives $x^2 - 2x + x - 2$
$= x^2 - x - 2$
and so $x^2 - x - 2 = (x + 1)(x - 2)$

---

3 Copy and complete:

a) $x^2 + 4x + 3 = (x + 1)(x \ldots\ldots)$ b) $x^2 + 8x + 12 = (x + 2)(x \ldots\ldots)$
c) $x^2 + x - 6 = (x - 2)(x \ldots\ldots)$ d) $x^2 - 2x - 3 = (x \ldots 3)(x \ldots\ldots)$
e) $x^2 - 5x + 6 = (x - 3)(x \ldots\ldots)$ f) $x^2 - 7x + 10 = (x \ldots 2)(x \ldots\ldots)$

4 Factorise:

a) $x^2 + 6x + 5$ b) $x^2 + 9x + 14$ c) $x^2 + 10x + 9$
d) $x^2 + 12x - 3$ e) $x^2 + 5x - 6$ f) $x^2 - 3x - 10$
g) $x^2 - 5x - 14$ h) $x^2 - 9x + 20$ i) $x^2 - 11x + 28$

As before, once a quadratic equation is factorised the solutions may be found quite easily.

Example

Solve $x^2 - 7x - 18 = 0$.

Answer

Factorising gives $(x + 2)(x - 9) = 0$
so, either $x + 2 = 0$ giving $x = -2$
or $x - 9 = 0$ giving $x = 9$

Hence the solutions are $x = -2$ and $x = 9$.

5 Solve the following equations:

a) $x^2 + 3x - 28 = 0$ b) $x^2 - 9x + 20 = 0$ c) $x^2 - 12x + 35 = 0$

d) $x^2 - 5x - 24 = 0$ e) $x^2 - 9x + 18 = 0$ f) $x^2 - 9x + 10 = 0$

6 Use your answers to question 5 to sketch the graphs of these equations:

a) $y = x^2 + 3x - 28$ b) $y = x^2 - 9x + 20$ c) $y = x^2 - 12x + 35$

d) $y = x^2 - 5x - 24$ e) $y = x^2 - 9x + 18$ f) $y = x^2 - 9x + 10$

39.3 Further trial and improvement

Under certain conditions the *maximum* distance d metres that a stunt rider can travel horizontally, to land (safely) h metres below the top of the launching ramp, is given by:

$$0.004d^2 - 0.09d = h$$

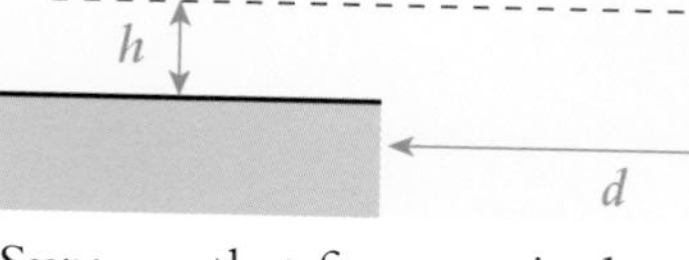

Suppose that for a particular stunt, the height of the ramp is to be set at 2 m but the horizontal distance is unknown. There is a strong connection between the practical and theoretical approaches to finding the value of d.

Practical	Theoretical
Experiment with different take-off speeds, length of ramp, etc., building up to maximum speed for a 2 m drop in height. Gather information from every attempt and make adjustments in the light of experience.	Experiment with different values of d in the equation: $0.004d^2 - 0.09d = 2$ Gather information from every attempt and refine estimates in the light of experience.

Both methods involve a form of trial and improvement.

1 Describe any problems that you would foresee with using a *purely* practical approach to finding the maximum value.

2 In what way might the theoretical approach be useful?

The table below shows how trial and improvement may be used to calculate the maximum horizontal distance when $h = 2$. Different values of d are substituted into the equation in an attempt to produce 2 as the target figure.

The change from 'too small' to 'too large' shows that the solution lies between these values. Further estimates now trap the solution in a smaller and smaller interval.

d	h	
10	–0.5	
20	–0.2	
30	0.9	too small
40	2.8	too large
35	1.75	too small
38	2.356	too large
37	2.146	too large
36	1.944	too small

The negative values of h indicate that the rider is still above the ramp.

At this stage, the required solution is trapped between two whole numbers but we need more information to decide which is the best estimate. To help us decide, we substitute the mid-value, i.e. 36.5, giving 2.044 (which is too large). A diagram now helps to make the situation clear.

Too small → 36 — 36.5 — 37 ← Too large

The solution must lie in here and so is nearer to 36 than 37.

The theory suggests that the maximum horizontal distance corresponding to a loss in height of 2 m is 36 m to the nearest metre.

Use the trial and improvement method to answer these questions.

3 The values in the table above suggest that $h = 0$ for some value of d between 20 and 30. Find this value to give the horizontal distance, to the nearest metre, that the rider travels to reach the same level as the take-off point.

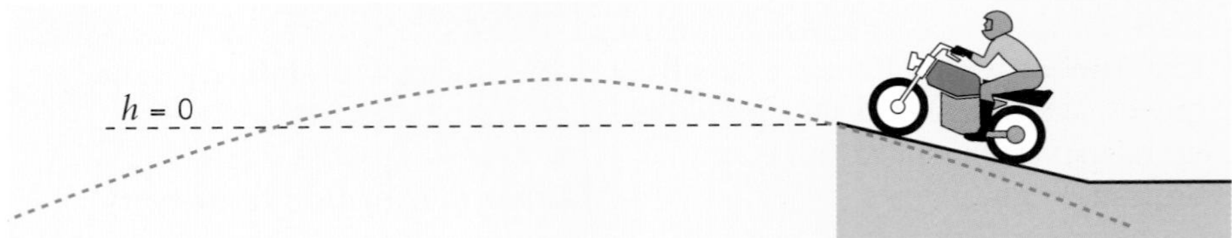

4 Greater horizontal distances can be achieved by increasing the value of h.

a) Describe the problems faced by the rider as h is increased.

b) The rider considers increasing h to 2.5 m. Use trial and improvement to find the difference that this should make to the horizontal distance.

5 Instead of altering the value of h, the effect of changing the angle of the ramp while keeping the same take-off speed is explored.

a) What difference should the rider experience if the angle is increased? Will it make the stunt more, or less, dangerous?

b) Altering the angle of the ramp in a precise way takes time. The engineers want to change the angle sufficiently to make a difference but not so much that the effect is too dramatic. Make a guess at the best increase in angle.

c) Theory suggests that increasing the angle by 2° changes the formula connecting d and h to $0.004d^2 - 0.12d = h$.

i.e. the coefficient of d^2 remains the same but the coefficient of d is changed.

Use trial and improvement with this formula to find the value of d when $h = 2$.

d) Compare the new value of d with the previous value and comment on the value of using theory when making changes to a stunt.

One of the problems that we have in solving equations by trial and improvement is that we don't know what values to start with. A good way to get started is to find approximate solutions by drawing graphs – particularly if a graphics calculator or computer graph plotter is available.

Example

Solve the equation $\frac{1}{x} = 2x - 3$, for $x > 0$, giving the value of x to 2 D.P.

Answer

The graphs of $y = \frac{1}{x}$ and $y = 2x - 3$ are already familiar to us and the diagram below shows both graphs on the same axes. At points where the graphs intersect, the value of the x coordinate gives a solution to the equation given above.

Another advantage of using graphs is that we can tell how many solutions there are. In this case there are two but only one of them is *positive*.

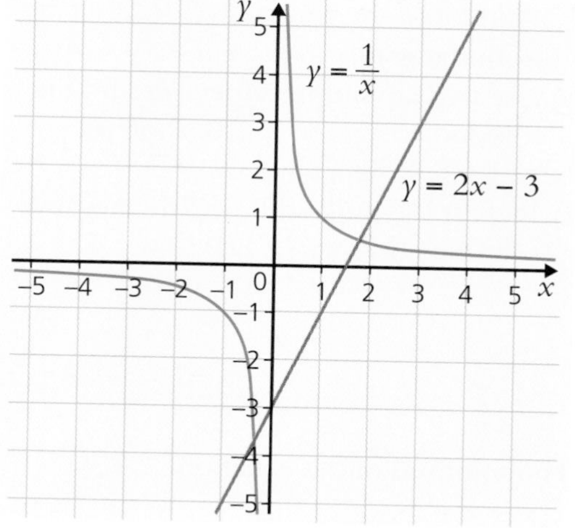

The graphs show that the positive solution is approximately 1.7. We now take this value as a starting point for the trial and improvement method.

The trial and improvement method is easier to work with if all the terms involving x are on one side of the equation.

$\frac{1}{x} = 2x - 3$ subtract $\frac{1}{x}$ from both sides

$0 = 2x - \frac{1}{x} - 3$ add 3 to both sides

$3 = 2x - \frac{1}{x}$ i.e. $2x - \frac{1}{x} = 3$

The solution is now trapped between consecutive values to 2 D.P.

To decide on the best answer to 2 D.P. we must try the mid-value.

x	$2x - \frac{1}{x}$	
1.7	2.812	too small
1.8	3.044	too large
1.75	2.929	too small
1.78	2.998	too small
1.79	3.021	too large
1.785	3.009	too large

Note how these results influence the next value to try.

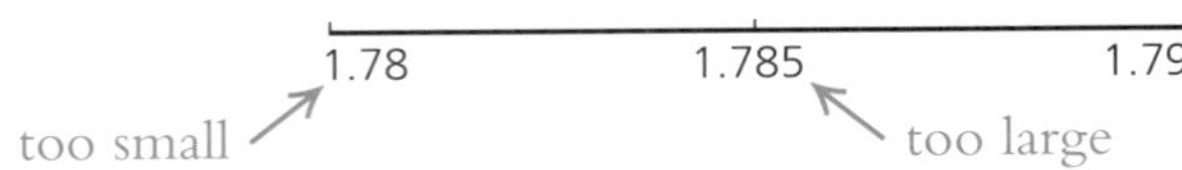

The required solution is 1.78 to 2 D.P.

---

6 Copy the table and complete this solution of the equation

$x^2 + x = 5$

to find x correct to 2 D.P.

x	$x^2 + x$
1	2
2	6
1.5	3.75

7 a) Take a first estimate of the positive solution to the equation $x^2 - 2x = 6$ from the graph.

b) Use trial and improvement to find the solution correct to 2 D.P. Show all your results in a table.

c) Repeat the process to find the negative solution correct to 2 D.P.

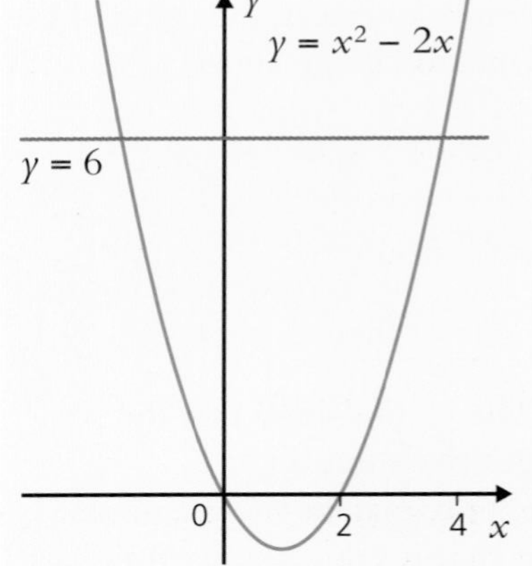

8 The solutions of the equation

$x^2 - x = 3$

are given by the intersection of the graphs shown in the diagram.

a) State the equations of the graphs shown.

b) Use trial and improvement to find both solutions to 1 D.P. (Show your results in a table).

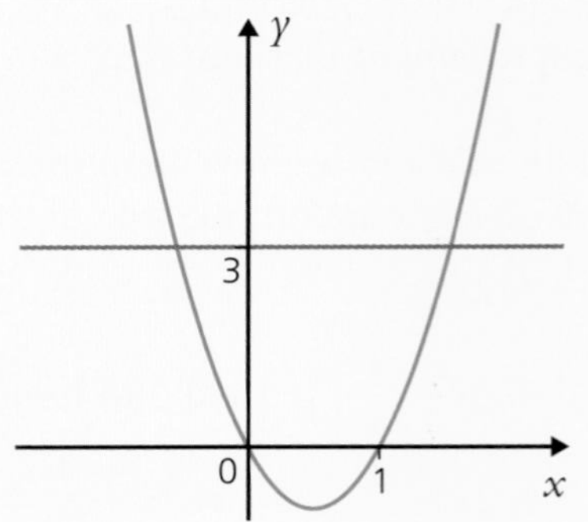

9 The diagram shows the graphs of the equations $y = x^2$ and $y = 3x + 1$.

a) State the equation satisfied by the x coordinates at the intersection of these graphs.

b) Rearrange the equation so that all of the terms involving x are on the same side.

c) Find the positive solution correct to 2 D.P.

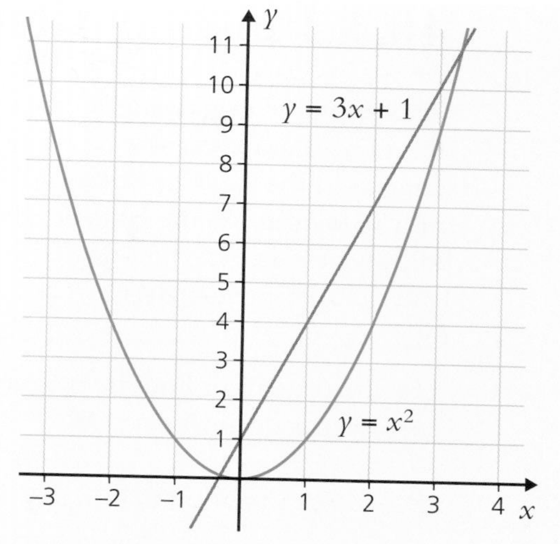

10 Draw the graphs of $y = x^2$ and $y = 5x - 3$ on the same diagram using values of x from -1 to 5 and values of y from -3 to 20.

a) Give the equation satisfied by the x coordinates at the intersection of the graphs. ✔

b) Is there a negative solution to this equation? Explain your answer by referring to the graphs.

c) Rearrange the equation so that the terms in x appear on one side only. ✔

d) Use trial and improvement to find both solutions to 1 D.P.

11 a) Draw the graphs of $y = x^{-1}$ and $y = x + 1$ for $0 < x \leq 3$ and $0 < y < 5$ on the same diagram.

b) Write down the equation satisfied by the x coordinate at the point of intersection of the two graphs.

c) Explain why there can only be one positive solution to this equation.

d) Multiply both sides of the equation by x so that the terms in x appear on only one side of the equation.

e) Use the graphs to obtain a suitable starting value and solve the equation by trial and improvement giving the value of x to 3 D.P.

12 a) Draw the graph of $y = x^3 + x$ for values of x from 0 to 3.

b) Use the graph to find the value of x to 1 D.P. such that $x^3 + x = 12$.

c) Use trial and improvement to refine the solution to 3 D.P.

40 SINE, COSINE AND TANGENT

40.1 Finding heights

The height of a right-angled triangle can be found by multiplying the base by the tangent of the angle of elevation (see Unit 36). So we can use the tangent when we know one side of a right-angled triangle and the adjoining angle.

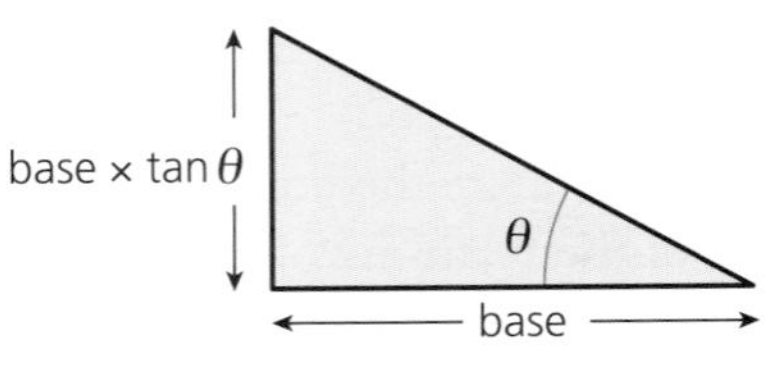

1 Use the tangent to find the heights of these triangles. Give your answer correct to 1 decimal place. ✓

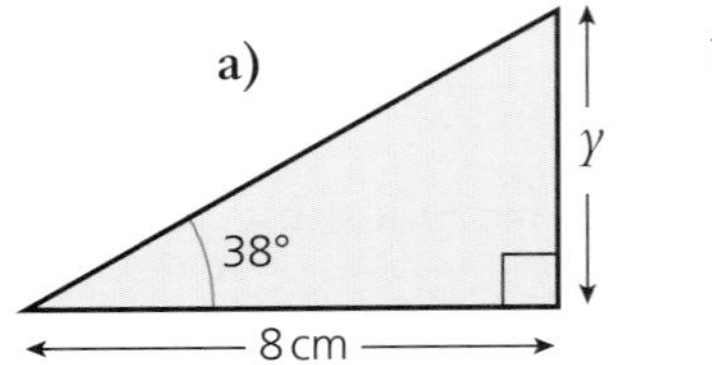

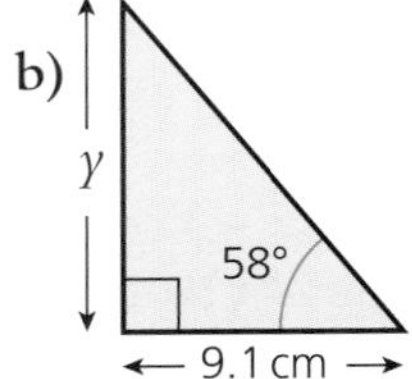

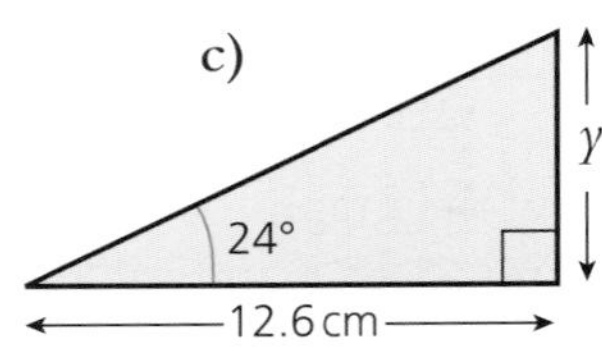

The tangent can be used to find the height of a building providing the angle of elevation is measured at a known distance away.

2 Find the height of this block of flats.

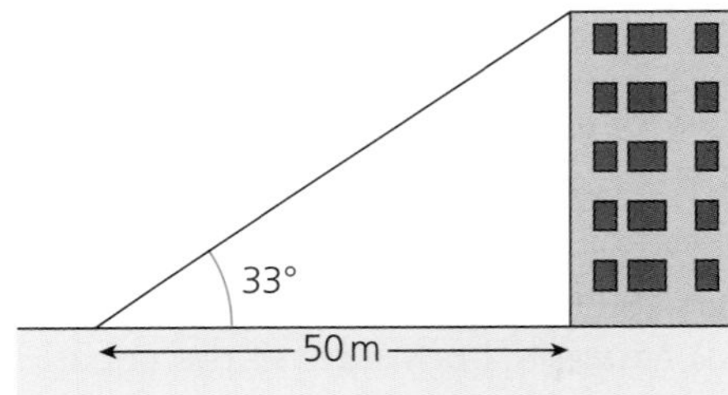

Sometimes we have the wrong information to use the tangent.

Investigation

Campbell has a stunt kite which he sometimes flies in competitions. He lets his kite out on 50 m of string and measures the angle of elevation as 60°. Can he use this information to find the height of the kite?

He cannot use the tangent because he knows the length of the hypotenuse and an adjoining angle. Here is an alternative method of solving this problem.

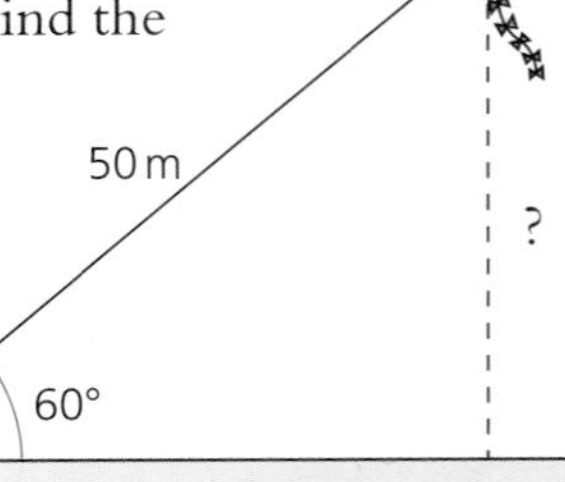

For this activity you need a protractor, 1 cm graph paper, ruler and pencil.

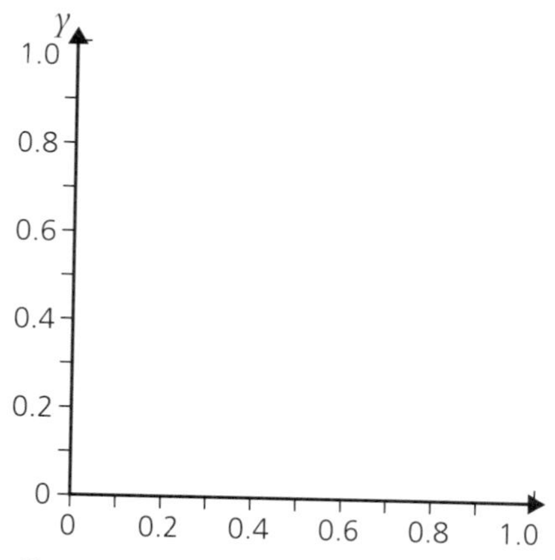

1 On your graph paper draw x and y axes, both 10 cm in length, as shown here. Use a scale of 1 cm for each 0.1 interval.

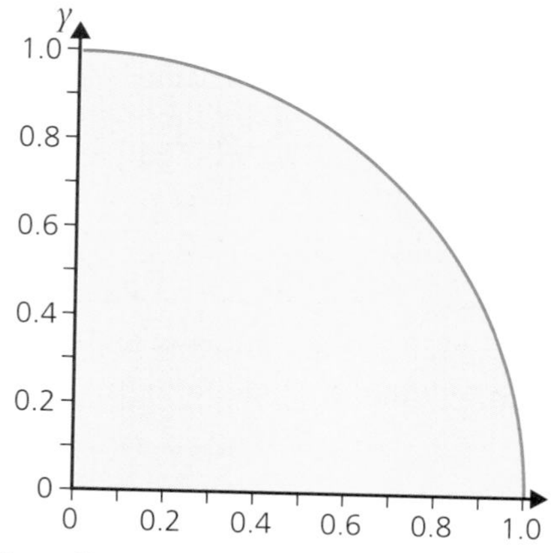

2 Set a pair of compasses so that they will draw a circle of 10 cm radius. Draw a quarter circle onto your diagram.

3 Use a protractor to draw an angle of 10°, up from the horizontal axis. Extend the line you have drawn out to the circle.

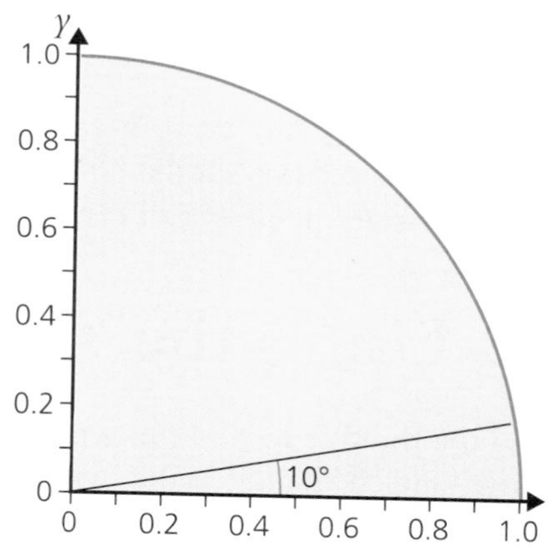

4 What are the coordinates of the point where your 10° line reaches the circle?

5 Repeat the process for 20°.

Continue in this way making your angle 10° larger each time.
Set out your answers in a table like this.

Angle	x coordinate	y coordinate
10°	0.98	0.17
20°		
30°		
40°		
50°		
60°		
70°		
80°		
90°		

6 ✔ Look at your table of results. Use it to find the heights of these triangles.

a) 1 cm 60° y

b)

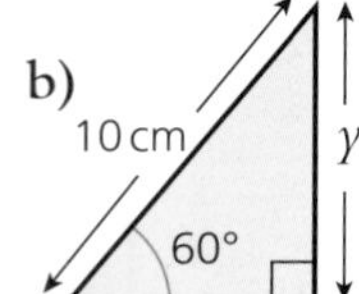

c)

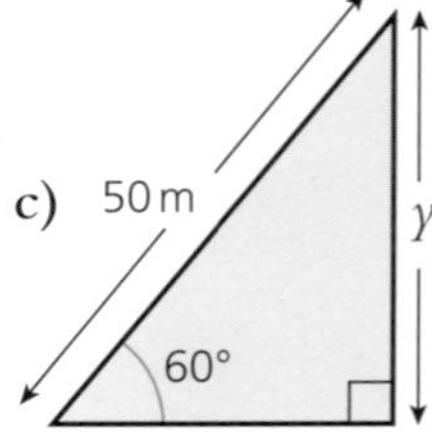

The accuracy of your answers will obviously depend on the accuracy of your drawing.

A more accurate result can be found using the **sine** of an angle.

This is abbreviated to sin on your calculator. To find the sine on your calculator, press:
[sin] 60 [=]

(An older calculator may require 60 [sin])

If you multiply this answer by 50 you will have an accurate answer for the height of the kite.

---

7 Now use the [sin] key on your calculator to find the sine for all the angles you drew. Your answers should correspond to the last column on your table where you wrote the height of each triangle.

40.2 Using the sine and cosine

We can use the sine to find the *height* of a right-angled triangle if the hypotenuse is known.

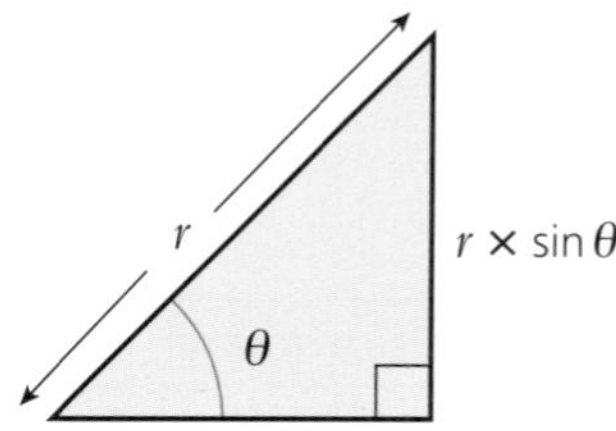

The height of the triangle is found using the formula:

height = $r \times \sin \theta$

Example

Use the sine to find the height (y) of this triangle.

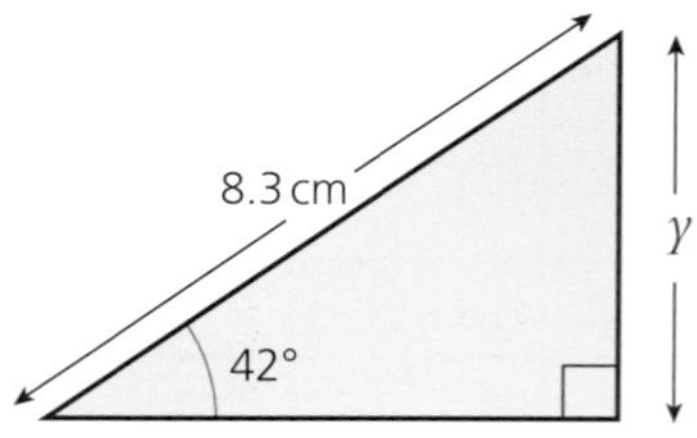

Answer

$y = 8.3 \times \sin 42°$

Use your calculator to check that $y = 5.553\,784$.

So the height is 5.6 cm correct to 1 D.P.

1 ✔ Use the sin key on your calculator to find the value for y in each triangle.

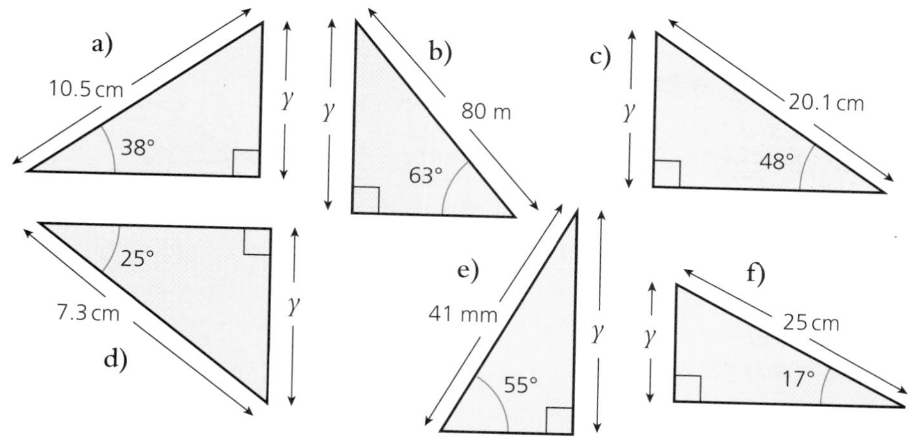

2 A playground slide has a 6 m slope. How high is the top of the slide above the ground?

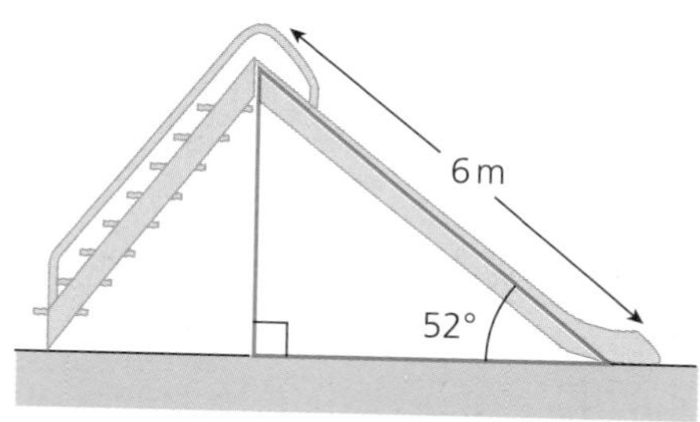

3 ✔ A ship sails out of harbour (H) on a bearing of 050°. It continues on this bearing for 10 km. To find how far north of the harbour it is now:

a) first find the size of the angle marked θ

b) use this to calculate the distance marked y.

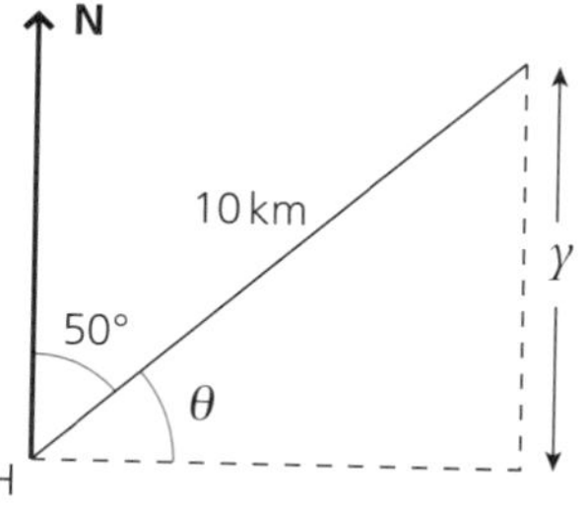

4 ✔ a) Suppose we had wanted to find the ship's distance *East* of the harbour. Look back at the table of results you completed for the Investigation on page 379. Can you find a result there which will help you to find the base of each of these triangles?

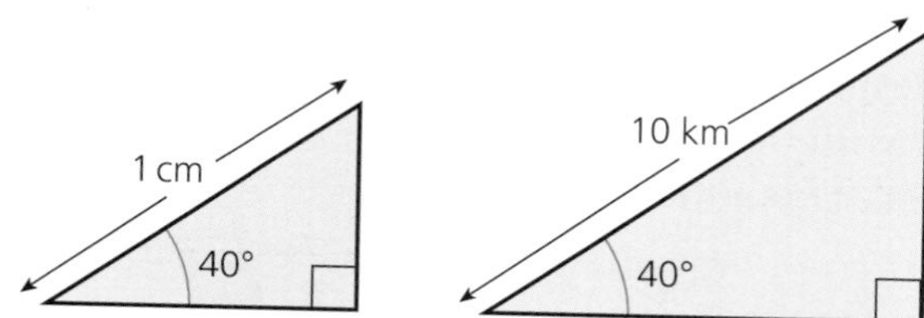

b) How far East has the ship in question 3 sailed?

The results listed in the Investigation table (page 379) as the x coordinates can all be found more accurately using the **cos** key on your calculator (cos stands for cosine).

Check that the results in the second column of your table are close to those given by the **cos** key on your calculator.

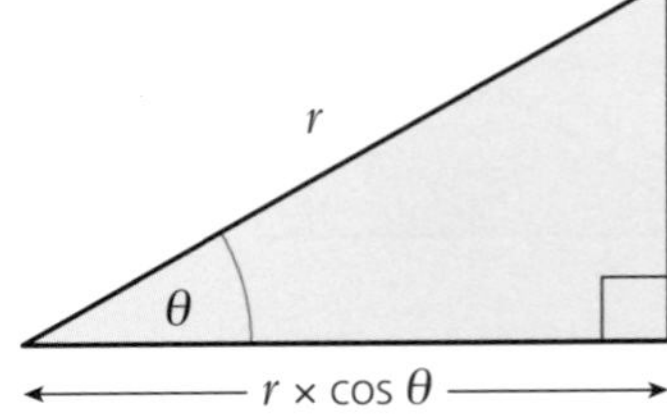

We can use the cosine to find the *base* of a right-angled triangle, if the hypotenuse is known.

The base of the triangle is found using the formula:

$$\text{base} = r \times \cos \theta$$

Example

Find the base (x) of this right-angled triangle.

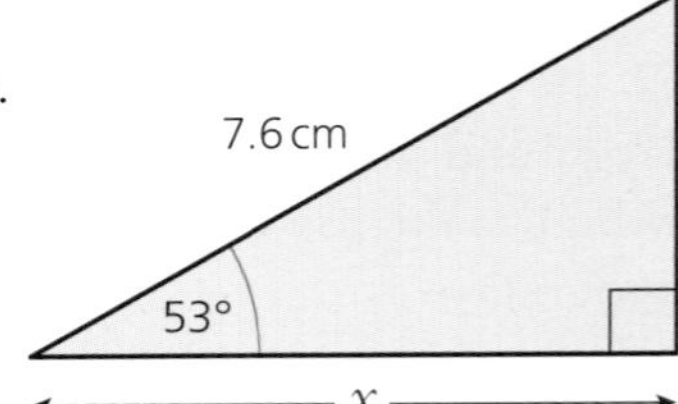

Answer

$x = 7.6 \times \cos 53° = 4.573\,79$

The base is 4.6 cm (correct to 1 D.P.)

5 ✔ Use the cosine to find the length of the side marked x in these triangles.

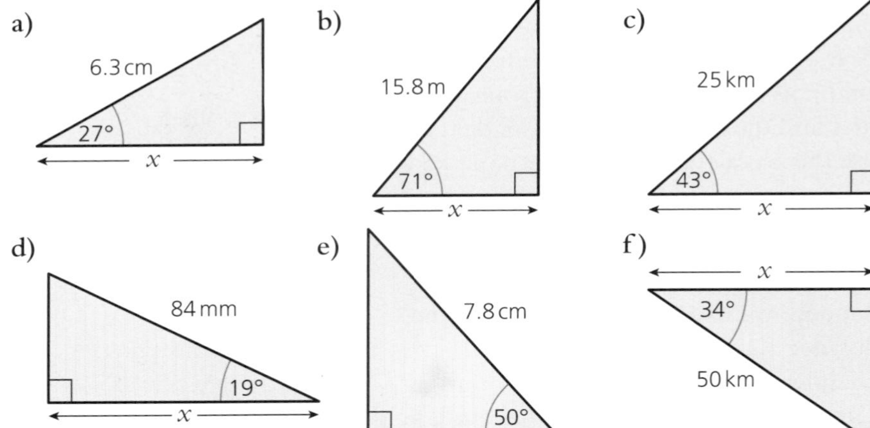

6 A ladder 7 metres long is leaning against a wall. If it makes an angle of 72° with the ground, how far is the bottom of the ladder from the wall?

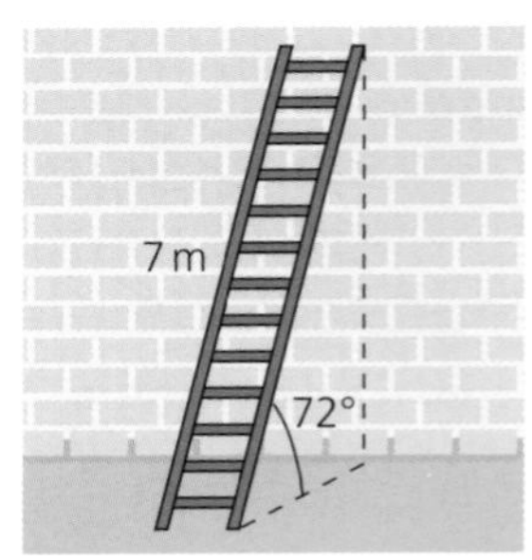

7 ✓ An isosceles triangle has two sides of 6 cm and an angle of 50° between them. Find θ and hence find the length of the third side.

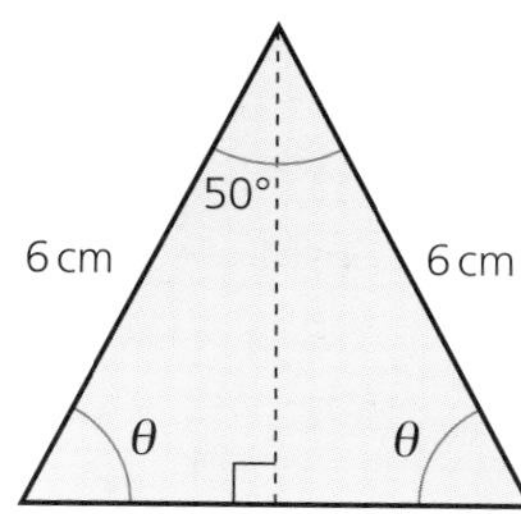

40.3 Sine, cosine and tangent

You have now used three trigonometrical (or trig) ratios: sine, cosine and tangent.

The sine and cosine are used when the hypotenuse of the right-angled triangle is known. The tangent is used when the hypotenuse is not known or needed.

It is easy to get confused when thinking about which of the three to use. It is customary to name the sides of the triangle as:

- hypotenuse — longest side
- adjacent — *next to* the angle which is known
- opposite — *opposite* the angle which is known

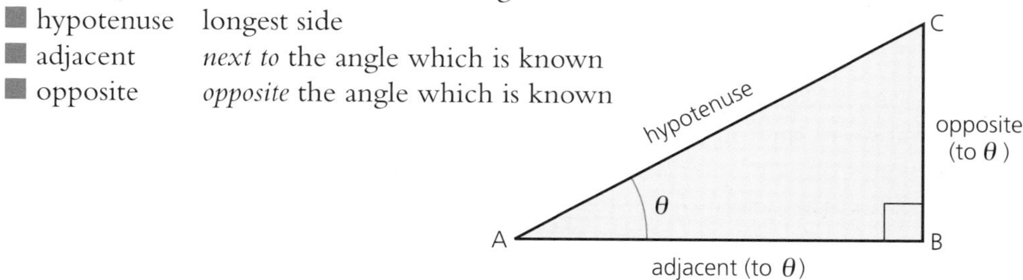

Sine
If you know the hypotenuse, the sine can be used to find the *opposite* side.
opposite = hypotenuse × sin θ

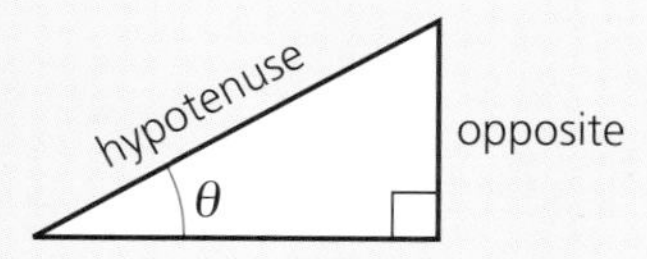

Cosine
If you know the hypotenuse, the cosine can be used to find the *adjacent* side.
adjacent = hypotenuse × cos θ

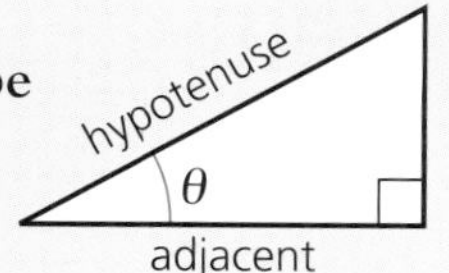

Tangent
If you know the adjacent side, the tangent can be used to find the opposite side.
opposite = adjacent × tan θ

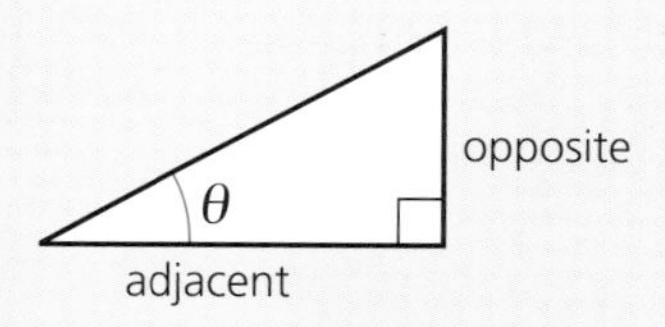

All these formulae will be given to you in your GCSE examination.

1 ✔ Which trig ratio (sin, cos or tan) would you use to find x in each of these triangles?

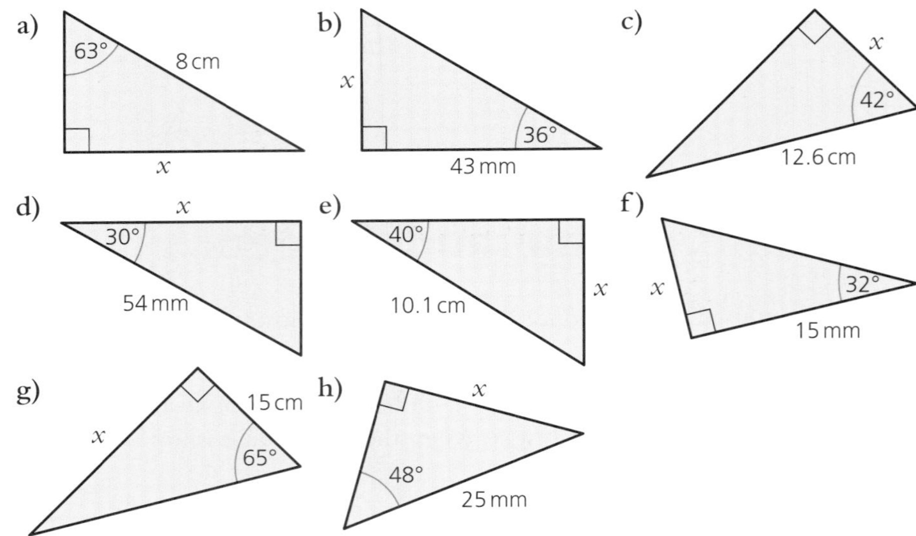

2 ✔ Find x for each of the triangles in question 1, giving your answer correct to 1 decimal place.

3 A woman walks 12 m away from a tree. From that position the angle of elevation to the top of the tree is 24°. If the measurement is taken from a point 1.5 m above the ground level, find the height of the tree.

4 A ladder leaning against a vertical wall makes an angle of 24° with the wall. If the ladder is 5 m long, how far out from the bottom of the wall is the foot of the ladder?

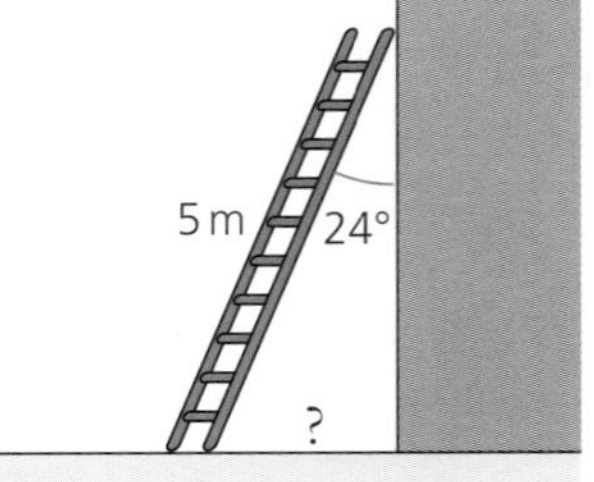

5 A slab of stone measuring 2 feet by 5 feet is left propped up against a wall. What is the height of D above the ground?

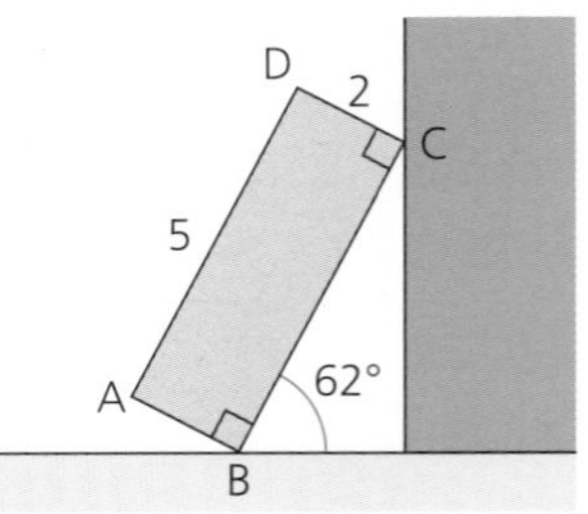

40.4 Finding the size of an angle

If you wish to find the size of an angle in a right-angled triangle, any of the three sin, cos, tan formulae can be re-arranged.

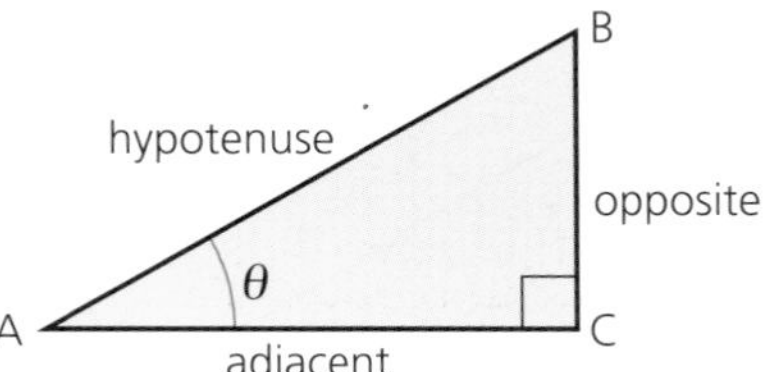

- Opposite = hypotenuse × sin θ
  Dividing both sides by the hypotenuse and rearranging:

  $$\sin \theta = \frac{\text{opposite}}{\text{hypotenuse}}$$

- Adjacent = hypotenuse × cos θ
  Dividing both sides by the hypotenuse and rearranging:

  $$\cos \theta = \frac{\text{adjacent}}{\text{hypotenuse}}$$

- Opposite = adjacent × tan θ
  Dividing both sides by the adjacent side and rearranging:

  $$\tan \theta = \frac{\text{opposite}}{\text{adjacent}}$$

The ratios sin θ, cos θ and tan θ are *only* true for right-angled triangles.

Example

Write as a fraction:

a) sin A b) cos A
c) tan C d) cos C

Answer

For angle A: AC is the hypotenuse
AB is the adjacent side
BC is the opposite side.

For angle C: AC is the hypotenuse
BC is the adjacent side
AB is the opposite side.

a) $\sin A = \frac{\text{opposite}}{\text{hypotenuse}} = \frac{5}{13}$

b) $\cos A = \frac{\text{adjacent}}{\text{hypotenuse}} = \frac{12}{13}$

c) $\tan C = \frac{\text{opposite}}{\text{adjacent}} = \frac{12}{5}$

d) $\cos C = \frac{\text{adjacent}}{\text{hypotenuse}} = \frac{5}{13}$

1 ✔ Write $\sin\theta$ as a fraction for each of these triangles.

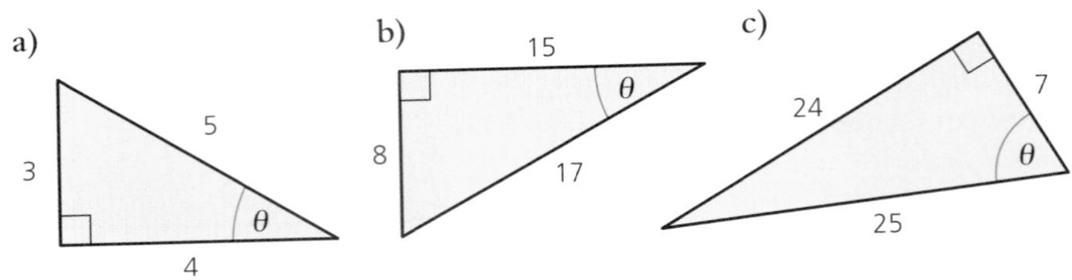

2 ✔ Write $\cos\theta$ as a fraction for each of the triangles in question 1.

3 ✔ Write $\tan\theta$ as a fraction for each of the triangles in question 1.

4 Find the trig ratios needed for each triangle. Write your answer first as a fraction, then as a decimal.

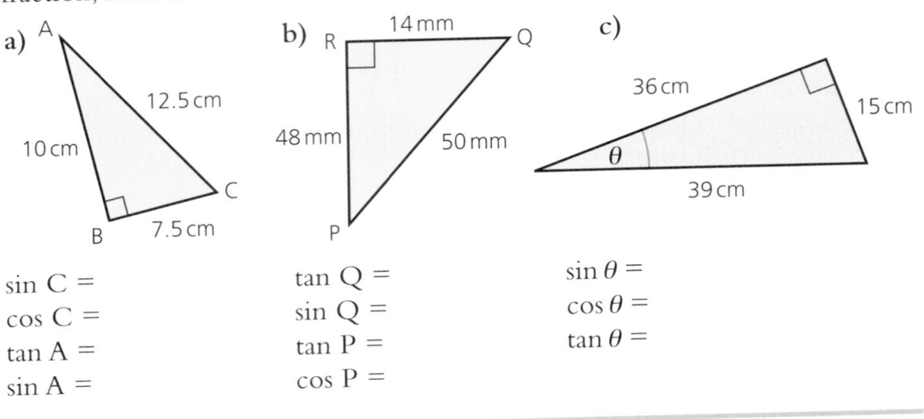

a)	b)	c)
sin C =	tan Q =	$\sin\theta$ =
cos C =	sin Q =	$\cos\theta$ =
tan A =	tan P =	$\tan\theta$ =
sin A =	cos P =	

Once the sine, cosine or tangent of an angle is known, we can use a calculator to find the size of the angle.

Example

Given that $\tan\theta = 1.3$, find the value of θ correct to 1 D.P.

Answer

Method (i) (trial and improvement)

tan 50° = 1.191	too small
tan 55° = 1.428	too big
tan 52.5° = 1.303	too big
tan 52.4° = 1.298	too small
tan 52.45° = 1.3008	too big

It follows that $\theta = 52.4°$ to 1 D.P.

Method (ii) (reversing the process)

Your calculator will have a SHIFT, 2nd F or INV key that may be used with the tan key to find the angle.

e.g. key in:

SHIFT tan 1.3 =

giving $\theta = 52.4314\ldots°$
$= 52.4°$ to 1 D.P.

For older calculators try 1.3 SHIFT tan

Note: it is much easier to find an angle by the second method but you should keep a note of the key sequence for *your* calculator. The reverse process works in the same way for sin and cos.

5 Use your answers to question 4 to find the size of the angles.

6 ✓ a) Decide which trig ratio – sine, cosine or tangent – you need to find θ in each of these triangles.

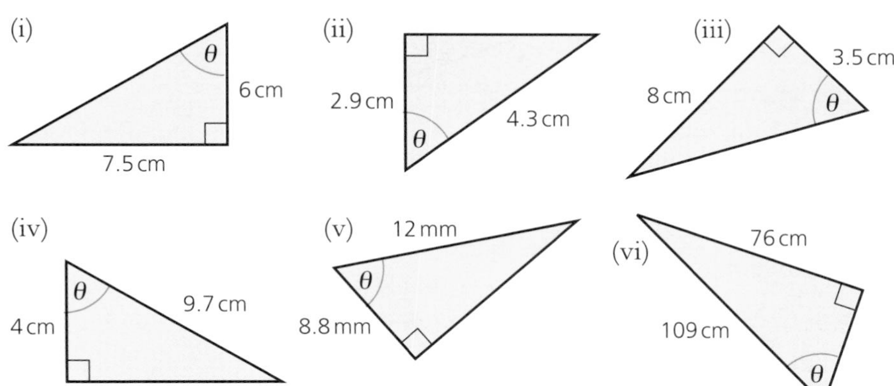

b) Use the correct trig ratio to find the value of θ for each of the triangles in part a).

7 A ship sails 3 km due East and then 4 km due North. Find the bearing from its original position. (Remember that the bearing is the clockwise angle from North.)

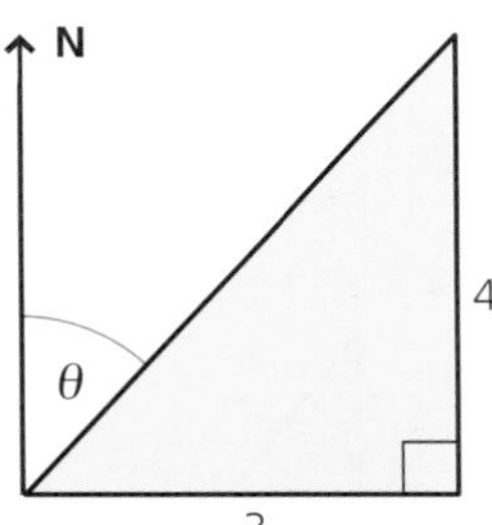

8 A pole 8 m high casts a shadow 6 m long. What is the angle of elevation of the Sun?

9 The legs of a pair of compasses are each 6 cm long, and they are used to draw a circle with a radius of 4 cm. Find the angle between the legs.

10 A bicycle shed is 3 m high at the back and 2.5 m high at the front. If the shed is 3.5 m wide, find the angle of slope of the roof.

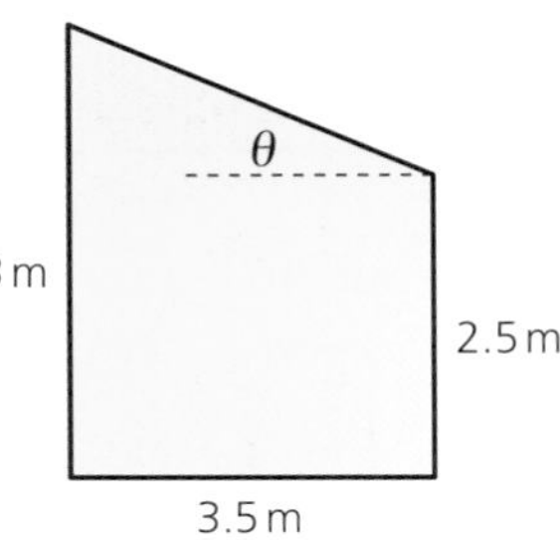

40.5 Harder problems

Example

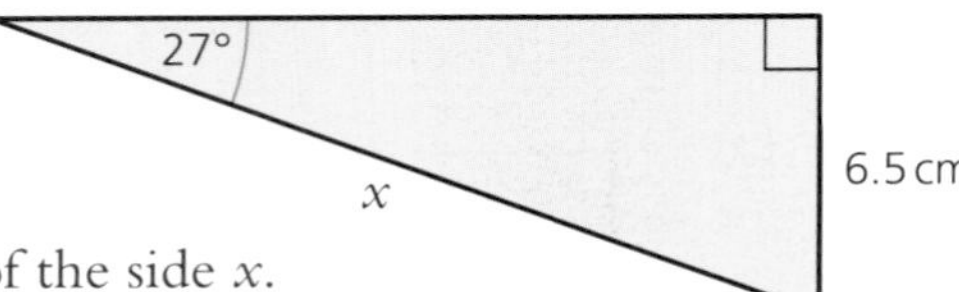

Find the length of the side x.

Answer

x is the hypotenuse and the side 6.5 cm is *opposite* the angle 27°. So we choose the sin ratio:

$$\sin\theta = \frac{\text{opposite}}{\text{hypotenuse}}$$

$\sin 27° = \frac{6.5}{x}$ multiply both sides by x

$x \times \sin 27° = 6.5$ cm divide both sides by sin 27°

$x = \frac{6.5}{\sin 27°}$ Using a calculator 6.5 [÷] [sin] 27 [=]

(or 6.5 [÷] 27 [sin] [=])

$x = 14.3$ cm (to 1 D.P.)

1 ✔ Find the length of d in each of these triangles. (Give your answer correct to 1 D.P.)

a)

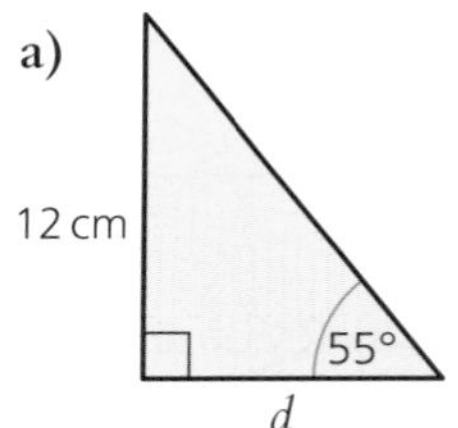

b)

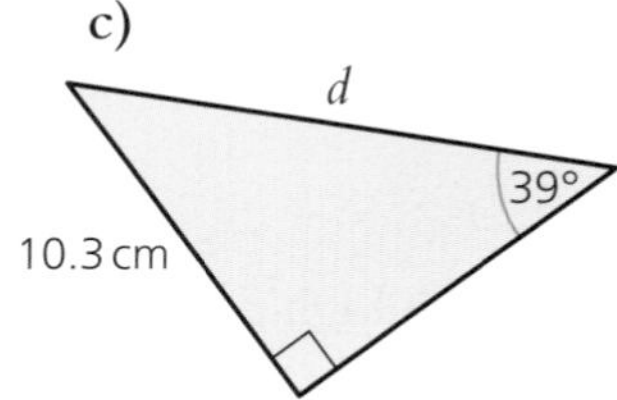

c)

d)

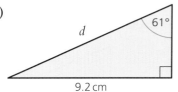

e)

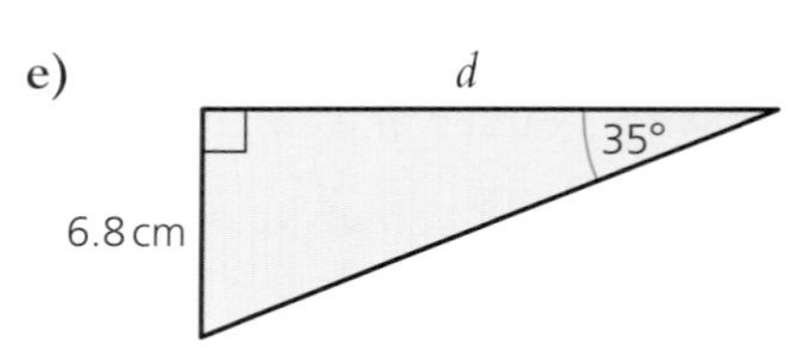

2 A ship sails 10 km on a bearing of 050°. How far North is it from its original position?

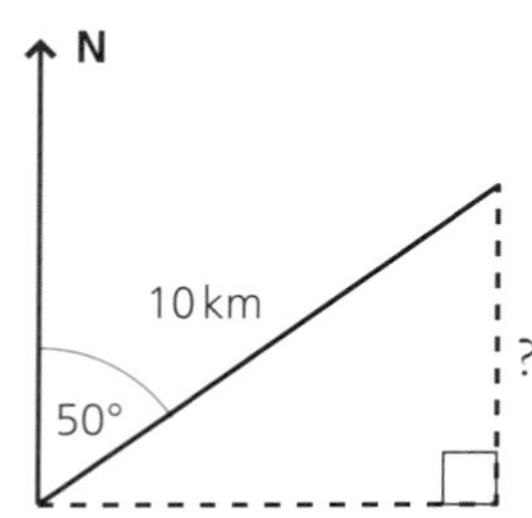

3 Two people are standing on opposite sides of a tower.

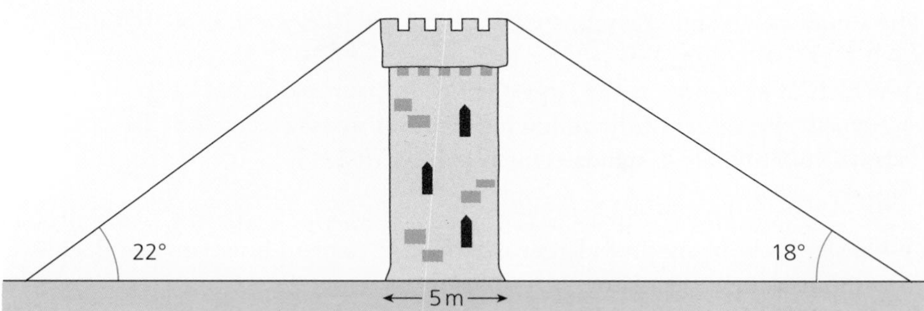

They measure the angles of elevation to the top of the tower as 22° and 18° respectively. If the height of the tower is 20 m, find the distance between the two people.

4 A kite is flying at a height of 67.2 m. It is attached to a string which makes an angle of 55° to the horizontal. What is the length of the string?

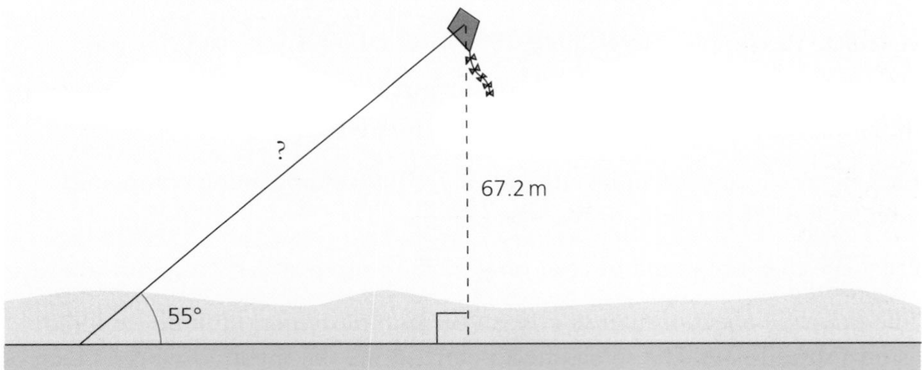

REVIEW 5

Unit 33 Calculator problems

1 The values of x, y and z are given by $x = 3.15 \times 10^{22}$, $y = 9.53 \times 10^{16}$ and $z = 6.27 \times 10^{23}$.

a) Which of x, y and z is the largest? Explain your reasoning.

b) *Estimate* the values of the following without using a calculator. In each case, leave your answer in standard form correct to 1 S.F.

(i) x^2 (ii) yz (iii) $\frac{y}{x}$ (iv) $\frac{x}{y}$

c) *Roughly*, how many times larger is z than x? Explain how you can decide without using a calculator.

d) Use a calculator to find the value of the expressions given in b) in standard form correct to 3 S.F.

2 Taking the speed of light as 1.86×10^5 miles per second and the distance of Neptune from the Sun as 2.794×10^9 miles, calculate the length of time needed for light from the Sun to reach Neptune.

Give your answer: a) to the nearest hour

b) in hours and minutes to the nearest minute.

3 Calculate the simple interest on £7500 invested for 4 years at 6.7% p.a.

4 How many complete years would it take for an initial investment of £3800 to more than double its value at 5.8% simple interest?

5 Find the total value of an investment of £10 000 after gaining compound interest at 8.3% per year for five years.

6 Calculate the compound interest on £9250 invested at 7.1% p.a. for three years.

7 The dramatic effect of interest charges on loan repayments can be explored using a spreadsheet. The spreadsheet below shows the situation where a loan of £10 000 is repaid at the rate of £2000 per year assuming that interest charges of 16% are added on at the end of each year.

Spreadsheet

	A	B	C	D	E
1	Years	Year's		Total	Current
2	completed	payment		repaid	balance
3	0			0	10000
4	1	2000		2000	9600
5	2	2000		4000	9136
6	3	2000		6000	8597.76
7	4	2000		8000	7973.402
8	5	2000		10000	7249.146
9	6	2000		12000	6409.009
10					

Find out how much money is borrowed on a mortgage by a typical first-time house buyer. Ask a local Building Society (or look at their website!) what the monthly repayments are and the interest charged on the loan. Use a spreadsheet to investigate what happens . How much will the interest charges total over the 25-year term of the loan?

The spreadsheet may be set up by copying the given formulae downwards.

Spreadsheet

	A	B	C	D	E
1	Years	Year's		Total	Current
2	completed	payment		repaid	balance
3	0			0	10000
4	=A3+1	2000		=D3+B4	=E3*1.16-B4

Use the spreadsheet to answer these questions assuming that interest continues to be charged in the same way.

a) If the pattern of payments remains the same, how much will have been repaid on the loan after 10 years?
b) What is the balance still to be paid after 10 years?
c) By how much does the balance reduce in the first year?
d) By how much does the balance reduce in the tenth year?
e) Explain why the balance doesn't reduce in equal amounts from year to year even though the payments are the same in each year.
f) If no payment is made in the third year but payments resume as normal afterwards, what difference does this make to the balance after 10 years?
g) If, instead, the payment in the third year is increased by £500 but all other payments remain the same, what is the new balance after 10 years?
h) Does it make any difference in which year an under-payment or over-payment is made? Explain your answer.
i) What is the balance after 10 years if the regular annual payment is £2069? How much has been repaid on the £10 000 loan?

8 Set up a spreadsheet to investigate mortgage repayments based on a standard 25-year loan. Consider the influence of interest rate changes and the effect of under and over-payments.
Find out about property price changes in the last twenty years and explain how positive and negative equity can occur.

Unit 34 Cumulative frequency

9 As part of an experiment, a group of students timed how long they could hold their breath. Here are their results timed in seconds:

a) How many students took part in the experiment?
b) Find the median time for holding their breath.
c) Find the interquartile range.

Time (seconds)	Frequency
$40 \le x < 50$	6
$50 \le x < 60$	8
$60 \le x < 70$	14
$70 \le x < 80$	21
$80 \le x < 90$	26
$90 \le x < 100$	14
$100 \le x < 110$	7
$110 \le x < 120$	4

10 Guy counted the number of matches in 50 matchboxes and obtained the following results:

a) Find the median number of matches in a box.
b) What is the interquartile range?

No. of matches	No. of boxes
42	10
43	6
44	20
45	6
46	5
47	2
48	1

11 A market gardener weighed a sample of tomatoes grown using a new brand of fertiliser. He recorded the weight of each individual fruit and drew up the frequency table shown here:

a) How many fruits did he weigh?
b) What was the median weight?
c) What is the interquartile range?

Weight of fruit (g)	Frequency
$35 \leq x < 45$	3
$45 \leq x < 55$	7
$55 \leq x < 65$	10
$65 \leq x < 75$	18
$75 \leq x < 85$	12
$85 \leq x < 95$	6
$95 \leq x < 105$	4

Unit 35 Further equations

12 Rearrange each of the following equations to make x the subject:

a) $x - h = k$ b) $x + nt = y$

c) $\frac{x}{k} = h$ d) $\frac{x}{j+k} = h$

e) $\frac{k}{x} = h$ f) $\frac{h}{x-k} = r$

g) $\sqrt{x - k} = h$ h) $\sqrt{k - x} = h$

i) $\sqrt{\frac{x}{k}} = h$ j) $\sqrt{\frac{x}{k}} - j = h$

13 a) Make l the subject of the formula $T = 2\pi\sqrt{\frac{l}{g}}$.

b) Find the value of l given that $T = 0.5$ and $g = 9.8$ (use the value of π given by your calculator).

14 Solve these simultaneous equations using the substitution method.

a) $2x + y = 18$
$y = x - 3$

b) $3x - y = 11$
$x = y + 5$

15 Solve the following simultaneous equations by the most convenient method:

a) $5u - 2v = 20$
$u + 2v = 16$

b) $m = 2n + 7$
$m + 3n = 22$

c) $3p - 4q = -22$
$p + q = 10$

d) $4a + 3b = 11$
$b - 6 = a$

16 Expand and simplify each of the following:

a) $3x(x + 5) + 2x$
b) $7x(2x - 1) + 3x - 5$
c) $(x + 5)(x + 4)$
d) $(x - 5)(x + 3)$
e) $(x + 8)(x - 1)$
f) $(x - 6)(x - 5)$
g) $(x + 4)^2$
h) $(x - 6)^2$
i) $(x + 5)(x - 5)$
j) $(x - 11)(x + 11)$

17 Given that: $9945 = 3^2 \times 5 \times 13 \times 17$
$25\,025 = 5^2 \times 7 \times 11 \times 13$
and $9537 = 3 \times 11 \times 17^2$

a) Find the highest common factor of:
(i) 9945 and 9537
(ii) 9537 and 25 025
(iii) 9945, 25 025 and 9537

b) What is the smallest whole number that 9537 must be multiplied by to make it a multiple of 9945?

18 Factorise fully:

a) $x^2y + xy^2$
b) $xyz + x^2yz$
c) $12x - 8xy$
d) $14pq^2 + 21p^2q - 7pq$
e) $9abc - 6ab - 15bc$
f) $x^2 - 36$

Unit 36 Dimensions

19 The area of fabric required to make this skirt can be found using one of the formulae listed below. Check the dimensions of each one to decide which one is likely to be correct.

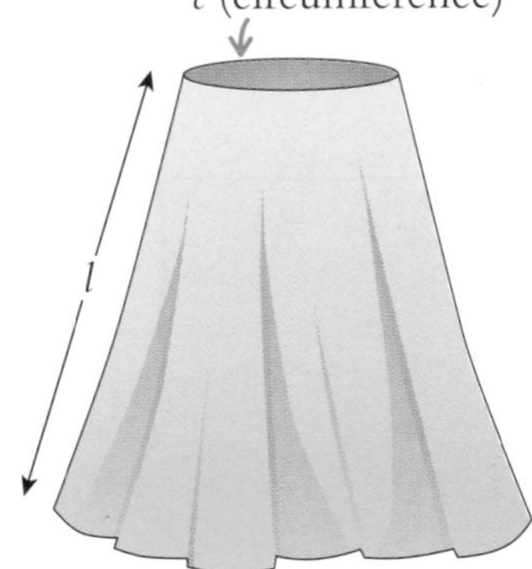

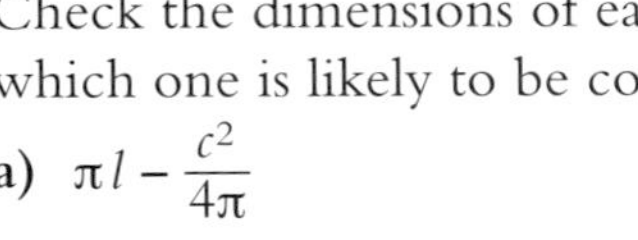

a) $\pi l - \dfrac{c^2}{4\pi}$

b) $cl + \pi l^2$

c) $\pi c^2 l - \pi c^2$

d) $\pi(l + c)$

20 A vertical pole casts a shadow 20 m long when the altitude of the Sun (angle of elevation) is 52°. Find the height of the pole.

52°
?
20 m

21 A person stands 30 m away from the foot of a tower, which has a flagpole on top. The angle of elevation to the bottom of the flagpole is 63°, while the angle of elevation to the top of the pole is 65°.

a) Draw a sketch to show this information.
b) How tall is the tower?
c) How high is the top of the flagpole?
d) How tall is the flagpole?

Unit 37 Algebra and graphs (3)

22 a) Using values of x from –4 to 4 draw the graphs of the equations $y = \frac{2}{x^2}$ and $y = x + 3$ on the same diagram.

b) Use the diagram to find the values of x that satisfy the following equations correct to 1 D.P.

(i) $\frac{2}{x^2} = 0.5$ (ii) $\frac{2}{x^2} = 4$ (iii) $x^3 + 3x^2 = 2$

c) Find the equation of the straight line which may be added to the diagram to solve the equation $x^3 = 2$. Explain how the diagram shows that the equation has only one solution and find its value correct to 1 D.P.

23 a) Give the coordinates of the points where the graph of $y = x(x - 4)$ crosses the x axis.

b) Sketch the graph and use it to find the values of x such that $x^2 - 4x < 0$.

24 Use a graphics calculator or computer graph plotter to produce displays that resemble the diagrams below. Write a list of your equations and describe any connections between them.

a)

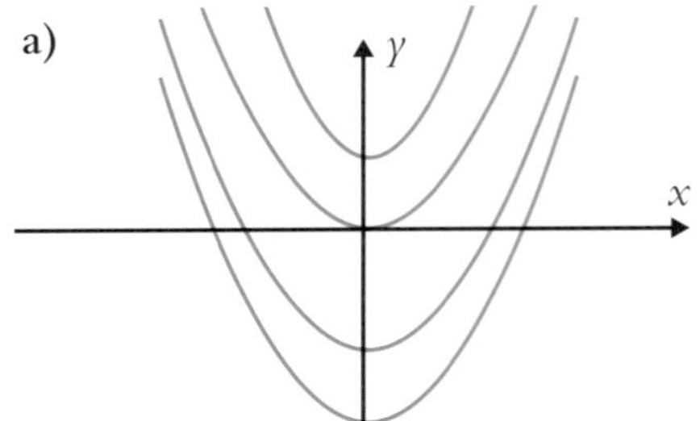

b)

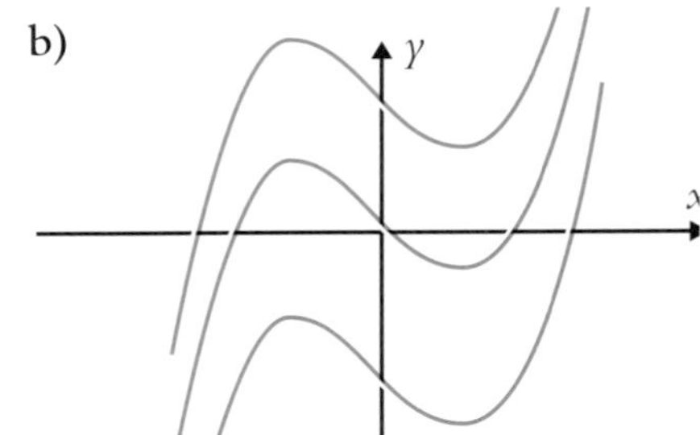

Unit 38 Combining probabilities

25 Ben knows from experience that when he catches a fish, the probability that it is too small to take home to eat for his tea is 0.9. Find the probability that if he catches three fish, exactly one will be large enough to take home.

26 The probability that a household living in a certain area owns a car is 0.7. Find the probability that:

a) two households selected at random both own cars
b) if the two households are selected at random only one owns a car
c) three households are selected at random and none of them owns a car.

27 The seeds for wallflowers sold by a nursery produce plants with either red or yellow flowers. The probability that a plant has yellow flowers is $\frac{2}{5}$. If two plants are grown from these seeds, find the probability that:

a) both have yellow flowers

b) both have red flowers

c) one has red and the other has yellow flowers.

Draw a tree diagram to help you work out these probabilities.

28 The probability that Jackie wakes up late in the morning is 0.6. When she does wake up late, she has a probability of arriving late for work of 0.85. If she wakes up on time, the probability that she arrives late for work is 0.4.

a) Copy and complete the following tree diagram.

Waking up		Arriving at work		Outcome	Probability
		?	on time	O,O	
?	on time				
		0.4	late	O,L	
		?	on time	L,O	
0.6	late				
		0.85	late	L,L	

b) Find the probability that Jackie arrives on time.

Unit 39 Problem solving

29 Emma and Vicky set off from their own separate homes at 2.58 p.m. to meet each other. The graph below shows their progress.

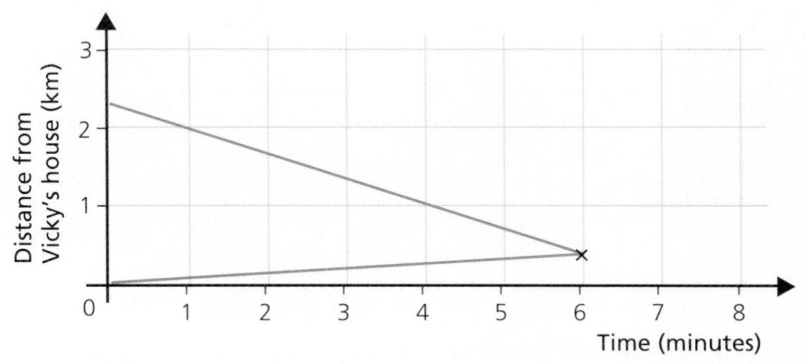

a) How far apart do Emma and Vicky live?

b) At what time did they meet?

c) Only one of them rode a bicycle and the other walked. Who do you think rode the bicycle? Explain your reasoning.

d) What feature of the graph shows that they both travelled at a steady speed?

e) Find their speeds in km/h.

30 Solve these equations:

a) $x^2 - 6x + 5 = 0$ b) $x^2 - 8x + 15 = 0$
c) $x^2 + x - 20 = 0$ d) $x^2 - 3x - 28 = 0$

31 Sketch the graphs of these equations:

a) $y = x(x - 5)$ b) $y = x^2 + 3x$
c) $y = (x - 4)^2$ d) $y = (x + 3)^2$
e) $y = x(x - 2)(x - 5)$ f) $y = (x + 3)(x - 1)(x - 4)$
g) $y = x^2 + 2x - 15$ h) $y = x^2 - 8x + 16$

32 The distance d metres that a parachutist falls during the t seconds before his parachute opens is given by the formula $d = 5t^2 - 0.3t$.
Use trial and improvement to find to 1 D.P. the time taken to fall:

a) 100 m b) 200 m.

Unit 40 Sine, cosine and tangent

33 Find the length x in each of these triangles correct to 3 S.F.

a)

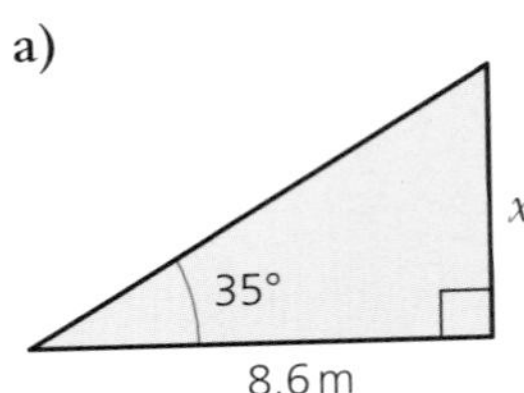

b)

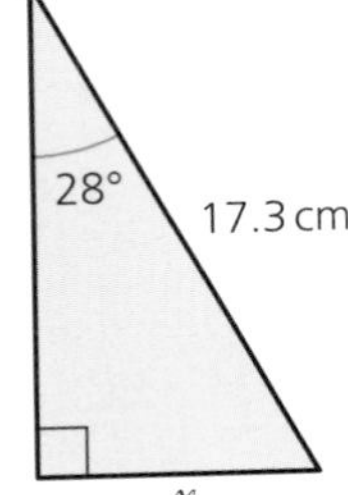

c)

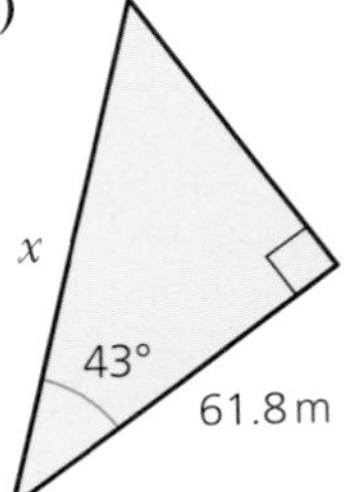

34 Calculate the value of θ correst to 1 D.P. in each case:

a)

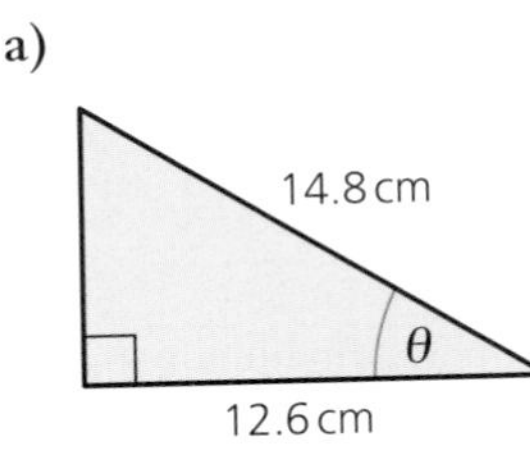

b)

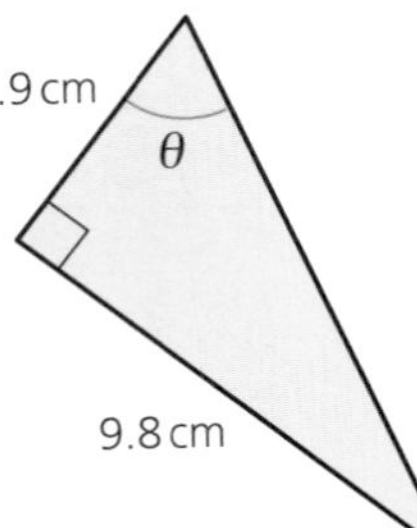

c)

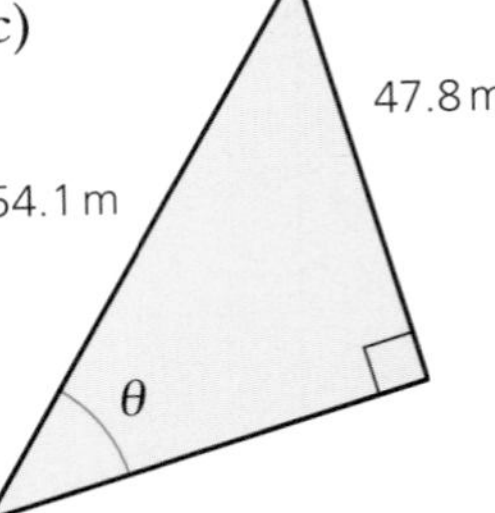

35 A flagpole is 17 m high. Find the length of its shadow when the altitude of the Sun (angle of elevation) is 58°.

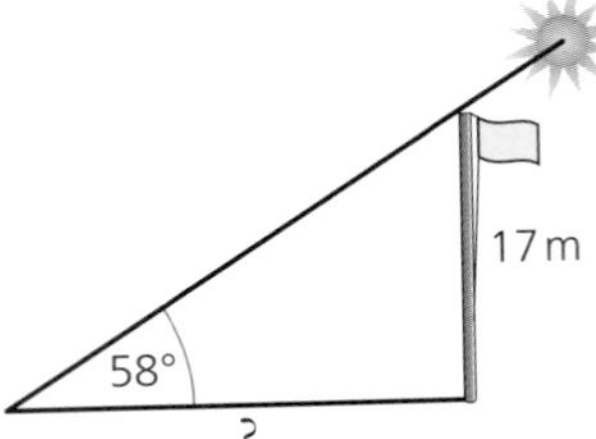

36 A girl standing on top of a mountain looks down towards the tower on a village church. She measures the angle of depression of the tower to be 42°. The mountain is 500 m high.

a) Draw a sketch diagram showing the information given in this question.

b) How far is the girl away from the church tower?

37 A ladder 6 m long is leaning against a wall with its base 2 m away from the wall.

a) Sketch this, and calculate the angle between the ladder and the ground.

b) The bottom of the ladder is then pulled 1 m further away from the wall. Make a new sketch and find how far down the wall the top of the ladder must have moved correct to the nearest centimetre.

38 A is 4 km East of B and C is 6 km South of A. Calculate the bearing of C from B.

39 An equilateral triangle has a vertical height of 10 cm. Calculate the lengths of its sides.

40 Make a scale drawing to represent the journey described in this question:

A ship sails at 18 km/h on a bearing of 160° for 1.5 hours. It then changes course to 076° and sails at 16 km/h for half an hour. For the final stage of the journey its bearing is 348° and it maintains a speed of 10 km/h for one hour.

Find its bearing and distance from its starting point.

41 a) Given that $\cos A = \frac{3}{5}$, sketch a right-angled triangle which would give that result.

b) Find the values of sin A and tan A.

42 A triangle has sides of 47 mm and 59 mm and a right angle between those two sides.

Find the smallest angle in that triangle (without making an accurate drawing).

EXAM PRACTICE

Number and algebra

When working through the questions in this section, make a point of checking your answers as if you were in the examination. Ask yourself:

1 **Have I answered the question?**
2 **Does the answer look reasonable?**

It's all too easy, under exam pressure, to misinterpret a question or to produce a silly answer. Carrying out these simple checks may help you spot the errors and save you valuable marks.

---

1 The sides of a quadrilateral, measured in cm, are:
$x, x + 2, x + 3$ and $x + 4$
a) Write a formula for the perimeter P of this quadrilateral.
b) The perimeter of the quadrilateral is 41 cm.
(i) Write an equation in x.
(ii) Find the side lengths of the quadrilateral by solving the equation.

2 A useful approximate value of π is $\sqrt{10}$.
Find the difference to 3 decimal places between this value and the value of π given by your calculator.

3 **a)** Solve the inequality $5x + 17 < 7$.
b) Write down all the integer solutions to $x^2 \leq 4$.
c) List all the values of x, which are integers that fit:
$-3 \leq x < 3$

4 Solve these equations:
a) $\dfrac{x-1}{2} = 4$ **b)** $\dfrac{1}{2}(45 - y) = 18$
c) $8(r - 1) - 3(2r - 2) = 2r - 2$ **d)** $x + 8.4(x - 1) = 10.4$

5 The length of a man's forearm (f cm) and his height (h cm) are approximately connected by the formula:
$$h = \frac{10f + 256}{3}$$
Use this approximate formula to answer these questions.
a) Part of a male human skeleton is found in an old plague pit.
The forearm is measured and found to be 20 cm long.
How tall might the man have been?
b) Write an expression for f in terms of h.
c) Does the formula hold for toddlers?
Give some figures and reasons to support your answer.

6 Find two numbers whose sum is 7 and whose product is 10.

7 A theatre has 500 seats. Tickets on the door cost £7 each, but advance tickets only cost £6. On a night the theatre was full, the total takings were £3425.
Let the number of tickets sold on the door be x.
a) Write down, in terms of x, the number of tickets sold in advance.
b) Use the information above to write down an equation satisfied by x.
c) Solve the equation to find the number of tickets sold in advance and at the door.

8 There is a solution to the equation $x^3 - 2x^2 = 1$ between 1 and 3.
Find this solution by trial and improvement to two decimal places.

9 Amy, Beth and Carol share £100 so that Amy has twice as much as Beth who has three times as much as Carol.
a) Rewrite this information in the form of an equation.
b) Solve the equation and find out how much Amy has.

10 Plot the graph of $y = 5x - x^2$ for values of x from 0 to 5.
Use your graph to solve these equations:
a) $5x - x^2 = 0$
b) $5x - x^2 = 5$

11 Use a graphical method to solve the simultaneous equations:
$$7x + 4y = 28$$
$$4x + 5y = 20$$

12 Write 125 as a power of 5.

13 According to the *Gazetteer of British Ghosts*, ghosts fade away after 400 years.
A ghost has been haunting a castle for x years.
How much longer can it go on haunting?

14 I am thinking of two numbers. Twice the first minus the second is 2 and three times the first number plus the second is 13. Find the two numbers.

15 A mother is 35 years old and her son is 7 years old. In how many years time will the mother be three times as old as her son?

16 Jim states that the winner of a race took 26.4 seconds.
Jules states that the winner took 26.40 seconds.
Is there any difference in these times?
Give a reason for your answer.

17 Pam conducted a survey about microwave cookers.
40% of the people she interviewed were women.
25% of these women owned a microwave.
30% of the men she interviewed owned a microwave.

a) What percentage of the people she interviewed were men?
b) What percentage of the people she interviewed were women owning a microwave?
c) What percentage of all the people interviewed owned a microwave?

18 In 1994 the price of a washing machine rose by 15%.
In 1995 the price was reduced by 15%.
Diane says 'The prices are back to what they were in 1994'.
Is she right? Give a reason for your answer.

19 Three people share a job cleaning offices each week.
Tom works for 12 hours.
Fred works for 4 hours.
Sally works for 8 hours.
They are paid £144 for the work which they share in proportion to the time they each worked. How much does each person get paid?

20 A recent newspaper report claimed that:
'Concorde planes have now flown 71 million miles. This is equivalent to 150 return trips to the Moon.'
Using this information, work out the distance from Earth to the Moon.

21 A woman is x years old now. In 12 years time she will be three times as old as she was 12 years ago. Use this information to set up an equation in x and solve it.

22 Jayne is a careers teacher. She does a survey each year to find out what the pupils do when they leave school at the end of year 11.
In 1995 there were 240 pupils.
110 went into the sixth form.
80 went into employment.
35 went to college.
15 were unemployed.

a) Draw a pie chart to show this and label each sector.
b) In 1990 360 pupils left school. 25% went into employment. Jayne said that more pupils were employed in 1995 than in 1990.
Why is she wrong?

23 A home brewer uses the rule that, if he puts x g of sugar per litre, the percentage alcohol in his beer will be $A\%$, where

$$A = \frac{x}{16} - 1 .$$

This holds for $20 \leq x \leq 208$.

a) What are the greatest and smallest values of A for which the formula holds?
b) Write down a formula for x in terms of A.

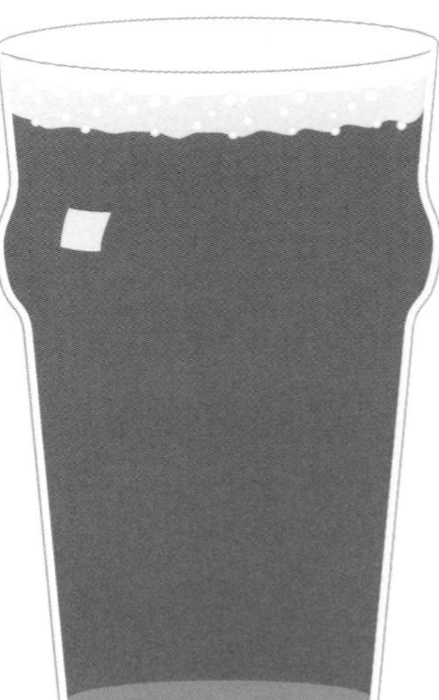

24 A sweet-vending machine only takes 20p and 50p coins.
There are ten more 20p coins than there are 50p coins.
The total amount of money in the machine is £26.50.
Let x be the number of 20p coins and y the number of 50p coins.

a) Write down two equations connecting x and y.
b) Solve these two equations to find the values of x and y.

25 Plot the graph of $y = x^2 - 2.9x + 1.9$ for values of x from 0 to 3.

a) Estimate, from your graph, solutions to the equation $x^2 + 1.9 = 2.9x$.
b) Add a line $y = 1.9$ to your graph.
c) State the equation satisfied by the x values where the graphs intersect.

26 a) Solve the equations:
$x + y = 201$
$x - y = 1$

b) For the values of x and y you found in a), find $x^2 - y^2$.
c) Find the values of x and y that satisfy the equations:
$x - y = 1$
$x^2 - y^2 = 2001$

27 Here is information on distances and times for a trained sprinter running a 100 metre race.

Time (s)	Distance from start
0	0
1	2.5
2	9.5
3	19.0
4	27.5
5	37.5
6	45.0
7	52.0
8	60.0
9	70.5
10	78.0
11	87.0
12	94.5
12.6	100.0

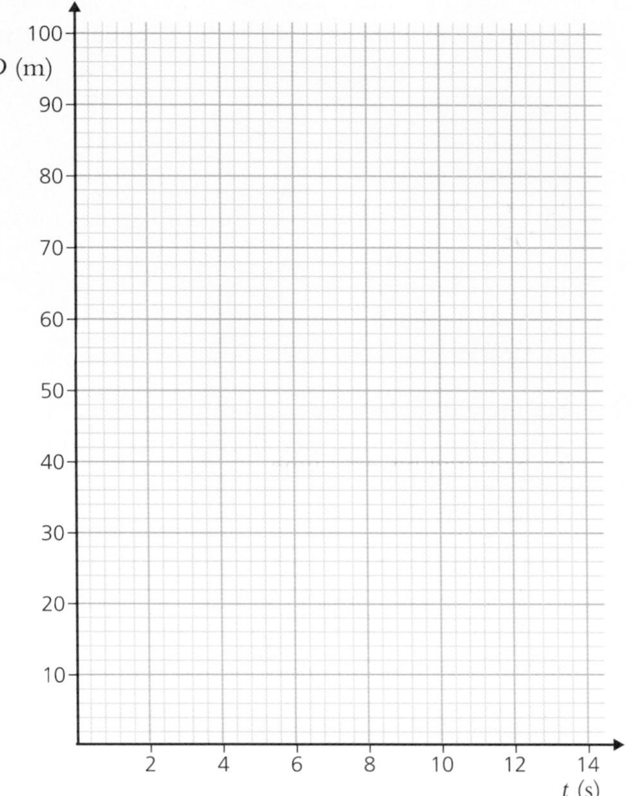

a) Plot this information on the grid above.
b) Use your graph to find when the sprinter had the greatest velocity.
c) What was his maximum velocity?

28 The water near to the bottom of a river does not flow as fast as the water at the surface. The two speeds are connected by the formula:

$$\sqrt{s} = \sqrt{b} + 1$$

where s is the speed in mph at the surface and b the speed in mph near to the bottom of the river.
Use the formula to find:
a) the speed on the surface when the speed near the bottom of the river is 5 mph.
b) the speed near the bottom when the river speed at the surface is 10 mph.

29 The thirteen cards in a bridge hand can be arranged in more than 6.227×10^9 different ways. Write this number without using standard form.

30 Rumours can spread very fast in a crowd.
A typical formula showing this is $n = 3^x$, where x is the time in minutes since the rumour began and n the number of people who heard it.
According to the formula, how many people will have heard the rumour ten minutes after it began?

31 The speed at which a certain species of ant crawls is a function of temperature. This table shows how speed (s cm per second) and temperature (t °C) are related.

Speed of ant (s)	2	3	4	5
Temperature (t)	16	22	28	34

a) Use this information to find a formula connecting the ant's speed and the temperature.
b) Use your formula to predict the temperature below which the ant will not crawl.
c) Will the formula work for all temperatures? Give a reason for your answer.

32 Set up and solve the equation representing this four thousand-year-old riddle: 'If a certain number, two thirds of it, half of it and one seventh of it, are added together the result is 97.'
What is the number?'

33 The planet Saturn's largest ring has a radius of 1.35×10^5 km.
a) What is the diameter of this ring?
b) What is the circumference of the ring?
Give both answers in standard form correct to 2 S.F.

34 A coil of wire a metres long has a mass of b kg.
If c metres are cut off, what is the weight of the remaining wire?

35 Draw the graph for the function:

$$y = 6 + x - x^2$$

Use your graph to solve the equations:
a) $6 + x - x^2 = 0$
b) $6 + x - x^2 = 2$

36 A chocolate firm claims that over 16 000 of their sweets are eaten throughout the World every minute.
a) How many is this in a year? Give your answer in standard form correct to two significant figures.
b) Each sweet is 1 cm in diameter. If the sweets eaten in a year were laid in a line, how many kilometres long would the line be?

37 In 1994 a local council received the following complaints about noise:

Domestic noise	20%
Music	34%
Dogs and other animals	34%
Building repairs, etc.	12%

There were 2000 complaints about music.
How many complaints were there altogether?

38 Work out $\frac{2}{3}$ of £21.

39 Given that x is an integer such that:

$3 < x \leq 21$

a) State the largest possible value of x.
b) State the smallest possible value of x.
c) List the values of x that are prime numbers.
d) List the values of x that are square numbers.
e) Explain why your answers to parts c) and d) should have no values in common.

40 Solve the equations:

a) $5x - 3 = 27$ b) $2(y - 5) = 12$ c) $17 + 2z = z + 8$

41 a) Estimate the value of 49.7×9.8 by rounding each number to one significant figure. Show all your working.
b) Find the percentage error in your estimate correct to two significant figures.

42 James wanted to calculate:

$$\frac{3.5 + 2.7}{4} - \frac{1}{2.8}$$

He considered two possible key sequences:

a) [3] [.] [5] [+] [2] [.] [7] [ ] [÷] [4] [−] [ ] [ ] [2] [.] [8] [=]

and

b) [(] [3] [.] [5] [+] [2] [.] [7] [ ] [÷] [4] [−] [2] [.] [8] [ ] [=]

List the missing steps (blank keys) for each key sequence.

43 If three out of five year 11 students at a school stay on for the sixth form, what percentage go elsewhere?

44 Identical pairs of jeans are sold in two shops. Which pair will cost less to buy?
Show your working.

45 Emma rounds her calculator answer to 2 D.P. to give 8.34. What is the smallest possible value displayed?

46 When switched off, the temperature inside a freezer increases from – 18 °C at the rate of 2 °C per hour.

a) Find the temperature after $2\frac{1}{2}$ hours.

b) After $2\frac{1}{2}$ hours, the door is opened and the temperature increases rapidly by 16 °C. What is the new temperature?

47 Write $\frac{1}{4}+\frac{2}{3}$ in its simplest form.

48 Find the *n*th term of these sequences in terms of *n*:

a) –2, 3, 8, 13, ...

b) $\frac{1}{2}$, $\frac{1}{4}$, $\frac{1}{8}$, $\frac{1}{16}$, ...

49 The diagrams represent the equations $x + y = a$, $y = bx + c$, $y = x^2 + d$ and $y = ex^2$.
Find the values of a, b, c, d and e.

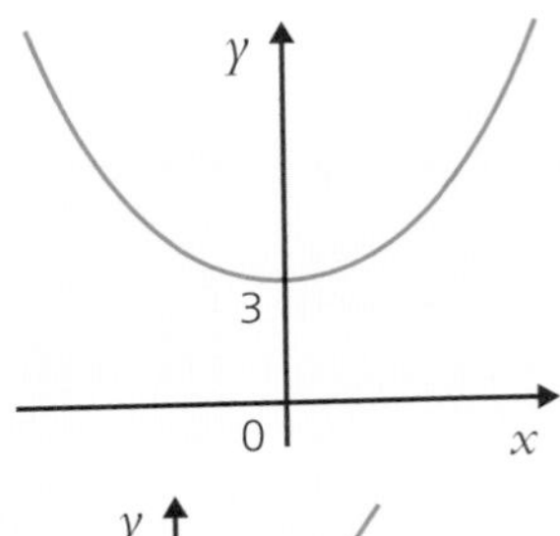

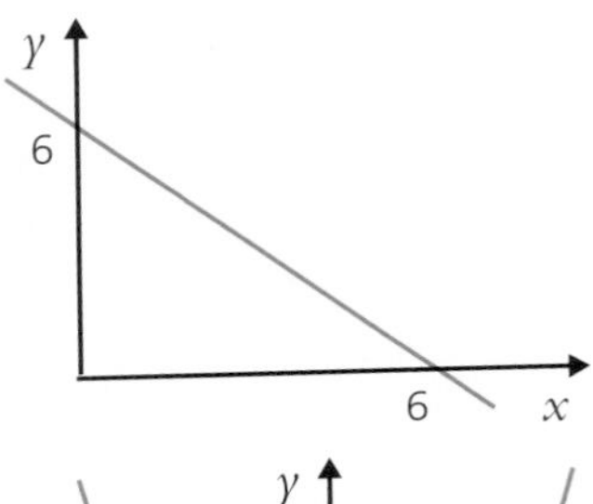

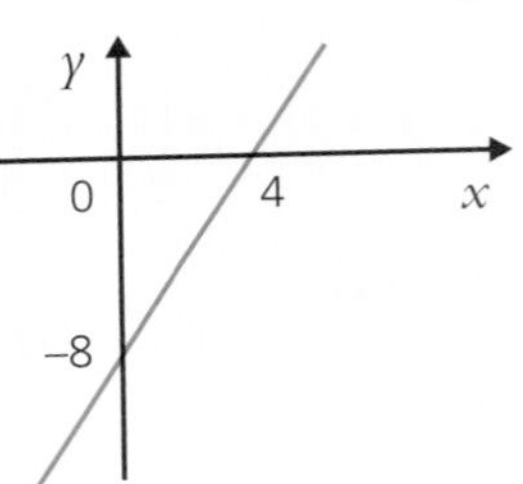

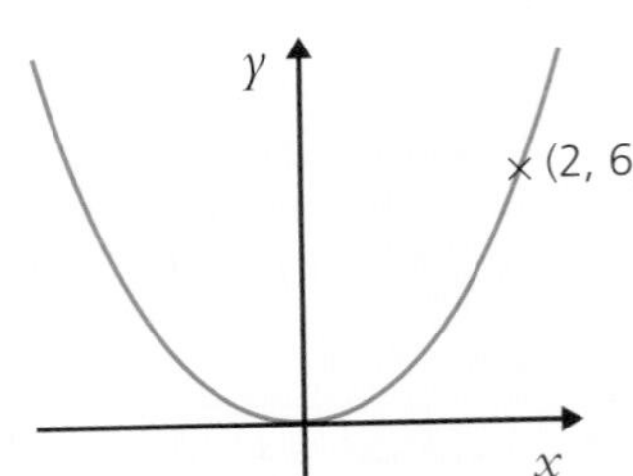

50 Use inequalities to describe region R in this diagram, including the boundary lines.

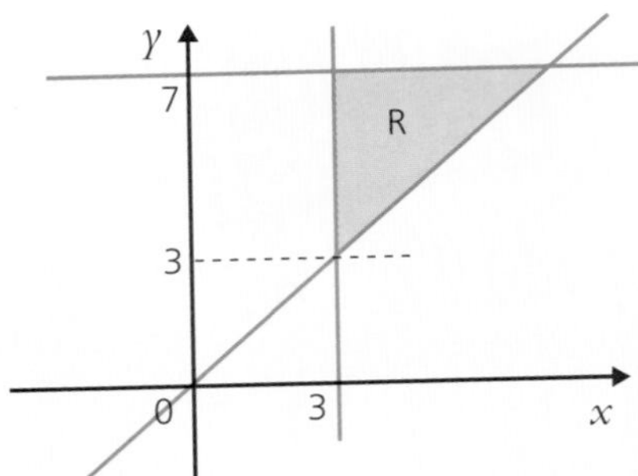

51 Factorise fully:

a) $12 - 8x$

b) $6x - 9xy$

52 Solve these inequalities:

a) $\frac{x+3}{5} > 2$

b) $x^2 + 1 < 10$

53 Multiply out and simplify:

a) $(2x + 3)(3x - 1)$

b) $(x + 5)^2 - 2(x - 3)$

54 Use a calculator to find the value of:

a) $\frac{17.9 - 11.3}{5}$

b) $\frac{15.3}{6.8 \times 4.5}$

c) $\sqrt{5.7^2 + 1.15}$

EXAM PRACTICE

Shape, space and measures

When working through the questions in this section, make a point of checking your answers as if you were in the examination. Ask yourself:

1 Have I answered the question?
2 Does the answer look reasonable?

It's all too easy, under exam pressure, to misinterpret a question or to produce a silly answer. Carrying out these simple checks may help you spot the errors and save you valuable marks.

1

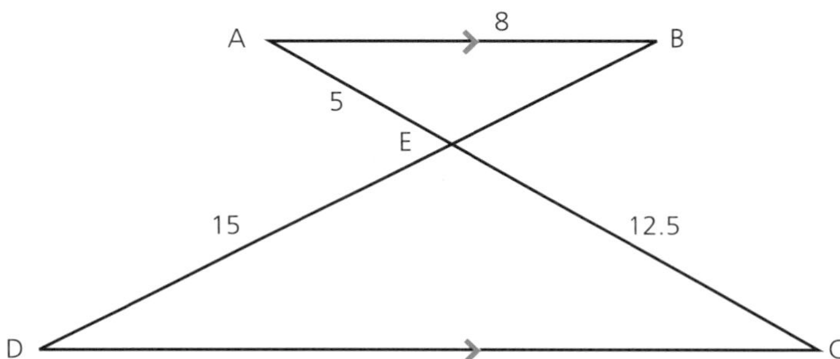

Triangles ABE and CDE are similar.
AB is parallel to DC.
AE = 5 cm, EC = 12.5 cm, AB = 6 cm and ED = 15 cm.
Calculate the lengths of a) DC, b) EB.

2 The diagram shows a rectangular gate.
Angle FAE = 66° and side AF is 90 cm long.
BC = CD = DE = 30 cm

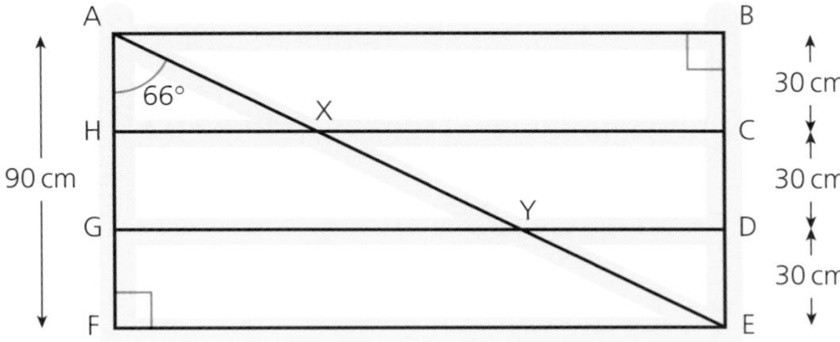

Find:
a) the width of the gate EF
b) the length XY.

3 O is the centre of a circle. The diameter AB is 13 cm long. PB is 6 cm.

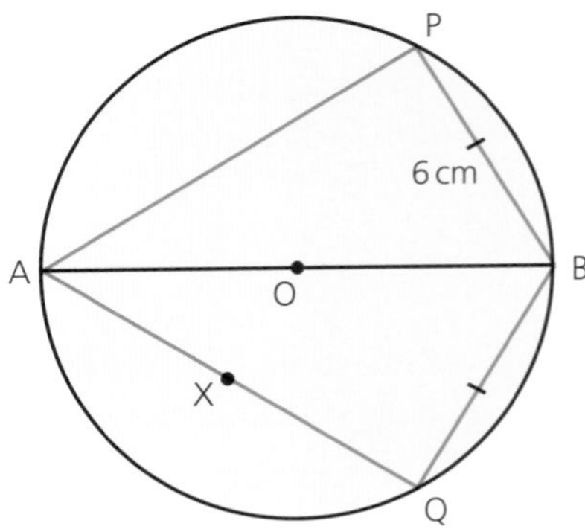

a) What is the size of angle APB?
b) Work out the size of angle BAP.
c) X is the midpoint of AQ. What is the length of the line OX?

4 A sailing dinghy leaves a buoy B and travels 200 m due North. It then travels 325 m due East to a point E.

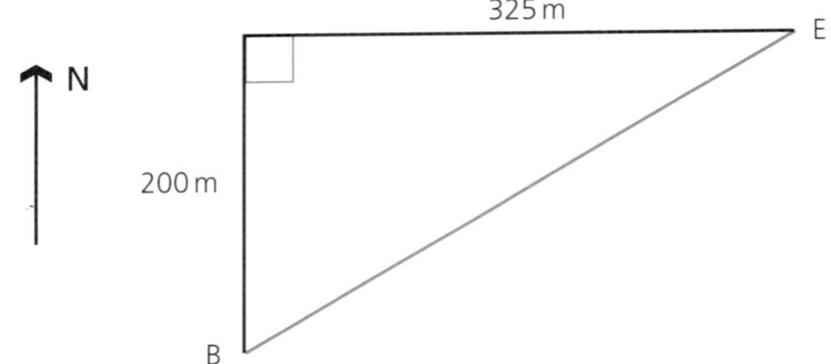

a) Calculate how far it is from the buoy.
b) What is the bearing of the buoy from the dinghy?

5 This is the logo of a yacht club.

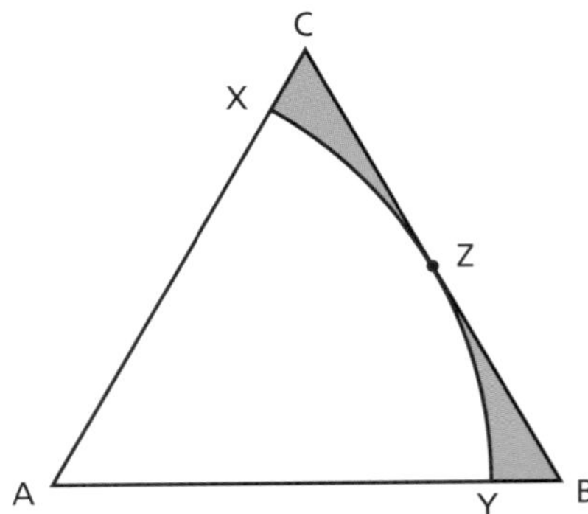

ABC is an equilateral triangle. AXY is a sector of a circle centre A. Calculate the area of the shaded part of the logo if side AC is 20 cm.

6 The diagram shows a view of a swimming pool.

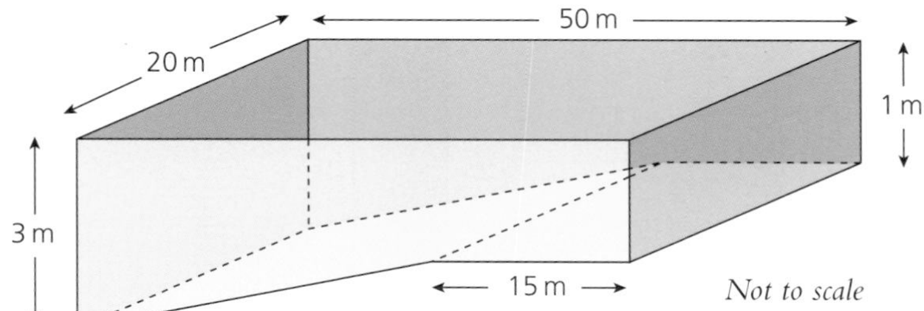

a) Calculate the volume of the pool in cubic metres.

b) When the pool is ready for use the water level is 20 cm below the top of the sides. How many litres of water are in the pool?

7 This sketch shows a metal container for holding milk bottles. The measurements are in centimetres.

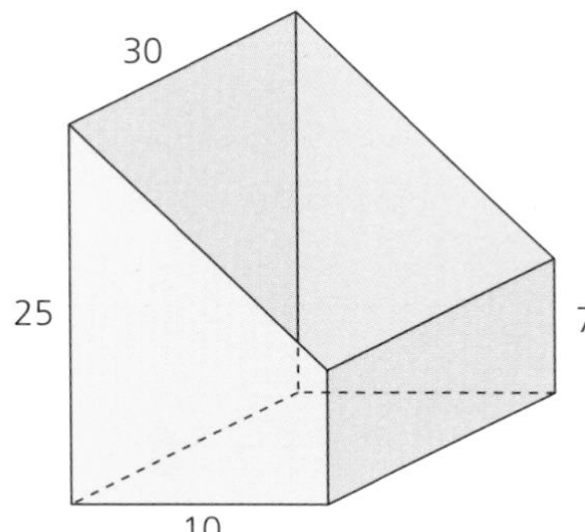

Using a scale of 1 cm to 5 cm, make a scale drawing of a net for the container.

8 A new, full tin of paint has a base radius of 10 cm and a height of 25 cm.

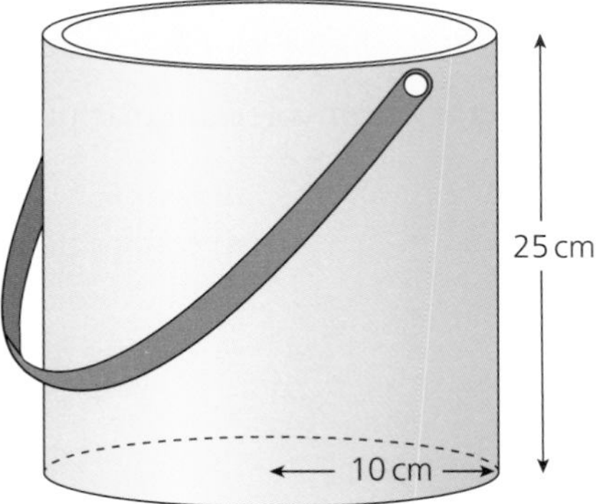

John removes the lid using a screwdriver which he drops into the paint.
The screwdriver disappears completely.
What is the maximum possible length (to the nearest cm) of the screwdriver?

9 What is the ratio of the surface areas of a cube with edges all 8 cm long and a cube with a volume of 8 cm^3?

10

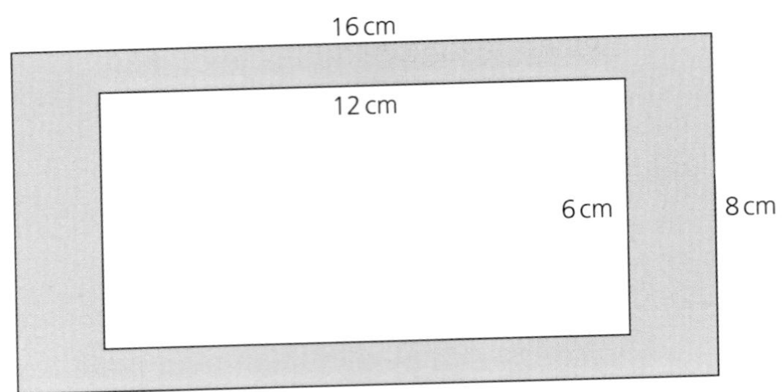

A rectangular picture frame measures 16 cm by 8 cm.
The picture measures 12 cm by 6 cm.
If all measurements are correct to the nearest cm, calculate the maximum possible area of the shaded border.

11 Brian has to park 12 vans in a circle.

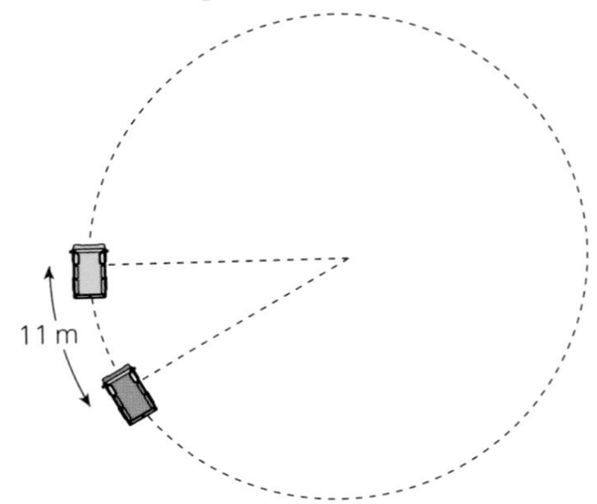

The vans must be 11 m apart.
Calculate the radius of the circle (ignore the size of the vans).

12 The diagram shows a steel plate made by a factory from a rectangular piece of metal. The cut-out ends are semi-circular.

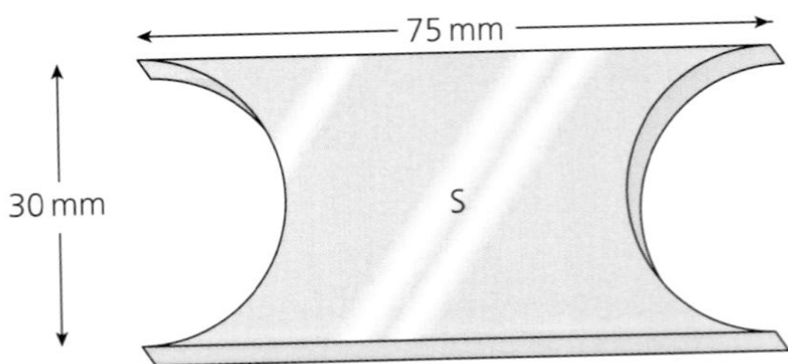

a) Calculate the area of the flat face labelled S.
b) The metal is 3 mm thick. Calculate the volume of the steel plate.

13 These circles are all the same size.

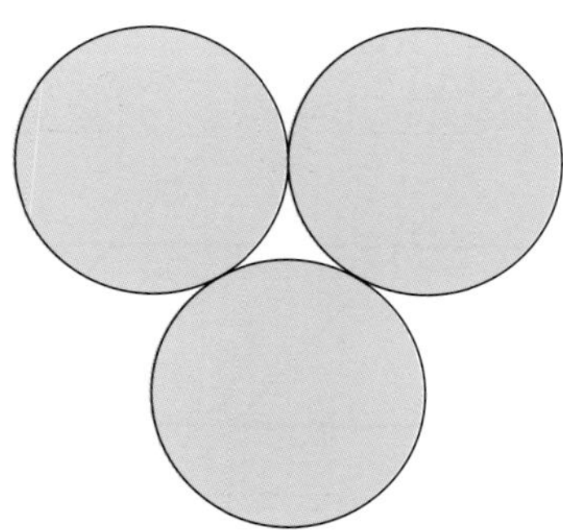

a) Draw in all the lines of reflection symmetry.
b) What order of rotational symmetry does the shape have?

14 A is the point (–3, 2). B is the point (1, 4). C is the point (3, –2).

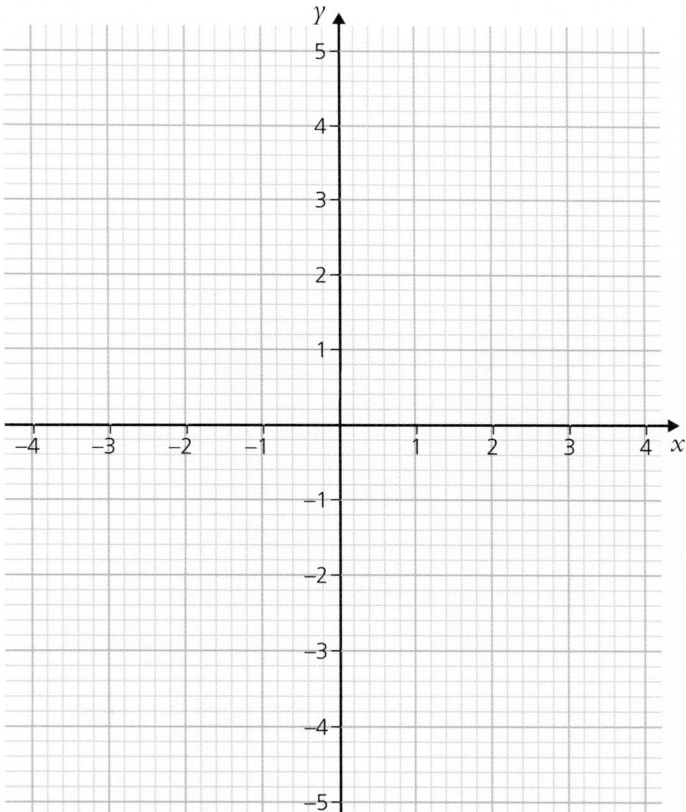

a) Copy the grid and mark these points on it.
b) The shape ABCD is a parallelogram. Mark a possible position of point D.
c) Draw the shape ABCD.
d) Draw in the diagonals and write down the coordinates of the point where they intersect.

15 AB = BC = AD = DG = GJ.
Angle GEH = 68°.

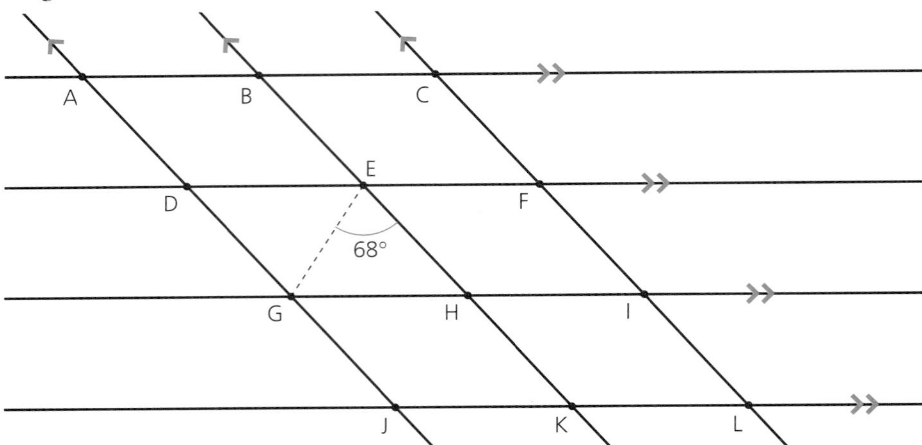

Write down the sizes of these angles:
a) DGE b) GDE c) EHI d) JKH.

16 The diagram shows a pen where two goats are kept.

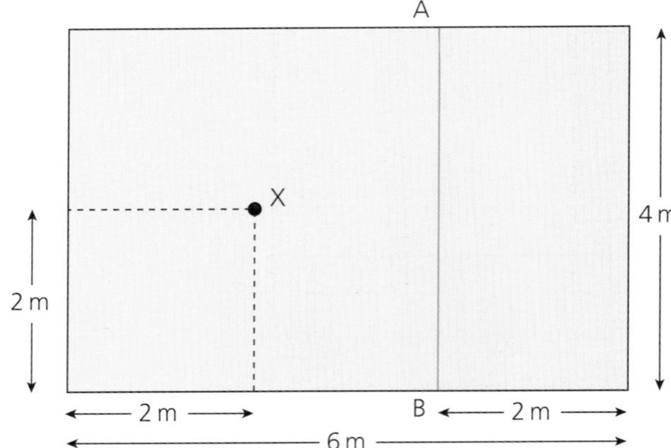

The first goat is tethered to the peg marked X and can graze anywhere within 1.5 m of the peg.
The second goat is tethered to a wire marked AB. This goat can graze anywhere within 0.75 m of AB.
a) Show the areas that can be grazed by each goat.
b) Mark with the letter G the area where both goats can graze.

17 Using the origin as the centre of enlargement, enlarge the shape ABCDE by scale factor 2.5.

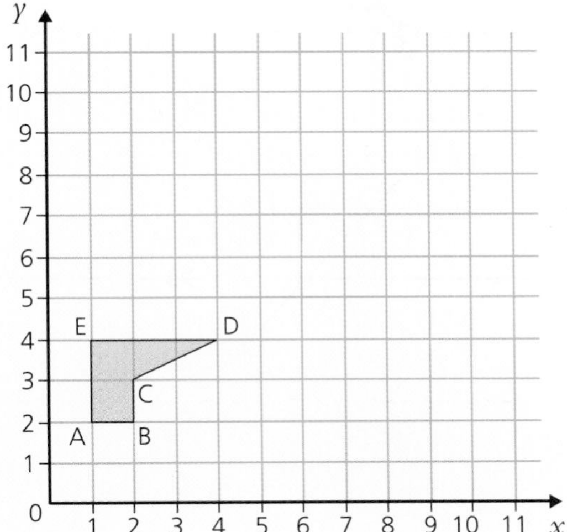

18 The two shapes A and B can be joined together to make other shapes.

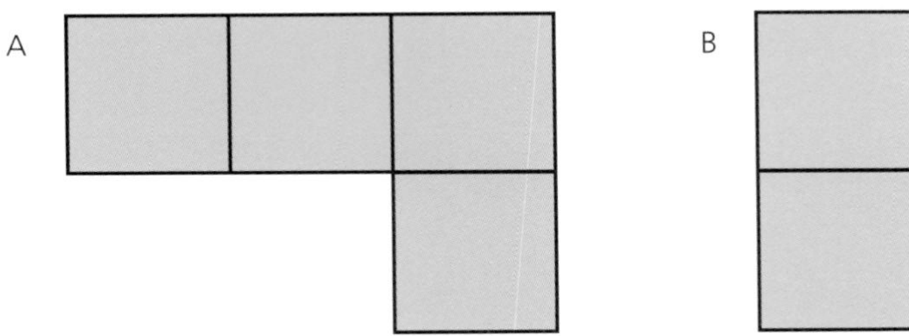

Draw a shape (using both pieces) that has:

a) two lines of symmetry and rotational symmetry of order 2.

b) one line of symmetry and rotational symmetry of order 1.

c) no lines of symmetry and rotational symmetry of order 2.

Handling data

When working through the questions in this section, make a point of checking your answers as if you were in the examination. Ask yourself:

1 Have I answered the question?
2 Does the answer look reasonable?

It's all too easy, under exam pressure, to misinterpret a question or to produce a silly answer. Carrying out these simple checks may help you spot the errors and save you valuable marks.

---

1 Peter is conducting a survey to find out about the use made of the drinks vending machine at his school. One of the questions he asks is:

How often do you buy a drink from the machine?	Sometimes	
	Never	
	Often	
	Hardly at all	

a) What is wrong with Peter's question?
b) How would you rewrite it?

2 Katie is buying an ice-cream. She has a choice of these flavours and toppings:

Flavours	Toppings
Vanilla	Flake
Lemon	Chocolate chips
Chocolate	Hundreds and thousands
Strawberry	Nuts

a) How many different combinations of flavours and toppings are there to choose from?
b) Katie remembers that she is allergic to nuts. How many combinations can she choose from now?
c) For a cone, the assistant tells Katie she can have any combination of two flavours. Make a list of all the possible combinations of two flavours, like this:

Vanilla and lemon
... and ...

3 Yvonne is buying some pansies to plant in her garden. The flowers have not yet opened. She buys five boxes of pansies with six in each box.
The probability of obtaining different coloured flowers is shown in the following table:

Red	0.3
White	0.2
Yellow	0.4
Purple	0.1

a) What is the probability that a pansy will be white or yellow?
b) What is the probability that a pansy will not be red?
c) How many pansies would Yvonne expect to be purple?

4

The diagram shows a fair dice and a fair spinner.
The dice is an ordinary dice.
The triangular spinner is labelled F for forward, B for backwards and M for miss your turn.
If the score on the dice is 2, and the spinner shows B, this means move two squares backwards.

a) The dice is thrown and the spinner is spun. What is the probability of missing your turn?
b) Calculate the probability of moving forwards three or more squares.

5 Paul recorded the number of birds that visited his bird table from 5 pm to 5.30 pm each day for two weeks. The results were:

28, 32, 14, 19, 18, 26, 34, 15, 18, 25, 33, 19, 28, 9

a) For these results, find:
   (i) the mean
   (ii) the median
   (iii) the range
b) Peter also recorded the birds that visited his table. His results gave a mean of 25, a median of 23 and a range of 20 birds.
Which bird table, Paul's or Peter's, was visited by the most birds? Give a reason for your answer.

6 Lucy and Amy each buy a bag of fruit gums.
Lucy's bag contains 6 red, 3 black and 3 green fruit gums.
Amy's bag contains 4 red, 5 black and 3 green fruit gums.
They each take a fruit gum from their bag without looking.

a) On the tree diagram below, write the probability of each event on the appropriate line.

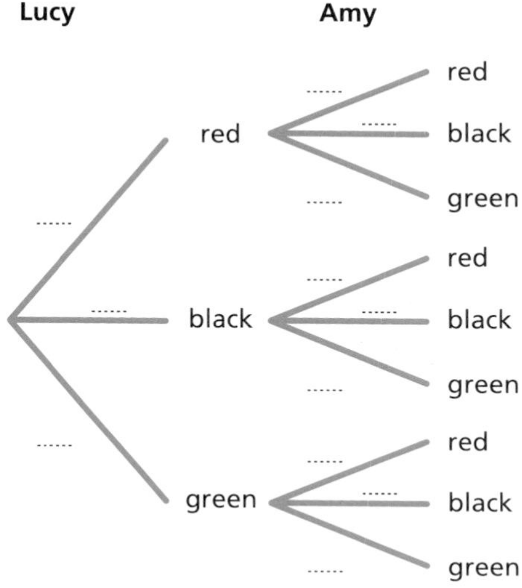

b) Calculate the probability that Lucy chooses a red fruit gum and Amy a green one.

c) Calculate the probability that they both choose the same colour fruit gum.

7 There are 350 000 km of public roads in Britain, as shown in the table below:

Motorways	3000 km
Dual carriageways	12 000 km
'A' roads	38 000 km
Other roads	297 000 km

Draw a clearly labelled pie chart to show this information.

8 A dice is made in the shape of a square-based pyramid.
The four triangular faces are numbered 1 to 4 and the square face is labelled 0.
The score is given by the face which is flat on the table.
John says the probability of scoring 3 is $\frac{1}{5}$ or 0.2.
Do you agree with John?
Give a reason for your answer.

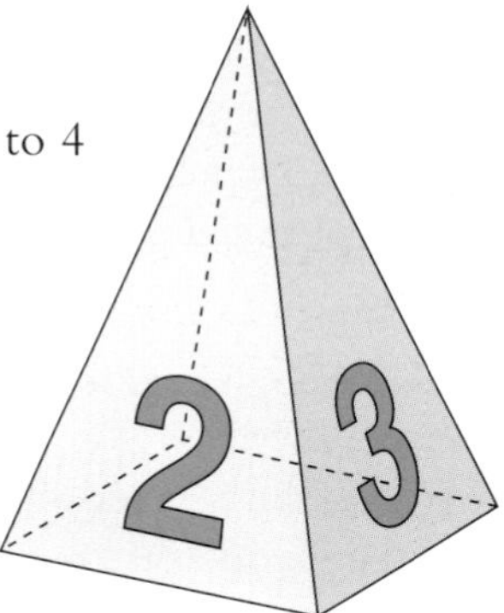

9 Copy the axes below and draw scatter diagrams which show:

a) a weak positive correlation between time spent revising and GCSE results

b) a strong negative correlation between the speed of a car and time take to travel around the M25.

Include at least 10 points.

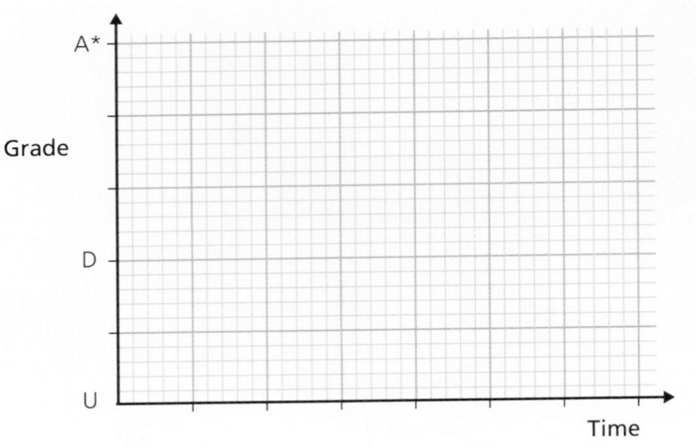

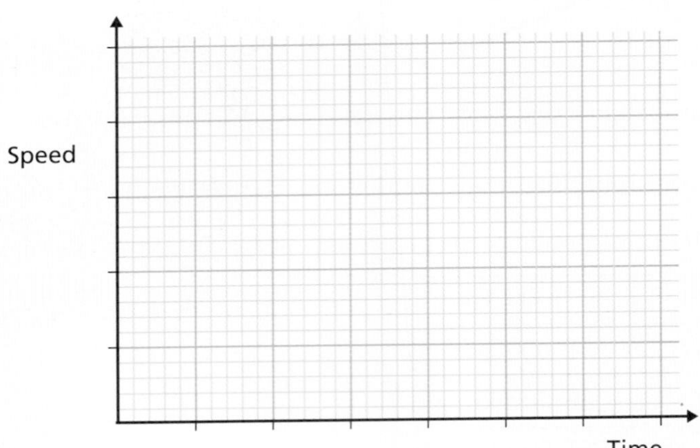

10 After every match pupils in the school football team are given a 'performance' mark out of 10. To qualify for an 'outstanding player' award pupils must get a mean score of at least 7.5.
After eight matches Paul has a mean score of 6.5.
There are only two games left to play.
Is it possible for Paul to get an 'outstanding player' award? You must show all your working.

11 Carol has to pass through two sets of traffic lights on her way to work. They operate independently.
The probability that the first set of lights are on green is 60% and the probability that the second set are green is 50%. What is the probability that she will pass through both sets of traffic lights without having to stop?

12 The dipper is a small bird which lives on rivers. This bar chart shows the number of dippers in Derbyshire in 1993.

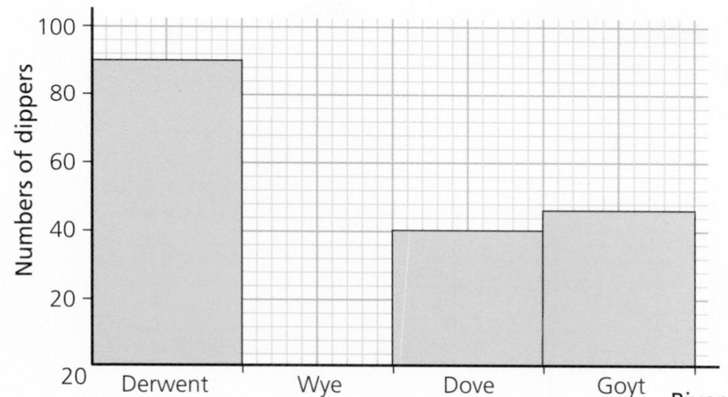

a) 44 lived on the river Wye. Add this bar to the chart.
b) How many dippers lived in Derbyshire altogether?
c) This pie chart shows the relative length of each river in Derbyshire. Which river are you least likely to see a dipper on?

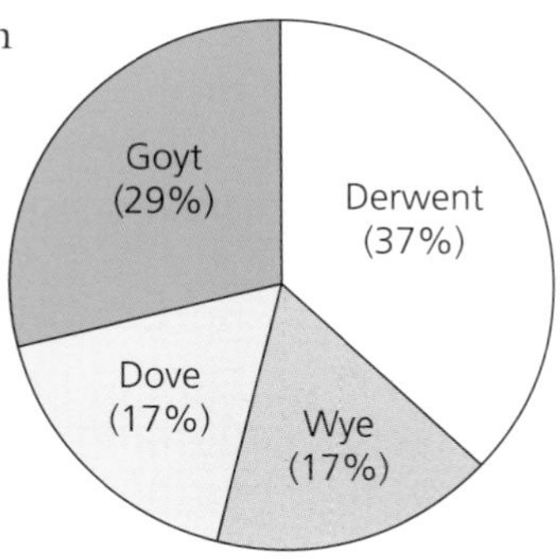

13 This table shows the number of goals scored by Paul's football team in each game last season.

Number of goals scored	Number of matches
0	6
1	3
2	5
3	3
4	2
6	1

a) What is the modal number of goals scored per match?
b) What is the median number of goals scored per match?
c) Calculate the mean number of goals scored per match.
d) Paul's team has lost its last five matches. Which average would you use if you were the manager trying to encourage them?

14 This table shows the probability that a car will break down during a 12-month period.

	Age (years)		
Make	**0–3**	**3–6**	**6–9**
Ford	0.13	0.28	0.35
Nissan	0.02	0.07	0.16
Renault	0.07	0.23	0.44
Rover	0.08	0.17	0.37
Mitsubishi	0.01	0.10	0.17

a) What is the probability that an 8-year-old Rover will break down once in a year?
b) Which is the most reliable make of brand new car?
c) Which make of car is generally the most reliable?

15 A. Wainwright divided the mountains of the Lake District into seven areas. These are the heights in feet of the mountains that make up the Southern Fells.

2572	1056	2960
2611	2259	2633
2816	2555	2903
2560	2575	2984
1602	2536	1803
2140	1040	1983
2649	1530	2304
2106	1807	3162
3210	1970	2499
2630	2502	1755

a) Complete this tally chart.

Height	Tally	Frequency
$1000 < h \leq 1500$		
$1500 < h \leq 2000$		
$2000 < h \leq 2500$		
$2500 < h \leq 3000$		
$3000 < h \leq 3500$		

b) This frequency polygon show the heights of the Western Fells. Draw the frequency polygon to show the heights of the Southern Fells.

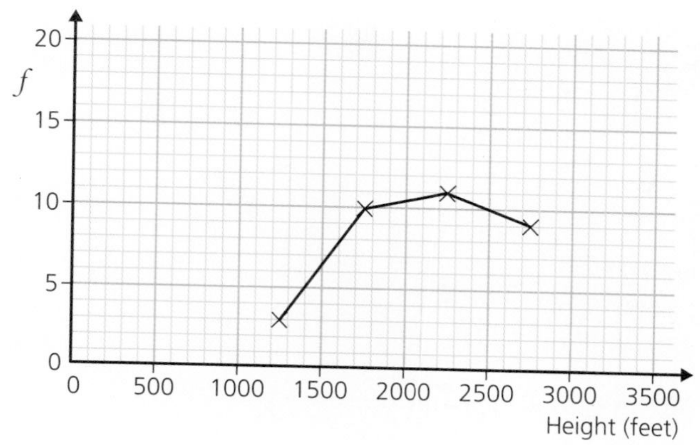

c) Which area, Southern or Western, has the most mountains over 2000 feet? Show your working clearly.

16 David, Ellen and Farah have made 8-sided spinners. They have tested them to see if they are fair or biased. Here are their results:

	Number of spins	Number of 6s	Relative frequency
David	50	6	
Ellen	100	20	
Farah	500	43	

a) Complete the relative frequency column.
b) Are the spinners fair?
Explain how you decided in each case.

17 This table shows the time one hundred Year 10 pupils spent watching television after school yesterday.

Time (hours)	Frequency	Cumulative frequency
0	9	
$0 < t < 1$	23	
$1 \le t < 2$	29	
$2 \le t < 3$	20	
$3 \le t < 5$	19	

a) Complete the cumulative frequency column.
b) Draw the cumulative frequency graph.
c) Use the graph to estimate:
(i) the median time spent watching TV
(ii) the interquartile range of the time spent watching TV.

18 Two twins, Tim and Tom, take their driving test on the same day. They each have a probability of $\frac{2}{3}$ of passing.
What is the probability that:
a) both of them pass
b) neither of them pass
c) only one of them passes?

19 The mean of the values:
x, 3.5, 6.7, 5.0 and 7.3
is 6.5. Calculate x.

20 This table shows the population of the UK to the nearest million.

Country	Population
England	48
Wales	3
Scotland	5
N. Ireland	2

a) Draw a pie chart to show this distribution and label it clearly.

The pie chart below shows the area of the UK each country occupies.

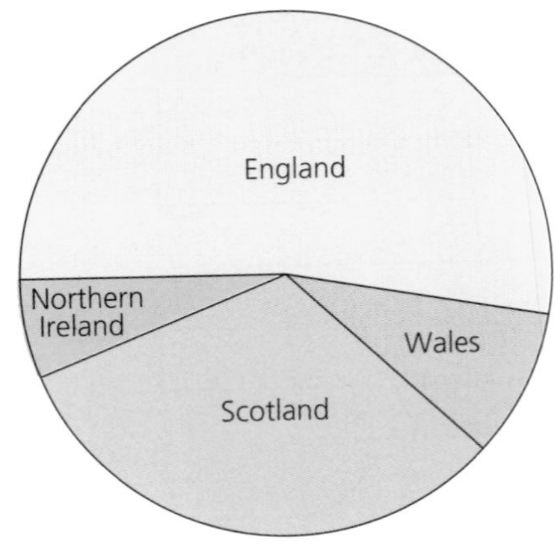

b) What do the two pie charts tell you about Scotland?
c) If the total area of the UK is 244 000 km^2, estimate the area of Scotland.

21 A firm manufactures a device, called an RCD, which protects users of electric machines from getting an electric shock. The device turns off, or 'trips', the power when the current reaches a certain level.
The firm tests the efficiency of two prototypes A and B. Below is a cumulative frequency graph showing the results of the tests:

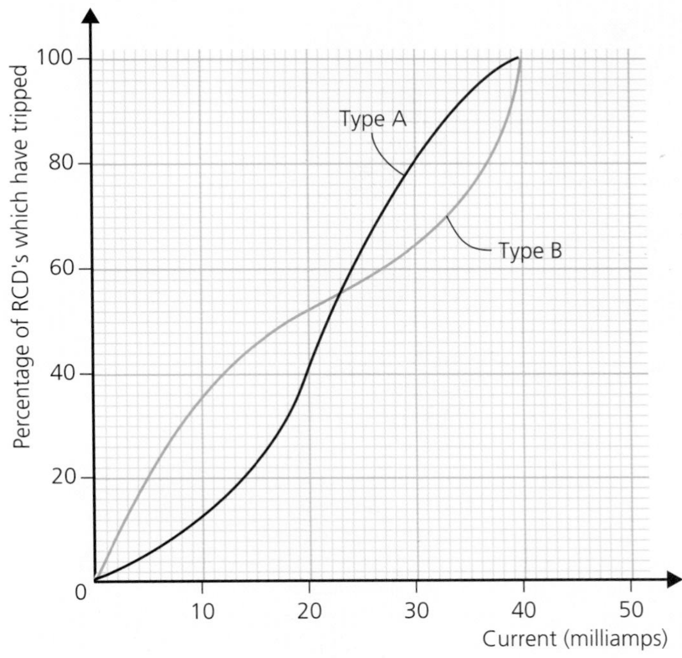

a) What is the median current that will trip the type B prototype?

b) What percentage of the type A prototypes have not tripped after the current reaches 30 milliamps?

c) The final version of the RCD must trip at or before 30 milliamps. Which of the prototypes should the firm continue to develop?

ANSWERS TO ✓ QUESTIONS

Unit 1 Number systems

1 **1 d)** 490
e) 25

1 **3 b)** CD
i) DCCCIL

1 **4 a)** 1925

2 **6 b)** LX
g) DLXXX

2 **1 c)** 7 thousands

3 **7 c)** 2486
i) 2961

4 **9 a)** 60.03

4 **10 a)** 100

4 **1 a)** 0.3

4 **2 c)** 7.4

5 **6 a)** 8.6

5 **7 b)** 3.7

6 **1 a)** 2.1 and 2.2

6 **2 e)** 6.0

7 **8 a)** £5.68

8 **3** 2.4

8 **6** 60×0.04 and 600×0.004

8 **8 b)** $900 \times 7 = 6300$
c) $90 \times 7 = 630$

9 **11 c)** 0.112

Unit 2 Angles and symmetry

14 **1** Corresponding angles are equal.

14 **2** Alternate angles are equal.

15 **3** Vertically opposite angles are equal.

15 **4** $a = 47°, b = 133°, c = 133°$

16 **1 a)** 4
b) 2

18 **1 a)** 2
b) 5

Unit 3 Division

20 **4 a)** 2

23 **4** The denominator must be multiplied by the same value.

23 **5 a)** $\frac{20}{24}$

24 **1 b)** 0.75

25 **5** It suggests that $\frac{7}{7} = 0.9999\ldots$

25 **1 a)** $\frac{47.1}{3}$

t 4 Probability (1)

30 5 $\frac{4}{6}=\frac{2}{3}$

30 **8** a) $\frac{1}{2}$

31 **12** $\frac{10}{49}$

32 **1** The relative frequency may have quite large fluctuations in value at the beginning of the experiment (for smaller numbers of throws). As the number of throws increases the graph should level off and the fluctuations should be smaller. The relative frequency at the end of the experiment should be close in value to the theoretical probability (i.e. $\frac{1}{6}$ or 0.17).

33 *Discussion point*
The proportion of people who wear glasses can be estimated by counting the number of people wearing glasses in a large sample of people. The larger the sample, the more likely your answer is to be correct.

34 **7** The *centre* of the penny must be at least 1 cm away from the lines.

35 **10** Yes, the probability will change. b) is correct. The coin is less likely to land crossing a line so you are more likely to score a point.

36 **6 b)**
[SHIFT] [RAN#] [×] [5] [=]
c)
[SHIFT] [RAN#] [+] [1] [=]

Unit 5 Working with fractions

38 **1 a)** $6\frac{1}{4}$

39 **5 a)** 35 min

39 **7 a)** $8\frac{3}{4}$

41 **11 a)** 21 h 2 min

42 **3 a)** 6000

42 **4 d)** 0.10

43 **1 a)** $5 \times 0.2 = 1$

46 **3 a)** £52.20

46 **8 a)** 8 (over-estimate)

48 **14 a)** £8.40

48 **15 a)** 68.1

Unit 6 Organising data

50 **1 a)** Year 7: median = 5
mean = 4.23
mode = 6
Year 10: median = 2
mean = 1.86
mode = 3

55 **8 a)** A bar graph or pictogram.
c) A pie chart would be better than a bar graph or pictogram.

Unit 7 Process and priority

58 **1 a)** $y = x + 4$

58 **2 a)** $4x = x + 50$

60 **1 e)** $3p + 2q$
f) $12p^2q$
i) $5a^2b$

61 **4 a)** Sometimes true. The result holds whenever a or b is zero but otherwise it is false.

63 **4 a)** -1
f) -6
j) -1.4

64 **5 a)** $-5 - -7$
$= -5 + 7$
$= 2$
e) $4 + (3 - 9)$
$= 4 + -6$
$= 4 - 6$
$= -2$

65 **2 a)** 273 K

65 **3 b)** -753

Unit 8 Length, weight and capacity

67 **2** 54 mm long and 33 mm wide

68 **6 b)** 58
d) 14 000

68 **7 a)** 4.8

68 **8 a)** 1.53

69 **9 a)** 15 feet

70 **2 a)** 2930 g or 2.93 kg

7 a) 4 oz

Unit 9 Signs, equations, sequences

86 **1 a)** $\frac{11}{3}$

b) $3\frac{2}{3}$

c) $3.\dot{6}$

d) 3.667

e) 3.67

87 **5 a)** $x = 15$

88 **6 a)** $x = 24$

88 **8 a)** $x = \pm 4$

d) $x = 1, x = -11$

88 **9 f)** – 0.048 0

88 **12 b)** $99x = 37$

Unit 10 Probability (2)

92 **1 a)** $\frac{15}{30} = \frac{1}{2}$

92 **2 a)** 15, 17, 19, 51, 57, 59, 71, 75, 79, 91, 95, 97

93 **3 b)** 16

93 **5 a)** 250

100 **1 a)** See table below

e) Roughly, 40

100 **2 a)** 9

c) 27

		spinner 1			
		blue	yellow	red	green
spinner 2	blue	B, B	Y, B	R, B	G, B
	yellow	B, Y	Y, Y	R, Y	G, Y
	red	B, R	Y, R	R, R	G, R
	green	B, G	Y, G	R, G	G, G

Unit 11 Straight lines

102 **1 a)** 20 shovels

102 **4 a)** 6 : 14

102 **5 a)** 3 : 4

103 **6 a)** 1 : 2

105 **5 a)** 1

106 **9 a)** $-\frac{1}{2}$

107 **2 a)** $-\frac{3}{5}$

108 **8 c)** $y = 3$

108 **12 c)** The x value plus the y value must be equal to 6.

Unit 12 Bearings and plans

111 **2 a)** The bearing of OA is 063°.

112 **4 a)** 84°
b) 85°

112 **5** 045°

113 **1 a)** The bearing of AO is 243°.

113 **2** For (i), OX is 049°, XO is 229°.

113 **3 a)** 190°

114 **1** 32 km, 235°

116 **2 a)** 55.98 m^2 (say 56 m^2)

117 **1 a)** A 1:100, 4 cm by 3 cm

Unit 13 Algebra and graphs (1)

119 **2 a)** $p - q + r$

119 **5 b)** $p - q + r + s$

119 **7** If the sign outside the brackets is a '+', then the signs stay the same when the brackets are removed. If the sign outside the brackets is a '–', then the signs *inside* the brackets are all changed when the brackets are removed.

121 **11 a)** $7x - 6$

121 **12 a)** $3x - 5y$

122 **15 a)** $5x - 18$

122 **16 c)** $-8x + 2y - 4$

122 **17 a)** $2y$

125 **9 a)** $y = 3x + 5$

125 **12 a)** $y = x + 2$

Unit 14 Charts, graphs, histograms

130 **2 a)** 2

132 **2 b)** Frequencies are 3, 9, 8, 6 and 4.

134 **1 a)** Group in 2s. The first group will be 0–1, then 2–3, 4–5, etc.

Unit 15 Ratio, percentage, proportion

139 **3 c)** 10 gallons of white and 2 gallons of red

139 **5**

Foundation	22
Intermediate	88
Higher	44

140 **3 a)** 40%

141 **1 a)** $\dfrac{\text{loss in value}}{\text{original value}} \times 100\%$

Unit 16 Polygons and circles

149 **5** a and c are alternate angles.
b and c are corresponding angles.
It shows that opposite angles in a parallelogram are equal.

150 **1** Area of a parallelogram
= base × height = bh

150 **2** Area of a kite
= $\frac{1}{2}$ width × height = $\frac{1}{2}wh$

150 **3 a)** Area of triangle A
= $\frac{1}{2}a$ × height
Area of triangle B
= $\frac{1}{2}b$ × height
Area of trapezium
= area of triangle A
+ area of triangle B
= $\frac{1}{2}(a + b)$ × height

151 **4 a)** 27.3 cm^2

151 **6 a)** Height = 3.5 cm,
area = 17.5 cm^2,
perimeter = 18 cm

152 **2 f)** 720°
h) 120°

153 **2 j)** ... 2 less than ...

154 **7 b)** An octagon

154 **8 a)** A hexagon

154 **10** $a = 72°$, $b = 108°$, $c = 36°$

155 **1** Circumference = 6 × radius (approximately)

156 **2 a)** 24.9 cm

157 **8 a)** 12.3 m

159 **3 a)** 62.2 cm^2

160 **4 a)** 62.14 cm^2

Unit 17 Numbers and equations

171 **3** They are all greater than 1.

171 **6 a)** $<$

172 **9** $0.876 \times 1.25 < 1.25$
$0.876 \times 1.25 > 0.876$

$0.876 < 0.876 \times 1.25 < 1.25$

0.876 1.25

172 **13 a)** $>$

174 **4 a)** 17.3

174 **5 c)** 14.6

177 **5 a)** $x = 16$

177 **6 a)** $x = -6$

Unit 18 Hypotheses

178 **1** State the hypothesis
Decide which data to collect
Collect the data
Analyse the data
Interpret the results
Report your findings with reference to the original hypothesis

179 **3 a)** Whether the student dropping the bag is female or male.

181 **1** People will catch the ruler quicker using the hand they write with.

183 **2 a)** This may be considered an embarrassing question. People may not be willing to admit that they never clean their teeth. So will you be able to find out the truth?

Unit 19 Factors and inequalities

185 **1 a)** 0.75

186 **4 a)** 32.8

186 **5 n)** 2.2

187 **6 a)** £558.13

187 **7 i)** 151

188 **5 a)** Divide by 1.15

189 **2 a)** $x < 4$

190 **5 g)** 3

190 **6 a)** 3, 4, 5, 6, 7, 8, 9, 10

Unit 20 Transformations

191 **2** (1, 1)

192 **4 a)** 3
b) (10, 10)
c) It is three times greater.

194 **2 a)** $a = 9$ cm, $b = 3$ cm

194 **3 b)** Angles in both triangles are equal.
BC is parallel to DE.
So ∠ABC = ∠ADE corresponding angles
∠ACB = ∠AED corresponding angles
∠A is common to both triangles.

195 **1 a)** (10, 5)

196 **1 c)** (i) The mirror line is the y-axis, i.e. $x = 0$.
e) (i) Change the sign of the x coordinate. The y coordinate stays the same.

197 **2** The image must be the same distance on the other side of the mirror line.

200 **1 b)** $A_1 = (2, -4)$, $B_1 = (8, -4)$, $C_1 = (8, -7)$
c) $A_2 = (-2, -4)$, $B_2 = (-8, -4)$ $C_2 = (-8, -7)$
d) Rotation 180° about (0, 0)

Unit 21 Simultaneous equations

207 **4 a)** $5x = 29$

208 **5 a)** $h = x + 3$ (isosceles triangle)

Unit 22 Frequency tables

211 **1 a)** At the bottom of the cumulative frequency column.
b) They must be in the group which has a cumulative frequency of 18 (i.e. 12 packets).
c) 12 packets. This agrees with the answer to question 2 f).

211 **2 a)** Cumulative frequencies are 5, 9, 15, 18, 18, 20, 21.
b) 21
c) 8 pieces of work

212 **1 a)** The missing figures are 22, 60, 26, 28, 30, 48, 17, 0, 19, 20, 25 and 38.
b) The total for $x \times f = 431$ gives you the number of packets of cereal bought altogether.
c) The total frequency = 32 gives you the number of students in the class.
d) Mean = 431 ÷ 32
e) 13.47
f) The mean is higher than the median.
g) The mean is boosted by some unusually high results and so the median is probably more representative.

214 **3 a)** 62 kg
b) 5.57°

217 **7** Middle of each interval: 36.1°, 36.3°, 36.5°, etc. Mean = 36.9°

Unit 23 Patterns and primes

220 **9 a)** $2n + 3$
i) $12 - 2n$

225 **5 a)** $2^4 \times 3^6 \times 7$

226 **7 a)** $2^3 \times 5^2 \times 19$

Unit 24 Areas and volumes

227 **1 a)** 16.605 cm^2
b) 37.95 cm^2
c) 58.56 m^2
d) 6.64 cm^2

227 **3** 62.83 cm^2

228 **1 b)** 1100 m

228 **2 a)** 18.85 cm
b) $\frac{1}{6}$
c) 3.14 cm
d) 4.71 cm^2

228 **6 a)** The diameter is 70 m.

229 **1 a)** 196 000 cm^3

230 **1 a)** 53.76 cm^3

231 **1 a)** 235.62 cm^3

232 **5** 56 cups

Unit 25 Algebra and graphs (2)

242 **4 d)** $n = 1.4$

242 **5 b)** $m > 2$

243 **7 a)** $x = 46.2$

243 **8 a)** $x = \frac{2}{3}$

245 **8 a)** $\frac{1}{5}$

245 **9 a)** 8

245 **12 a)** $\frac{4}{5}$

246 **15 a)** $x = \frac{1}{11}$

246 **17 a)** 2.61 ohms (3 S.F.)

Unit 26 Pythagoras and loci

248 **1 c)** 34 cm^2

248 **2** Square C has an area equal to the areas of the other two squares added together.

248 **3 a)** 20 cm^2
b) 4.5 cm correct to 1 decimal place

250 **3 a)** (i) z

250 **4 a)** Yes, $6^2 + 8^2 = 10^2$
b) No, $1^2 + 2^2 \neq 3^2$

251 **1 a)** $x = 2.5$ cm

252 **4** 187.35 cm

253 **7 a)** 12 units
b) 5 units
c) 13 units

254 **1 a)** The locus is a circle round the plate with radius equal to the radius of plate + radius of coin.

b)

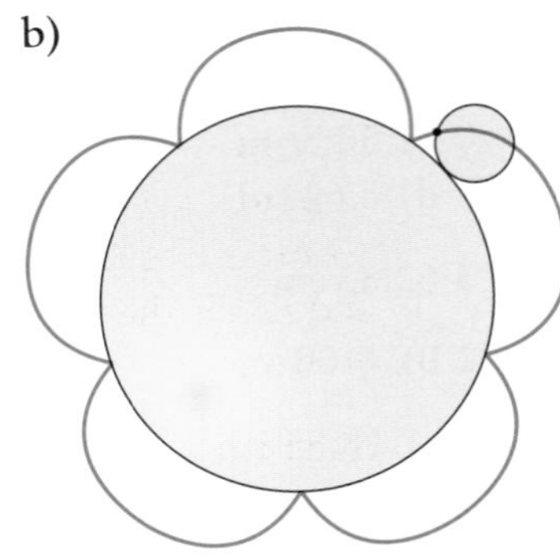

254 **4** I must walk on a path which is the perpendicular bisector of AB.

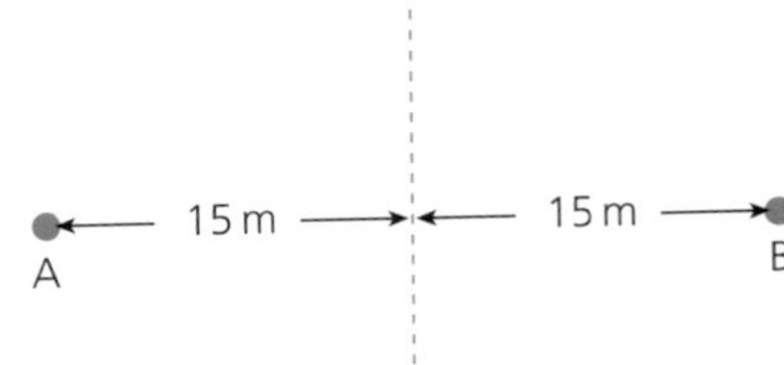

Unit 27 Trial and improvement

258 **4 a)** $x = 5.85$

258 **5 e)** $x = 6.16$

260 **4 a)** $x = 11.35$

262 **8 a)** $x = -5.9$
h) $x = -1.4$ and $x = -3.6$

263 **9 a)** 30.25

Unit 28 Predictions and comparisons

265 **2 a)** 97 cm

d) The answer to c) tells you how much the y variable changes for an increase in 1 unit in the x variable, and this is the same as the gradient.

265 **3 c)** 31 cm

d) Multiply 10 by π.

f) The gradient should be close in value to π because this is the amount by which the circumference changes if the diameter is increased by 1 cm.

265 **4 e)** $y = x$ is below the line of best fit, so the actual distances are always greater than Sarah's estimates.

266 **1 c)** Not that accurate; the points are not that close to the straight line.

267 **2 d)** This is a prediction for the average score. It is based only on results from players in one particular club. It does not take into account extra features such as lakes, trees, bunkers, etc. which will tend to increase the average score.

269 **3** See below

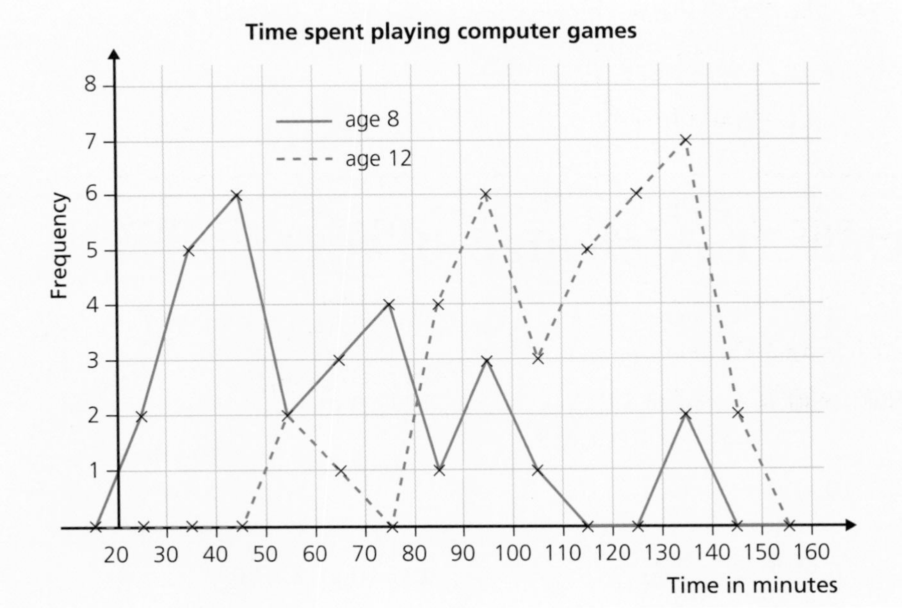

There is a huge range of results for both age groups.
Range (age 8) = 120 minutes
Range (age 12) = 100 minutes
However the older age group do spend more time playing computer games with a mode at 130–140 minutes as opposed to 40–50 minutes for the age 8 group.

Unit 29 Fractions

270 **1 a)** $\frac{12}{19}$

h) $\frac{17}{29}$

j) $\frac{6}{x}$

271 **2 a)** $1\frac{8}{15}$

h) $\frac{3}{4}$

271 **3 a)** $\frac{12}{3x}$

271 **4 a)** $\frac{7}{3x}$

272 **5 a)** $\frac{7}{12}$

272 **6 g)** $\frac{19}{x}$, $\frac{23}{x}$

272 **8 a)** $11\frac{11}{12}$

h) $5\frac{1}{6}$

273 **14 a)** 22

f) $3\frac{1}{3}$

274 **16 a)** 52

Unit 30 Using probability

278 **2 a)** 150

b) $\frac{16}{150} = 0.10\dot{6}$

278 **3 a)** 25 people (all lefthanded)

b) $\frac{9}{25} = 0.36$

283 **5** 10 eggs

283 **7** $\frac{1}{3}$ using dice;

$\frac{3}{10}$ using a calculator

Unit 31 A change of form

286 **1 a)** 17% increase

d) 7% reduction

287 **2 a)** 46.0% (to 3 S.F.)
(23.5 ÷ 16.1 = 1.459…)

289 **10 a)** A reduction of 16.7% (to 3 S.F.)

g) An increase of 42.9% (to 3 S.F.)

291 **5 a)** $9x^4$

g) $2x^2$

292 **12 a)** 1100 (to 3 S.F.)

293 **1 a)** 9×10^6

g) 3.7×10^6

294 **3 a)** 7.2×10^9

294 **4 a)** 2.54×10^{16} (It works out as 25.4×10^{15} but this is not in standard form.)

295 **10 a)** 7×10^{-6}

e) 7.4×10^{-4}

296 **14 a)** 7.2×10^{-12} (This looks reasonable since two very small numbers have been multiplied to give a result that is even smaller.)

Unit 32 Measurements

298 **2 a)** 174.5 cm

299 **3 a)** 175.25 cm
c) 175.25 cm $\leq h <$ 175.35 cm

299 **4 b)** 12.25 km $\leq x <$ 12.35 km

300 **5 b)** 4150 mm $\leq x <$ 4250 mm

300 **2** Lower limit for volume
$= 9.5 \times 5.5 \times 7.5$
$= 391.875$ cm^3
Upper limit for volume
$= 10.5 \times 6.5 \times 8.5$
$= 580.125$ cm^3

302 **1 a)** $5 \leq x < 6$
b) $0 \leq x < 2$
c) $10 \leq x < 20$
d) $70 \leq x < 85$

302 **2 e)** 31.04 years

303 **1** 13.9 m/s

303 **3** 25 mph

303 **6** $194.\dot{4}$ miles

304 **1 b)** 3.6 hours (this is 3 hours 36 minutes)

304 **3 a)** 30 km/h
b) 27 km/h
c) 10 hours

304 **6 a)** $4\frac{1}{4}$ hours (4 hours 15 minutes)
b) 3.4 hours (3 hours 24 minutes)
c) $35.\dot{5}$ mph

Unit 33 Calculator problems

312 **1 a)** 3.06×10^{12}

312 **2 a)** 9.02×10^{-11}

313 **5 a)** 3.25×10^{22}
c) 8.13×10^{9}

314 **1** £4672.50

316 **8 a)** 1.068

316 **9 a)** £14 223.24 ($10\,000 \times 1.073^5$)

316 **10 a)** £3312.58 (remember to subtract £4900)

317 **1 c)** 7.1% (1 D.P.). This is roughly half of the APR.

Unit 34 Cumulative frequency

320 **1** Results in order are:

65 72 81 82 (89 93) 93 95 97 130

Median = 91 seconds

Range = 130 – 65

= 65 seconds

320 **2** Find the value midway between the two middle results.

320 **3** The highest and lowest values may not be typical.

321 **1** 65 89 93 130

72 82 93 97

81 95

First quartile = 81

Third quartile = 95

Interquartile range = 14

321 **2** 11 15 15 19

13 14 15 17

14 14 16 16

First quartile = 14

Third quartile = 16

Interquartile range = 2

321 **3 b)** Make a list of results.

323 **1 a)** 26 people

b) It is the average of the ages of the thirteenth and fourteenth people. They are both between 50 and 60 years old.

325 **2 a)** 75 years

b) Q_1 = 65 years, Q_3 = 88 years

c) 18%

325 **3 a)** See table below

Females	Cumulative percentage	Males	Cumulative percentage
up to 150	2	up to 160	2
up to 155	12	up to 165	8
up to 160	42	up to 170	23
up to 165	73	up to 175	51
up to 170	92	up to 180	82
up to 175	99	up to 185	95
up to 180	100	up to 190	99
		up to 195	100

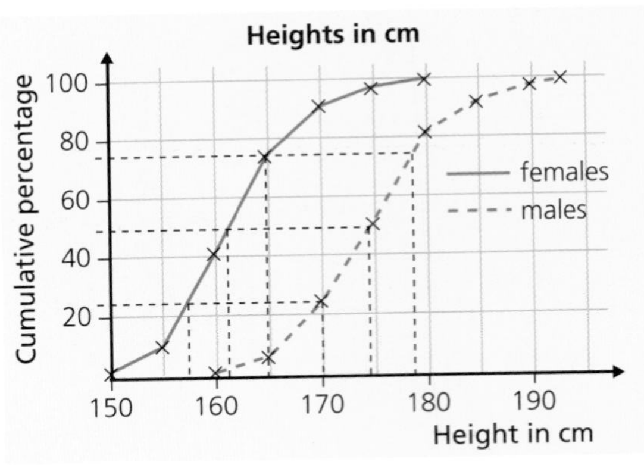

b) See graph

c) 162 cm

326 **4 a)**

Temperature	Frequency
$36.0 \le x < 36.2$	1
$36.2 \le x < 36.4$	1
$36.4 \le x < 36.6$	3
$36.6 \le x < 36.8$	8
$36.8 \le x < 37.0$	17
$37.0 \le x < 37.2$	12
$37.2 \le x < 37.4$	6
$37.4 \le x < 37.6$	2

326 **5 e)** At 10 am the median age is 54 years compared with only 17 years at 4 pm. At 10 am the interquartile range is 43 years whereas at 4 pm it is only 23 years. So at 10 am the passengers are generally older and also more variable in age.

327 **1 a)**

Beats	Cumulative frequency
≤ 64	2
≤ 69	7
≤ 74	11
≤ 79	23
≤ 84	27
≤ 89	29
≤ 94	30

b) See graph below

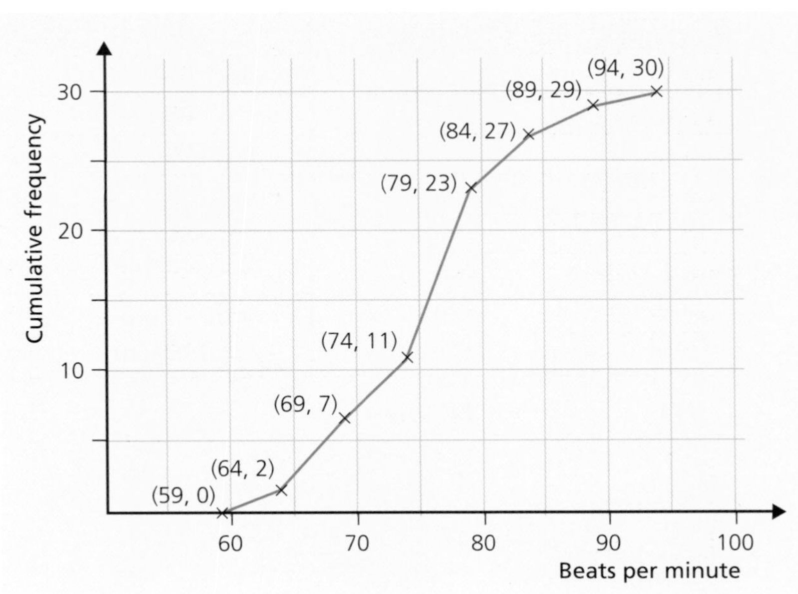

Unit 35 Further equations

329 **1 a)** $y = 2x + 3$;
gradient = 2, intercept = 3
i) $y = x + 1$;
gradient = 1, intercept = 1

331 **5 f)** $x = \frac{d - bc}{a}$
h) $x = bc + a$
n) $x = \frac{cd - b}{a}$

333 **1 a)** $x = 3, y = 3$

333 **2 a)** $a = 7, b = 2$
e) $m = 9, n = 6$

335 **2 a)** $x^2 + 7x + 12$

335 **3 a)** $x^2 + 8x + 16$

335 **4 a)** $x^2 + 2x - 24$
f) $x^2 - 7x + 12$

335 **5 a)** $x^2 - 8x + 16$

336 **6 a)** $2x^2 + 13x + 15$
g) $12c^2 - 7cd + d^2$

336 **7 a)** $4x^2 + 16x + 16$

336 **8 a)** $4x + 6$

339 **9 a)** $xy(y + 1 + z)$

339 **10 a)** $ab^2(ab + 1 - a^2 + a^3b)$

Unit 36 Dimensions

340 **3 a)** $V = x^3$
b) cm^3
c) (iii) L^3

340 **4 c)** (ii) L^2

342 **1** Dimension = L^4. This cannot be a formula for area.

342 **2 a)** Dimension of s is L.
b) $\sqrt{\text{L}^4} = \text{L}^2$

342 **3**

(i) $\text{L}^3 - \text{L}^3 = \text{L}^3$	No
(ii) $\text{L} - \text{L} = \text{L}$	No
(iii) L^3	No
(iv) $\text{L}^2 + \text{L}^2 = \text{L}^2$	Yes
(v) L^3	No

343 **1 e)** The picture gives the impression that the value of money went down to $\frac{1}{4}$ of what it was.

346 **1 c)** (i) No
(ii) No
(iii) No
(iv) Yes
d) 45°

346 **2 a)** 0.84 cm

347 **3** (i) 2.7 cm
(ii) 6.9 cm

Unit 37 Algebra and graphs (3)

350 **3 d)** $y = 3$
(Add 2 to both sides of the given equation to make use of this graph.)
e) $y = 2$

351 **4 a)** $y = 5x + 4$

351 **5 a)** $y = 2x$
(Add $2x$ to both sides of the given equation.)

352 **8 a)** $x = 2$ and $x = 7$

354 **14 a)** 15.625

356 **2 a)**

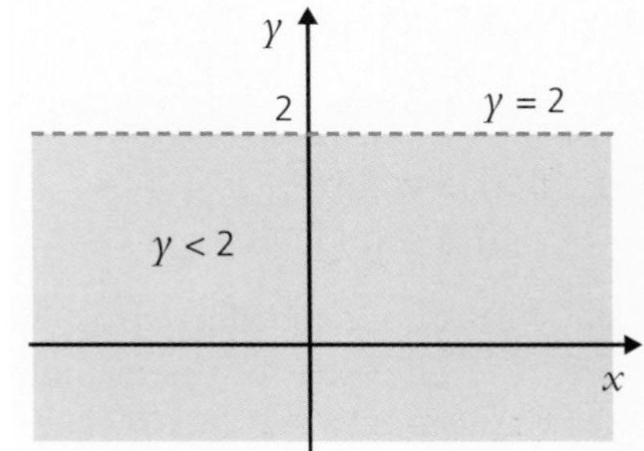

357 **6 a)** D

Unit 38 Combining probabilities

358 **1 a)** Yes
b) No

358 **2** Yes

359 **3 a)** $\frac{2}{13}$
b) $\frac{4}{13}$
c) $\frac{1}{2}$

360 **1** A No
B Yes

362 **2** $\frac{1}{2} \times \frac{1}{4} = \frac{1}{8}$. It does work.

362 **3 a)** $\frac{1}{2} \times \frac{1}{2} = \frac{1}{4}$
b) $\frac{1}{2} \times \frac{1}{2} = \frac{1}{4}$

367 **9 a)** $\frac{4}{5} \times \frac{1}{4} = \frac{1}{5}$

Unit 39 Problem solving

371 **1 a)** $x = 0$ or $x = 7$
g) $x = 0$ or $x = 2$

371 **2 a)** See graph

377 **10 a)** $x^2 = 5x - 3$
c) $x^2 - 5x = -3$

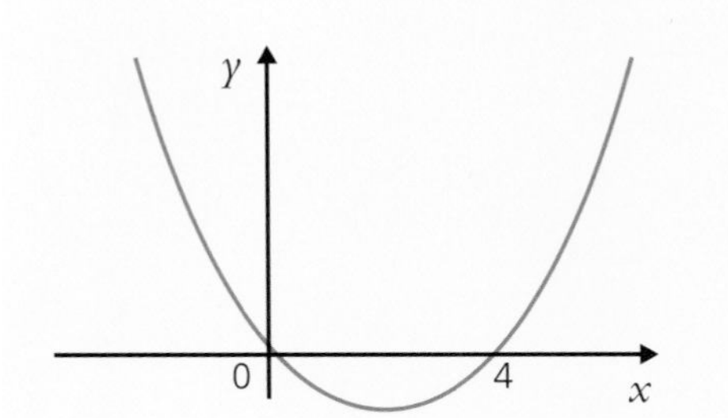

Unit 40 Trigonometry

378 **1 a)** 6.3 cm

380 **6 a)** 0.87 cm

381 **1 a)** 6.5 cm

381 **3 a)** $\theta = 40°$
b) 6.4 km

381 **4 a)** The x coordinate for 40°. The bases of the triangles are 0.77 cm and 7.7 km.
b) 7.7 km

382 **5 a)** 5.6 cm

383 **7** $\theta = 65°$
Base of triangle
$= 2 \times 2.54$ cm
$= 5.1$ cm

384 **1 a)** sine
b) tan
c) cosine

384 **2 a)** 7.1 cm
b) 31.2 mm
c) 9.4 cm

386 **1 a)** $\sin \theta = \frac{3}{5}$

386 **2 a)** $\cos \theta = \frac{4}{5}$

386 **3 a)** $\tan \theta = \frac{3}{4}$

387 **6** (i) **a)** tan
b) 51.3°

388 **1 a)** 8.4 cm

KEY SKILLS

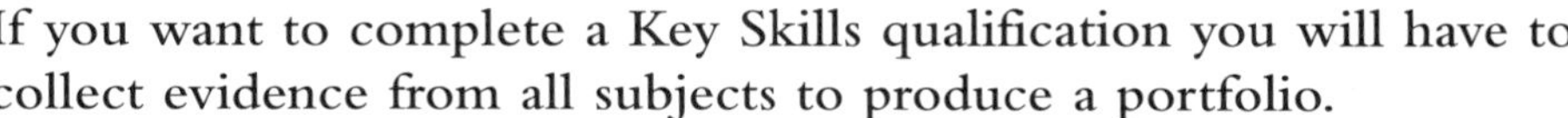

If you want to complete a Key Skills qualification you will have to collect evidence from all subjects to produce a portfolio.

The tables below show you how you can build a portfolio for Key Skills level 2. Each table focuses on one of the six Key Skills and gives examples of where these skills are covered in the classbook. Your teacher will be able to advise you on how to choose the best examples and where you might be able to find more evidence.

NUMBER	
Interpret information from different sources	
Interpretation of graphs from Social Trends	*page* 130
Plan of house from 1851	*page* 115
Interpretation of graphs	*pages* 129–31, 264–9
Code cracking	*page* 279
Designing a questionnaire	*pages* 182–4
Gathering information from a secondary source	*ICT Extra! box page* 133
Carry out calculations	
Calculations	*pages* 1–9, 20–28, 171–174
Calculations with angles	*pages* 15, 54–55, 111–3, 152–155, 378–389
Calculations with fractions	*pages* 38–48, 273–276
Calculations with measurements	*pages* 67–74, 250–3, 298–304
Calculations with ratios and percentages	*pages* 138–147, 185–189, 286–297, 312–9,
Calculations with areas and volumes	*pages* 156–160, 227–233,
Interpret results and present findings	
Presentation of results and graphs	*pages* 49–55, 128–133, 264–9, 320–6
Results of simulations and experiments	*page* 209, 280–2

COMMUNICATION	
Discussion	
Discussion of probabilities	*page* 33
Discussion of results	*page* 52, 94, 95, 279
Discussion of correlations	*page* 136
Discussion of experimental design	*page* 179, 209
Give a short talk	
Following on from the work in Unit 10 you could give a short talk	*pages* 95–100
Talk about the results of surveys done by pupils in your class	*pages* 178–184
Talk about one of the games in this section or one of your own invention	
Give a talk about mortgages and interest payments	*ICT Extra! page* 390

COMMUNICATION (continued)	
Read and summarise	
Information on measuring angles in Ancient Egypt	*page* 249
Information on large distances	*page* 293
Write different kinds of documents	
Design a questionnaire	*pages* 178–184
Write a report of findings	*pages* 178–184

INFORMATION TECHNOLOGY	
Search and select information	
Gather information from government websites	*ICT Extra! page* 133
Explore and develop information, derive new information	
Use of spreadsheet for simulation	*page* 36–7, 101
LOGO investigation	*page* 161
Use of spreadsheet for iterative processes	*page* 258–263
Present combined information	
Present results of search of websites using graphs	*ICT Extra! page* 133

WORKING WITH OTHERS	
Plan work with others	
Plan a survey	*page* 52, 182
Work cooperatively	
Shove penny experiment	*page* 32–3
Probability games	*pages* 95–99
Testing reaction times	*page* 180
Simulation	*page* 209
Exchange information	
Shove penny experiment	*page* 32–3
Angles experiment	*page* 131–132
Simulation	*page* 209

IMPROVING OWN LEARNING	
Set short term targets and get support from others	
Throughout the book , you will find that you can check the answers to questions marked with a 'tick'. These answers appear on page 427 onwards.	
Review progress	
Review Sections appear throughout the book	*pages* 75, 162, 234, 305, 390
Exam practice questions	*pages* 399–425

PROBLEM SOLVING

GLOSSARY

A

acceleration the rate of change of velocity with time

acute angle angle which is less than 90°

alternate angles angles formed between parallel lines on alternate sides of a line crossing them (Z angles)

angle of depression angle measured from the horizontal downwards

angle of elevation angle measured from the horizontal upwards

arc part of the circumference of a circle

B

bearings a bearing gives a direction measured in degrees clockwise from North; it must have 3 figures so 50° from North is written as 050°

bisect cut in half (exactly)

C

capacity measure of the amount of space inside a three-dimensional object

chord straight line which joins two points on the circumference of a circle

circumference distance round the outside of a circle, $C = 2\pi r$

coefficient number in front of a letter in an algebraic expression

complementary angles angles which add up to 90°

compound interest interest is added to the original sum of money invested, so that in the following year interest is paid on that also

congruent shapes are congruent if they are exactly the same size and shape (reflected shapes can be congruent)

continuous data a set of results resulting from measurements being taken; while continuous data can take any value, measurements can be rounded to the nearest whole number or to a convenient number of decimal places

correlation indicates a relationship between two sets of measurements; e.g. height and weight or age of child and amount of pocket-money received

corresponding angles angles in similar positions on the same side of a line crossing parallel lines (F angles)

cosine a trigonometric function; in a right-angled triangle, the cosine of an angle is found by dividing the adjacent side by the hypotenuse

cumulative frequency a running total of the frequency

D

degree unit for measuring angles; a complete revolution is divided into 360°

denominator number on the bottom of a fraction

diameter straight line passing through the centre of a circle from one side of the circumference to the other

difference of two squares $a^2 - b^2 = (a - b)(a + b)$

discrete data a set of results obtained by counting; e.g. the number of rooms in a building

E

elevation view of a three-dimensional shape from its front or side

equilateral triangle has all its sides equal in length and all its angles equal to 60°

exterior angles angles on the outside of a polygon adding up to 360°

F

factor a number which divides exactly into another number, e.g. 1,2,4 and 8 are all factors of 8

Fibonacci numbers sequence where each number is obtained by adding the two previous numbers: e.g. 1, 1, 2, 3, 5, 8, 13 etc.

fraction result of dividing one whole number (numerator) by another whole number (denominator)

frequency the number of times an event has occurred

G

gradient slope of a graph found by dividing vertical distance by the horizontal distance; a negative gradient indicates that the graph is going down as it goes across the page to the right.

H

highest common factor (HCF) largest factor that two numbers have in common: e.g. the HCF of 45 and 75 is 15

histogram graph used to illustrate continuous data; it is similar to a bar chart except that there are no gaps between the blocks

horizontal a line which goes straight across; the horizontal axis is often referred to as the x-axis on a graph

hypotenuse longest side of a right-angled triangle

I

improper fraction has the numerator bigger than the denominator: e.g. $\frac{9}{8}$

independent if two events have no effect on each other, they are independent (used in probability)

integer whole number, e.g. –25, –2, 4, 176

intercept the point at which a line crosses an axis on a graph

interior angles angles on the inside of a polygon; these add up to $180(n-2)$ degrees for a polygon with n sides

interquartile range difference between the upper quartile and the lower quartile; giving the spread for the middle 50% of a set of results

inverse variation two quantities vary inversely if one quantity increases while the other decreases

isosceles triangle has two sides and two angles equal

L

locus set of all possible positions a point can occupy, subject to some given condition

lower quartile the value below which 25% of results lie

lowest common multiple (LCM) the lowest number which is a multiple of two other numbers is called their LCM, e.g. the LCM of 6 and 4 is 12.

lowest terms a fraction is in its lowest terms when it cannot be cancelled down any further

M

mean straight-forward average obtained by dividing the total of a set of results by the number of results

median middle value when a set of results is arranged in order of size

mode the value which occurs most often in a set of results

mutually exclusive events which cannot happen at the same time are mutually exclusive

N

natural number positive whole number e.g. 1, 27, 379

numerator number on the top of a fraction

O

obtuse angle angle greater than 90° but less than 180°

order of rotational symmetry number of positions a shape can occupy while still looking the same as it turns about the centre of rotation

P

parallel lines lines which will never meet and are always the same distance apart

parallelogram quadrilateral with opposite sides parallel (and equal)

percentage fraction with a denominator of 100, so that 17% means 17 parts out of 100

perpendicular lines are at 90° to each other

pictogram statistical diagram using symbols, each of which represents units of data.

pie chart circular diagram used to represent statistical data

plan view of a three-dimensional object as seen from above

plane figure two-dimensional shape

polygon plane figure having 3 or more sides; a regular polygon has all its sides and all its angles equal

prime number has only two factors; itself and 1, e.g. 2, 3, 5, 7, 11 etc.

prism three-dimensional shape having the same cross-section throughout its length (it can be cut into slices which are all the same shape)

probability chance of something happening; its value must lie between 0 and 1; it can be found by dividing the number of ways an event can happen by the total number of possible outcomes

product the answer obtained when two or more numbers are multiplied together.

Pythagoras' theorem states that in a right-angled triangle, the square on the hypotenuse is equal to the sum of the squares on the other two sides

Q

quadratic equation is an equation containing a squared term e.g. $x^2 + 2x - 3 = 0$

quadrilateral polygon with four sides

R

radius distance from the centre of a circle to the circumference

range difference between the highest result and the lowest in a set of data

reciprocal multiplicative inverse of a number, e.g. the reciprocal of $\frac{a}{b}$ is $\frac{b}{a}$; the reciprocal of 5 is $\frac{1}{5}$

recurring decimal decimal number whose decimal places keep on repeating in a set pattern

reflection transformation in which an object appears to have been reflected in a mirror

reflex angle angle greater than 180° but less than 360°

regular a figure is regular if all its sides are equal in length and all its angles are equal

relative frequency is used as an estimate of probability; it is found by dividing the number of times that event occurred by the total number of trials

S

scalene triangle has no two sides equal in length (and therefore no two angles equal)

scattergraph graph drawn to investigate whether two sets of measurements are related; a scattergraph could be drawn showing height on the horizontal axis and weight on the vertical axis; each member of the sample is shown by a point on the graph

sector part of a circle enclosed between two radii

segment part of a circle between a chord and an arc

significant figures the number of digits in a number, not counting noughts at the beginning or end of the number

similar figures are the same shape but not necessarily the same size; their corresponding sides will be in the same ratio and corresponding angles will be equal

simultaneous equations two (or more) equations which connect the same two (or more) unknown values

sine trigonometric function; in a right-angled triangle the sine of an angle is found by dividing the opposite side by the hypotenuse

speed rate of change of distance with time; it can be found as the gradient on a distance-time graph;
speed = distance travelled/time taken

standard index form is a more economical way of writing very large or very small numbers. e.g. $46\,300 = 4.63 \times 10^4$
$0.000\,33 = 3.3 \times 10^{-4}$

supplementary angles add up to 180°

T

tangent trigonometric function; in a right-angled triangle the tangent of an angle is found by dividing the opposite side by the adjacent side

tessellation a regular pattern of identical shapes which fit together without leaving any gaps

U

upper quartile value below which 75% of the results in a set of data lie

V

velocity measure of speed in a particular direction

vertex point where two or more lines or edges meet (i.e. a corner)

vertically opposite angles are formed where two lines cross (X angles); vertically opposite angles are equal

volume amount of space occupied by a three-dimensional object, always measured in cubic units

vulgar fraction has a smaller number for the numerator than for the denominator: e.g. $\frac{2}{5}$

INDEX

J

L

M

N

O

P

Q

R

S

T

U

V

W

Y

Z